INTERNATIONAL

REVIEW OF CYTOLOGY

VOLUME 95

INTERNATIONAL

Review of Cytology

EDITED BY

G. H. BOURNE
St. George's University School of Medicine
St. George's, Grenada, West Indies

J. F. DANIELLI
(Deceased April 22, 1984)

ASSISTANT EDITOR
K. W. JEON
Department of Zoology
University of Tennessee
Knoxville, Tennessee

VOLUME 95

1985

ACADEMIC PRESS, INC.
(Harcourt Brace Jovanovich, Publishers)
Orlando   San Diego   New York   London
Toronto   Montreal   Sydney   Tokyo

ACADEMIC PRESS, INC.
Orlando, Florida 32887

United Kingdom Edition published by
ACADEMIC PRESS INC. (LONDON) LTD.
24–28 Oval Road, London NW1 7DX

LIBRARY OF CONGRESS CATALOG CARD NUMBER: 52-5203

ISBN 0–12–364495–X

PRINTED IN THE UNITED STATES OF AMERICA

85 86 87 88   9 8 7 6 5 4 3 2 1

Contents

v

Genetic Aspects of *Drosophila* as a Model System of Eukaryotic Aging

PETER J. MAYER AND GEORGE T. BAKER III

Histogenesis of the Cells of the Anterior and Intermediate Lobes of Human Pituitary Glands: Immunohistochemical Studies

R. YOSHIYUKI OSAMURA AND KEIICHI WATANABE

Peroxisomes of the Kidney

SHINICHI OHNO

Enzyme Cytochemistry

M. BORGERS AND A. VERHEYEN

Cell Position and Cell Interactions in Expression of Fetal Phenotype of Hepatocyte

A. S. GLEIBERMAN AND G. I. ABELEV

Primitive Never-Dividing Macronuclei of Some Lower Ciliates

IGOR B. RAIKOV

The Unicellular Tetrahymena as a Model Cell for Receptor Research

G. CSABA

Contributors

Numbers in parentheses indicate the pages on which the authors' contributions begin.

G. I. ABELEV (229), *Laboratory of Tumor Immunochemistry, Cancer Research Center, Moscow 115478, USSR*

GEORGE T. BAKER III (61), *Center on Aging, University of Maryland, College Park, Maryland 20742*

M. BORGERS (163), *Laboratory of Cell Biology, Janssen Pharmaceutica Research Laboratories, B-2340 Beerse, Belgium*

G. CSABA (327), *Department of Biology, Semmelweis University of Medicine, H-1445 Budapest, Hungary*

A. S. GLEIBERMAN (229), *Laboratory of Tumor Immunochemistry, Cancer Research Center, Moscow 115478, USSR*

PETER J. MAYER (61), *Merck Sharp & Dohme, West Point, Pennsylvania 19486*

JANET M. NOLIN (45), *Department of Biology, University of Richmond, Richmond, Virginia 23173*

SHINICHI OHNO (131), *Department of Anatomy, Shinshu University School of Medicine, Matsumoto 390, Japan*

R. YOSHIYUKI OSAMURA (103), *Department of Pathology, Tokai University School of Medicine, Boseidai Isehara-city, Kanagawa 259-11, Japan*

IGOR B. RAIKOV (267), *Institute of Cytology of the Academy of Sciences, 194064 Leningrad, USSR*

ALLAN TEREBA (1), *Department of Virology and Molecular Biology, St. Jude Children's Research Hospital, Memphis, Tennessee 38101*

A. VERHEYEN (163), *Laboratory of Cell Biology, Janssen Pharmaceutica Research Laboratories, B-2340 Beerse, Belgium*

KEIICHI WATANABE (103), *Department of Pathology, Tokai University School of Medicine, Boseidai Isehara-city, Kanagawa 259-11, Japan*

INTERNATIONAL REVIEW OF CYTOLOGY, VOL. 95

Chromosomal Localization of Protooncogenes

ALLAN TEREBA

Department of Virology and Molecular Biology, St. Jude Children's Research Hospital, Memphis, Tennessee

1

I. Introduction

During the last several years, the general area of tumor biology coalesced into a tighter, more unified discipline when it was discovered that the transforming activity of retroviruses was due to a series of cellular genes that had been acquired by retrovirus genomes (Bishop and Varmus, 1982). These cellular-derived sequences apparently acquired their transforming activity either by being placed under the control of an active viral transcriptional promoter or by acquiring limited mutational events which altered their activity or interaction with other molecules. (For a review on retrovirus oncogenes, see Bishop and Varmus, 1982; Bishop, 1983.) This unification has gained additional importance with the realization that at least some of these cellular genes have been implicated in the formation of several human cancers, as judged by *in vitro* transfection assays (Bishop, 1983).

During 1982, this fast-moving area of tumor biology began to merge into yet another discipline, tumor cytology. It has been known for many years that certain tumors have specific chromosomal structural abnormalities. The Philadelphia chromosome associated with chronic myelogenous leukemia (CML) (Sandberg,

1980; Mitelman and Levan, 1981) and the translocation t(8;14) associated with Burkitt's lymphoma (Yunis, 1981; Rowley, 1982) are among the best examples, but several other abnormalities frequently associated with a variety of human neoplasia also have been described (Sandberg, 1980; Yunis, 1983). Although these structural changes were deemed important, it was not until the chromosomal location of several oncogenes was determined that the real molecular significance became apparent. It now appears that many of the genes associated with animal tumors are located near specific translocations in human cancers.

The following discussion will define and briefly discuss the concept of protooncogenes and will then describe the studies by which these genes have been located in a variety of species, with a marked emphasis on man. Although the theme of this article is pointing out the close proximity of protooncogenes with tumor-associated chromosomal anomalies, it should be stated that no protooncogene has definitively been shown to be converted to an oncogene as a direct consequence of a translocation. In fact, the complex nature of most human tumors would suggest that multiple events are required and that gross chromosomal alterations play a significant but limited role in the formation of some tumors.

II. What Are Protooncogenes?

During the early 1970s it was discovered that most retrovirus strains were composed of two genome types: one, a replication-competent virus which would not cause an actue disease; and the other, a replication-defective genome that contained sequences unrelated to the nondefective viral genome. Through the use of temperature-sensitive (ts) and deletion mutants, it was conclusively shown that these replacement sequences were responsible for rapidly transforming cells *in vitro* and *in vivo* and were aptly called oncogenes (Linial and Blair, 1982). An examination of various retrovirus strains associated with a variety of animals has uncovered approximately 20 distinct oncogenes, although recent evaluation of nucleic acid sequences and deduced protein sequences has suggested that several of these genes have evolved from common progenitors (Levinson *et al.*, 1981).

During this period, it was also discovered that normal, uninfected cells contained sequences related to the viral oncogenes (Stehelin *et al.*, 1976). These cellular sequences were later shown to be distinct from endogenous retrovirus genomes (Padgett *et al.*, 1977; Tereba *et al.*, 1979), were present in most species (Shilo and Weinberg, 1981), were typical eukaryotic genes containing from none to many introns (Bishop, 1983), and were normally expressed in a variety of tissues (Muller *et al.*, 1982). Manipulation of some of these cellular sequences showed that they had the potential for causing oncogenesis when placed in the right environment (Osharsson *et al.*, 1980; Defeo *et al.*, 1981; Chang *et al.*,

1982). These sequences were thus termed protooncogenes with a "c" for cellular prefixing the three-letter code for the viral or v-*onc* genes.

Recently, oncogenesis by cellular genes has been successfully assayed by transfecting tumor DNA into NIH-3T3 cells. This procedure has resulted in an additional set of oncogenes overlapping their corresponding normal protooncogene counterparts. In this assay, the *ras* gene family has been implicated in many solid tumors, although several transforming genes associated with hematopoietic cancers have been detected which show no homology to sequences incorporated into known retrovirus genomes.

Of particular importance to speculations about the normal function of these protooncogenes is their highly conserved nature. All vertebrates examined contain an array of these genes, and some protooncogenes such as c-*myc* and c-*src* have been detected by nucleic acid hybridization in the DNA from *Drosophila* and the worm *Caenorhabditis elegans* (Shilo and Weinberg, 1981). Their omnipresent and highly conserved nature implies that these genes are important for fundamental cell functions. Indeed, the expression of several protooncogenes in a variety of species has been detected in most cell types examined (Muller *et al.*, 1982). Other protooncogenes appear to be expressed in specific cell types and at select stages of differentiation (Muller *et al.*, 1982; Chen, 1980; Westin *et al.*, 1982; Rosson and Tereba, 1983). This selectivity may account in part for the cell-type specificity that certain v-*onc* genes display. In support of these genes having fundamental roles in the growth of cells, it has been shown by deduced amino acid sequence that B*lym* shares a domain of partial homology with the transferrin gene family (Goubin *et al.*, 1983); v-*sis* shows an extensive homology with the platelet-derived growth factor (Doolittle *et al.*, 1983; Waterfield *et al.*, 1983) and v-*erb*-B corresponds to a truncated version of the epidermal growth factor receptor (Ullrich *et al.*, 1984). In any event, a knowledge as to which normal functions these gene products perform will greatly help our understanding of their role in oncogenesis.

III. Chromosomal Localization of Unique Gene Sequences

Localization of single copy gene sequences to distinct chromosomes has been accomplished by a variety of techniques. Each procedure has its advantages and disadvantages and is dependent to some extent on the species being examined and the detail that is desired. As in most investigations, it is desirable to use at least two approaches, if possible, since all of these procedures rely on somewhat subjective evaluations of chromosomes that are sometimes prone to artifacts. This section is designed to acquaint the reader with the various techniques utilized to localize distinct protooncogenes. The procedures are presented in sufficient detail to make clear the difficulties of each technique and their advantages and disadvantages. Detailed techniques should, however, be obtained from the cited references.

A. CHROMOSOME FRACTIONATION

Although chromosome fractionation has severe limitations regarding resolution and the type of cells that are suitable for this procedure, it has been successfully used and shows promise as a first step in performing other techniques. This procedure requires a cell line with a reasonably short generation time or normal cells that can be more or less induced into synchronous growth such as hematopoietic B and T cells. Early experiments utilized large-scale fractionation in sucrose gradients (Padgett *et al.*, 1977), a technique that is effective at separating chicken chromosomes into several enriched chromosome fractions due to the wide distribution in chromosome size. However, this procedure would be unsuitable for human and mouse chromosomes. Further separation of chromosomes has been accomplished using a fluorescent activated cell sorter (FACS) which separates chromosomes mainly on the basis of DNA content. The degree of separation is dependent upon which fluorescent DNA binding dye is used, the compactness and aggregation of the chromosomes, and whether one or two lasers are employed. Current techniques can separate all but one of the first nine chicken chromosomes (Stubblefield and Oro, 1982) and 17 of the 23 human chromosomes (Gray *et al.*, 1979; Dean and Pinkel, 1978). In addition, enough DNA can be obtained from the separated chromosomes to perform Southern blot analyses so as to localize specific unique gene sequences to distinct chromosomes and to generate DNA libraries of specific chromosomes.

In general, while this technique has been successful, it has limitations and requires an expensive FACS to obtain resolution of distinct chromosomes. It does have potential as an initial step in the generation of somatic cell hybrids containing specific heterologous chromosomes and as an initial sorting step for *in situ* hybridization techniques.

B. SOMATIC CELL HYBRIDS

Somatic cell hybrids have been used extensively in the localization of many human genes, including several protooncogenes. The technique requires several cell clones containing a few defined heterologous chromosomes. This is easily accomplished as heterologous cells fused with polyethylene glycol randomly eliminate chromosomes from one parental line (human in hamster or mouse cells fused to human cells and mouse chromosomes in hamster–mouse hybrids). Parental lines are eliminated by selective growth conditions frequently involving gene complementation in the hybrid cells. Analysis of the DNA from these clones using Southern blot technology and knowledge of the karyotype of each clone, makes it possible to unambiguously determine which chromosome contains the gene of interest. Although this technique is very time consuming to set up because many clones are required, once in place, it is a very rapid approach to determining the chromosome that contains a particular gene.

Although the procedure can be done rapidly under certain conditions, several problems are associated with this approach. First, somatic cell hybrids are typically unstable. Clones will usually contain a varying percentage of cells with slightly different karyotypes. In addition, gross (and submicroscopic) chromosomal alterations may be induced by this technique. This requires constant monitoring by isoenzyme analysis and can lead to ambiguous results. Second, unless specific deletions or translocations are present in the donor chromosomes, the resolution is limited to the chromosomal level. However, in many instances involving chromosomal abnormalities, this technique may help to provide definitive evidence that a particular gene is actually translocated. Finally, this technique is unsuitable for analyzing a large number of cell samples because of the extensive cell culturing involved. This procedure is therefore used mainly as a first-line technique for quickly determining the chromosome in which a particular cloned gene is situated.

C. *In Situ* HYBRIDIZATION

The hybridization of nucleic acid probes directly to chromosomes provides the best resolution of gene localization short of detailed genetic analysis and nucleic acid sequencing. Developed in the late 1960s by Gall and Pardue (1969), this technique has been quite successful in localizing genes in polytene chromosomes and tandomly reiterated sequences in vertebrate species. Unfortunately, several attempts to localize unique sequences in human cells produced a wide range of artifacts attributed mainly to impure probes and resulted in skepticism about the usefulness of this technique. Within the last 5 years, procedures have gradually improved with the use of molecularly pure probes to the point where given a purified mRNA or a cloned DNA sequences, the chromosomal position of complementary sequences can be routinely determined in most species. One of the original approaches developed by Tereba *et al.* (1979) was to attach purified RNAs containing the sequences of interest to a heterologous double-stranded DNA which had been radioactively labeled with ^{125}I in such a manner as to retain a high molecular weight. The attachment was via hybrids between the poly(A) of the RNA and poly(BUdR) tails enzymatically attached to the heterologous DNA. Results of their studies were independently confirmed by chromosome fractionation studies and genetic analyses. The advantage of this approach was the relative quantitation available when more than one locus hybridized since the amount of radioactivity bound to any one locus was independent of the size of the hybridizing sequence. The disadvantage included the requirement for highly purified RNA and an extensive preparation of the probe.

More recently, with the advent of cloned DNA, successful *in situ* hybridizations have been performed with nick-translated, cloned DNA by using either ^{3}H or ^{125}I. The hybridization conditions have also been improved with the use of dextran sulfate to increase the hybridization rate and 70% formamide at 70°C to denature the chromosomal DNA without destroying the details of the chromosomal banding patterns (Harper and Saunders, 1981). Even with these improvements, it is difficult to rationalize why the hybridization reactions work with these probes. The probes are usually short (although relatively large fragments are an important necessary factor) and not of sufficient specific activity to be detectable in single copies. One possible explanation is that many molecules are arrached at each site, thereby forming large networks of radioactive probe molecules. Regardless of the actual mechanism involved, these reactions have been very dependable when proper controls have been used and due care has been taken in aging the slides and with the rapid or low-temperature development of autoradiographs to limit background grains. Typically 5 to 30% of the grains over chromosomes can be attributed to specific hybridization in a successful experiment.

IV. *myc* and Its Association with B Cell Tumors

Of all the oncogene-related sequences, the chromosomal localization of c-*myc* has been examined most often and has generated the most interest. The prototype sequence is derived from the avian acute leukemia virus MC29. The virus is unusual in that it causes a wide range of diseases of both hematopoietic and solid tumor origin. The cell counterpart is highly conserved and can be detected in a wide variety of species (Shilo and Weinberg, 1981). Expression of the cellular gene has been observed in a variety of normal tissues at various stages of differentiation. It is thus likely that this gene plays a fundamental role in the growth or maintenance of cells. This gene is the first and prime example of a cellular gene's involvement in tumor formation. Neel *et al.* (1981), and others (Payne *et al.*, 1981, 1982; Hayward *et al.*, 1981), have shown that a large percentage of chicken bursal lymphomas induced by avian leukosis viruses are clonal and have the right-hand viral promoter region inserted near the cellular c-*myc* gene. High levels of c-*myc* mRNA containing viral sequences also were usually observed in these cells compared to 4-month normal bursal tissue (Hayward *et al.*, 1981). (It should be noted, though, that 5-day bursal tissue which contains actively growing B cells has elevated levels of c-*myc* mRNA also.) This discovery led to the promoter insertion model, which states that high levels of a cellular protooncogene mRNA induced by the placement of an active transcriptional promoter next to the gene is responsible for the induction of oncogenesis (Neel *et al.*, 1981). In theory, any active promoter or enhancer sequence placed near a protooncogene should accomplish the same function as the viral promoter. Thus, transformation could, in practice, be accomplished by a chromosomal translocation. This theory is, in essence, at the heart of the rush to localize the protooncogenes.

A. Chromosomal Localization of c-*myc* on Chicken Chromosomes

The motivation for localizing the cellular c-*myc* gene in chickens was associated not with chromosomal translocations but rather with the desire to answer the question whether exogenous or endogenous retrovirus genomes were physically associated with protooncogenes. An understanding of this situation was important in ultimately determining the mechanism by which retroviruses occasionally incorporated protooncogenes into their genomes as well as determining the viral or cellular origin of this gene. The first approach was to partially separate chicken metaphase chromosomes from a fast-growing lymphoid cell line, MSB-1, by means of a sucrose gradient (Sheiness *et al.*, 1980). Due to the large size differential of the various chicken chromosomes, reasonable separation was accomplished between large, medium, and small chromosomes. Analysis of the extracted DNA from these fractionated chromosomes with a v-*myc* probe suggested that the c-*myc* sequences were located on a large chromosome.

In an independent set of experiments, Tereba and Lai (1982) analyzed chromosomes from normal chicken fibroblasts using *in situ* hybridization of RNA from MC29 virus, the prototype *myc*-containing virus, and MH2, a related virus also containing *myc* sequences, as well as cloned DNA containing the c-*myc* chicken sequences. All experiments showed hybridization over a large microchromosome probably between numbers 12 and 15. Exact determination was impossible because of the small size and uniform morphology of this group of chromosomes. Internal controls showing the location of *ev*1, an endogenous retrovirus locus, were consistent with previous studies (Tereba and Astrin, 1980). The inconsistency in these two sets of experiments are hard to rationalize, as other genes localized by these two methods have provided compatible results (i.e., *ev*1 and c-*src*). One explanation given has been the possibility that the *myc* gene was translocated in the MSB-1 cell line. A few alterations do exist in the karyotype of MSB-1, including an extra region on one of the number 1 chromosomes. However, unless MSB-1 cells only have one *myc* gene, this translocation theory would not easily explain the two divergent results. One approach that may resolve this discrepancy would be to perform *in situ* hybridization on chromosomes from MSB-1.

B. Mouse c-*myc* and Its Association with the t(12;15) Translocation of Plasmacytomas

Murine plasmacytomas have a frequently occurring specific translocation in which there is a reciprocal exchange between the distal part of chromosome 15 (15 D3/E) and chromosome 12 (12F2) or occasionally chromosome 6C2. In addition, trisomy of chromosome 15 is common in most T cell and some B cell leukemias. Since the immunoglobulin heavy chain gene had been localized to the breakpoint on chromosome 12 and the κ light chain gene was located on chromosome 6, this translocation event appeared very similar to the human Burkitt's lymphoma t(8;14) translocation to be described in Section IV,C and suggested some common mechanism of oncogenesis.

An examination of DNA clones containing the constant portion of the α immunoglobulin heavy chain gene from plasmacytomas revealed a rearrangement with nonimmunoglobulin DNA sequences being present near the α switch region. These sequences were called nonimmunoglobulin-associated rearranging DNA (NIARD) or lymphoid rearranging DNA (LYR) (Harris *et al.*, 1982a; Adams *et al.*, 1982). The identity of these sequences was determined by hybridizing this cloned DNA with a v-*myc* probe (Adams *et al.*, 1983). As suggested by the chicken bursal lymphoma model system, the rearranging sequences did indeed contain the mouse c-*myc* gene. Examination of several plasmacytomas revealed that this rearrangement was not very specific at the molecular level with respect to the breakpoint on chromosome 12, that the c-*myc* gene had been decapitated of its 5′ intron in at least some cases leaving an altered gene, and that the union between the immunoglobulin gene and c-*myc* was in a 5′-to-5′ orientation.

As mouse chromosomes are very similar in morphology and form a continuous size gradient, *in situ* hybridization of these chromosomes is rarely attempted. Thus, the approach to confirm the chromosome position of c-*myc*—assumed to be on chromosome 15 from the molecular data described earlier and from the fact that the immunoglobulin heavy chain gene was previously localized to chromosome 12—relied on Chinese hamster–mouse somatic cell hybrids. Using cloned DNA probes containing NIARD sequences (shown to contain c-*myc* sequences), Harris *et al.* (1982b) and Calame *et al.* (1982) both showed a direct relationship between the presence of chromosome 15 and the NIARD sequences. Thus, by the combination of these data and the molecular analysis of the heavy chain gene in plasmacytomas, conclusive evidence is available that the c-*myc* gene is directly involved in the t(12;15) translocation.

Although the positions of the heavy chain immunoglobulin and the c-*myc* genes have been determined in the germline and have been shown to be rearranged in the t(12;15) translocation, the location of these genes in the translocated chromosomes remains to be determined. Either the heavy chain genes could be transposed to chromosome 15 or c-*myc* to chromosome 12. From genetic and molecular considerations, Harris *et al.* (1982b) have proposed that the translocation is reciprocal with the breakpoint occurring at position 15D3 on chromosome 15, leaving all but the extreme 5' terminus of c-*myc* on chromosome 15. The breakpoint on chromosome 12 would be at position 12F1, frequently in the C^α switch region. As a result of the orientation of the immunoglobulin genes, most of the constant region and all of the variable region would be retained on chromosome 12. The C^α region, however, would be translocated to chromosome 15. One consequence of this model would be the transposition of the c-*myc* promoter region and presumably regulator sequences to chromosome 12.

Unfortunately, as with the chicken c-*myc* gene, no direct evidence has been obtained concerning the oncogenic potential of the mouse c-*myc* gene involved in this translocation. The frequent relationship between translocation of this gene and plasmacytomas strongly implies that the gene is involved in some aspect of the oncogenic process. However, when plasmacytoma DNA is transfected into mouse NIH-3T3 cells, transformed cells are obtained which do not contain the rearranged c-*myc* gene (Lane *et al.*, 1982). In addition, levels of expression of c-*myc* may not be altered in all plasmacytomas as compared to normal B cells (Shen-Ong *et al.*, 1982), although other groups have noticed such changes (Muskinski *et al.*, 1983; Marcu *et al.*, 1983). Thus, a two-step process must be envisioned if c-*myc* is to be part of the oncogenic mechanism.

C. Involvement of Human c-*myc* in the t(8;14) Translocation of Burkitt's Lymphoma

With the discovery that c-*myc* was involved in chicken lymphomas via a viral integration mechanism, there was a concerted effort to show a linkage between human c-*myc* and Burkitt's lymphoma. As mentioned in the introduction to Section IV, translocations fit into the general hypothesis of the promoter insertion theory. Previous karyotology on chromosomes obtained from Burkitt's lymphoma revealed a consistent reciprocal translocation between chromosomes 8 at band q24 and chromosome 14 at band q32. Occasional variations in the translocation were also observed between chromosome 8q24 and 2p12 or 22q11 (Sandberg, 1980). Previous studies, including *in situ* hybridization studies, revealed that the immunoglobulin heavy chain gene family was located on chromosome 14q32 (Croce *et al.*, 1979; Kirsch *et al.*, 1982) and that the light chain κ and λ genes were located on chromosomes 2 and 22, respectively (Erikson *et al.*, 1981; McBride *et al.*, 1982a; Malcolm *et al.*, 1982). It was therefore theorized that c-*myc* would be found on chromosome 8.

Several groups independently showed that this postulated position was indeed correct. Both Taub *et al.* (1982) and Neel *et al.* (1982) used *in situ* hybridization techniques to localize *myc*-related sequences to 8q24 on chromosomes from normal peripheral leukocytes (Fig. 1). The sensitivity and specificity of the results of these two groups were quite similar even though Neel *et al.* used a cloned v-*myc* [³H]nicked translated probe, and Taub *et al.* used nicked translated cellular mouse *myc* probe. Between 10 and 20% of the grains were associated with 8q24 in these sets of experiments, a finding that was sufficient to demonstrate specificity. Chromosome 1p in one set of experiments also contained a significant excess of grains ($p \leq 0.001$), but these grains were distributed along the chromosome arm in contrast to the sharp localization on 8q24. Without information on grain clusters of individual spreads, the meaning of the grains over 1p must remain inconclusive. One possible explanation given is that *myc*-related sequences are located on chromosome 1. Although N-*myc* has been localized to chromosome 2 (see Section IV,E), thus showing that the c-*myc* gene family is dispersed, the disperse nature of the grains along the chromosome would imply that these excess grains were just an artifact.

Although the *in situ* hybridization studies conclusively demonstrated the close association of c-*myc* to the breakpoint in the t(8;14) translocation of Burkitt's lymphoma, two other methods were used to decisively show that c-*myc* was actually translocated. Using a panel of mouse–human somatic cell hybrids, Dalla-Favera *et al.* (1982a) confirmed that human chromosome 8 contained the c-*myc* gene when DNA from these hybrids were assayed on Southern blots. To circumvent detection of pseudogenes, the 3′ portion of the human c-*myc* gene was used as the probe. The data was confirmed with a Chinese hamster–human somatic cell hybrid that contained only human chromosome 8. In addition, cell hybrids derived from Burkitt's lymphoma cell lines were analyzed. Using three lines which retained the 14q⁺ but not the 14, 8, or 8q⁻, it was shown that there was a direct correspondence between this chromosome and the presence of c-*myc*. Thus, c-*myc* was directly shown to be translocated to chromosome 14. It should be noted that this mechanism is in contrast to the mouse c-*myc* gene which appears to remain on chromosome 15.

To determine an actual molecular involvement of c-*myc* in the translocations, molecular analyses of the DNA surrounding c-*myc* in Burkitt's lymphoma were undertaken. Taub *et al.* (1982) showed that in a certain percentage of cases, a molecular recombination could be observed between the immunoglobulin gene containing the μ chain sequences and the c-*myc* gene. This finding has been confirmed by several laboratories, and several cloned DNA sequences that have been obtained demonstrate this union. It now appears that the c-*myc* and μ chain-encoded genes are joined head to head so that a simple promoter insertion model could not explain this activation event. In addition, the breakage and joining regions appear to have considerable flexibility, sometimes leaving the immu-

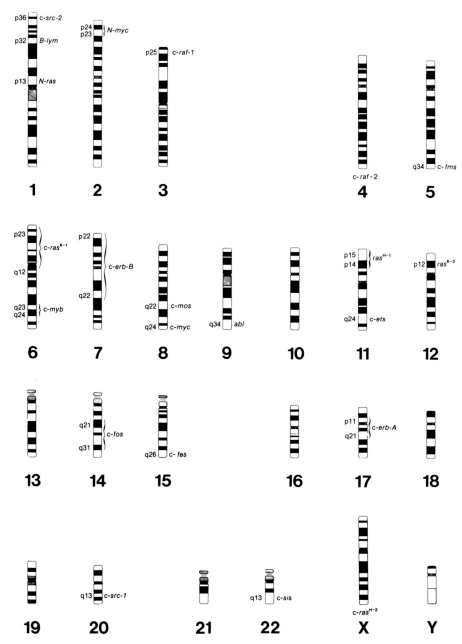

Fig. 1. The chromosomal location of human protooncogenes. The chromosomal location of 16 protooncogenes and 6 apparent pseudogenes containing oncogene-related sequences are displayed on a human karyotype showing the G banding pattern at the 400-band stage. The location of each gene is given in Table I, and the methods used to localize the genes are described in the text.

noglobulin and *myc* genes several kilobases apart. Thus, what appeared to be a distinct event at the chromosomal level is, in fact, quite variable at the molecular level.

The conclusive demonstration that c-*myc* is translocated to chromosome 14 in the Burkitt's lymphoma t(8;14) translocation still leaves the involvement of this gene in the process of oncogenesis up in the air. Although some reports have demonstrated an increased transcription of this gene from the translocated chromosome (Erikson *et al.*, 1983), no direct biological assay has shown that this event is oncogenic. Indeed, another gene, B*lym,* has been associated with oncogenesis in Burkitt's lymphoma using transfection assays with NIH-3T3 assay cells (Cooper and Neiman, 1981). Recent evidence using v-*myc* in transfection assays has shown that this gene may play a role in immortalization of cells but requires an additional oncogene such as *ras* for tumorigenesis of primary rat fibroblasts (Land *et al.*, 1983).

D. HUMAN c-*myc* AMPLIFICATION AND APPARENT CHROMOSOMAL REARRANGEMENT

In addition to the promoter insertion model, gene amplification of protooncogenes has been proposed as a mechanism for oncogenesis. Two human cell lines containing amplified c-*myc* genes have been detected (Dalla-Favera *et al.,* 1982b; Collins and Groudine, 1982; Alitalo *et al.,* 1983). One of these cell lines, the neuroendocrine tumor cells COLO 320, has been examined by *in situ* hybridization (Alitalo *et al.,* 1983). This cell line contains both double minute chromosomes (DMs) and two homogeneous staining regions (HSR) on a marker chromosome believed to be derived from an X chromosome. From previous model systems, these two karyotypic abnormalities would be prime sites for the *myc* amplification. Indeed, Alitalo *et al.* (1983) observed clustering of grains over both HSRs of the marker chromosome when *in situ* hybridization was performed with a v-*myc* probe. Unfortunately, no statistical analysis of the grain distribution or examination of other chromosomes were presented and only two partial spreads were shown. In addition, no detectable hybridization was observed over the double minute (DM) chromosomes and no mention was made of chromosome 8, the defined location of c-*myc*.

As to the role of this amplification in the oncogenic process, more information is needed. This gene amplification is still highly unusual among cancer cells and its amplification theoretically could be accounted for by the amplification of a nearby gene involved in metabolism. Amplifications by this mechanism span relatively large regions and involve many genes. In addition, as discussed above, the c-*myc* gene has not been shown to be oncogenic in biological assays. This mechanism of transcriptional amplification of c-*myc* by gene amplification must await further analysis before it can be concluded to be an important mechanism of oncogenesis.

E. Chromosomal Location of Human N-*myc*

Several human neuroblastoma cell lines contain an amplified DNA sequence that contains *myc*-related sequences (Schwab *et al.*, 1983; Kanda *et al.*, 1983; Kohl *et al.*, 1983). This sequence shares 78% homology with human c-*myc* over two stretches comprising 133 base pairs of the 5' exon (Schwab *et al.*, 1983). The amplified DNA appears to be in HSRs and/or DMs that are present at a large variety of chromosomal places. To determine the location of the unamplified copy, cloned DNA was isolated and used as a probe with somatic cell hybrids (Kanda *et al.*, 1983; Kohl *et al.*, 1983). Using both human–hamster and human–mouse hybrids, concordance of a specific 2.0-kb *Eco*RI *myc*-related fragment was observed only with human chromosome 2. In addition, two hybrids that retained only the short arm of chromosome 2 had the specific sequences whereas a hybrid that retained only the long arm of chromosome 2 did not retain the sequences. Thus, the *myc*-related sequence, called N-*myc*, has been assigned to the short arm of chromosome 2.

To further localize this gene, Schwab *et al.* (1984) used both *in situ* hybridization and somatic cell hybrids that had deletions in chromosome 2. A hybrid containing only region p23–pter of chromosome 2 retained N-*myc*. *In situ* hybridization confirmed the result, showing 35% of the grains on chromosome 2 localized to p23 and p24 (Fig. 1). Although most neuroblastoma cell lines examined contain this amplified sequence, no direct biological evidence is available that shows this sequence to be oncogenic or immortalizing.

V. B*lym*: An Oncogene Discovered by Transfection Assays

The discovery that avian leukosis virus genomes frequently integrated near c-*myc* in infected chicken cells provided hope that at least one mechanism of oncogenesis involving a protooncogene had been established. However, *in vitro* oncogenic assays involving the transfer of bursal lymphoma DNA into the non-oncogenic NIH-3T3 mouse fibroblast cell line soon dispelled these early hopes. The oncogenic agent, when cloned, turned out to be not c-*myc* but a small gene called B*lym* (Cooper and Neiman, 1981). Transfection experiments with mouse plasmacytoma and human Burkitt's lymphoma DNA also revealed the B*lym* gene to be the oncogenic agent in the *in vitro* assay (Diamond *et al.*, 1983). As expected, this gene was highly conserved between species; and, interestingly, a region of the gene showed some homology with the transferrin gene family (Goubin *et al.*, 1983). *In situ* hybridization was performed on human chromosomes with this probe, and the gene was localized to 1p32 (Morton *et al.*, 1984) (Fig. 1). Although chromosome 1 frequently contains alterations in tumor cells, it is not frequently involved in human Burkitt's lymphoma. In addition, analyses have shown that the B*lym* gene is neither amplified nor grossly rearranged. Thus, whatever alteration has occurred, it is probably associated with point mutations and not due to chromosomal rearrangement.

VI. *myb:* A Hematopoietic-Associated Oncogene

The oncogene v-*myb* is present in avian myeloblastosis virus (AMV) and a related virus E26. Both viruses transform macrophages *in vitro* and AMV produces myeloid leukemia. Interestingly, E26 produces mainly erythroblastosis. Using v-*myb* probes derived from AMV, investigators have determined that the c-*myb* gene is transcribed primarily in myeloid cells in human samples although expression is largely associated with myeloblasts rather than with granulocytes (Westin *et al.*, 1982; Rosson and Tereba, 1983). Although this gene is conserved among a large variety of species, it is significantly more divergent than some of the other c-*onc* genes. This may signify a developmental role in one of the hematopoietic lineages that is not present or is substantially altered in invertebrates.

A. Localization of c-*myb* in Chickens

The localization of chicken c-*myb* has been performed using two methods: *in situ* hybridization and chromosome separation by sucrose gradient. Using *in situ* hybridization, AMV RNA, containing the v-*myb* oncogene, was attached to ^{125}I-labeled high-molecular-weight sea urchin DNA as described above and hybridized to metaphase chromosomes from chicken fibroblasts containing the endogenous retrovirus genome, *ev*1 (Tereba and Lai, 1982). Examination of the chromosomes revealed hybridization over chromosome 1 at the location previously assigned to *ev*1, and to the microchromosomes. Some hybridization occurred over the chromosome group 10–12 (the group slightly larger than the microchromosomes), but further examination indicated that this was probably the result of misidentification and that the gene was probably on a larger microchromosome (13–16).

Using gradient-separated chromosomes from the cell line MSB-1 and a c-*myb* probe, Symonds *et al.* (1984) localized c-*myb* to an intermediate chromosome group (2 to 4/Z). Of some concern in this experiment is the very broad spread of chromosomes containing c-*myb* (half of the gradient containing chromosomes) and the uniform amount of c-*myb* DNA in each fraction. This pattern did not correspond to any one particular chromosome as judged by visual examination of the fractions. In any case both results point out the fact that different oncogenes reside on different chromosomes (see Section XV).

B. LOCATION OF c-*myb* ON MOUSE CHROMOSOME 10

Salaguchi *et al.* (1984) used a v-*myb* probe to detect related sequences in mouse–hamster hybrids. Only one mouse DNA fragment and two hamster DNA fragments were observed allowing for easy analysis of this gene. When 15 hybrids were examined, complete concordancy was observed between this gene fragment and mouse chromosome 10.

C. HUMAN c-*myb* AND 6q⁻ ABERRATIONS

The discovery that c-*myc* was located in the vicinity of a translocation associated with Burkitt's lymphoma stimulated the attempts to localize other protooncogenes. The hope was that transformation could be accounted for by the activation of c-*onc* genes during chromosomal translocations. This would account for the specific translocations common to many tumors. The localization of c-*myb* was not disappointing in this regard.

Localization of c-*myb* was first accomplished by examining somatic cell hybrids (Dalla-Favera *et al.*, 1982c). The DNA from 27 mouse–human hybrids was analyzed for a characteristic 2.0 kb *Eco*RI digest fragment that hybridized with a human cloned DNA fragment which showed homology with v-*myb*. Concordance was shown only with chromosome 6. Further localization of this gene was accomplished by *in situ* hybridization using the same probe (Harper *et al.*, 1983). Metaphase chromosomes from 163 cells were examined. Although the grains were distributed widely over all the chromosomes, 7.4% of the grains occurred over 6q2. This was statistically significant (one would expect about 2% by random distribution) but was not as impressive as other localizations. However, since this agreed with the somatic cell hybrid data, it is likely that this observation is correct. Analysis of the grain distribution along chromosome 6 suggested that the gene was probably in the vicinity of 6q22 to 24 (Fig. 1).

In examining this gene location in relationship to chromosomal aberrations associated with tumor cells, two examples stand out. First, acute lymphocytic leukemia patients occasionally have a deletion or sometimes a translocation involving 6q21–qter (Oshimura *et al.*, 1977). Unfortunately, this is not observed in the majority of cases. In addition, ovarian carcinoma cells frequently have a t(6;14) translocation with the breakpoint at 6q21 (Wake *et al.*, 1980; Trent and Salmon, 1981). Thus, common chromosomal aberrations can be found near c-*myb* in specific tumor cells. However, it must be pointed out that c-*myb* appears to be at least one to two subbands away from these deletions and translocations. It should also be pointed out that these are deletions which appear to eliminate the c-*myb* gene. Thus, one must consider the possibility that the remaining c-*myb* gene is altered and that the altered gene is recessive. An alternative explanation is that c-*myb* is fortuitously near these deletions and that it has nothing to do with tumor formation.

VII. Location of c-*ets* on Human Chromosome 11

The oncogenic potential of v-*ets* is at present unknown since this gene is found in conjunction with another oncogene, v-*myb*. The avian retrovirus E26 is capable of transforming erythroid and myeloid hematopoietic cells and except for its erythroid tropism is very similar to avian myeloblastosis virus (AMV). When the sequences of the two viruses were compared (Nunn *et al.*, 1984), it was observed that E26 contains a v-*myb* gene that has deletions at both the 5' and the 3' ends when compared with v-*myb* from AMV. In addition, E26 contains extra sequences 3' to the *myb* gene that have been defined as v-*ets*. These sequences abut v-*myb* and form a continuous reading frame, a finding suggesting that the two oncogenes are made as a polyprotein. Whether this *ets* gene has any inherent oncogenic potential or is responsible for the erythroid tropism is a matter of speculation.

The localization of the human c-*ets* gene was accomplished using two methods. First, metaphase chromosomes were sorted, immobilized on nitrocellulose filters, and hybridized with a human c-*ets* cloned DNA probe. The results suggested that the gene was on chromosome 10, 11, or 12. By analyzing chromosomes from a cell that contained a t(11;22)(p11;q22) translocation, the investigators determined that the gene was now on two chromosomes of different sizes, presumably the normal chromosome 11 and the 11p⁻. To obtain a more precise localization of c-*ets, in situ* hybridization was used. Of 148 grains observed, 22 grains were located on 11q24. However, because of discrepancies in band assignments, 11q23 could not be ruled out. Thus, c-*ets* is located between 11q23 and 11q24. Several rearrangements have been associated with these two bands, especially involving acute monocytic leukemia (AML). However, no evidence is available to support any alterations of c-*ets* structure or transcription in neoplastic cells containing alterations in the 11q23–24 region.

VIII. Chromosomal Location of c-*erb*-A and c-*erb*-B

The v-*erb* oncogene was detected in avian erythroblastosis virus (AEV) as a 3.0-kb region showing no homology to replicative retrovirus genes (Bister and Duesberg, 1979; Lai *et al.*, 1979). The viral oncogene will transform both erythroid cells and fibroblasts *in vitro* and causes erythroblastosis and sarcomas *in vivo*. Of interest is the fact that v-*erb* is composed of two protein-coding regions that have been designated v-*erb*-A and v-*erb*-B. although *erb*-B appears to be sufficient for oncogenesis. In a major step linking oncogenes with growth, it was shown through sequence analysis that v-*erb*-B was a truncated version of the epidermal growth factor (EGF) receptor (Ullrich *et al.*, 1984). It appears that AEV acquired the receptor gene but in the process deleted the 5′ portion of the gene containing the coding sequence for the EGF binding site. The resulting molecule may be permanently signaling the cell to initiate growth.

A. LOCATION OF CHICKEN c-*erb*-A AND c-*erb*-B ON DIFFERENT CHROMOSOMES

Wong *et al.* (1981) localized the chicken c-*erb* genes by *in situ* hybridization, using a probe that contained both *erb*-A and *erb*-B. AEV RNA was attached via its poly(A) tail to ^{125}I-labeled sea urchin DNA as described before. This probe was hybridized to metaphase chromosomes from line 15_B fibroblasts which contains retrovirus loci on chromosomes 1 (*ev*1) and the Z sex chromosome (*ev*7). Analysis of the grain distribution from 119 chromosome spreads revealed cross-hybridizing sequences on chromosome 1 at the position of *ev*1, on the Z chromosome at the position of *ev*7, and over the chromosome group 10–12. This finding indicated that at least one of the *erb* genes was located on the chromosome group 10–12.

Using DNA from gradient-purified chromosome preparations, Symonds *et al.* (1984) localized the c-*erb* genes using probes specific for *erb*-A and *erb*-B. The c-*erb*-A gene was localized to the group of chromosomes smaller than number 8 and the c-*erb*-B gene was located on a larger chromosome, possibly number 2, although hybridization occurred significantly with half of the fractions containing chromosomes. The discrepancy between the two results can be explained by the failure of the *in situ* hybridization study to detect the c-*erb*-B gene. These results demonstrate that AEV acquired nonlinked genes most likely through a two-step mechanism.

B. LOCATION OF MOUSE c-*erb*-A AND c-*erb*-B ON THE SAME CHROMOSOME

The c-*erb*-A and c-*erb*-B genes were localized to chromosome 11 using a combination of mouse–hamster somatic cell hybrids and interspecies microcell hybrids. Initial experiments using defined hybrids suggested both c-*erb*-A and c-*erb*-B were on chromosome 11. To confirm this finding, mouse chromosome 11 was inserted into a hamster cell by microcell fusion (Fournier and Frelinger, 1982). This hybrid, which only contained mouse chromosome 11, and a BUdR-counterselected clone lacking the mouse chromosome were then analyzed for the presence of the mouse *erb* genes. The hybrid containing chromosome 11 had both genes, whole; the revertant lacked both genes. Additional experiments with hybrids containing deletions on chromosome 11 suggested that *erb*-A and *erb*-B are not closely linked. Thus, although these genes reside on the same chromosome, they appear to be separated by a considerable distance; this findings supports the general findings in other species that these genes are physically quite separate.

C. LOCATION OF HUMAN c-*erb*-A AND c-*erb*-B ON DIFFERENT CHROMOSOMES

The chromosomal location of c-*erb*-A was determined using somatic cell hybrids. Using seven hybrids, investigators provisionally assigned the gene to chromosome 17. To confirm this location, a hybrid containing only human chromosome 17 was shown to have the human c-*erb*-A gene. To further localize the gene, two hybrids containing chromosome 17 translocations were analyzed. The results indicated that c-*erb*-A is located at 17p11–q21 (Fig. 1). Zabel *et al.* (1984) have confirmed the chromosome 17 location of c-*erb*-A by somatic cell hybrids and also concluded that the gene is between 17p11 and 17qter.

The localization of c-*erb*-B was accomplished by analyzing the DNA from somatic cell hybrids. Results indicated concordancy with chromosome 7; the hybrids used included one hybrid that only had human chromosome 7. To further localize the gene, a hybrid containing an X;7 translocation was used. This hybrid only retained 7pter–q22 but still retained human c-*erb*-B, thus indicating the gene's chromosomal position (Fig. 1). Using similar hybrids, Zabel *et al.* (1984) arrived at the same conclusions including the sublocalization of the gene.

IX. Localization of c-*abl*

The viral oncogene v-*abl* is present in the Abelson strain of murine leukemia virus. This strain has several variants which code for *abl* specific sequences of different lengths and appear to be the result of deletions near the middle of the oncogenic sequences. Although this virus can transform fibroblasts *in vitro, in vivo* it acts solely as a hematopoietic oncogenic agent. The target cells appear to be immature B lymphocytes. The protein product is of some interest since it is the only hematopoietic-associated oncogene product that appears to have tyrosine-specific protein kinase activity. The c-*abl* gene appears to be transcribed in many types of tissues.

A. LOCATION OF MURINE c-*abl* ON CHROMOSOME 2

The localization of murine c-*abl* to chromosome 2 was accomplished using mouse–hamster somatic cell hybrids (Goff *et al.*, 1982). Restriction endonuclease-digested DNAs from 11 hybrids were analyzed for the presence of v-*abl*-related sequences that corresponded in size to the mouse c-*abl* fragments. From this initial screen, two chromosomes, 2 and 19, showed complete concordance with mouse c-*abl*. One clone containing these chromosomes was subcloned, and in one of four cases chromosome 2 was lost. This subclone also lost the mouse c-*abl* gene, thus indicating that c-*abl* was on chromosome 2.

Interestingly, the murine adenylate kinase (AK) gene is located on chromosome 2 while the human counterpart is located on human chromosome 9 near the location of the human c-*abl* gene. Thus, the murine c-*abl* locus is probably located near this kinase gene also.

B. INVOLVEMENT OF HUMAN c-*abl* WITH THE t(9;22) TRANSLOCATION OF CML

Several groups were involved in the localization of the human c-*abl* protooncogene. The first step in localization utilized somatic cell hybrids. DNA from 16 hybrids were analyzed for the presence of human c-*abl* using both v-*abl* and human c-*abl* probes (Heisterkamp *et al.*, 1982). Concordance between this gene and chromosome 9 were shown, including one clone that retained only chromosomes 1, 9, 14, and X. This localization was improved by using a subclone of a human–hamster hybrid. The original clone contained human c-*abl* and the three isoenzymes used to identify human chromosome 9. A subclone of this hybrid was shown to have lost the human c-*abl* gene along with the marker enzyme AK1 but retained the other two markers for chromosome 9. Thus, it was concluded that c-*abl* was on the long arm of chromosome 9 (the location of AK1) and not on the short arm, which contains the other two markers.

The sublocalization of c-*abl*, as well as the localization of murine c-*abl*, implied that c-*abl* was near the breakpoint in the t(9;22)(q34;q11) translocation associated with CML (Rowley, 1973, 1980a; Lawler, 1977). To confirm this, de Klein *et al.* (1982) utilized somatic cell hybrids made with leukocytes from CML patients. In this way, both normal 9 and 22, as well as the translocated chromosomes, could be analyzed. Using probes derived from both the 5′ and the 3′ ends of human c-*abl*, Klein *et al.* showed that all of c-*abl* was translocated to chromosome 22q$^+$ and that 9q$^+$ no longer contains c-*abl*. Thus, this gene must reside near the terminus of chromosome 9 (9q34) and is indeed involved in the translocation. This finding has been confirmed by Jhanwar *et al.* (1984) who used *in situ* hybridization to pachytene cells. Only 13 of 49 total grains occurred at position 9q34, data that are far from conclusive. However, because of the agreement with the somatic cell hybrid data, it can be concluded that this experiment was indeed detecting the c-*abl* gene.

Finally, Heisterkamp *et al.* (1983) used a 5′ c-*abl* cloned DNA probe to isolate the junction fragment in the t(9;22) translocation of one CML patient. DNA 5′ to the c-*abl* gene was isolated and used as probes to test for rearranged sequences in

CML DNA. In one case, an alteration was observed and the DNA fragment was cloned. This fragment, which had sequences normally within 15 kb of the c-*abl* gene, contained DNA from both chromosome 9 and chromosome 22, as determined by hybridization of the appropriate human–mouse somatic cell hybrids. Thus, the breakpoint in the DNA from this CML patient appears to occur about 14.5 kb 5' to the c-*abl* gene. It is possible that the breakpoint is even closer, as the exact 5' terminus of c-*abl* is unknown. Interestingly, the use of *Bam*HI digestion produces a 24-kb c-*abl*-containing fragment in normal human DNA that does not contain the translocated area and thus points out the problems associated with this type of analysis in detecting translocations. Finally, the breakpoint in the t(9;22) translocation of two other CML patients could not be identified, a result suggesting that the breakpoint is variable as with c-*myc* in the t(8;14) translocation of Burkitt's lymphoma.

The localization of c-*abl* at the breakpoint of a major translocation associated with CML and its known movement to the Ph' chromosome is reminiscent of the *myc*-involved translocation in Burkitt's lymphoma. So far, transcriptional amplification of this gene and structural alterations have not been reported in cells from CML patients. More disturbing is the occurrence of alternative translocations (Sandberg, 1980). In these cases (more than 30), simple translocations are observed between 22q and a chromosome other than 9. Thus, it appears that something on chromosome 22 is likely to be the important factor. This would exclude c-*abl* involvement unless some unobserved complex translocations involving three chromosomes (including 9) were occurring. Indeed, this situation has been observed in a number of other cases and in most cases includes chromosome 9. At the present time, the involvement of c-*abl* in CML appears strong.

X. c-*ras* Family

The retrovirus strains, Harvey sarcoma virus and Kirsten sarcoma virus, contain sequences that have oncogenic potential. Although distinct, these oncogenes are distantly related and have been placed in the same family, designated *ras*. As expected, homologous protooncogenes can be found in a large variety of mammalian species. These two protooncogenes are only part of a larger family in human cells, a family which presently includes five distinct genetic loci. As three of these loci have been shown to possess transcriptional activity in at least some cells, it is highly unlikely that the large size of the family represents a collection of pseudogenes.

The most interesting feature about this class of oncogenes is its biological activity. Whereas other protoncogenes have shown little or no transforming activity when assayed in standard transfection assays employing NIH-3T3 cells, the first, and at present, vast majority of transforming genes derived from human cell lines have been characterized as *ras* related. Thus, this group of protoon-cogenes is the primary link between viral oncogenes and human cancer.

A. LOCATION OF c-*ras*[H-1] ON MOUSE CHROMOSOME 7

The chromosomal localization of the mouse c-*ras*[H-1] gene was determined using hamster–mouse somatic cell hybrids (Kozak *et al.*, 1983a). Thirty somatic cell hybrids were examined for the presence of the mouse 4.5-kb *Hin*dIII-digested DNA fragment that cross-hybridized to a human c-*ras*[H-1] probe. Hamster DNA contained two cross-hybridizing kilobase fragments, 12.2 kb and 2.1 kb; but these were far in size removed from the 4.5-kb fragments and thus allowed easy identification of the mouse gene. There were 18 hybrids that contained the mouse c-*ras*[H-1] gene and all contained chromosome 7. Of the 12 hybrids lacking the gene, none contained chromosome 7 as judged by Giemsa–trypsin banding. No other chromosome correlated with the presence of this mouse gene. Thus, c-*ras*[H-1] has been assigned to mouse chromosome 7. Using hamster–mouse hybrids, Pravtcheva *et al.* (1983) and Sakaguchi *et al.* (1984) have confirmed the chromosome 7 location of c-*ras*[H-1].

The localization of c-*ras*[H-1] to chromosome 7 is not surprising in light of the previous localization of human c-*ras*[H-1] to chromosome 11p14–15 (see Section X,D). The human lactate dehydrogenase A and non-α-globin genes have been located to this region on chromosome 11 and the mouse counterparts (*LdH-1* and *Hbb*) have been mapped to mouse chromosome 7. No tumor-specific transloca-tion associated with mouse chromosome 7 has been reported. Thus, it appears that activation of this protooncogene would likely involve point mutations. This is in agreement with the current model for the activation of the human c-*ras*[H-1] gene.

B. LOCATION OF c-*ras*[K] ON MOUSE CHROMOSOME 6

The chromosomal location of mouse c-*ras*[K] was determined by Sakaguchi *et al.* (1984) using mouse–hamster hybrids. Complicating this approach was the fact that Chinese hamsters contain a large number of Kirsten v-*ras*-related genes. However, by using digests of hybrid cell DNA by two restriction endonucleases, they were able to identify a 7.0-kb fragment of mouse c-*ras*[K] that was not obscured by the Chinese hamster-related genes in Southern blots. Using 15 hybrids, these investigators observed complete concordancy between this frag-ment and chromosome 6.

Because two of the mouse cross-hybridizing fragments were obscured by hamster *ras*-related fragments, it was impossible to determine whether the mouse genome contains one or, as in the case of human cells, two Kirsten-related genes. However, by examining the chromosomal location of this mouse gene and the human Kirsten-related genes (see Sections X,F–G), it appears likely that the localized mouse gene correlates with the human c-ras^{K-2} locus. The human *ras* gene is located on chromosome 12p as are the genes for glyceraldehyde-3-phosphate dehydrogenase and triosephosphate isomerase. The homologues of the latter genes are located on mouse chromosome 6, a finding suggesting that the c-ras^{K-2} gene is in a conserved chromosomal region.

C. Location of N-*ras* on Mouse Chromosome 3

Ryan *et al.* (1984) used the human N-*ras* gene as a probe to isolate the related gene from a mouse genomic library. Subclones which were made lacked repetitive murine DNA sequences and did not hybridize with hamster DNA. These subclones were then used to determine the chromosomal location of the gene by analyzing the DNA from 40 mouse–hamster hybrids. The best concordancy with this gene was with chromosome 3, where only one discordant event was observed. All other chromosomes had at least five discordant events. This assignment appears logical as chromosome 3 also contains amylase 1 and amylase 2. These two genes map to human chromosome 1p221–q11, the region containing the human N-*ras* gene. Thus, as with the other *ras*-related genes, N-*ras* appears to be in a conserved chromosomal block between mice and humans.

D. Chromosomal Location of Human c-ras^{H-1}

The chromosomal localization of c-ras^{H-1} was determined first by using the transforming gene derived from the T24 human bladder carcinoma cell line rather than a v-ras^H probe. Sequencing has shown that this transforming gene is very similar to the v-ras^H genes and contains only minor point mutations. Using the T24 oncogene, McBride *et al.* (1982b) examined the DNA from 18 hamster–human cell lines derived from nine independent clones. The c-ras^{H-1} gene was detected in two sets of clones, the only sets that retained human chromosome 11. To confirm this observation, subclones were prepared from three lines containing chromosome 11 and three lacking this chromosome. The loss of chromosome 11 was correlated with a concomitant loss of human c-ras^{H-1} in 14 of 32 subclones originally containing this chromosome.

More recently, De Martinville *et al.* (1983b) examined DNA from 24 rodent–human hybrid cell lines derived from Chinese hamster or mouse cell lines and normal diploid human fibroblasts or leukocytes. In this case, the probe used was the transforming gene from the human EJ bladder carcinoma cell line. This gene has been shown to be identical to the T24 oncogene. Their results confirmed the presence of c-ras^{H-1} on human chromosome 11. To refine this localization, several somatic cell hybrids containing only a part of chromosome 11 were studied. DNA from lines containing the short arm retained the c-ras^{H-1} gene, whereas DNA from lines containing only the long arm lacked this gene. Thus, $c\text{-}ras^{H\text{-}1}$ was localized to the region 11p11→11p15.

This regional localization provided considerable speculation regarding chromosomal abnormalities frequently associated with Wilms's tumor (Riccardi *et al.*, 1978; Yunis and Ramsay, 1980). Aniridia patients typically have a deletion in the short arm of chromosome 11. Although this deletion can vary in size and location, it always involves band 11p13. Of interest is the fact that aniridia predisposes patients to Wilms's tumors. Investigators speculated that this chromosomal abnormality either deleted $c\text{-}ras^{H\text{-}1}$ or altered it, possibly in a manner similar to that proposed in the *myc*-associated t(8;14) translocation. Evidence for this hypothesis, however, is lacking as Southern analysis of DNA from Wilms's tumor patients, including several patients with the aniridia-associated 11p13 deletion, failed to detect any alteration in the $c\text{-}ras^{H\text{-}1}$ gene compared to normal DNA (Huerre *et al.*, 1983; G. Kitchingman, D. Rosson, and A. Tereba, personal observation). In addition, transfection assays in our laboratory have shown that transforming activity from primary Wilms's tumor is associated with N-*ras* (Rosson and Tereba, personal observations). Finally, Jhanwar *et al.* (1983) have used *in situ* hybridization to localize this gene to 11p14.1. In this experiment 19% of the grains were localized to this site on pachytene chromosomes and 21% of the grains were localized to two sites on chromosome 12 associated with $c\text{-}ras^{K\text{-}2}$. This places the gene outside of the deletion.

Two genetic studies of aniridia patients and their families support the lack of $c\text{-}ras^{H\text{-}1}$ involvement in the 11p13 deletion, although the studies do suggest that the oncogene is closer to the terminus of chromosome 11 than 11p14.1. Huerre *et al.* (1983) analyzed the DNA of four aniridia patients. Three of the patients had deletions of 11p13 and the fourth had a deletion 11p13 to p15.1. In all cases the DNA analyses indicated two $c\text{-}ras^{H\text{-}1}$ alleles, thus suggesting that this gene is located between 11p15.2 and pter. In the second case, de Martinville and Francke (1983) analyzed a family in which the 11p12.2 to p14.2 from one chromosome was translocated to 11q22. A subsequent crossover event resulted in a chromosome lacking this region and a chromosome containing two of these regions. Thus, the members of this family had one, two, or three copies of this 11p region. When the $c\text{-}ras^{H\text{-}1}$ gene was analyzed in the three members, no quantitative difference was observed. Thus, $c\text{-}ras^{H\text{-}1}$ was assigned to 11p14.2 to pter. The discrepancies in these studies and the *in situ* hybridization results may be due either to inherent problems in quantitating Southern blots or to an error in interpreting banding patterns.

E. Location of Human N-*ras* on Chromosome 1

The N-*ras* gene was identified by transfection assays using three diverse cell types. Shimizu *et al.* (1983) isolated and cloned the transforming gene from a human neuroblastoma cell line, SK-N-SH. This gene showed weak but significant hybridization with the v-ras^H gene. More recently, Murray et al. (1983) have cloned the transforming gene from a human promyelocytic cell line, HL60, and Hall et al. (1983) cloned the transforming gene from two human sarcoma cell lines. After examination of the restriction patterns, these three clones were determined to be the same and were designated N-ras.

To determine the chromosomal location of human N-ras, 17 somatic cell hybrids were used (Hall et al., 1983). N-ras was detected in all seven clones that contained chromosome 1 and was absent in the 10 clones that lacked chromosome 1. This assignment was independently determined by Ryan et al. (1983), using mouse–human hybrids, and by McBride et al. (1983), using hamster–human hybrids. Using five somatic cell hybrids that contained only part of human chromosome 1, de Martinville et al. (1983a) sublocalized this gene between the centromere and p31. This finding sparked some speculation as alterations in chromosome 1, including deletions, duplications, and trisomy are quite common in human tumors, especially neuroblastoma. Unfortunately, examination of the endonuclease restriction patterns of activated and normal N-ras have uncovered no observable changes as seen with myc rearrangement in Burkitt's lymphoma. In addition, the level of transcription of the N-ras gene also appears to be identical in tumor and normal fibroblasts. Indeed, recent evidence has shown that N-ras is activated by a point mutation (Taparowsky et al., 1983). Finally, Davis et al. (1983) and Rabin et al. (1984) both have been able to further localize this gene using in situ hybridization. Hybridization occurred chiefly on chromosome 1 between 1p11 and 1p13 (Fig. 1). This more precise localization demonstrates that the major chromosomal structural alterations in neuroblastoma (1p31–p36) are probably not responsible for the activation of N-ras and agrees with the model of activation by point mutation discussed above.

F. Localization of Human c-ras^{K-2}

The human genome contains at least two genes sharing significant homology with v-ras^K. Because of this multiplicity, it was necessary to examine the chromosomal location of these genes by biochemical means, i.e., analysis of somatic cell hybrids to discriminate these genes. The c-ras^{K-2} gene, which has been isolated as an activated transforming gene from human tumors (Der et al., 1982), can be identified by a 14-kb HindIII fragment when a human DNA clone containing a small region of v-ras^K homology is used. Forty mouse–human hybrids were screened for this 14-kb fragment, and the results were correlated with the presence of particular human chromosomes (O'Brien et al., 1983). Only chromosome 12 showed complete concordance. In independent experiments using a cloned DNA segment of a human colon transforming gene (shown to be related to v-ras^K) a unique 2.9-kb EcoRI cross-hybridizing fragment could be detected in human cells but not in mouse cells (Sakaguchi *et al.*, 1983a). When 38 mouse–human somatic cell hybrids were examined, only those hybrids that contained chromosome 12 had this sequence. Finally, using mouse–human hybrids, Ryan *et al.* (1983) demonstrated that a lung carcinoma transforming gene (shown to be related to v-*ras*^{K}) was on chromosome 12. In analyzing the hybrids, they discovered that two hybrids lacked markers for the long arm of chromosome 12 but retained the transforming gene and the short arm markers. This implies that c-*ras*$^{K-2}$ is on the short arm of chromosome 12. Sakaguchi *et al.* (1984) confirmed this 12p location when they detected the gene in a somatic cell hybrid containing only human 12p12–pter. Thus, the four sets of experiments are in agreement. This finding was anticipated as chromosomes 11 and 12 have similar banding patterns and several genetic homologies that suggest that the two chromosomes were derived from a common precursor. As noted earlier, c-*ras*$^{H-1}$ is located on 11p14 to pter. Indeed, recent *in situ* hybridization data with a *ras*^{K}-related probe suggests that the chromosomal location of c-*ras*$^{K-2}$ may be at 12p12 (Jhanwar *et al.*, 1983). Complicating the results of these experiments is the observation of a second locus on chromosome 12 at position 12q24. Because of the nature of these experiments, either locus could represent c-*ras*$^{K-2}$. Surprisingly, the somatic cell hybrid experiments reveal only one *ras*-related gene on chromosome 12 (see Section X,G) unless that gene were duplicated exactly. This discrepancy will have to await further analysis. In any event, it is likely that c-*ras*$^{K-2}$ is located at 12p12 (Fig. 1).

G. Other Human *ras*-Related Protooncogenes

As previously mentioned, the human genome contains several *ras*-related genes. Besides the three genes of this family that show transforming activity (c-*ras*$^{H-1}$, c-*ras*$^{K-2}$, and N-*ras*), two other *ras*-related genes have been localized to specific chromosomes (O'Brien *et al.*, 1983). The c-*ras*$^{H-2}$ gene appears to lack introns and thus is probably transcriptionally inactive. This locus can be detected as a 3.6-kb *Bam*HI fragment using human c-*ras*$^{H-2}$ cloned DNA as a probe. When 20 somatic cell hybrids were examined, only the X chromosome showed complete concordance with this gene. Examination of one mutant that had lost the X chromosome but retained the terminus of the long arm of X (q26-ter) through a translocation revealed that the c-*ras*$^{H-2}$ gene was absent. Thus, it is likely that this gene is located on the short arm or proximal part of the long arm of the X chromosome (Fig. 1).

Using a different set of somatic cell hybrids, O'Brien *et al.* (1983) also localized the c-*ras*$^{K-1}$ gene. Using *Bgl*II-digested DNA from 14 mouse–human somatic cell hybrids, they were able to detect a 4.0-kb fragment cross-hybridizing with v-*ras*^{K} in eight cases. The presence of this gene was only observed with the presence of chromosome 6. This gene has therefore been assigned to chromosome 6.

To sublocalize this gene, Sakaguchi *et al.* (1984) made somatic cell hybrids containing different deletions in human chromosome 6. The analysis of six of these hybrids revealed that the c-*ras*[K-1] gene was present only when the chromosome segment p23–q12 was present. McBride *et al.* (1983), using hybrids containing the short arm of the chromosome, obtained similar results. This effectively localizes the gene to 6p23–q12 (Fig. 1).

XI. Chromosomal Location of c-*sis*

The v-*sis* oncogene is contained within the simian sarcoma virus and has been identified through molecular cloning and its conserved sequence, which is present in a wide variety of species. The oncogene codes for a protein of 28,000 daltons, designated p28[sis]; the sequence of the protein has been derived from the nucleic acid sequence of the oncogene (Devare *et al.*, 1983). Surprisingly, this sequence shares extensive homology for over 90 amino acids with the recently sequenced platelet-derived growth factor (PDGF) (Doolittle *et al.*, 1983; Waterfield *et al.*, 1983). This is the first instance where an oncogene has been shown to be almost identical to a known protein subunit. The fact that PDGF is a growth factor increases the likelihood that other oncogenes will be involved in growth regulation.

A. LOCATION OF MOUSE c-*sis* ON CHROMOSOME 15

When mouse and Chinese hamster DNA is digested with *Bam*HI restriction endonuclease and analyzed with a *sis*-specific probe, bands of 6.9 and 17 kb can be observed, respectively. Kozak *et al.* (1983b) utilized this observation to localize the mouse c-*sis* gene, employing hamster–mouse somatic cell hybrids. Nineteen hybrids were analyzed for the presence of the *Bam*HI mouse c-*sis*-specific fragment using a human cloned c-*sis* probe. Chromosome 15 showed 95% concordancy, whereas all other chromosomes showed better than 20% discordancy. The one discordant hybrid in this group contained c-*sis*, but it lacked karyotypic evidence of chromosome 15. However, this hybrid was shown to contain mouse c-*myc* sequences (15D3/E) and thus must contain some of chromosome 15 translocated to another chromosome. Thus, c-*sis* appears to be relatively close to c-*myc* on chromosome 15. This location is consistent with genetic data which place the mouse NADH diaphorase and arylsulfatase A genes on chromosome 15 (Franke *et al.*, 1981) and the human counterparts on chromosome 22, the location of the human c-*sis* gene (see the following section).

B. Location of Human c-*sis* on Chromosome 22

The chromosomal location of human c-*sis* was first determined by using human–rodent somatic cell hybrids and a fragment of the v-*sis* gene as probe (Swan *et al.*, 1982a). Analyzing the *Eco*RI-digested DNA from 28 hybrids, the presence and absence of human c-*sis* could only be correlated with chromosome 22. This assignment was confirmed by using a probe made from DNA 9 kb upstream from human c-*sis*. In addition, the presence of the human λ immunoglobulin gene, which is on chromosome 22 (McBride *et al.*, 1982a; Erickson *et al.*, 1981), correlated exactly with the presence of human c-*sis*.

The assignment of c-*sis* to chromosome 22 suggested that this gene may be involved in the t(9;22) translocation observed in CML (Rowley, 1980b) or the t(8;22) occasionally seen in Burkitt's lymphoma (Bernheim *et al.*, 1981). In both of these cases, the breakpoint is at 22q11. In this regard, Dalla-Favera *et al.* (1982d) used mouse–human hybrids in which the region q11–qter of human chromosome 22 was translocated to chromosome 17. When these hybrids were analyzed, only those cells that contained the 17q$^+$ retained human c-*sis*. Thus, the c-*sis* gene was sublocalized to this lower portion of chromosome 22. However, when the location of c-*sis* was determined by *in situ* hybridization (Jhanwar *et al.*, 1984), the breakpoints proved to be at some distance from this gene. Seventeen of 55 grains occurred at position 22q13 (Fig. 1) representing the location of c-*sis*. This location does result in its translocation from chromosome 22 to chromosome 9 or 8 in the two translocations mentioned above. Whether this rearrangement results in an activation of c-*sis* is unknown; but in a limited series of cells containing the t(9;22) or t(8;22), no increase in expression has been observed (Swan *et al.*, 1982a). As a result of the distance of c-*sis* from the breakpoints and the lack of expression in these cells, it is likely that c-*sis* is fortuitously being rearranged with no effect on its structure or expression.

XII. Localization of c-*fes*

Two feline sarcoma virus (FeSV) strains (Snyder-Theilen and Gardner) contain homologous oncogene sequences which are referred to as v-*fes*. These v-*fes* sequences are also hmologous to the v-*fps* oncogene present in the defective avian sarcoma viruses FuSV and PRC11 and probably are derived from the same gene present in the two host species (Shibuya *et al.*, 1980). These sequences are associated with fibroblast transformation *in vitro* and with sarcomas *in vivo*. The oncogene products of the two FeSV are associated with tyrosine kinase activity (Barbacid *et al.*, 1980; Reynolds *et al.*, 1980) and even share some amino acid homology with several other sarcoma-associated oncogenes, v-*src*, v-*yes*, and v-*mos* (Hampe *et al.*, 1982; Kitamura *et al.*, 1982; Van Beveren *et al.*, 1981).

Thus, v-*fes* and its protooncogenes c-*fes* most likely are derived from some ancestral kinase gene now represented by several protooncogenes.

A. Location of Mouse c-*fes* on Chromosome 7

The location of c-*fes* in mice was accomplished using hamster–mouse somatic cell hybrids (Kozak *et al.*, 1983a). A 4.4-kb *Hind*III-digested mouse DNA fragment cross-hybridizes with a number of v-*fes* probes. This could be distinguished from the 4.0-kb fragment found in hamster DNA. Using 22 hybrid clones, 12 were found to contain the mouse c-*fes* gene. All of these clones contained chromosome 7, and conversely none of the 10 clones which lacked mouse c-*fes* retained chromosome 7. The percentage of discordance with the other chromosomes was greater than 23. This localization was not unexpected as the *IDH2* locus closely associated with the location of human c-*fes* (see the following section) has its mouse counterpart, *Idh-2*, on chromosome 7. No disease-specific translocations have been associated with mouse chromosome 7.

To further localize this gene, Blatt *et al.* (1984) used recognizable allelic variations in genetic experiments involving inbred strains of mice. They observed that the A/J strain of mice had a slightly larger *Eco*RI restriction fragment containing c-*fes* than the C57BL/6J strain. This polymorphic variation allowed them to analyze the distribution of each parental c-*fes* gene in a series of 23 recombinant inbred strains of mice derived from these parents. The distribution was compared with the distribution of other loci that could be distinguished between the two parental strains. As a result of the mating procedure, linked loci would have a similar distribution. The results showed that c-*fes* mapped to the proximal portion of chromosome 7 between the *Gpi-1* and *Tam-1* genes.

B. Human c-*fes* and the t(15;17) Translocation of Promyelocytic Leukemia

The initial localization of human c-*fes* was accomplished using mouse–human somatic cell hybrids (Dalla-Favera *et al.*, 1982c). DNA from a battery of cell hybrids was analyzed for a 3.9-kb *Bam*HI-digested DNA fragment that hybridized to a human c-*fes* cloned DNA probe. Complete concordance for the presence of the human c-*fes* gene was only observed with chromosome 15. In an independent experiment using eight somatic cell hybrids, Heisterkamp *et al.* (1982) arrived at the same conclusion. To obtain a more precise localization of this gene, *in situ* hybridization was performed using the same probe as the first set of experiments (Harper *et al.*, 1983). Specific hybridization of 119 metaphase spreads revealed that 12% of the 393 independent sites showing grains occurred over 15q2. This was statistically highly significant and represented the only major hybridization. Examination of the grain distribution along chromosome 15 showed that most of the grains were located on 15q26 (Fig. 1). Jhanwar *et al.* (1984) have confirmed this location using *in situ* hybridization to pachytene chromosomes.

It has been suggested that the location of this gene is near a very frequent translocation found in promyelocytic leukemia patients t(15;17) (q22;q21). Three sets of data suggest that this association may be misleading. First, while the translocation breakpoint is poorly defined, the current interpretation is that it occurs at 15q22 (Rowley, 1983). This is significantly far from the suggested location of c-*fes*. Second, Sheer *et al.* (1983) have determined that the 15q$^+$ rearranged chromosome does not contain c-*fes*. However, observations on complex translocations have suggested to Rowley (1983) that 15q$^+$ is the important factor observed in this disease. Thus, if an activated c-*fes* were involved, it would have to work in a different way than that predicted for *myc* or *abl*. Finally, v-*fes* has not been associated with promyelocytic leukemia or, for that matter, with any hematopoietic tumor. Indeed, the activated oncogene derived from the promyelocytic cell line HL60 has turned out to be N-*ras* (Murray *et al.*, 1983). Third, *myc* has been suggested as playing a role in oncogenesis of this cell line as a result of its amplification (Collins and Groudine, 1982; Dalla-Favera *et al.*, 1982b). Further examination of this possible association will have to be performed before any theory can be substantiated.

XIII. Localization of c-*mos*

The v-*mos* gene is defined as the transforming component present in the Moloney and Gazdar strains of murine sarcoma virus. Several mutants have been obtained (Blair *et al.*, 1979) and subgenomic fragments have been utilized to show that this gene is directly involved in the transformation of fibroblasts *in vitro* (Anderson *et al.*, 1979; Canaani *et al.*, 1979; Blair *et al.*, 1980). The gene has been cloned and sequenced and, surprisingly, the predicted carboxy-terminal region shows significant amino acid homology with the avian v-*src* gene (van Beveren *et al.*, 1981). However, there is evidence to suggest that v-*mos* does not possess a tyrosine-specific kinase activity.

A. Location of Mouse c-*mos* on Chromosome 4

Although mouse genetic analysis has been very extensive, few protooncogenes have been localized in this species. The c-*mos* gene was localized by using mouse–hamster hybrids in which mouse chromosomes are segregated on a background of a full complement of hamster chromosomes (Swan *et al.*, 1982b).

Using a probe derived from c-*mos* cloned DNA, a 4.3-kb cross-hybridizing fragment is observed when mouse DNA is digested with *Sst*-1. The hamster c-*mos* cross-hybridizing fragment can be distinguished easily from this as it migrates as a 6.0-kb fragment. Looking at the DNA from eight somatic cell hybrids, complete concordance for mouse c-*mos* was observed only with chromosome 4. Although there were not many somatic cell hybrids used in this study, one of them contained only chromosome 4 and had the mouse c-*mos* gene. Thus, it can be concluded with reasonable certainty that c-*mos* is on chromosome 4. Although chromosomal abnormalities do exist in association with certain tumors, chromosome 4 has not been implicated in this regard.

B. LOCATION OF HUMAN c-*mos* NEAR THE t(8;21) TRANSLOCATION ASSOCIATED WITH AML

The localization of human c-*mos* was first determined by use of human–hamster and human–mouse somatic cell hybrids (Prakash *et al.*, 1982). Using a human c-*mos* probe that contained v-*mos*-related sequences, the DNA from 24 human–rodent somatic cell hybrids was analyzed. Although significant discordancy was observed between the presence of human c-*mos* and all human chromosomes except 8, the presence of human chromosome 8 was ambiguous in the human–mouse hybrids. Additional human–hamster subclones were analyzed and eventually confirmed that the location of c-*mos* was on chromosome 8.

This localization was further analyzed by *in situ* hybridization using the human c-*mos* probe (Neel *et al.*, 1982). A total of 333 grains were observed over 48 pachytene and metaphase spreads. Of these grains, only 8q and 9q contained significantly larger numbers of grains than were expected by random distribution. However, when the grain distribution was analyzed on the long arm of each of these chromosomes, only chromosome 8 had a nonrandom distribution. The majority of grains were located at 8q22. Thus, the location of c-*mos* has been assigned to this site (Fig. 1).

In examining common translocations associated with tumors, one aberration was found to be near the site of c-*mos*. The most frequent translocation of AML (around 10 to 15% of the cases) have a t(8;21)(q22;q22) translocation. In addition, trisomy of chromosome 8 is very frequent. This close agreement between this translocation breakpoint and the location of c-*mos* is, with the exception of the *myc, raf,* and *abl* genes, the closest any protooncogene has been shown to be to a common translocation associated with a disease. Unfortunately, v-*mos* is not associated with hematopoietic tumors and no increase in expression nor structural abnormalities of c-*mos* have been reported in AML cells. Thus, until further evidence is obtained, it is uncertain whether the t(8;21) translocation affects the c-*mos* gene in any way.

XIV. Chromosomal Location of Human c-*fos*

The c-*fos* protooncogene is homologous to the oncogene present in the Finkel-Biskis-Jinkins murine osteosarcoma virus. This gene is expressed primarily in the extraembryonic tissues during normal development (Muller *et al.*, 1983). Evidence for its role in growth regulation was obtained when it was discovered that stimulation of quiescent fibroblasts with growth factors resulted in the rapid synthesis of c-*fos* mRNA followed by the synthesis of c-*myc* mRNA and the subsequent rapid degradation of c-*fos* mRNA (Muller *et al.*, 1984). This suggests that c-*fos* functions at a very early stage in the induction of growth.

The localization of the human c-*fos* gene was performed both by analysis of somatic cell hybrids and by *in situ* hybridization (Barker *et al.*, 1984). The analysis of a panel of 31 mouse–human hybrids using both v-*fos* and c-*fos* probes showed that c-*fos* was on chromosome 14. One discordancy contained a t(5;14) translocation and suggested that the gene was distal to 14q21. *In situ* hybridization confirmed this location, revealing 40% of the grains associated with 14q21–q31 (Fig. 1).

XV. Chromosomal Location of c-*src*

The v-*src* gene is present in Rous sarcoma virus (RSV) and represents a unique case in that the oncogene has not displaced any viral sequence. Thus, the virus is replication competent. The *src* gene is by far the most studied of all the oncogenes, and more is known about its gene product, pp60, than about any other gene. Originally detected as an additional sequence when compared to avian leukosis viruses (ALV) (Duesberg and Vogt, 1970; Martin and Duesberg, 1972; Lai *et al.*, 1973), many ts mutants have been obtained to confirm its oncogenic property (Martin, 1970; Friis *et al.*, 1971; Kawai and Hanafusa, 1971; Wyke and Linial, 1973). The v-*src* product is a protein kinase that is present in infected cells in the membrane at the attachment sites between the cell and the surface it is growing on (Wellingham *et al.*, 1979; Rohrschneider, 1980). Using this gene as a probe, it was first discovered that both chickens, the natural host of these viruses, and other widely divergent species contain related sequences (Stehelin *et al.*, 1976). This original observation has become the norm for oncogenes in general. Being the first and most extensively studied oncogene, it is not surprising that it was also the first protooncogene to be localized to a particular set of chromosomes.

A. CHICKEN c-*src:* THE FIRST LOCALIZED PROTOONCOGENE

The localization of c-*src* to a particular chromosome group was accomplished by separating metaphase chromosomes from a T cell leukemia cell line, MSB-1, on a sucrose gradient (Padgett *et al.*, 1977). The DNA from each fraction of chromosomes was then analyzed with a v-*src* probe. The c-*src* gene was present in the fractions containing the microchromosomes. In another experiment in which separation was better, it was determined that the gene was on a large microchromosome (Hughes *et al.*, 1979), possibly between 13 and 16.

In an independent set of experiments, the c-*src* gene was localized using *in situ* hybridization to metaphase chromosomes from normal chicken fibroblast cultures (Tereba *et al.*, 1979). Retroviral RNAs containing (RSV) and lacking (ALV) v-*src* were attached to ^{125}I-labeled sea urchin DNA as described in Section III,C. Hybridization with the RSV RNA occurred on chromosome 1 and the chromosome group 10–12, whereas hybridization with ALV RNA occurred only on chromosome 1. Thus, the c-*src* gene was probably on one of the large microchromosomes. Several additional experiments using embryos that contained one or two known endogenous retrovirus loci substantiated the earlier results and suggested that c-*src* was probably on chromosome 12 (Tereba and Astrin, 1980, 1982; Tereba *et al.*, 1981; Tereba, 1981; Tereba and Lai, 1982). Since chromosome 12–15 are very similar in size, additional work would be required to further localize this gene. It should also be pointed out that the c-*src* gene was localized to the same set of chromosomes in Japanese quail (Tereba *et al.*, 1979). This is not surprising since these two birds have very similar karyotypes.

B. Location of c-*src* on Mouse Chromosome 2

The c-*src* gene was localized to mouse chromosome 2 using two approaches. First, Sakaguchi *et al.* (1984) analyzed the DNA from 15 mouse–hamster hybrids with a v-*src* probe. The two mouse-related fragments were observed only with the presence of chromosome 2. This location is not surprising since the genes for adenosine deaminase and inosine triphosphatase are found on this chromosome and on human chromosome 20, the location of c-*src*-1.

The second approach utilized recognizable allelic variations between two strains of mice as described in Section XII,A. Examination of the recombination frequency between *Psp* (parotic secretory protein gene on chromosome 2) and the restriction site polymorphism of c-*src* observed between the two strains of mice showed that they were linked and were 2.2 ± 1.6 centimorgans apart (Blatt *et al.*, 1984). This places c-*src* on the distal half of chromosome 2.

C. Human c-*src*

When a v-*src* probe is used, a large 28-kb *Eco*RI-digested fragment of human DNA can be detected along with additional minor bands. These major large fragments can be easily distinguished from *Eco*RI-digested mouse DNA containing c-*src*. Sakaguchi *et al*. (1983b) utilized this observation and somatic cell hybrids to localize the human c-*src* gene. Thirty human–mouse hybrids were examined for the presence of the *src*-related human fragments. Only chromosome 20, as determined by the chromosome marker adenosine deaminase, had a perfect concordancy. To further localize this gene, Le Beau *et al*. (1984) used *in situ* hybridization with a c-*src* probe. Specific hybridization was observed over two regions: 1p34–p36 (13.5% of grains) and 20q12–q13 (9.9% of grains). Hybridization at high strigency or with a v-*src* probe also identified these sites, but the hybridization was weaker. Although this experiment does not determine which of the sites represents the c-*src*-1 locus, from the somatic cell hybrid data it is safe to conclude that this locus resides at 20q12–q13 (Fig. 1). The second locus identified on chromosome 1 probably represents the c-*src*-2 locus, a gene somewhat less related to v-*src* than is c-*src*-1.

XVI. Chromosomal Location of Human c-*fms*

The SM strain of feline sarcoma virus obtained by McDonough *et al*. (1971) contains an oncogene that is different from the other two v-*fes*-containing FeSV. The oncogene v-*fms* shows no homology to v-*fes*, and unlike v-*fes*, it is neither phosphorylated at tyrosine residues nor contains any protein kinase activity. Thus, *fms* appears to act differently than the other cat sarcoma-inducing oncogene.

The chromosomal localization of human c-*fms* was determined by two groups using somatic cell hybrids. Roussel *et al*. (1983) used a fragment of the human c-*fms* gene to analyze 32 mouse–human somatic cell hybrids. This probe detected only the human c-*fms* sequence and thus simplified the analysis. Complete concordance of c-*fms* was only observed with chromosome 5. As a confirmation of this, three hybrids containing chromosome 5 were treated with diphtheria toxin to eliminate chromosome 5, which contains the gene coding for the toxin receptor. All hybrid clones that lost chromosome 5 also lost the c-*fms* gene.

Groffen *et al*. (1983) utilized the same approach, screening 15 mouse–human hybrids with a human c-*fms* probe. Chromosome 5 showed complete concordance with the presence of c-*fms*. To regionally localize the gene, six hamster–human hybrids were analyzed. One hybrid contained only human chromosome 5 and the other hybrids were derivatives which contained deletions in chromosome 5. Only those hybrids that contained q34 retained c-*fms* sequences. This included two hybrids which had deletions of q12 to q33 and q35, respectively. Hybrids that lacked q3 lacked c-*fms*. Thus, this gene was localized to 5q34 (Fig. 1).

XVII. Localization of the Human c-*raf* Gene Family

The selection of oncogenes in nature has been accomplished by retroviruses through a very inefficient, poorly understood process of gene transfer from a tumor cell to a retrovirus genome. In an effort to help this natural selection, Rapp *et al.* (1983a) used iododeoxyuridine to induce retrovirus production in a methylcholanthrene-induced murine cell line. One isolate, 3611-MSV, obtained from this experiment was an acute transforming replication-defective murine retrovirus. When injected into newborn mice, it caused rapid fibrosarcomas and could transform both fibroblasts and epithelial cells in tissue culture. Of importance, cloned viral DNA transformed NIH-3T3 cells in transfection assays (Rapp *et al.*, 1983b), thus extending the association between transforming genes and viral oncogenes. The transforming agent appears to be a unique sequence called v-*raf* which, like other oncogenes, contains extensive homology to sequences in a variety of species. The oncogene shares extensive homology with v-*mil*, a second oncogene present in the avian *myc*-containing retrovirus MH2 (Jansen *et al.*, 1983).

Two loci showing homology with *raf* can be detected in human cells. The c-*raf*-1 locus appears to contain sequences homologous with the entire v-*raf* gene and has at least eight introns. The c-*raf*-2 locus contains no introns and lacks extensive open reading frames. For this reason c-*raf*-2 is probably a pseudogene. To identify the human chromosomes that contain these genes, Southern blot analysis of human–mouse and human–hamster somatic cell hybrids was performed (Bonner *et al.*, 1984). The analysis of 35 hybrids showed the location of c-*raf*-1 on chromosome 3 and c-*raf*-2 on chromosome 4 (Fig. 1). In both cases, a single hybrid contained the protooncogene but lacked the appropriate chromosome as determined by karyotypic and isoenzyme analyses. Marker chromosomes in each of these hybrids, however, could explain the discrepancies.

To sublocalize the c-*raf*-1 locus, *in situ* hybridization was performed using a probe containing the 3' flanking region of c-*raf*-1. Eleven of 70 chromosomal spreads showed hybridization over 3p25, with this region containing approximately 9% of the total grains. This was highly significant and suggests that c-*raf*-1 is located at 3p25 (Fig. 1). This location correlates with a specific translocation (t(3;8)(p25;q21) in mixed parotid gland tumors. It will be of interest to determine whether the structure or level of transcriptional expression of c-*raf* is altered in these tumors.

XVIII. Summary and Perspectus

Table I contains a summary of the chromosomal location of 22 protooncogenes in chicken, mouse, and human cells. The table also lists the diseases

TABLE I
CHROMOSOMAL LOCATION OF PROTOONCOGENES

Protooncogene	Disease caused by homologous v-onc	Chromosomal location		
		Chicken	Mouse	Human
c-myc	Myelocytoma, carcinoma	1–3[b]		
	Lymphoma[a]	13–16[c]	15D3	8q24
N-myc	Neuroblastoma[a]			2p23–p24
Blym	B lymphoma[d]			1p32
c-myb	Myeloblastic leukemia	13–16[c]; 2–Z[b]	10	6q22–q24
c-ets				11q23–q24
c-erb-B	Erythroleukemia	2–3	11	7p22–q22
c-erb-A		10–12[c]; > 8[b]	11	17p11–q21
c-abl	B cell lymphoma, leukemia[a]		2	9q34
c-ras^{H-1}	Sarcoma, erythroleukemia		7	11p14.1[c]
	Carcinoma[d]			11p15.2–pter[e]
c-ras^{H-2}				Xq25–pter
c-ras^{K-1}				6p23–q12
c-ras^{K-2}	Sarcoma, erythroleukemia			
	Carcinoma[d]		6	12p12
N-ras	Sarcoma[d], carcinoma[d]			
	Leukemia[d]		3	1p11–1p13
c-sis	Sarcoma		15	22q13
c-fes	Sarcoma		7	15q26
c-mos	Sarcoma		4	8q22
c-fos	Osteosarcoma			14q21–q31
c-src-1	Sarcoma	12–16	2	20q12–q13
c-src-2				1p34–p36
c-fms	Sarcoma			5q34
c-raf-1	Sarcoma			3p25
c-raf-2				4

[a]Disease association inferred from proven chromosome alterations near protooncogene.
[b]Determined by analysis of fractionated chromosomes.
[c]Determined by in situ hybridization.
[d]Disease associated with activated protooncogene using transfection assays.
[e]Determined by analysis of DNA from somatic cell hybrids.

associated with the homologous retrovirus oncogene and associations with naturally occurring tumors. The chicken protooncogenes were the first examined, mainly for the purpose of determining the chromosomal association between endogenous retrovirus loci and protooncogenes. This examination, along with Southern blot analyses of diverse species, has revealed no correlation, and it is now assumed that these protooncogenes are important growth and/or regulatory genes that infrequently act as nonspecific targets for exogenous retrovirus genomes. Because of the almost invarient structure of avian chromosomes and the many small unidentifiable microchromosomes, this system has proved unsuitable for protooncogene localization studies beyond the initial examination. Indeed, the nomenclature of these chromosomes has even led to some confusion concerning protooncogene location. Tereba *et al.* (1979) and Tereba and Astrin (1980), using *in situ* hybridization, described the localization of c-*src* on a *large microchromosome* group, 10–12. Hughes *et al.* (1979), using chromosome fractionation suggested that c-*src* was on a *small macrochromosome* somewhat larger than the chromosome containing the ribosomal RNA genes (15–18). Chromosomes 12 to 15 are very close in size, a fact indicating that the two sets of data are really compatible.

The localization of protooncogenes in mouse chromosomes, with the notable exception of c-*myc*, has proved to be no great revelation either. Because of the similarity of chromosomes, localization has been accomplished by analysis of DNA from somatic cell hybrids. Thus, there is a general lack of sublocalization. Nevertheless, with the exception of c-*myc*-involved rearrangement in plasmacytomas, no gross chromosomal abnormalities have been associated with protooncogene locations. It is likely, therefore, that the major emphasis will be centered around the localization of protooncogenes on human chromosomes.

The localization of human protooncogenes has progressed at breakneck speed since the discovery that chicken c-*myc* was involved in avian leukosis virus-induced bursal lymphomas. The localization of c-*myc* and c-*abl* to the breakpoints of very consistent translocations in Burkitt's lymphoma and chronic myelogenous leukemia, respectively, support the importance of pursuing the localization of protooncogenes by linking specific genes with the disease state of human malignancies. With the isolation of molecularly cloned DNA spanning the translocation junction, it will now become possible to examine why and how these translocations occur and what mechanism is involved in supposedly activating these protooncogenes.

With the localization of other protooncogenes, the task became finding the appropriate disease-related translocation. As Yunis (1983) pointed out, many tumors contain specific chromosomal abnormalities. Thus, it was not hard to correlate the location of these protooncogenes with a particular disease. Unfortunately, in many cases, the correlations have been applied to less frequent abnormalities and the required molecular interactions have stretched to thousands of kilobase pairs. These dubious correlations have many times linked protooncogenes with diseases never associated with the homologous viral oncogene. Finally, activation mechanisms of protooncogenes determined by transfection assays and DNA sequencing have been ignored in this matching game. As examples, c-*ras*[H-1], c-*ras*[K-2], and N-*ras* are all located in the general area of chromosomal abnormalities associated with specific diseases. These genes, however, have been shown to be activated by single point mutations (Tabin *et al.,*

1982; Reddy *et al.*, 1982; Taparowsky *et al.*, 1982, 1983). Although point mutations have been associated with the process of transposition in the case of c-*myc* (Rabbitts *et al.*, 1983), this was a special case probably involving the hypermutation mechanism of the variable portion of the immunoglobulin genes. Thus, on several counts, correlations of several protooncogene locations with deletions and translocations appear weak. This should not detract from the molecularly proven correlations such as c-*myc* with Burkitt's lymphoma-associated t(8;14) translocations.

From the fall of 1982 until the end of 1984, most of the known protooncogenes have been localized on normal human chromosomes. Future advances will utilize cells that contain the abnormal karyotypes of interest in order to assess the earlier suppositions of gene translocation and deletion. The ultimate experiments, however, will have to await the development of new assay systems that can determine the oncogenic and immortalizing activities of a wide range of activated protooncogenes. Until then the chromosomal localization data will only be able to point an accusing finger.

ACKNOWLEDGMENTS

This project has been supported in part by Grant CA-34759 from the National Cancer Institute, by Cancer Center Support (CORE) Grant CA-21765, and by ALSAC.

REFERENCES

Adams, J. M., Gerondakis, S., Webb, E., Mitchell, J., Berard, O., and Cory, S. (1982). *Proc. Natl. Acad. Sci. U.S.A.* **79,** 6966–6970.
Adams, J. M., Gerondakis, S., Webb, E., Corcoran, L. M., and Cory, S. (1983). *Proc. Natl. Acad. Sci. U.S.A.* **80,** 1982–1986.
Alitalo, K., Schwab, M., Lin, C. C., Varmus, H. E., and Bishop, J. M. (1983). *Proc. Natl. Acad. Sci. U.S.A.* **80,** 1707–1711.
Anderson, G. R., Mariott, K. R., and Whitaker-Dowling, P. A. (1979). *Virology* **99,** 31–48.
Barbacid, M., Lauver, A. V., and Devare, S. G. (1980). *J. Virol.* **33,** 196–207.
Barker, P. E., Rabviin, M., Watson, M., Berg, W. R., Ruddle, F. H., and Verma, I. M. (1984). *Proc. Natl. Acad. Sci. U.S.A.* **81,** 5826–5830.
Bernheim, A., Berger, R., and Lenoir, G. (1981). *Cancer Genet. Cytogenet.* **3,** 307–315.
Bishop, J. M. (1983). *Annu. Rev. Biochem.* **52,** 301–354.
Bishop, J. M., and Varnus, H. E. (1982). In "RNA Tumor Viruses" (R. Weiss, N. Teich, H. Varmus, and J. Coffin, eds.), pp. 999–1108. Cold Spring Harbor Laboratory, Cold Spring Harbor, New York.
Bister, K., and Duesberg, P. H. (1979). *Proc. Natl. Acad. Sci. U.S.A.* **76,** 5023–5027.
Blair, D. G., Hull, M. A., and Finch, E. A. (1979). *Virology* **95,** 303–316.
Blair, D. G., McClements, W. L., Oskarsson, M. K., Fishinger, P. J., and Vande Woude, G. F. (1980). *Proc. Natl. Acad. Sci. U.S.A.* **77,** 3504–3508.

Blatt, C., Harper, M. E., Franchini, G., Nesbitt, N., and Simon, M. I. (1984). *Mol. Cell. Biol.* **4,** 978–981.

Bonner, T., O'Brien, S. J., Nash, W. G., Rapp, U. R., Morton, C. C., and Leder, P. (1984). *Science* **223,** 71–74.

Calame, K., Kim, S., Lalley, P., Hill, R., Davis, M., and Hood, L. (1982). *Proc. Natl. Acad. Sci. U.S.A.* **79,** 6994–6998.

Canaani, E., Robbins, K. C., and Aaronson, S. A. (1979). *Nature (London)* **282,** 378–383.

Chang, E. H., Furth, M. E., Scolnick, E. M., and Lowy, D. R. (1982). *Nature (London)* **297,** 479–484.

Chen, J. H. (1980). *J. Virol.* **36,** 162–170.

Collins, S., and Groudine, M. (1982). *Nature (London)* **298,** 679–681.

Cooper, G. M., and Neiman, P. E. (1981). *Nature (London)* **292,** 857–858.

Croce, C. M., Shander, M., Martinis, J., Circurel, L., D'Aconna, G. G., Dolby, T. W., and Koprowski, H. (1979). *Proc. Natl. Acad. Sci. U.S.A.* **76,** 3416–3419.

Dalla-Favera, R., Bregni, M., Erikson, J., Patterson, D., Gallo, R. C., and Croce, C. M. (1982a). *Proc. Natl. Acad. Sci. U.S.A.* **79,** 7824–7827.

Dalla-Favera, R., Wong-Staal, F., and Gallo, R. C. (1982b). *Nature (London)* **299,** 61–63.

Dalla-Favera, R., Franchini, G., Martinotti, S., Wong-Staal, F., Gallo, R. C., and Croce, C. M. (1982c). *Proc. Natl. Acad. Sci. U.S.A.* **79,** 4714–4717.

Dalla-Favera, R., Gallo, R. C., Giallongo, A., and Croce, C. M. (1982d). *Science* **218,** 686–688.

Davis, M., Malcolm, S., Hall, A., and Marshall, C. J. (1983). *EMBO J.* **2,** 2281–2283.

Dean, P. N., and Pinkel, D. (1978). *J. Histochem. Cytochem.* **26,** 622–627.

De Feo, D., Gonda, M. A., Young, H. A., Chang, E. H., Lowy, D. R., Scolnick, E. M., and Ellis, R. W. (1981). *Proc. Natl. Acad. Sci. U.S.A.* **78,** 3328–3332.

de Klein, A., Van Kessel, A. G., Grosueld, G., Bartram, C. R., Hagemeijer, A., Bootsma, D., Spurr, N. K., Heisterkamp, N., Groffen, J., and Stephensen, J. R. (1982). *Nature (London)* **300,** 765–767.

de Martinville, B., and Francke, U. (1983). *Nature (London)* **305,** 641–643.

de Martinville, B., Cunningham, J. M., Murray, M. J., and Francke, U. (1983a). *Nucleic Acids Res.* **11,** 5267–5275.

De Martinville, B., Giacalone, J., Shih, C., Weinberg, R. A., and Francke, U. (1983b). *Science* **219,** 498–501.

Der, C. J., Krontiris, T. G., and Cooper, G. M. (1982). *Proc. Natl. Acad. Sci. U.S.A.* **79,** 3637–3640.

de Taisne, C., Gegonne, A., Stehelin, D., Bernheim, A., and Berger, R. (1984). *Nature (London)* **310,** 581–583.

Devare, S. G., Reddy, E. P., Law, J. D., Robbins, K. C., and Aaronson, S. A. (1983). *Proc. Natl. Acad. Sci. U.S.A.* **80,** 731–735.

Diamond, A., Cooper, G. M., Ritz, J., and Lane, M-A. (1983). *Nature (London)* **305,** 112–116.

Doolittle, R. F., Hunkapiller, M. W., Hood, L. E., Devare, S. G., Robbins, K. C., Aaronson, S. A., and Antoniades, H. N. (1983). *Science* **221,** 275–277.

Duesberg, P. H., and Vogt, P. K. (1970). *Proc. Natl. Acad. Sci. U.S.A.* **67,** 1673–1680.

Erikson, J., Martines, J., and Croce, C. M. (1981). *Nature (London)* **294,** 173–175.

Erikson, J., Ar-Rushdi, A., Drwinga, H. L., Nowell, P. C., and Croce, C. M. (1983). *Proc. Natl. Acad. Sci. U.S.A.* **80,** 820–824.

Fournier, R. E. K., and Frelinger, J. A. (1982). *Mol. Cell. Biol.* **2,** 526–534.

Franke, U., Tetri, P., Taggart, R. T., and Oliver, N. (1981). *Cytogenet. Cell Genet* **31,** 58–69.

Friis, R. R., Toyoshima, K., and Vogt, P. K. (1971). *Virology* **43,** 375–389.

Gall, J. G., and Pardue, L. L. (1969). *Proc. Natl. Acad. Sci. U.S.A.* **63,** 378–383.

Goff, S. P., D'Eustachio, P., Ruddle, F. H., and Baltimore, D. (1982). *Science* **218,** 1317–1319.

Goubin, G., Goldman, D. S., Luce, J., Neiman, P. E., and Cooper, G. M. (1983). *Nature (London)* **302,** 114–119.

Gray, J. W., Langlois, R. G., Carrano, A. V., Burkhart-Schultz, K., and Van Dilla, M. A. (1979). *Chromosoma* **73,** 9–27.

Groffen, J., Heisterkamp, N., Spurr, N., Dana, S., Wasmuth, J. J., and Stephenson, J. R. (1983). *Nucleic Acids Res.* **11,** 6331–6339.

Hall, A., Marshall, C. J., Spurr, N. K., and Weiss, R. A. (1983). *Nature (London)* **303,** 396–400.

Hampe, A., Lapnevotte, J., Galibert, F., Fedele, L. A., and Sherr, C. J. (1982). *Cell* **30,** 775–785.

Harper, M. E., and Saunders, G. F. (1981). *Chromosome* **83,** 431–439.

Harper, M. E., Franchini, G., Love, J., Simon, M. I., Gallo, R. C., and Wong-Staal, F. (1983). *Nature (London)* **304,** 169–171.

Harris, L. J., D'Eustachio, P., Ruddle, F. H., and Marcu, K. B. (1982a). *Proc. Natl. Acad. Sci. U.S.A.* **79,** 6622–6626.

Harris, L. J., Lang, R. B., and Marcu, K. B. (1982b). *Proc. Natl. Acad. Sci. U.S.A.* **79,** 4175–4179.

Hayward, W. S., Neel, B. G., and Astrin, S. M. (1981). *Nature (London)* **290,** 475–479.

Heisterkamp, N., Groffen, J., Stephenson, J. R., Spurr, N. K., Goodfellow, P. N., Solomon, E., Carritt, B., and Bodmer, W. F. (1982). *Nature (London)* **299,** 747–749.

Heisterkamp, N., Stephenson, J. R., Groffen, J., Hansen, P. F., de Klein, A., Bartram, C. R., and Grosveld, G. (1983). *Nature (London)* **306,** 239–242.

Huerre, C., Despoisse, S., Gilgenkrantz, S., Lenoir, G. M., and Junien, C. (1983). *Nature (London)* **305,** 638–641.

Hughes, S. H., Stubblefield, E., Payvar, F., Engel, J. D., Dodgson, J. B., Spector, D., Cordell, B., Schimke, R. T., and Varmus, H. E. (1979). *Proc. Natl. Acad. Sci. U.S.A.* **76,** 1348–1352.

Jansen, H. W., Ruckert, B., Lurz, R., and Bister, K. (1983). *EMBO J.* **2,** 1969–1975.

Jhanwar, S. C., Neel, B. G., Hayward, W. S., and Chaganti, R. S. K. (1983). *Proc. Natl. Acad. Sci. U.S.A.* **80,** 4794–4797.

Jhanwar, S. C., Neel, B. G., Hayward, W. S., and Chaganti, R. S. K. (1984). *Cytogenet. Cell Genet.* **38,** 73–75.

Kanda, N., Schreck, R., Alt, F., Bruns, G., Baltimore, D., and Latt, S. (1983). *Proc. Natl. Acad. Sci. U.S.A.* **80,** 4069–4073.

Kawai, S., and Hanafusa, H. (1971). *Virology* **46,** 470–479.

Kirsch, I. R., Morton, C. C., Nakahara, K., and Leder, P. (1982). *Science* **216,** 301–303.

Kitamura, N., Kitamura, A., Toyoshima, K., Hirayama, Y., and Yoshida, M. (1982). *Nature (London)* **297,** 205–207.

Kohl, N. E., Kanda, N., Schreck, R. R., Bruns, G., Latt, S. A., Gilbert, F., and Alt, F. W. (1983). *Cell* **35,** 359–367.

Kozak, C. A., Sears, J. F., and Hoggan, M. D. (1983a). *J. Virol.* **47,** 217–220.

Kozak, C. A., Sears, J. F., and Hoggan, M. D. (1983b). *Science* **271,** 867–869.

Lai, M. M. C., Duesberg, P. H., Horst, J., and Vogt, P. K. (1973). *Proc. Natl. Acad. Sci. U.S.A.* **70,** 2266–2270.

Lai, M. M. C., Hu, S. S. F., and Vogt, P. K. (1979). *Virology* **97,** 366–377.

Land, H., Parada, L. F., and Weinberg, R. A. (1983). *Nature (London)* **304,** 596–602.

Lane, M. A., Sainten, A., and Cooper, G. (1982). *Cell* **28,** 873–880.

Lawler, S. D. (1977). *Clin. Haematol.* **6,** 55–75.

Le Beau, M. M., Westbrook, C. A., Diaz, M. O., and Rowley, J. D. (1984). *Nature (London)* **312,** 70–71.

Levinson, A. D. Courtneidge S. A. and Bishop, J. M. (1981). *Proc. Natl. Acad. Sci. U.S.A.* **78,** 1624–1628.

Linial, M., and Blair, D. (1982). *In,* "RNA Tumor Viruses" (R. Weiss, N. Teich, H. Varmus, and J. Coffin, eds.), pp 649–784. Cold Spring Harbor Laboratory, Cold Spring Harbor, New York.

McBride, O. W., Hieter, P. A., Hollis, G. F., Swan, D., Otey, M. C., and Leder, P. (1982a). *J. Exp. Med.* **155,** 1480–1490.

McBride, O. W., Swan, D. C., Santos, E., Barbacid, M., Tronick, S. R., and Aaronson, S. A. (1982b). *Nature (London)* **300,** 773–774.

McBride, O. W., Swan, D. C., Tronick, S. R., Gol, R., Klimanis, D., Moore, D. E., and Aaronson, S. A. (1983). *Nucleic Acids Res.* **11,** 8222–8237.

McDonough, S. K., Larsen, S., Brodey, R. S., Stock, N. D., and Hardy, W. D., Jr. (1971). *Cancer Res.* **31,** 953–956.

Malcolm, S., Barton, P., Murphy, C., Fergusson-Smith, M. A., Bentley, D. L., and Rabbits, T. H. (1982). *Proc. Natl. Acad. Sci. U.S.A.* **79,** 4957–4961.

Marcu, K. B., Harris, L. J., Stanton, L. W., Erikson, J., Watt, R., and Croce, C. (1983). *Proc. Natl. Acad. Sci. U.S.A.* **80,** 519–523.

Martin, G. S. (1970). *Nature (London)* **227,** 1021–1023.

Martin, G. S., and Duesberg, P. H. (1972). *Virology* **47,** 494–497.

Mitelman, F., and Levan, G. (1981). *Hereditas* **95,** 79–140.

Morton, C. C., Taub, R., Diamond, A., Lane, M. A., Cooper, G. M., and Leder, P. (1984). *Science* **223,** 173–175.

Muller, R., Slamon, D. J., Tremblay, J. M., Cline, M. J., and Verma, I. M. (1982). *Nature (London)* **299,** 640–644.

Muller, R., Tremblay, G. M., Adamson, E. D., and Verma, I. M. (1983). *Nature (London)* **304,** 454–456.

Muller, R., Bravo, R., Burckhardt, J., and Curran, T. (1984). *Nature (London)* **312,** 716–720.

Murray, M. J., Cunningham, J. M., Parada, L. F., Dautry, P., Lebowitz, P., and Weinberg, R. A. (1983). *Cell* **33,** 749–757.

Muskinski, J. F., Bauer, S. R., Potter, M., and Reddy, E. P. (1983). *Proc. Natl. Acad. Sci. U.S.A.* **80,** 1073–1077.

Neel, B. G., Hayward, W. S., Robinson, H. L., Fang, J., and Astrin, S. M. (1981). *Cell* **23,** 323–334.

Neel, B. G., Jhanwar, S. C., Chaganti, R. S. K., and Hayward, W. S. (1982). *Proc. Natl. Acad. Sci. U.S.A.* **79,** 7842–7846.

Nunn, M., Weiher, H., Bullock, P., and Duesberg, P. (1984). *Virology* **139,** 330–339.

O'Brien, S. J., Nash, W. G., Goodwin, J. L., Lowy, D. R., and Chang, E. H. (1983). *Nature (London)* **302,** 839–842.

Osharsson, M., McClements, W. L., Blair, D. G., Maizel, J. V., and Vande Woude, G. F. (1980). *Science* **207,** 1222–1224.

Oshimura, M., Freeman, A. I., and Sandberg, A. A. (1977). *Cancer* **40,** 1161–1172.

Padgett, T. G., Stubblefield, E., and Varmus, H. E. (1977). *Cell* **10,** 649–657.

Payne, G. S., Courtneidge, S. A., Crittenden, L. B., Fadley, A. M., and Bishop, J. M. (1981). *Cell* **23,** 311–322.

Payne, G. S., Bishop, J. M., and Varmus, H. E. (1982). *Nature (London)* **294,** 574–576.

Prakash, K., McBride, O. W., Swan, D. C., Devare, S. G., Tronick, S. R., and Aaronson, S. A. (1982). *Proc. Natl. Acad. Sci. U.S.A.* **79,** 5210–5214.

Pravtcheva, D. D., Ruddle, F. H., Ellis, R. W., and Scolnick, E. M. (1983). *Somatic Cell Genet.* **9,** 681–686.

Rabbitts, T. H., Hamlyn, P. H., and Baer, R. (1983). *Nature (London)* **306,** 760–765.

Rabin, M., Watson, M., Barker, P. E., Ryan, J., Breg, W. R., and Ruddle, F. H. (1984). *Cytogenet. Cell Genet.* **38,** 70–72.

Rapp, U. R., Reynolds, F. H., Jr., and Stephenson, J. R. (1983a). *J. Virol.* **45,** 914–924.

Rapp, U. R., Goldsborough, M. D., Mark, G. E., Bonner, T. I., Groffen, J., Reynolds, F. H., Jr., and Stephenson, J. R. (1983b). *Proc. Natl. Acad. Sci. U.S.A.* **80,** 4218–4222.

Reddy, E., Reynolds, R., Santos, E., and Barbacid, M. (1982). *Nature (London)* **300,** 149–152.

Reynolds, F. H., Jr., Vande Ven, W. J. M., and Stephenson, J. R. (1980). *J. Biol. Chem.* **255,** 11040–11047.

Riccardi, V. M., Sumansky, E., Smith, A. C., and Francke, U. (1978). *Pediatrics* **61,** 604–610.

Rohrschneider, L. R. (1980). *Proc. Natl. Acad. Sci. U.S.A.* **77,** 3514–3518.

Rosson, D., and Tereba, A. (1983). *Cancer Res.* **43,** 3912–3918.

Roussel, M. F., Sherr, C. J., Barker, P. E., and Ruddle, F. H. (1983). *J. Virol.* **48,** 770–773.

Rowley, J. D. (1973). *Nature (London)* **243,** 290–293.

Rowley, J. D. (1980a). *Clin. Haematol.* **9,** 55–86.

Rowley, J. D. (1980b). *Annu. Rev. Genet.* **14,** 17–39.

Rowley, J. D. (1982). *Science* **216,** 749–751.

Rowley, J. D. (1983). *Nature (London)* **301,** 290–291.

Ryan, J., Barker, P. E., Shimizu, K., Wigley, M., and Ruddle, F. H. (1983). *Proc. Natl. Acad. Sci. U.S.A.* **80,** 4460–4463.

Ryan, J., Hart, C. P., and Ruddle, F. H. (1984). *Nucleic Acids Res.* **12,** 6063–6072.

Sakaguchi, A. Y., Naylor, S. L., Shows, T. B., Toole, J. J., McCoy, M., and Weinberg, R. A. (1983a). *Science* **219,** 1081–1083.

Sakaguchi, A. Y., Naylor, S. L., and Shows, T. B. (1983b). *Prog. Nucleic Acid. Res. Mol. Biol.* **29,** 279–283.

Sakagucki, A. Y., Lalley, P. A., Zabel, B. U., Ellis, R. W. Scolnik, S. M., and Naylor, S. L. (1984a). *Proc. Natl. Acad. Sci. U.S.A.* **81,** 525–529.

Sakaguchi, A. Y., Zabel, B. U., Grzeschik, K-H., Law, M. L., Ellis, R. W., Scolnick, E. M., and Naylor, S. L. (1984b). *Mol. Cell. Biol.* **4,** 989–993.

Sandberg, A. A. (1980). "The Chromosomes in Human Cancer and Leukemia." Elsevier, Amsterdam.

Schwab, M., Alitalo, K., Klempnauer, K.-H., Varmus, H. E., Bishop, J. M., Gilbert, F., Brodeur, G., Goldstein, M., and Trent, J. (1983). *Nature (London)* **305,** 245–248.

Schwab, M., Varmus, H. E., Bishop, J. M., Grzeschik, K-H., Naylor, S. L., Sakaguchi, A. Y., Brodeur, G., and Trent, J. (1984). *Nature (London)* **308,** 288–291.

Sheer, D., Hiorus, L. R., Stanely, K. F., Goodfellow, P. N., Shallow, D. M., Povey, S., Heisterkamp, N., Groffen, J., Stephenson, J. R., and Solomon, E. (1983). *Proc. Natl. Acad. Sci. U.S.A.* **80,** 5007–5011.

Sheiness, D. K., Hughes, S. H., Varmus, H. E., Stubblefield, E., and Bishop, J. M. (1980). *Virology* **105,** 415–424.

Shen-Ong, G. L. C., Keath, E. J., Piccoli, S. P., and Cole, M. D. (1982). *Cell* **31,** 443–452.

Shibuya, M., Hanafusa, T., Hanafusa, H., and Stephenson, J. R. (1980). *Proc. Natl. Acad. Sci. U.S.A.* **77,** 6536–6540.

Shilo, B.-Z., and Weinberg, R. A. (1981). *Proc. Natl. Acad. Sci. U.S.A.* **78,** 6789–6792.

Shimizu, K., Goldfarb, M., Perucho, M., and Wigler, M. (1983). *Proc. Natl. Acad. Sci. U.S.A.* **80,** 383–387.

Spurr, K., Solomon, E., Jansson, M., Sheer, D., Goodfellow, P. N., Bodmer, W. F., and Vennstrom, B. (1984). *EMBO J.* **3,** 159–163.

Stehelin, D., Varmus, H. E., Bishop, J. M., and Vogt, P. K. (1976). *Nature (London)* **260,** 170–173.

Stubblefield, E., and Oro, J. (1982). *Cytometry* **2,** 273–281.

Swan, D. C., McBride, O. W., Robbins, K. C., Keithley, D. A., Reddy, E. P., and Aaronson, S. A. (1982a). *Proc. Natl. Acad. Sci. U.S.A.* **79,** 4691–4695.

Swan, D., Oskarsson, M., Keithley, D., Ruddle, F. H., D'Eustachio, P., and Vande Woude, G. F. (1982b). *J. Virol.* **44,** 752–754.

Symonds, G., Stubblefield, E., Guyaux, M., and Bishop, J. M. (1984). *Mol. Cell. Biol.* **4,** 1627–1630.

Tabin, C., Bradley, S., Bargmann, C., Weinberg, R., Papageorge, A., Scolnick, E., Dhar, R., Lowy, D., and Chang, E. (1982). *Nature (London)* **300,** 143–148.

Taparowsky, E., Suard, Y., Fasano, O., Shimizu, K., Goldfarb, M., and Wigler, M. (1982). *Nature (London)* **300,** 762–765.

Taparowsky, E., Shimizu, K., Goldfarb, M., and Wigler, M. (1983). *Cell* **34,** 581–586.

Taub, R., Kirsch, I., Morton, C., Lenoir, G., Swan, D., Tronick, S., Aaronson, S., and Leder, P. (1982). *Proc. Natl. Acad. Sci. U.S.A.* **79,** 7837–7841.

Tereba, A. (1981). *J. Virol.* **40,** 920–926.

Tereba, A., and Astrin, S. M. (1980). *J. Virol.* **35,** 888–894.

Tereba, A., and Astrin, S. M. (1982). *J. Virol.* **43,** 737–740.

Tereba, A., and Lai, M. M. C. (1982). *Virology* **116,** 654–657.

Tereba, A., Lai, M. M. C., and Murti, K. G. (1979). *Proc. Natl. Acad. Sci. U.S.A.* **76,** 6486–6490.

Tereba, A., Crittenden, L. B., and Astrin, S. M. (1981). *J. Virol.* **39,** 282–289.

Trent, J. M., and Salmon, S. E. (1981). *Cancer Genet. Cytogenet.* **3,** 279–291.

Ullrich, A., Coussens, L., Hayflick, J. S., Dull, T. J., Gray, A., Tam, A. W., Lee, J., Yarden, Y., Libermann, T. A., Schlessinger, J., Downward, J., Mayes, E. L. V., Whittle, N., Waterfield, M. D., and Seeburg, P. H. (1984). *Nature (London)* **309,** 418–425.

Van Beveren, G., Galleshaw, J. A., Jonas, V., Berns, A. J. M., and Doolittle, R. F. (1981). *Nature (London)* **289,** 258–262.

Wake, N., Hreshchyshyn, M. M., Piver, S. M., Matsui, S., and Sandberg, A. A. (1980). *Cancer Res.* **40,** 4512–4518.

Waterfield, M. D., Scrace, G. T., Whittle, N., Stroobant, P., Johnson, A., Wasteson, A., Westermark, B., Heldin, C.-H., Huang, J. D., and Deuel, T. F. (1983). *Nature (London)* **304,** 35–39.

Wellingham, M. C., Jay, G., and Paston, I. (1979). *Cell* **18,** 125–134.

Westin, E. H., Gallo, R. C., Arya, S. K., Eva, A., Souza, L. M., Baluda, M. A., Aaronson, S. A., and Wong-Staal, F. (1982). *Proc. Natl. Acad. Sci. U.S.A.* **79,** 2194–2198.

Wong, T. C., Tereba, A., Vogt, P. K., and Lai, M. M. C. (1981). *Virology* **111,** 418–426.

Wyke, J. A., and Linial, M. (1973). *Virology* **53,** 152–161.

Yunis, J. J. (1981). *Hum. Pathol.* **12,** 494–503.

Yunis, J. J. (1983). *Science* **221,** 227–236.

Yunis, J. J., and Ramsay, N. (1980). *J. Pediatr.* **96,** 1027–1030.

Zabel, B. U., Fournier, R. E. K., Lalley, P. A., Naylor, S. L., and Sakaguchi, A. Y. (1984). *Proc. Natl. Acad. Sci. U.S.A.* **81,** 4874–4878.

INTERNATIONAL REVIEW OF CYTOLOGY, VOL. 95

Target Cell Prolactin, II

JANET M. NOLIN

Department of Biology, University of Richmond, Richmond, Virginia

I. Introduction

This story began in 1928 during the period described by Greep (1974) as the golden age of elucidation of the physiology of the anterior lobe of the pituitary gland. In that year, interested initially in the known gonadotropic properties of anterior pituitary extracts, Stricker and Grueter published their chance observations that, given enough extract, rabbits would begin to lactate (see also Grueter, 1928; Grueter and Stricker, 1929). Shortly thereafter, Evans and Simpson (1929) reported similar findings in the rat.

On the other hand, this story also began in 1786, the year John Hunter described the process in which birds such as ring doves and pigeons feed their young on crop "milk" epithelium (Greep, 1974). Oscar Riddle and his colleagues were studying this phenomenon during the golden age of pituitary physiology and discovered that, like mammalian milk production, crop "milk" production is also under the control of a pituitary factor (Riddle and Braucher, 1931; Riddle et al., 1932). That the same hormone was responsible for both avian and mammalian effects was communicated by Riddle et al. in 1933, and the active substance was given the name "prolactin."

This peptide hormone is now known, not only as a pro-"lactin" (and a gonadotropin and an adrenocorticotropin, as well), but also as a hormone central to an enormous number of diverse life processes, in an enormous number of diverse vertebrate forms—extending on the evolutionary scale from cyclostomes

45

to humans (Bern and Nicoll, 1968; Nicoll and Bern, 1972; Clarke and Bern, 1978; Devlaming, 1979). To date, however, the mechanism(s) of action of Riddle's "prolactin," not only in the mammary gland, where mechanisms have been most studied, but also in all its other targets, remains, in legacy (?), just that, a riddle.

II. Background

The study of the molecular events in peptide hormone action began its remarkably sharp ascent to its present-day transcendence with the enunciation of a "second messenger" concept by E. W. Sutherland (Sutherland and Rall, 1957, 1960; Sutherland, 1972). With the impetus given by Sutherland's guidelines, a large body of evidence began to accrue in favor of the following scheme: peptide hormones, unlike the steroids and other small regulatory molecules, do not enter their target cells to interact directly with subcellular constituents; nor is there any need for them to do so because their activity can be entirely (?) accounted for on the basis of their ability to touch down at the target cell interface (by way of a specific receptor in the plasma membrane) and, with the resulting perturbation of the membrane, to induce the formation of a single, simple, totipotent (?), ubiquitous "second messenger"—cAMP.

The applicability of this scheme to prolactin was first evaluated by Turkington and his colleagues in a series of experiments using the classic target, the mammary gland (Majumder and Turkington, 1971; reviewed by Turkington, 1972; Turkington et al., 1973). Their results were subsequently confirmed and extended in a number of laboratories (Sapag-Hagar et al., 1974; Loizzi et al., 1975; Loizzi, 1978; Rillema, 1975; Speake et al., 1976; Chomczynski and Zwierzchowski, 1978). No one succeeded in demonstrating a surrogate role of cAMP for prolactin; rather, elevated cAMP levels were universally associated with inhibition (inter alia Louis and Baldwin, 1975; Sapag-Hagar and Greenbaum, 1973, 1974a,b; Rillema, 1976). However, because few could argue against the value of the second-messenger concept to the overall advance of knowledge in other areas of endocrinology, there seemed to be no implicit need, despite these findings, to "throw out the baby with the bathwater." Curiously, it was considered heresy at this point (Szego 1974, 1975, 1978) to wonder whether there might be no baby to begin with, i.e., whether the underlying maxim of the second-messenger hypothesis—nonentry—might itself be open to question. Thus, the hunt for a mediator other than cAMP began. The list of experiments is long and the data often conflicting, but neither cGMP (Rillema, 1975; Kleczkowska and Chomczynski, 1976; Matusik and Rosen, 1980; Anderson et al., 1981), nor cCMP (Matusik and Rosen, 1980; Anderson et al., 1981), nor cUMP or cTMP (Anderson et al., 1981), nor polyamines (reviewed in Rillema, 1980a; Houdebine, 1983; see also Frazier and Costlow, 1982), nor prostaglandins (reviewed in Rillema, 1980a;

Knazek *et al.*, 1981; Dave *et al.*, 1982; cf. Houdebine and Lacroix, 1980), nor Ca^{2+}/calmodulin (Rillema, 1980b; Pizarro *et al.*, 1981; cf. Houdebine, 1981), nor Na^+,K^+-ATPase (Falconer and Rowe, 1975; cf. Houdebine and Djiane, 1980a; Bisbee, 1981), nor (currently ephemeral) peptides derived from cell membranes (Houdebine, 1983; cf. Teyssot and Houdebine, 1980) can be unequivocally invoked as the totipotent second for prolactin.

Heresy or not, in the midst of all this, there appeared two papers with the potential for intricately confounding this search. One described a direct effect of prolactin on isolated mammary cell nuclei (Chomczynski and Topper, 1974); the other presented evidence that prolactin can indeed enter the milk secretory cell, that it does so physiologically, and, moreover, that it can reach the cell nucleus (Nolin and Witorsch, 1976). Confirmation of the Chomczynski and Topper experiments remains singular and indirect; namely, the onset of lactational failure, inducible by estrogen, coincides with inhibition of translocation of prolactin into the cell nucleus, at doses of estrogen that still permit uptake into the cell (Nolin and Bogdanove, 1980). On the other hand, confirmation of entry, and, in some targets, of nuclear localization, has been abundant and has been extended by way of a variety of methodologies to a number of species, including humans, and to a number of prolactin targets including target cells that, unlike the milk secretory cell (McMurtry and Malven, 1974; Nolin and Witorsch, 1976; Grosvenor and Whitworth, 1976; Gala and Van de Walle, 1977), do not appear to process the hormone transcellulary (representative citations: Nolin, 1978a,b, 1979, 1980a,b, 1981a,b, 1982; Suard *et al.*, 1979; Josefsberg *et al.*, 1979; Nolin and Bogdanove, 1980; Purnell *et al.*, 1982; Costlow and Hample, 1982b; Paterson *et al.*, 1982; Malven and Keenan, 1983).

With this discovery, it became crystal clear that an important conceptual constraint had been removed, and one is no longer limited to a description of the molecular basis of prolactin action within the dogma of nonentry.

III. Clearance and Internalization

The first among the new questions was, What is the evidence that uptake into the cell does not, simply and exclusively, subserve a mechanism for intracellular degradative "clearance" of bioactive hormone? One set of experiments dealing with this question was reported by Shiu (1980). In human breast cancer cells, incubated with ^{125}I-labeled human prolactin for 5 days, as much as 70% of receptor binding activity was lost; with normal cells, derived from milk, loss was reported to be less, but nevertheless significant (57%). By contrast, when incubated with native prolactin for as long as 6 days, cancer cells behaved much as they did toward the iodinated material, but normal cells did not, i.e., "normal" prolactin incubated with normal cells remained biologically intact. These experiments suggested two important things. First, the use of iodinated hormone is, at best, less than ideal for such studies; and, second, there may be notable differences in the ways cancer cells and normal cells deal with prolactin (and vice versa?). Other experiments have shown important related differences between normal and cancerous prolactin targets (Costlow and Hample, 1982a).

Still other experiments having a bearing on the question of clearance in the normal gland include those of Gala *et al.* (1980), who showed that the immunoreactive prolactin, recoverable from milk, has not lost bioactivity. This and the high concentrations of prolactin in the milk of a number of species (Malven, 1983) suggest that the major pathway for clearance of prolactin is transcellular, at least in normally lactating tissue, and that it occurs without loss of bioactivity. Subcellular localization studies also shed light on this question. In addition to the detectability of a form of prolactin sufficiently intact to be immunoreactive in cell nuclei, the detectability of prolactin, in relatively high concentrations, bound to other anabolic subcellular organelles such as rough endoplasmic reticulum (RER) and the Golgi apparatus (Malven and Keenan, 1983) is rather strong evidence for the idea of intracellular sites of prolactin action—excluding deactivation, whether within or across the cell—as the sole purpose of entry. The mode of eventual clearance of the prolactin that interacts with these organelles may or may not be transcellular. All that is known, regarding this point, is that all of the immunoreactive intracellular prolaction in the milk secretory cell is lost by the end of each functional alveolar cycle, the duration of which is about 8 hours in the rat (Nolin and Bogdanove, 1980).

IV. Involvement of Lysosomes

Is the hydrolytic lysosome a candidate for clearance of any prolactin that might not be removed via a transcellular route, either in milk secretory cells or, particularly, in target cells such as those of the adrenal cortex and ovarian corpus luteum, that do not appear to exercise a transcellular pathway? Nothing is known about adrenal or ovarian cells. As for normally lactating cells, prolactin has not been identified in association with lysosomes. This, of course, is not at all surprising. Morphologically identifiable lysosomes themselves are a rarity in lactating cells (Hollmann, 1974, and personal observations), and lysosomal enzyme activity is, correspondingly, low or nondetectable (Baldwin and Yang, 1974).

On the other side of the coin, what about the possibility that lysosomes might actually modulate the effects of prolactin as a function of lysosomal membrane labilization, as they appear to do for a number of other hormones, both steroid and peptide (Szego, 1974, 1975, 1978)? The answers to this question may be target-cell dependent. Prolactin itself is a stabilizer of lysosomal membranes

(Giunta *et al.*, 1972; Szego, 1975; Kikuyama *et al.*, 1980). However, prolactin often acts in synergy with other hormones, particularly steroids. In rat corpus luteum, for example, the synergistic steroid is estrogen (Nolin and Bogdanove, 1980). Estrogen is clearly a labilizer of lysosomal membrane (Szego 1974, 1975, 1978). Thus, in lutein cells, some sort of balance may be struck to allow the participation of lysosomes in this synergy. In the lactating cell, the situation is very different. It is well known that, in most species, prolactin's synergistic companion in this case is a glucocorticoid, both *in vivo* and *in vitro* (*inter alia*, Elias, 1980). The notable exception has been thought to be the rabbit, but there is compelling new evidence that for the full complement of the effects of prolactin in the rabbit gland this idea is erroneous (Sankaran and Topper, 1982). In contrast to estrogen, glucocorticoids are well known as remarkably efficient lysosomal membrane stabilizers. To add to this, insulin is also a requirement for lactation both *in vitro* (reviewed in Elias, 1980) and *in vivo* (Martin and Baldwin, 1971), and insulin is also a lysosomal stabilizer (summarized in Szego, 1975). Thus, all cogent parameters, namely, the rarity of the lysosome itself, the paucity of lysosomal enzymes, the "backup" membrane stabilizing effects of glucocorticoid (and insulin) and the stabilizing effect of prolactin itself, would mitigate against any involvement of the lysosome in prolactin action in milk synthesis. Pharmacological experiments that have been reported from Houdebine's laboratory seem to be in agreement with this line of reasoning (Houdebine, 1983).

V. Studies with Toxic Drugs

Houdebine's group has also taken a pharmacological approach to another question raised by the discovery of entry. *Do drugs, targeted to interfere with normal functioning of the elements of the cytoskeleton, affect response to prolactin?* Although their work with cytochalasin B, targeted to microfilaments, turned out to be equivocal (Houdebine and Djiane, 1980b), local anesthetics were reported to have no effect on response in hormone-supplemented explants of mammary tissue from pseudopregnant rabbits (Houdebine *et al.*, 1981). Whether these drugs can break the filamentous connection between the cell surface and subcellular systems in this preparation, as appears to be the case in cells of explants of lactating tissue (Houdebine *et al.*, 1981), remains to be answered. Griseofulvin was also studied by Houdebine *et al.* (1982) for its purported ability to alter microtubule structure. This drug also failed, like the local anesthetics, to alter response. It should be noted that three key questions remain unaddressed by these experiments: Is the cytoskeleton involved in uptake and/or intracellular redistribution of prolactin? What did these various drugs actually do to the cells being studied? What effect, if any, did these drugs have on intracellular prolactin topogenesis?

Unlike griseofulvin, colchicine, a tubulin-binding drug that can also alter microtubule function, blocked some responses completely (Houdebine and Djiane, 1980b). Because colchicine can bind not only to intracellular "cytosolic" tubulin but also to various cell membranes, including the plasmalemma, often nonspecifically (Stadler and Franke, 1974), inhibition of microtubule function could not be assigned as the cause of failed response. Subsequently, Houdebine *et al.* (1982) reported evidence, in fact, of both colchicine binding to mammary gland membranes and an inhibitory effect of colchicine on the formation of his newly discovered, membrane-derived, second-messsenger peptide(s) noted earier in this article (Section II). Although the discovery of this newest mediator awaits confirmation at this writing, from this it would appear that the effects of prolactin that are blocked by colchicine may be mediated by small, membrane-derived peptides. The caveat is that not all prolactin effects are blocked by colchicine (Teyssot and Houdebine, 1980; see also Bolander, 1983).

Houdebine's group has also reported another experiment, one that may, like the discovery of entry and of mediator peptides, lead to an entirely new approach in this area of research. Antiserum containing antibody to the prolactin receptor can mimic prolactin in terms of binding to cell membranes, generating the active peptide(s) and stimulating DNA synthesis, casein synthesis, and the accumulation of β-casein mRNA (Djiane *et al.*, 1981). Whether antireceptor mimics prolactin in terms of uptake into the cell and binding to nuclei has not yet been shown. Certainly, the mammary gland is well known for receptor-mediated uptake of immunoglobulins of all sorts: Why not antibody to the prolactin receptor? (See Anderson *et al.*, 1982, for uptake of antibody to the low-density lipoprotein receptor; Moncharmont *et al.*, 1982, for nuclear penetration of antibody to the estrogen receptor; and Kasuga *et al.*, 1983, for internalization of antibody to the insulin receptor.)

Note: With regard to the contributions of the Houdebine group—as potentially important and exciting as they may become—the task falls to this reviewer to note that most of their published work, in the opinions of several investigators, is seriously compromised by inadequate, imprecise RNA assay methodology (Chan *et al.*, 1978; Rosen *et al.*, 1980; discussion Rosenfeld *et al.*, 1983). One of the more outspoken critics in this regard has been Rosen (Rosen *et al.*, 1980; Hobbs *et al.*, 1982; Rodgers *et al.*, 1983), who, himself, has been working toward the development of what he and others (Hennighausen and Sippel, 1982) consider to be a far better mousetrap.

VI. The Anatomy of the Situation

What is known about concurrence of intracellular prolactin and biological effect from approaches other than pharmacological experiments? Much of what is known comes from morphological studies. The use of mammary tissue from normally lactating rats serves as an excellent model for this sort of coordinate approach (Nolin, 1979; Nolin and Bogdanove, 1980). Even a single section for light microscopy can show the anatomy of the entire spectrum of metabolic alveolar activity, i.e., from the onset of milk synthesis, through the stages of gradual repletion of the alveolar lumen, to the completion of the cycle when the lumen is at capacity. Cell shape and size vary according to the stage of the cycle. At the beginning, when the lumen contains little or no milk, the milk secretory cells lining the alveolus are tall columnar and exhibit unmistakable signs of synthetic activity. As milk leaves the cells, to be stored temporarily in the lumen, the cells gradually decrease in apparent volume and change shape, becoming cuboidal. By the time the alveolus is filled, having completed their mission for this cycle, they become squamous and appear to be metabolically resting. An estimate for the time span for these three broad categories of the cycle has been given as lactogenic, 1.5 hours; galactopoietic, 4 hours; resting, 2.5 hours (Nolin and Bogdanove, 1980; Nolin, 1981a).

From immunocytochemical studies (Nolin, 1979; Nolin and Bogdanove, 1980) it would appear that prolactin uptake begins, appropriately, at the beginning of this cycle. In the columnar cells that characterize the onset of the cycle, prolactin appears to undergo intracellular topogenesis in distinguishable steps: internalization into the basal pole of the cell, polar translocation, nuclear uptake, aggregation in the apical pole, and, as this phase gets well under way, eventual excretion from the cell apex. These steps are asynchronous among cells in a given alveolus. By contrast, during the galactopoietic phase, movement through the cell appears to be continuous (or more rapid?) and synchronous, cell–cell. Finally, during the resting period, even though free binding sites, available to the investigator, are present in the cells, prolactin itself is undetectable. Interestingly, the only time in this cycle that prolactin can be seen in nuclei, where it appears to reside for about 20–25 minutes, is during the early part of the lactogenic phase, a finding that is clearly in harmony with a direct effect on nuclear events.

In other, more highly resolved experiments that employed dispersed mammary epithelial cells isolated from pregnant rabbits and incubated with ^{125}I-labeled ovine prolactin, Suard et al. (1979) found 63%[1] of the label already inside the cell after a 5-minute period of heat activation at 37°C. Of this, 17% was associated with vesicles/vacuoles, 27% with RER/cytoplasm, 4% with mitochondria. For the nucleus and Golgi apparatus, it was 6 and 8%, respectively. At 15 minutes, another 14% of the label had entered the cells but 14%[1] entering does not alone account for the percentage of grains recorded for individual cell com-

---

[1]These two numbers are not exactly the same as the authors of this work presented because my calculations start at 100% on the plasmalemma.

partments. The evidence would point to redistribution among cell compartments as an important factor as well; the percentage in vesicles/vacuoles decreased by 4%, in RER/cytoplasm by 3%, and in mitochondria by 1%. The 14% entering, with 8% redistributed, brought an increased 11% to the nucleus and 9% to the Golgi, for a total of 17% in each of these compartments. By 30 minutes of incubation, an additional 5% had entered. The concentration of label over vesicles/vacuoles was unchanged. Mitochondria and RER/cytoplasm held a few more grains than at 15 minutes, an increase of 1 and 3% of the total number of cell-associated grains, respectively. At 30 minutes, the number of grains in the nucleus had dropped by 2%; but, in the Golgi, label was increased again by 3 to 20% of all the grains in the cell.

In addition to differences among relative concentrations in various cell compartments over time, these data also show differences in rates of accumulation. Whether drawn as a function of percentage of total grams per volume density over time (for volume density data, see original report) or of percentage of total grains alone over time, plots of the data reveal that during the first 5 minutes the rate of accumulation was greater into RER/cytoplasm than into the nucleus, with the Golgi rate between these two. Between 5 and 15 minutes, accumulation by the nuclear membrane and into euchromatin continued, at a linear rate. Golgi accumulation also continued, but when volume density was taken into account, at a much sharper rate that became even more rapid between 15 and 30 minutes. Nuclear accumulation appeared to cease completely during this period; in fact, the authors report a net loss of accumulated label. No association of label with lysosomes was clearly defined at any point during the 30-minute incubation and only by 30 minutes did there appear to be any tenable suggestion of such an association.

Although there are a number of questions raised by this experiment, particularly as regards the direction and/or subdirections of intracellular distribution pathways, the observation that label accumulates to its 30-minute maximum first in nuclei, then in Golgi, and (perhaps) finally in lysosomes clearly supports a direct effect of prolactin on nuclear metabolism that is followed by a direct effect on a predictably anabolic pathway prior to any putative lysosomal interaction.

There is another important duo of experiments that ought be mentioned with regard to pathways. Lyons showed nearly 50 years ago (1942) that prolactin can induce a lactational response in the pseudopregnant rabbit mammary gland when delivered "backward," i.e., through a mammary duct. More recently, using this route and ^{125}I-labeled ovine prolactin, Birkinshaw and Falconer 1972) showed an accumulation of radioactivity in the basal portion of mammary epithelial cells, much like what we observed at the onset of response during a normal alveolar milk-secretory cycle (Nolin and Bogdanove, 1980). No information was given regarding intracellular retrotransport, but it seems likely that, in this model, the absence of tight junctions prior to prolactin administration (Pitelka *et al.*, 1973) would permit pericellular transport.

VII. Receptors

Is intracellular prolactin bound to its receptor? Although this has generally been assumed to be the case, there is not much in the way of direct evidence. As for the transcellular pathway, Waters *et al.* (1980) found prolactin receptors on the milk-derived membranes that are thought to derive wholly or in part from apical cell membrane that envelops fat globules during their extrusion from the cell. Although free receptors were detectable, there was no measure of the prolactin that might (or might not) have been bound to these receptors prior to exposure of the test membranes to the apparent low-pH dissociation effects of $MgCl_2$ (Costlow and Hample, 1982a; Necessary and Ebner, 1983). On the other hand, there is evidence of prolactin, but not $MgCl_2$-independent, i.e., not physiologically free receptor, on such membranes (Nolin and Witorsch, 1976). It is quite possible, of course, that any prolactin–receptor complexes that might be found in milk membranes reflect the binding, to apically available receptors, of previously non-receptor- (and non-fat-globule-) associated intracellular prolactin, on its way out of the cell (Nolin and Witorsch, 1976). In line with this, in the Suard *et al.* (1979) experiments discussed earlier, fat globules, still inside the cell, were strikingly devoid of label. Furthermore, milk fat itself appears to contain no prolactin (Gala, 1980). By contrast, there are other studies (Costlow and Hample, 1982b; Necessary and Ebner, 1983) that do suggest intracellular binding to receptor, at least in target cells that exhibit lysosomal dormancy (see Section IV). These studies showed that the best *in vitro* condition for dissociating prolactin from its receptor appears to be a highly acid environment (pH 3.0–4.0). Dissociation occurred, incidentally, without loss of either prolactin or receptor binding activity. *In vivo,* such a low pH environment would be available, as far as we know, only in lysosomes.

None of the experiments dealing directly with intracellular prolactin, i.e., with prolactin that had entered an intact cell, have revealed, nor could they reveal (Nolin, 1979), whether prolactin had carried along with it part or all of the surface receptor (R). Therefore, the question whether the detectability of the agonist portion of a potential agonist–receptor complex actually reflects the indirect detection of the R portion as well remains, although clearly a possibility, as yet unanswered. With the evidence of a polygamous receptor, and therefore, that it is not prolactin itself, but rather the agonist–receptor bond that is important (Houdebine, 1983), this question becomes paramount. The data so far (Section V), however, do not rule out a necessary, continued intracellular liaison between agonist and receptor and, in light of the evidence presented in the next section (Section VIII), an intracellular modification of this complex, analogous to the situation for steroid hormones.

VIII. Entry and Hormone Potentiation

In response to the new challenges presented by these recently evolved data, exploration of a novel hypothesis has begun. The tenability of this hypothesis derives from the detectability of target-cell prolactin by polyclonal antibody to pituitary prolactin being clearly compatible with the possibility that target-cell "prolactin" represents a population of fragments of the original, pituitary molecule. Such fragmentation could account for both the remarkable pluritropism of this molecule, i.e., the diversity of its targets, and, perhaps, its even more remarkable pleiotropism, i.e., the diversity of its effects, not only among targets, but even within a single target. Thus, the multiple actions of the larger pituitary peptide would be inherent in single actions of small fragments. This hypothesis would suggest that specificity of the response resides in a particular target cell's ability to "clip" the multifaceted pituitary (or better, blood-borne) precursor into the number of selectively active fragments needed by each cell type.

The nature of polyclonal antisera to the pituitary molecule was put to use in the examination of this hypothesis, immunocytochemically (Nolin, 1982). The availability of a well-characterized small peptide from the ovarian follicle that is both prolactin-like in biological activity and "inducible" by prolactin (Channing et al., 1981; Channing and Evans, 1982) dictated that these initial studies be done in ovarian tissue rather than in mammary gland. Although these experiments required the use of cycling rats (Nolin, 1982), their feasibility was predicted on the basis of previous work that showed the immunohistochemical detectability of prolactin in ovarian follicles of lactating rats (Nolin, 1980a).

"Prolactin," detectable with unmodified antibody to homologous pituitary prolactin, was found in ovaries from cycling rats in all three major follicular compartments during preovulatory development: in granulosa cells, in follicular fluid, and in the oocyte. During the early stages of development, nuclear "prolactin" was evident in granulosa cells but not in the oocyte. Subsequent preovulatory development was characterized by an apparent gradual decrease in the concentration of prolactin in all three compartments, with a striking decrease—from relatively high concentrations to barely detectable levels—in follicular fluid. As predictable ovulation became imminent, not only was the concentration of "prolactin" in the oocyte further diminished, but a redistribution occurred. Whereas "prolactin" had been distributed in an overall filamentous pattern in oocyte cytoplasm, its cytoplasmic distribution became restricted to the oocyte periphery and an association with the membrane of the oocyte nucleus, or germinal vesicle, first became evident. Although nothing is known regarding a direct biological effect of "prolactin" on the oocyte itself, the overall distribution and the changes in the levels of prolactin in the various compartments of the ovarian follicle in these studies are in accord with expectations based on the effects of prolactin that have been established (Hamada *et al.*, 1980; Velduis *et al.*, 1980; Wang *et al.*, 1980; Kraiem, 1981; Dorrington and Gore-Langton, 1982).

Whether any of this follicular "prolactin" might be a fragment(s) of the whole molecule was examined with the antiserum modified by preexposure to the small-peptide ovarian material. In direct comparisons, as development progressed, fragmentation accounted for some but not all of the "prolactin" in mural granulosa cells and the oocyte, and, eventually, for all of it in follicular fluid and in the cumulus granulosa cells surrounding the oocyte. The distribution of oocyte "prolactin" along the germinal vesical membrane at ovulation-readiness was attributable exclusively to the presence of fragment(s). Cortical prolactin appeared not to be fragmented or perhaps, more accurately, not to be the same fragment(s).

Although fragmentation by granulosa cells might take place at the plasma membrane and/or through the action of neutral intracellular proteases (Goldstein and Livingston, 1981) and/or, in the case of ovarian follicle, in lysosomes, these experiments gave no information on this question. What they did suggest, on the basis of distributional data, is that in the multilayered granulosa, in which the inner layers of cells have no direct access to the bloodstream, "prolactin" can be carried from one layer to the next, in a cell–cell fashion and fragmented along the way, such that only fragments appear in deeper, cumulus layers. That this occurs independently of unmodified prolactin receptors in the deeper layers is supported by studies of the follicular distribution of free receptors for pituitary prolactin. They appear to be exclusively localized to granulosa cells nearest the blood supply (Oxberry and Greenwald, 1983).

Is there anything else in the literature that would suggest further worthwhile exploration of this "clipzyme" hypothesis? Not much as yet; but there are some tantalizing data. Grosvenor and Whitworth showed some time ago (1976) that milk prolactin is clearly different from pituitary prolactin. Whether it is "different" because it is protein bound, or phosphorylated, or methylated (and so on), or fragmented was not reported. Malven and Keenan (1983) and Gala and Van de Walle (1977), using radioimmunoassay and pituitary prolactin and prolactin-just-secreted-from-the-pituitary as assay standards, found some nonparallelism in nuclear "prolactin" and milk "prolactin," respectively, findings also suggesting that these two molecules are indeed "different." That they might not be totally different from prolactin was suggested by the lack of marked non-parallelism. Shiu (1980) was actually able to retrieve prolactin fragments from the medium after incubation of mammary cells with pituitary prolactin, but again, for the purpose here, a key element in the data was missing. There was no information about biological viability of these fragments. Evidence along these lines may be difficult to obtain. Fragments produced by the cell, i.e., after the initial binding to a recognizer protein on the cell surface, may no longer be "active" in the commonly used, whole-cell preparation. This would not be evidence that such fragments have no biological activity within the cell, i.e., after initial "binding" activity has fulfilled its purpose. (This is also true, incidentally, when using pituitary prolactin modified in the chemist's laboratory for the express purpose of studying this question.)

With regard to the wider implications of this question of target cell fragmentation, it is curious that the pituitary is apparently capable of selective secretion of a growth-promoting and a "metabolic" fragment of a presumably, stored, intact form of prolactin (Mittra, 1980a,b). Heterogeneity, limited to terms of molecular weight, has also been described for circulating radioimmunoassayable forms of prolactin, with only the "little" form finding its way into milk (Suh and Frantz, 1974; Gala and Van de Walle, 1977; Garnier *et al.*, 1978; Gala and Hart, 1980; Soong *et al.*, 1982). How "little" this form is, is not altogether certain. Perhaps prolactin's mechanisms of action involve modifications of a parent molecule all the way down the line, from within the pituitary, into and within the circulation and finally, into and within the target cell itself. That would be physiological conservation!

IX. Summary

Is the entry hypothesis compatible with all the existing data about "the" second messenger for prolactin listed in Section II? All of these messengers, in some way either participate in, or modify, prolactin's actions or, in an end point-dependent manner, may actually mimic prolactin. There remains considerable uncertainty as to whether these findings reflect phenomena, some independent of and others quite dependent upon entry, on the one hand, or merely portions of a relatively large number of molecular cascades, some (but not necessarily all) begun initially at the plasmalemma and many (if not all) orchestrated toward completion by intracellular prolactin or agonist–receptor complex.

X. Admonishment

On the other hand, maybe all of this deals with mere fantasy. Mention was made earlier of the oft-required synergism for the actions of prolactin. This synergism forces the realization of what may be an analytical impasse (even in the rabbit mammary gland; see Section IV). Where synergy of regulatory agents is required, how does one go about assigning an effect exclusively to one partner in the synergy, without such basic information as the time course of the presence of each of the specific elements of this synergy on, and/or, in the cell, much less their localization to the various domains of the cell that they might, individually or in concert, govern (Bolander *et al.*, 1979; Nolin, 1981b; Ganguly *et al.*, 1980; Oka, 1983)? In this respect, but still without comparable evidence regarding its synergistic partners, that body of data that shows correlation of the presence of prolactin in subcellular compartments with responses, or responsive states, of those compartments may constitute a major step forward.

At this writing, one other aspect of this story is "crystal clear." We are still left with Riddle's riddle . . . is a riddle . . . is a riddle. . . .

ACKNOWLEDGMENTS

With this article my thanks goes particularly to Bob Bates, né: January 31, 1904, for his friendship and for his sharing with me some of the excitement of the early days of discovery in this field. Who better? For it is this Bob Bates who was a member of the team that originally gave this hormone its proper christening (Riddle *et al.*, 1933).

I would also like to extend my thanks to all of the scientists whose work I have cited here, for the spice of controversy they have brought to this subject; to Anthony Padua for his forgiving, continuing surveillance; to my students, George Mulheron and Angus Grant, for the wonder still in their eyes; and to my family for their steadfastness. I also acknowledge both Jane Wait and Sarah Lehman for their generous technical expertise.

The work presented here, from my own laboratory, has been supported by grants from the University of Richmond, the National Science Foundation, U.S.A. (PCM 76-23641) and the National Institutes of Health, U.S.A. (HD 14478 and HD 16505), to whom I also express my gratitude.

REFERENCES

Anderson, R. G. W., Brown, M. S., Beisiegel, U., and Golstein, J. L. (1982). *J. Cell Biol.* **93**, 523–531.

Anderson, T. R., Mayer, G. L., and Nicoll, C. S. (1981). *J. Cyclic Nucleotide Res.* **7**, 225–233.

Baldwin, R. L., and Yang, Y. T. (1974). *In* "Lactation" (B. L. Larson and V. R. Smith, eds.), Vol. 1, pp. 349–411. Academic Press, New York.

Bergeron, J. J. M., Resch, L., Rachubinski, R., Patel, B. A., and Posner, B. I. (1983). *J. Cell Biol.* **96**, 875–886.

Bern, H. A., and Nicoll, C. S. (1968). *Recent Prog. Horm. Res.* **24**, 681–720.

Birkinshaw, M., and Falconer, I. R. (1972). *J. Endocrinol.* **55**, 323–334.

Bisbee, C. A. (1981). *Am. J. Physiol.* **240**, C110–C115.

Bolander, F. F., Jr. (1983). *Biochem. Biophys. Res. Commun.* **3**, 150–155.

Bolander, F. F., Jr., Nicholas, K. R., and Topper, Y. J. (1979). *Biochem. Biophys. Res. Commun.* **91**, 247–252.

Chan, L., Means, A. R., and O'Malley, B. W. (1978). *Vitamins Horm.* **36**, 259–295.

Channing, C. O., Anderson, L. D., Stone, S. L., and Batta, S. (1981). *In* "Reproductive Processes and Contraception" (K. W. McKerns, ed.), pp. 619–645. Plenum, New York.

Channing, C. P., and Evans, V. W. (1982). *Endocrinology* **111**, 1746–1748.

Chomszynski, P., and Topper, Y. J. (1974). *Biochem. Biophys. Res. Commun.* **60**, 56–63.

Chomczynski, P., and Zwierzchowski, L. (1978). *Acta Biochim. Pol.* **25**, 29–36.

Clarke, W. C., and Bern, H. A. (1978). *Horm. Proteins Pept.* **8**, 105–197.

Costlow, M. E., and Hample, A. (1982a). *J. Biol. Chem.* **257**, 6971–6977.

Costlow, M. E., and Hample, A. (1982b). *J. Biol. Chem.* **257**, 9330–9334.

Dave, J. R., Brown, N. V., and Knazek, R. A. (1982). *Biochem. Biophys. Res. Commun.* **108**, 193–199.

Devlaming, V. L. (1979). *In* "Hormones and Evolution" (E. J. W. Barrington, ed.), Vol. 2, pp. 561–642. Academic Press, New York.

Djiane, J., Kelly, P. A., and Houdebine, L.-M. (1980). *Mol. Cell. Endocrinol.* **18**, 87–98.

Djiane, J., Houdebine, L.-M., and Kelly, P. A. (1981). *Proc. Natl. Acad. Sci. U.S.A.* **78**, 7445–7448.

Dorrington, J. H., and Gore-Langton, R. E. (1982). *Endocrinology* **110**, 1701–1707.

Elias, J. J. (1980). *Horm. Proteins Pept.* **8**, 37–74.

Evans, H. M., and Simpson, M. E. (1929). *Proc. Soc. Exp. Biol. Med.* **26**, 598.

Falconer, I. R., and Rowe, J. M. (1975). *Nature (London)* **256**, 327–328.

Frazier, R. P., and Costlow, M. E. (1982). *Exp. Cell Res.* **138**, 39–45.

Gala, R. R. (1980). *Life Sci.* **26**, 783–788.

Gala, R. R., and Hart, I. C. (1980). *Life Sci.* **27**, 723–730.

Gala, R. R., and Van De Walle, C. (1977). *Life Sci.* **21**, 99–104.

Gala, R. R., Forsyth, I. A., and Turvey, A. (1980). *Life Sci.* **26**, 987–993.

Ganguly, R., Ganguly, N., Mehta, N. M., and Banerjee, M. R. (1980). *Proc. Natl. Acad. Sci. U.S.A.* **77**, 6003–6006.

Garnier, P. E., Aubert, M. L., Kaplan, S. M., and Grumbach, M. M. (1978). *J. Clin. Endocrinol. Metab.* **47**, 1273–1281.

Giunta, C., Campantico, E., Vietti, M., and Gustalla, A. (1972). *Gen. Comp. Endocrinol.* **18**, 568.

Goldstein, B. J., and Livingston, J. N. (1981). *Endocrinology* **108**, 953–961.

Greep, R. (1974). *Handb. Physiol. Sect. 7 Endocrinol.* **4**, 1–27.

Grosvenor, C. E., and Whitworth, N. S. (1976). *J. Endocrinol.* **70**, 1–9.

Grueter, F. (1928). *C. R. Soc. Biol.* **98**, 1215–1217.

Grueter, F., and Stricker, P. (1929). *Klin. Wochenschr.* **8**, 2322–2323.

Hamada, Y., Schlaff, S., Kobayashi, R., Santulli, R., Wright, K. H., and Wallach, E. E. (1980). *Nature (London)* **285**, 161–163.

Hennighausen, L. G., and Sippel, A. E. (1982). *Eur. J. Biochem.* **125**, 131–141.

Hobbs, A. A., Richards, D. A., Kessler, D. J., and Rosen, J. M. (1982). *J. Biol. Chem.* **257**, 3598–3605.

Hollmann, K. H. (1974). *In* "Lactation" (B. L. Larson and V. R. Smith, eds.), Vol. 1, pp. 3–95. Academic Press, New York.

Houdebine, L.-M. (1981). *Biol. Cell.* **40**, 129–134.

Houdebine, L.-M. (1983). *Ann. d'Endocrinol.* **44**, 85–100.

Houdebine, L.-M., and Djiane, J. (1980a). *Biochimie* **62**, 433–440.

Houdebine, L.-M., and Djiane, J. (1980b). *Mol. Cell. Endocrinol.* **17**, 1–15.

Houdebine, L.-M., and Lacroix, M. C. (1980). *Biochimie* **62**, 441–444.

Houdebine, L.-M., Djiane, J., and Ollivier-Bousquet, M. (1981). *Biol. Cell.* **41**, 231–234.

Houdebine, L.-M., Olliver-Bousquet, M., and Djiane, J. (1982). *Biochimie* **64**, 21–28.

Josefsberg, A., Posner, B. I., Patel, B., and Bergeron, J. J. M. (1979). *J. Biol. Chem.* **254**, 209–214.

Kasuga, M., Carpentier, J. L., Vanobberman, E., Orci, L., and Gorden, P. (1983). *Biochem. Biophys. Res. Commun.* **114**, 230–233.

Kikuyama, S., Yamanoto, K., and Seki, T. (1980). *Gunma Symp. Endocrinol.* **17**, 3–13.

Kleczkowska, D., and Chomczynski, P. (1976). *Bull. Acad. Pol. Sci., Ser. Sci. Biol.* **24**, 189–193.

Knazek, R. A., Christy, R. J., Watson, K. C., Lim, M. F., Van Gorder, P. N., Dave, J. R., Richardson, L. L., and Liu, S. C. (1981). *Endocrinology* **109**, 1566–1572.

Kraiem, Z. (1981). *Isr. J. Med. Sci.* **17**, 1200.

Loizzi, R. F. (1978). *Horm. Metab. Res.* **10**, 415–419.

Loizzi, R. F., de Pont, J. J. H. H. M., and Bonting, S. L. (1975). *Biochim. Biophys. Acta* **392**, 20–25.

Louis, S. L., and Baldwin, R. L. (1975). *J. Dairy Sci.* **58**, 861–869.

Lyons, W. R. (1942). *Proc. Soc. Exp. Biol. Med.* **51**, 309–311.

McMurtry, J. P., and Malven, P. V. (1974). *J. Endocrinol.* **61**, 211–217.

Majumder, G. C., and Turkington, R. W. (1971). *J. Biol. Chem.* **246**, 2650–2657.

Malven, P. V. (1983). *Endocrinol. Exp.* **17**, 283–299.

Malven, P. V., and Keenan, T. W. (1983). *J. Dairy Sci.* **66**, 1237–1242.

Martin, R. J., and Baldwin, R. L. (1971). *Endocrinology* **88**, 863–871.

Matusik, R. J., and Rosen, J. M. (1980). *Endocrinology* **106**, 252–259.

Mittra, I. (1980a). *Biochem. Biophys. Res. Commun.* **95**, 1750–1759.

Mittra, I. (1980b). *Biochem. Biophys. Res. Commun.* **95**, 1760–1767.

Moncharmont, B., Su, J.-L., and Parikh, I. (1982). *Biochemistry* **21**, 6916–6921.

Necessary, P. C., and Ebner, K. E. (1983). *Biochem. Biophys. Res. Commun.* **3**, 224–230.

Nicoll, C. A., and Bern, H. A. (1972). *In* "Lactogenic Hormones" (G. E. W. Wolstenholme and J. Knight, eds.), pp. 299–324. Churchill, London.

Nolin, J. M. (1978a). *Endocrinology* **102**, 402–406.

Nolin, J. M. (1978b). *In* "Structure and Function of the Gonadotropins" (K. W. McKerns, ed.), pp. 151–182. Plenum, New York.

Nolin, J. M. (1979). *J. Histochem. Cytochem.* **27**, 1203.

Nolin, J. M. (1980a). *Biol. Reprod.* **22**, 417–422.

Nolin, J. M. (1980b). *Peptides* **1**, 249–255.

Nolin, J. M. (1981a). *In* "Reproductive Processes and Contraception" (K. W. McKerns, ed.), pp. 195–213. Plenum, New York.

Nolin, J. M. (1981b). *J. Cell Biol.* **91**, 210a.

Nolin, J. M. (1982). *Peptides* **3**, 823–831.

Nolin, J. M., and Bogdanove, E. M. (1980). *Biol. Reprod.* **22**, 383–416.

Nolin, J. M., and Witorsch, R. J. (1976). *Endocrinology* **99**, 949–958.

Oka, T. (1983). *In* "Biochemistry of Lactation" (T. B. Mepham, ed.), pp. 381–398. Elsevier, Amsterdam.

Oxberry, B. A., and Greenwald, G. S. (1983). *Biol. Reprod.* **29**, 1255–1263.

Paterson, J. A., Salih, J., and Shiu, R. P. C. (1982). *J. Histochem. Cytochem.* **30**, 153–156.

Pitelka, D. R., Hamamoto, S. T., Duafala, J. G., and Nemanik, M. K. (1973). *J. Cell Biol.* **56**, 797–818.

Pizarro, M., Puente, J., and Sapag-Hagar, M. (1981). *Eur. Biochem. Soc. Lett.* **136**, 127–130.

Purnell, D. M., Hillman, E. A., Heatfiled, B. H., and Trump, B. F. (1982). *Cancer Res.* **42**, 2317–2324.

Riddle, O., and Braucher, P. F. (1931). *Am. J. Physiol.* **97**, 617–625.

Riddle, O., Bates, R. W., and Dykshorn, S. W. (1932). *Proc. Soc. Exp. Biol. Med.* **29**, 1211–1215.

Riddle, O., Bates, R. W., and Dykshorn, S. W. (1933). *Am. J. Physiol.* **105**, 191–216.

Rillema, J. A. (1975). *Horm. Metab. Res.* **7**, 45–49.

Rillema, J. A. (1976). *Proc. Soc. Exp. Biol. Med.* **151**, 748–751.

Rillema, J. A. (1980a). *Fed. Proc., Fed. Am. Soc. Exp. Biol.* **39**, 2593–2598.

Rillema, J. A. (1980b). *Endocrinology* **106**, 1360–1364.

Rodgers, J. R., Yu-Lee, L.-Y., and Rosen, J. M. (1983). *Proc. Endocrinol. Soc.* p. 569.

Rosen, J. M., Matusik, R. J., Richards, D. A., Gupta, P., and Rodgers, J. R. (1980). *Recent Prog. Horm. Res.* **36**, 157–239.

Rosenfeld, M. G., Amara, S. G., Birnberg, N. C., Mermod, J.-J., Murdoch, G. H., and Evans, R. M. (1983). *Recent Prog. Horm. Res.* **39**, 305–351.

Sankaran, L., and Topper, Y. J. (1982). *J. Cell Biol.* **95**, 181a.

Sapag-Hagar, M., and Greenbaum, A. I. (1973). *Biochem. Biophys. Res. Commun.* **53**, 982–987.

Sapag-Hagar, M., and Greenbaum, A. E. (1974a). *Eur. J. Biochem.* **47**, 303–312.

Sapag-Hagar, M., and Greenbaum, A. I. (1974b). *FEBS Lett.* **46**, 180–183.

Sapag-Hagar, M., Greenbaum, A. I., Lewis, D. J., and Hallowes, R. C. (1974). *Biochem. Biophys. Res. Commun.* **59**, 261–268.

Shiu, R. P. C. (1980). *J. Biol. Chem.* **255**, 4278–4281.

Soong, Y. K., Ferguson, K. M., McGarrick, G., and Jeffcoate, S. L. (1982). *Clin. Endocrinol.* **16**, 259–265.

Speake, B., Eils, R., and Mayer, R. J. (1976). *Biochem. J.* **154**, 359–370.

Stadler, J., and Franke, W. W. (1974). *J. Cell Biol.* **60**, 297–303.

Stricker, P., and Grueter, F. (1928). *Co. R. Soc. Biol.* **99**, 1978–1980.

Suard, Y. M. L., Kraehenbuhl, J.-P., and Aubert, M. L. (1979). *J. Biol. Chem.* **254**, 10466–10475.

Suh, H. K., and Frantz, A. G. (1974). *J. Clin. Endocrinol. Metab.* **39**, 928–935.

Sutherland, E. W. (1972). *Science* **177**, 401.

Sutherland, E. W., and Rall, T. W. (1957). *J. Am. Chem. Soc.* **79**, 3608.

Sutherland, E. W., and Rall, T. W. (1960). *Pharmacol. Rev.* **12**, 265.

Szego, C. M. (1974). *Recent Prog. Horm. Res.* **30**, 171–233.

Szego, C. M. (1975). *In* "Lysosomes in Biology and Pathology" (J. T. Dingle and R. T. Dean, eds.), Vol. 4, pp. 385–477. North-Holland Publ., Amsterdam.

Szego, D. M. (1978). *In* "Structure and Function of the Gonadotropins" (K. W. McKerns, ed.), pp. 431–472. Plenum, New York.

Teyssot, B., and Houdebine, L.-M. (1980). *Biochem. Biophys. Res. Commun.* **97**, 463–473.

Turkington, R. W. (1972). *In* "Lactogenic Hormones" (G. E. W. Wolstenholme and J. Knight, eds.), pp. 111–135. Churchill, London.

Turkington, R. W., Majumder, G. C., Kadohama, N., MacIndoe, J. H., and Frantz, W. L. (1973). *Recent Prog. Horm. Res.* **29**, 417–455.

Velduis, J. D., Klase, P., and Hammond, J. M. (1980). *Endocrinology* **107**, 40–46.

Waters, M. J., McNeilly, A. S., Ohgo, S., and Friesen, H. G. (1980). *Endocrinology* **107**, 816–821.

Wang, C. A., Hsueh, A. J. W., and Erickson, G. F. (1980). *Mol. Cell. Endocrinol.* **20**, 135–144.

NOTE ADDED IN PROOF. Regarding the work of Houdebine *et al.*, cited in this article, please see a retraction of data on their membrane-derived "second messenger" as well as their own description of the inadequacy of their nuclear response assay (*Proc. Natl. Acad. Sci. U.S.A.* **82**, 3062, 1985).

INTERNATIONAL REVIEW OF CYTOLOGY, VOL. 95

Genetic Aspects of *Drosophila* as a Model System of Eukaryotic Aging

PETER J. MAYER*,† AND GEORGE T. BAKER III†

*Merck Sharp & Dohme, West Point, Pennsylvania and
†Center on Aging, University of Maryland, College Park, Maryland

I. Introduction

We shall begin with a broad definition: Aging in eukaryotes refers to the sequential changes and endogenous processes (biochemical, physiological, etc.) that regularly occur over time in the phenotype and that influence the duration of life. In a population of organisms, aging is ultimately reflected in differential (adult) survival and, along with the effects of the environment, determines the shape of the survivorship curve. Using Fisher's concept of reproductive value (Fisher, 1930), we can show how changes in survivorship relate to evolutionary fitness. Thus, we shall focus upon the duration of life of the organism because it represents the manifestation of many complex, highly integrated, suborganismal phenomena and because the longevity of the phenotype evolves through natural selection.

61

Longevity is an easily measured property of individual organisms; life expectancy, readily calculated from the life table, is the analogous property of populations. Unfortunately from the viewpoint of comparative biology, life expectancy is rarely reported for nohuman data, although early investigations of aging in *Drosophila* contain life tables. Although age at death does not necessarily correlate strongly with all aspects of aging in the wild, under controlled conditions differences in age at death can indicate much about genetic differences in aging. It is in this context that *Drosophila* represent a potentially valuable model of eukaryotic aging.

In general, insect models of aging offer many advantages, such as ease of maintenance, availability of pure genetic lines and well-defined mutants, short life span, and existence of tremendous biological variability (Rockstein, 1966). In particular, *Drosophila* offer the advantages of a substantial literature detailing their genetic, biochemical, physiological, and behavioral characteristics in relation to aging (for reviews see Baker *et al.*, 1985; Lints, 1978). These holometabolous, dipteran poikilotherms are especially amenable to study from the perspective of the biogerontologist interested in the total life cycle (Fisher, 1930; Lints, 1978; Clark, 1964; Sondhi, 1967c, 1968; David and Cohet, 1971; Northrup, 1917; Miller and Thomas, 1958; Hiraizume and Crow, 1960; Lints and Lints, 1971a; Mayer and Baker, 1984; Alpatov and Pearl, 1929; Moment, 1982) because the developmental phase and the adult phase are so distinct. The preimaginal phase comprises growth and differentiation of the organism as it passes from the egg through the larval to the pupal stage. During the preadult period (which generally lasts for about 8–14 days), the phenotype undergoes highly regulated morphological and physiological changes associated with metabolic and genetic events. The imaginal phase begins with the emergence of the adult fly, which experiences a period of biochemical and physiological maturation referred to as metachemogenesis (Baker, 1975, 1976, 1978). With the exception of the reproductive tissues and some midgut cells, the adult phenotype can be considered a postmitotic organism (Maynard Smith, 1962; Hollingsworth, 1967; Bozcuk, 1972). Mean imaginal (adult) life spans range from 15 to 60 days, depending on genotype and environmental conditions.

We emphasize that aging is a developmental, highly complex trait to underline the significance of genetic and environmental factors in determining longevity and to highlight the dependence of later effects on earlier events. These two themes provide the framework around which this article is organized. In the next two sections we shall discuss the effects on adult longevity of experiments in which genotypes or environments (or both) are manipulated. Primary examples of experimental manipulations include mutant, inbred, and hybrid strains, on the one hand, and temperature, chemical, and radiation effects, on the other. Another area of investigation—the influence of parental age on certain traits of offspring (including longevity)—is also considered within the context of genotypic and environmental experimentation since germ cells ''age'' within the changing physiological milieux of aging postemergent adults.

In Section IV we shall consider studies that explicitly followed *Drosophila* throughout the life cycle to demonstrate relationships between development and adult longevity. Even though less research has been conducted in this area, our own recent work (Mayer and Baker, 1984) and the work of others using mammalian systems (e.g., McKay *et al.*, 1935; Birren, 1964; Byung *et al.*, 1982; Weindruch and Walford, 1982) suggest exciting prospects for complete life cycle studies.

The final section progresses from a summary of the previous work to suggestions and speculations concerning possible future investigations. The use of isofemale strains, selection under extreme environmental conditions, observations of phenotypic variance in minimal stress experiments, and life table (Clark, 1964), life history (Stearns, 1976, 1977; Barclay and Gregory, 1981; Giesel *et al.*, 1982) or life cycle analysis all present interesting possibilities with relevance to other model systems of aging.

This article is based on the excellent bibliography of Soliman and Lints (1976) and on examinations of the following journals from 1976 to 1982: *American Naturalist, American Zoologist, Annual Review of Genetics, Annual Review of Entomology, Evolution, Experimental Gerontology, Genetika, Genetical Research, Genetics, Gerontology, Hereditas, Heredity, Journal of Gerontology, Journal of Heredity,* and *Mechanisms of Ageing and Development*. It represents a comprehensive picture of investigations into genetic aspects of aging (as defined above), but it is not intended to be an exhaustive search of the literature.

II. Genotypic and Environmental Studies

Genotypic investigations that employ pure or inbred strains will be discussed first, followed by consideration of hybrids or outbred strains (and the effects of heterosis); we shall conclude with data on mutants and chromosomal variants. While the vast majority of mutations have lethal or sublethal effects, only those studied explicitly in relation to life span will be treated here. Elaboration of experimental procedures in which various environmental stresses are manipulated will comprise, in order, temperature; diet; metabolism, and chemical administrations; radiation; and other variables such as population density, light, and atmospheric perturbations.

A review of the genetics of resistance to environmental stresses can be found in Parsons (1973). His approach is especially valuable and complementary to the present one in that he emphasizes the ecological and evolutionary perspective by focusing on acclimatization and resistance to stress in the wild. However, most of the workers investigating the evolutionary fitness of *Drosophila* measure egg-to-adult viability and egg production. Studies of genetic variability and environmental stress generally do not take into account such variables as duration of development and adult longevity. This is indeed an unfortunate loss of information and is an issue raised at several points throughout this article.

A. INBRED LINES

The studies of Pearl and his co-workers (e.g., Pearl, 1928b; Pearl and Parker, 1922a,b,c, 1924a,b,c; Pearl et al., 1923) set an admirable standard for the description of longevity by investigating short-lived (e.g., vestigal, with mean adult life span of 14 to 17 days), long-lived (e.g., wild-type line 107, with mean adult longevity of 50 to 54 days), and intermediate-lived inbred lines of *Drosophila melanogaster*. Repeated samplings of successive brother × sister matings established that duration of life is a consistently stable trait under constant experimental conditions. Furthermore, the F_2 generations of crosses of short-lived and long-lived lines exhibited Mendelian segregation with respect to imaginal longevity; this was interpreted to mean that the mutant (vestigal) produces a life-shortening effect. More recent studies of hybrids have revealed F_1 superiority and F_2 inferiority among *D. pseudoobscura* (Maynard Smith, 1959), although over the course of 4.5 years there was substantial genetic divergence within these populations (Mourad, 1965). In other studies hybrids did not demonstrate greater mean adult survival than all wild types, although inbreds were consistently shorter lived (Gowen and Johnson, 1946). *D. melanogaster* hybrids showed no change in mean adult longevity between F_1 and F_2 offspring in one case (Woodhams and Hollingsworth, 1971), and a decrease in the F_2 in another (Bozcuk, 1978). The latter study used female virgins, and both males and females were maintained in darkness.

The rectangular shape of the survivorship curve of the long-lived lines and the diagonal shape of the curve of the short-lived lines approach the theoretical limits to genetically homogeneous populations reared under laboratory conditions (Pearl and Parker, 1924a). The former depicts the ideal situation in which all individuals of a population die at the same age, whereas the latter indicates a constant rate of mortality at all ages. Intermediate curves have an inflection point (rarely more than one) where the slope is steepest; this has been interpreted to indicate the initiation of, or the period of, maximal senescence (e.g., Clark, 1964). While it is often recognized that Pearl and his co-workers established an invaluable research baseline, unfortunately one aspect of their work, the presentation of life table data, has not continued. Even simple calculations of life expectancy values at different ages can provide meaningful comparative statistics which are informative about aging processes in populations. It also allows more detailed comparisons to be made between laboratories and among studies, while permitting theoretical biologists, modelers, and others to utilize data.

The usual practice of researchers involves reporting mean adult longevities or median (50%) survivorship values separately for each sex. A recent summary of these data for four species and 34 strains (Baker *et al.*, 1983) indicates a number of interesting trends. In both *D. melanogaster* and *D. subobscura,* female mean longevity exceeds male mean longevity in more than half the strains studied, although differences range from 27.0 to 0.9 days. Within each species, mean adult longevities for flies reared under the same temperature conditions extend from 38 to 74 days for *melanogaster* males, from 30 to 52 days for *melanogaster* females, from 17 to 69 days for *subobscura* males, and from 17 to 64 days for *subobscura* females. In *D. subobscura,* genetic sex-limited effects on adult longevity have been demonstrated (Maynard Smith, 1959), but generally there are no consistent sex differences with respect to longevity (Pearl, 1928b). Undoubtedly some of these life span differences reflect genuine species and strain genetic differences; nevertheless, it is also known that variability between labs, across seasons and climates, and among environmental conditions can explain differences in longevity. Caution in comparing results from different labs, or even from the same lab at different times, means that replication is essential to reaching sound conclusions. As an example, consider a study in which *D. melanogaster* and *D. simulans* were reared simultaneously in the same lab with the result that nonsignificant differences in adult longevity were reported both between species and within species between sexes (Tantawy and Rakha, 1961).

Finally, it is important to note that the significance of environmental variability in enhancing genotypic variability is supported by attempts to select for increased adult longevity. Given the heterogeneous character of imaginal life span for different strains of *D. melanogaster,* one might assume that there is a substantial amount of additive variance for the trait. Yet one study of selection for increased longevity over eight generations lead to the conclusion that only epistatic effects can explain the lack of response (Lints *et al.,* 1979), whereas another demonstrated a possibly pleiotropic response of longevity to selection for increased fecundity at later ages (Rose and Charlesworth, 1980). Moreover, selection of *D. subobscura,* using flies which survived 30 or more days (where mean adult longevity was 22–25 days), also yielded no increase in life expectancy (Comfort, 1953). Other research into the complex determination of life history traits such as longevity will be considered in Section V.

B. Hybrid Lines

The advantages of hybrid vigor include longevity superior to that of either inbred parental stock. For example, among 24 hybrids of *D. melanogaster* all reared at 25°C, the ranges of adult mean longevity were 31–90 days for males and 23–85 days for females (Baker *et al.,* 1983, Table 3). These ranges exceed those cited above (38–74 for males, 30–52 for females). Life expectancy at eclosion (emergence) can double when inbred lines of *D. subobscura* are out-crossed (Clarke and Maynard Smith, 1955), although the closely related *D. pseudoobscura* demonstrates no heterozygote superiority for wild second chromosomes [40]. Interestingly enough, in *D. subobscura* (Clark and Maynard Smith, 1955) and in 21 hybrids of different *D. melanogaster* strains (Baker *et al.*, 1983, Table 3) no consistent sex differences in adult longevity were found, although the parental inbred lines exhibit female superiority. Coefficients of variation for imaginal longevity of hybrids are consistently smaller than those of inbreds (Baker *et al.*, 1983; Clarke and Maynard Smith, 1955; Maynard Smith *et al.*, 1955). Moreover, heterotic effects on longevity are much more pronounced in crosses between genetically different populations than in crosses between mutants or stocks which are genetically similar (Zimina *et al.*, 1977).

These observations suggest that heterosis for adult longevity is multigenic and probably epistatic or regulatory in mechanism, with the further implication that genetic homeostasis (Lerner, 1954) affects the entire life span (see Section IV). In fact, among five strains of *D. funebris* and *D. pavani*, it has been shown that heterozygotes enjoy greater survival at both the preadult and the adult stages (Brncic and del Solar, 1961) and that, in crowded cultures, viability is higher for heterozygotes than for homozygotes among four species of *Drosophila* (Dobzhansky and Wallace, 1953).

C. Mutant and Chromosome Variants

Whereas heterozygosis in outbred lines increases the imaginal life span, homozygosity in mutant strains predictably decreases imaginal life span. Among 32 examples of single and multiple mutants of *D. melanogaster* reared at 25°C, longevity ranged from 9 to 64 days for males and from 11 to 57 days for females (Baker *et al.*, 1983, Table 4). In half of the cases males were longer lived, and in half the cases females were longer lived. This observation is consonant with the finding that while the genetic background into which a mutant line is bred conditions the effect of the mutant on life span, such studies reveal no consistent pattern with respect to sex differences in adult longevity (Lints, 1971; Clarke and Gould, 1970; Bozcuk, 1981). Interesting in this regard is the report that sex intergrades (2 X and 1 Y chromosome per genome) exhibit diagonal survival curves, whereas triploid females (3X chromosomes per genome) demonstrate mean adult longevity equal to that of wild-type (control) females (Gowen, 1931a), which typically yield rectangular-shaped survivorship.

While most studies have examined morphological mutants (e.g., Clarke and Gould, 1970; Bozcuk, 1981; Gonzalez, 1923; Brierley, 1938), behavioral or neurological mutants (Trout and Kaplan, 1970) and at least one physiological mutant (Doane, 1960) also demonstrate reduced adult longevity relative to wild type. As was found with crosses between wild-type flies, imaginal longevity has shown a heterotic effect among X-linked mutant strains (Unlu and Bozcuk, 1979a,b). However, the effects which multiple mutations exert on the life span depend on the particular loci involved and on the (epistatic) effects of their combinations (Gonzalez, 1923). Hence it is important to keep in mind the fact that even though mutant strains may breed true with respect to their particular markers, other as yet uncharacterized mutations may be present. This is probably true, for example, with a series of DNA repair-deficient mutants which were recovered from exposure of mass cultures to chemical mutagens (Green, 1970) and which exhibit reduced imaginal longevity relative to the parental stock (Baker *et al.*, 1983, Table 4; Daly *et al.*, 1979, 1980).

While many, if not most, identified mutants have reduced viability, adult longevity is rarely studied or reported. The assumption, presumably, is that mutation invariably disrupts a coadapted genotype (Dobzhansky and Wallace, 1953) to the detriment of the mutant organism. Thus, there is a pronounced negative skew to the distribution of imaginal life span among mutants (see Fig. 1). Moreover no mutation has yet been reported in *Drosophila* which acts to increase longevity. Here the assumption may be that untold generations of ancestral *Drosophila* have been subject to some type of stabilizing selection such that the optimal phenotype(s) we observe today (and have observed since the early twentieth century) attained an adaptive plateau. On the other hand, our inability to select successfully for increased life span may mean that intrinsic biochemical and physiological limits have been reached and that a form of macroevolution would be required to exceed them. What constitutes these limits, and how optimal phenotypes achieve their adaptive plateau, are questions which experimental gerontologists can pursue with the *Drosophila* model genetic system. Environmental stresses, for example, have been used to help define boundaries to survival and adaptation.

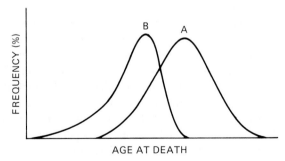

FIG. 1. Idealized frequency distributions of imaginal longevity for normal (A) and mutant (B) *Drosophila* populations.

D. Temperature Effects

Because of longstanding interest in the rate of living concept (Pearl, 1928a; Comfort, 1979), because of the ease with which it can be experimentally manipulated, because of the obvious occurrence of climatic variables in *Drosophila* ecology, and because *Drosophila* is a poikilotherm, studies abound on the effects of temperature on life span. One recent review lists more than 80 entries in which temperature varied either between the preadult and adult stages of the life cycle or during the imaginal period of replicate cultures (Baker *et al.*, 1983, Table 9). One nearly universal result is that lower temperatures prolong development or imaginal life span (or both), whereas higher temperatures decrease the lengths of these periods. Adult *Drosophila subobscura,* for example, can live as long as 100 days if kept at 18.5°C (Hollingsworth and Bowler, 1966) and beyond 150 days at 15°C (Hollingsworth, 1969). *D. melanogaster* imaginal longevity increases linearly from 14 days at 30°C to 120 days at 10°C (Loeb and Northrup, 1917). Exceptions to the inverse relationship between temperature and duration of life include reports on *D. melanogaster* (David *et al.,* 1975; Cohet, 1973; Lamb, 1968) and a range of other dipteran insects (Baumberger, 1914).

Yet even within the widespread validity of the inverse correlation, significant differences among strains have been reported. For example, consider two studies of *D. melanogaster* F_1 hybrids reared at a preadult temperature of 25°C: in one, mean female adult longevity declined from 67 to 44 days and from 55 to 35 days as imaginal temperature increased from 16° to 31°C (Lints and Lints, 1971); in another, mean female adult longevity decreased from 171 to 29 days and from 158 to 31 days as imaginal temperature was raised from 15° to 30°C (Burcombe and Hollingsworth, 1970). Moreover, female *D. melanogaster* (Burcombe and Hollingsworth, 1970) and *D. simulans* (Parsons, 1977) are able to survive better than are males at both lower and higher imaginal temperatures, and they suffer a smaller percentage reduction in mean longevity as temperature rises. Yet this sex difference is not seen when individually housed, virgin *D. melanogaster* are studied (Strehler, 1961).

While the rate of living theory of aging may have supplied the original impetus to research into temperature effects on longevity in *D. melanogaster* (Alpatov and Pearl, 1929), studies with *D. subobscura* have led to an alternative hypothesis. According to the threshhold theory of aging (Maynard Smith, 1962; Clarke and Maynard Smith, 1961a,b) there are two phases in the adult life span of *D. subobscura:* an "aging" phase that is temperature independent, followed by a "dying" phase that can be prolonged at lower temperatures. While the level of the threshhold between "aging" and "dying" is dependent on temperature, the rate of "aging" is irreversible in the range of 15° to 30°C. Lack of subsequent experimental support for this theory (which initially had been empirically derived) when it was tested with *D. melanogaster* (Hollingsworth, 1969; Miquel *et al.*, 1976) led one of its proponents to suggest an alternative explanation, namely, that previous findings of the independence of temperature effect on adult life span may have been due to reaching the upper temperature limit of variability for each species (Hollingsworth, 1966) or to irreversible effects at higher temperatures (Hollingsworth, 1968). The establishment of "boundary conditions" such as maximum temperature is important to the genetics of aging not only because it helps to constrain theories but also because it demonstrates the range of phenotypic plasticity and suggests limits to homeostatic and ontogenetic adaptation.

Two other issues relevant to all of the environmental studies on longevity can conveniently be raised here. The first concerns correlated response, whether this be due to selection for one trait or to experimental perturbation of the organism. The present example relates to the increase in body size (Alpatov and Pearl, 1929; Tantawy and Vetukhiv, 1960; Tantawy, 1961a) and in lifetime egg production (Tantawy and Vetukhiv, 1960; Tantawy, 1961a) which accompanies increased longevity at lower temperatures. While increased lifetime egg production may be due to larger body size per se (Roff, 1981), it is also a consequence of longer life span. More important, to the extent that increased body size is due to increased developmental time (Robertson, 1960), the positive relationship between body size and adult longevity may be due to a common factor, such as aging rate, that is affected by temperature throughout the life span. More will be said below about these sorts of interrelationships, which selection experiments might help to dissect. (For example, what are the effects on imaginal longevity of lines of flies selected for extreme body sizes or developmental times when they are reared at different temperatures?)

The second point to be made is a commonplace that bears repeating: Cognizance of gene–environment interaction is critical when interpreting the types of experiments reviewed here. For example, hybrids of *D. melanogaster* may (Tantawy *et al.*, 1973) or may not (Woodhams and Hollingsworth, 1971) exhibit increased heterotic effects for longevity at extreme temperatures (e.g., 28° to 30°C) as compared with more optimal temperatures (15° to 25°C). Furthermore, even sibling species of *Drosophila* differ with respect to the effects of temperature increase on preimaginal and imaginal longevity (Parsons, 1978a; McKenzie, 1978). Finally, environment by environment interactions must also be considered, as demonstrated, for example, by an elegant study of fitness-related traits in 12 strains of *D. pseudoobscura* using two culture media and two temperatures (Taylor and Condra, 1978).

E. Diet and Metabolic Effects

The rate of living theory (Pearl, 1928a) suggests that metabolic rate is directly related to the duration of life. For example, when medium containing ethidium bromide (which reduces mitochondrial respiratory efficiency) is fed to *D. melangoaster* as either larvae or imagoes, oxygen consumption is decreased and both developmental time and adult longevity increase (Fleming *et al.,* 1981). Yet when tested by oxygen consumption in *D. melanogaster* (Sheherbakov, 1935; Lints and Lints, 1968), *D. simulans* (Winberg, 1936), and *D. subobscura* (Bowler and Hollingsworth, 1966), or by carbon dioxide production in *Drosophila* with chromosomal imbalances (Gowen, 1931b), data do not adequately and consistently support the theory. One study which specifically examined the effects of differential developmental temperature (14, 22, 28°C) on O_2 consumption and adult longevity (at 22°C) in *D. melanogaster* reported no differences in respiration or longevity (Vinberg, 1937).

While these results may be surprising in light of the consistent inverse relationship between temperature and life span (*vide supra*), they probably reflect the existence of an optimal metabolic rate in much the same way that there appears to be a very narrow range of growth temperature (Cohet, 1975) and larval population density (Pearl and Parker, 1922b; Pearl *et al.,* 1927) optimal for longevity. Moreover, "buffering" of effects on life span by homeostatic adjustment to atmospheric conditions may be disrupted by specifically targeted biochemical interactions. Yet the analysis of an oxygen free-radical scavenger (superoxide dismutase) in *D. melanogaster* strains with markedly different adult longevities has led to contradictory results (Bartosz *et al.,* 1979; Massie *et al.,* 1981).

Nutritional requirements for *Drosophila* longevity (Hollingsworth and Burcombe, 1970) include water, a carbohydrate as a respiratory substrate, and yeast or bacteria (living or killed) to provide amino acids as well as other nutrients (Glaser, 1924). Among the factors added to media, and their effects on longevity, are the following: "embryonic juice" had no effect on *D. melanogaster* (Pearl and Parker, 1922b); amino acid analogues had no effect when fed to adult *subobscura* (Pearl and Parker, 1922a) or to adult *melanogaster* (Bozcuk, 1977), but they did when fed to larval *melanogaster* (Harrison and Holliday, 1967); deuterium oxide decreased life spans of *melanogaster* by diminishing amounts as temperature rose from 10° to 30°C (Samis *et al.,* 1974); arsenic killed *melanogaster* within 3.5 to 6.5 days, although hybrids and females were relatively more resistant (l'Heriter, 1932); lactic and gluconic acids extend life span of *D. melanogaster* (Massie and Williams, 1979) while ascorbic acid slightly decreases longevity (Massie *et al.,* 1976); vitamin E and centrophenoxine (a lipofuscinolytic agent) increase longevity in DNA repair deficient mutants of *D. melanogaster* (Daly *et al.,* 1980; Baker, 1981); other antioxidants (sodium and magnesium thiazolidine carboxylate) also increase longevity in wild-type *melanogaster* (Miquel and Economos, 1979); the mutagen nitrosodimethylurea decreases male but not female *melanogaster* life span, whereas a "geroprotector" (2-ethyl-6-methyl-3-hydroxypyridine·HCl) increases adult longevity of both sexes (Obukhova *et al.*, 1979); pH buffers increase life span of *D. melanogaster* (Massie *et al.*, 1981) and neutral pH also improves a synthetic medium with casein, sucrose, and a vitamin complex, which nevertheless reduces longevity when compared to a natural diet of killed yeast (van Herrewege, 1974).

In the absence of food, the following results have been obtained: *D. melanogaster* males live less than 36 hours at 21°C (Economos and Ballard, 1982), and females outlive males at 25°C (Pearl and Parker, 1924b); normally short-lived vestigal and long-lived wild-type flies exhibit equivalent survival of 42 to 52 hours (Pearl and Parker, 1924a), whereas ebony mutants outlive wild types when both are singly housed (Greiff, 1940); depending on humidity and population density, *D. pseudoobscura* males average 66 to 113 hours at 19°C and 38 to 88 hours at 24°C, while mean female adult longevities range from 63 to 128 hours at 19°C and from 35 to 92 hours at 24°C (Lilleland, 1938). Limited underfeeding as adults (by dilution of medium) does not appreciably affect female longevity of *D. melanogaster* until dilution reaches one-sixteenth of the normal concentration, while male life span is reduced at one-eighth (David *et al.*, 1971a). The greater ability of female *Drosophila* to tolerate nutritional stress (as well as other types of stress) has been reported by others (Bileva *et al.*, 1978; Alpatov, 1930).

Making food less accessible consistently reduces adult longevity (David and Cohet, 1972), as does intermittent starvation (Kopec, 1928) and feeding adults a yeastless medium (Alpatov, 1930). Conversely, "there is no reason for believing that a diet rich in nutrients is life-shortening for *Drosophila* adults" (Hollingsworth and Burcombe, 1970, p. 1017).

F. RADIATION

Various investigations of the effects of high-energy radiation on whole organisms lead to the suggestion that such effects mimic aging (e.g., Szilard, 1959; Failla, 1958; cf. Strehler, 1959). This view became incorporated into the somatic mutation theory of aging which attributes disruption of function and loss of physiological adaptation with age to unrepaired mutations in diverse tissues and organs (Comfort, 1979; Curtis, 1963). Since adult *Drosophila* are essentially postmitotic organisms (Bozcuk, 1972), the results of experiments irradiating imagoes are applicable only to the effects of somatic mutations in nondividing cells. To the extent that radiation causes life shortening (see later), the question arises as to whether the effect is due to a radiation-specific phenomenon or whether it represents a model of intensified "normal" aging. Similarly, distinction needs to be made between the results of "premature aging" in which there is *de novo* induction of a finite aging process and "accelerated aging" in which there is amplification of, or a contribution to, an on-going aging process (Lamb and Maynard Smith, 1969). Obviously age at exposure(s), as well as dosage level and frequency, becomes a critical variable in trying to test these hypotheses.

Low doses of ionizing radiation (less than 5–10 kR) increase adult longevity [103c], as seen, for example, with a single dose (5 kR) irradiating individually housed *D. melanogaster* (Strehler, 1962). But the F_2 males carrying an irradiated X chromosome (from F_1 males exposed to 2 kR), exhibited three identifiable life-shortening mutations (Gould and Clarke, 1977). Much larger doses (up to 225 kR, γ irradiation) given to 1-day-old imagoes proportionally decreased survival with increasing exposure (Baxter and Tuttle, 1957). A series of single exposures (33, 66, 93 kR) to 2- to 4-day-old flies revealed that males show a greater percentage reduction in adult longevity than do females at all doses (Gartner, 1973). A different series of exposures (15, 20, 25, 50, 75 kR), also with *D. melanogaster,* showed that males aged 1, 4, or 8 days all demonstrate similar decreases in longevity with increasing doses, whereas females seem to exhibit a more complex maturational effect at intermediate doses (Giess and Planel, 1977; Giess, 1980). Small daily doses (1–4 kR, X ray) throughout the life span increase longevity, whereas larger (up to 20 kR) periodic exposures decrease life span (Sacher, 1963). For *D. melanogaster* there does not appear to be a change with age in radiosensitivity to larger doses (up to 120 kR) at young ages (1–8 days) (Mill *et al.,* 1973) or to single small doses (5–50 kR) at older ages (up to 35 days) (Lamb, 1964a; Atlan *et al.,* 1969; Baxter and Blair, 1967). But at higher doses (up to 75 kR) results are contradictory (Baxter and Tuttle, 1957; Lamb, 1964a; Atlan *et al.,* 1969). *D. subobscura* males irradiated under various conditions of temperature and change of media, exhibited constant reduction in longevity such that 45 kR halved the life span (Lamb, 1964a). Longer-lived *D. melanogaster* males suffer a greater reduction in longevity than do shorter-lived males (when exposed to 10 daily doses of 20 kR), whereas females do not display this phenomenon (Baxter and Blair, 1967). Similarly, highly inbred female *D. melanogaster* are more resistant than males to irradiation exposure at 10 days of age, although at 5 days there is little gender difference (Lamb and Maynard Smith, 1964). However, virgin females show a much greater decrease in longevity than do either mated females, virgin males, or mated males when all are exposed to increasing but small doses of radiation (10, 15, 20 kR) as 4-day-old imagoes (Giess *et al.,* 1980).

Ordinarily, unmated males and females both outlive their mated counterparts, with females enjoying a greater increase due, presumably, to the lack of stress associated with egg laying (David and Cohet, 1971; Doane, 1960; Bilewicz, 1953; and see below). This might explain how low doses increase longevity by sterilizing the adults (Giess *et al.,* 1980; Alpatov, 1930), but it cannot account for the sex difference among virgins at higher doses. Apparently, triploid and diploid female *D. melanogaster* are equally radiosensitive (Lamb, 1965), which argues against an X-linked gene dosage effect to explain greater female radioresistance (Ogaski and Nakashima-Tanawa, 1966). Nevertheless, there does appear to be some autosomal genetic determination to radioresistance and radiosensitivity (Lamb and Maynard Smith, 1964; Ogaski and Nakashima-tanawa, 1966; Westerman and Parsons, 1973), although it does not appear to be associated with genes that determine longevity in untreated controls (MacBean, 1970). Additive gene effects for differential survival response to irradiation have been traced to the second and third chromosomes (Parsons et al., 1969).

While we are aware of only one study that looked at radiosensitivity throughout the life span (Giess and Pellannel, 1973), the intriguing results bear mentioning and may be worth further exploration. Radioprotection against background sources resulted in *reduced* adult longevity when both males and females were protected either throughout the life span or just during the imaginal period. Given the existence of inducible DNA repair systems in prokaryotes, and their arguable presence in mammalian systems (Nichols and Murphy, 1977; Hanawalt et al., 1977), it may be that under certain conditions low levels of ionizing radiation can induce longevity-enhancing responses in *Drosophila*. With the availability of DNA repair-deficient mutants, such a hypothesis may be testable, although it might not be straightforward inasmuch as the mutations identified thus far are on the X chromosome.

In summary, there is more evidence to support the age-independent effects of irradiation on longevity than the alternative of age sensitivity. However, the repeated findings of linear decreases in survival with age stand in contrast to the exponential declines observed at the oldest ages. Such synergistic effects suggest the occurrence of accelerated aging among longer-lived survivors and result in a two-phase model in which early mortality is strictly an effect of radiation (Dolkas et al., 1975). This interpretation is supported by histological analysis of control flies and of same-aged flies killed at 2–33 days but irradiated at age 1 day with 50 kR, which revealed substantial differences in a range of tissues (Miquel et al., 1972). The somatic mutation theory of aging cannot be definitively dismissed or confirmed by the data because of the inconsistency of the sex differences and because the presence of DNA repair systems presents an entirely new level of possible control of life span which remains to be fully evaluated.

G. OTHER STRESSES

As already mentioned, in both D. *melanogaster* and D. *subobscura* mating status influences adult longevity. Females are more dramatically affected than males, the effect consistently being that virgins outlive nonvirgins (David and Cohen, 1971; Hiraizume and Crow, 1960; Zimina et al., 1977; Doane, 1960; Giess et al., 1980; Bilewicz, 1953; O'Brian, 1962; Giess and Pianel, 1977; Giess, 1980; Kidwell and Malick, 1967; Cohet and David, 1973; Ramel and

Eiche, 1960). While there are no reported exceptions to this observaton, at least two related variables must also be taken into account. The first concerns the effects of egg laying on imaginal longevity, which are reported to be negative (Bilewicz, 1953; Maynard Smith, 1958) and positive (Lints and Lints, 1971b; Tantawy and Vetukhiv, 1960; McKenzie, 1978; Kidwell and Malick, 1967). Larger females live longer and lay more eggs (both on average and in total lifetime production) than smaller females (Lints and Lints, 1971b; Tantawy and Vetukhiv, 1960; cf. Kidwell and Malick, 1967). Heterozygous females lay more eggs than shorter-lived homozygotes (Sondhi, 1967c; Kidwell and Malick, 1967; Ohnisni, 1976; Giesel, 1979b; cf. Spiess *et al.*, 1952), even though the number of eggs laid per day diminishes with age after reaching a maximum by about age 10 (David *et al.*, 1975). Thus, there appears to be a "constellation of fitness characters" such that natural selection has favored a positive correlation between fertility and survival. This correlation yields what has been called a "higher evolutionary potential" of the population (Cannon, 1966), since it results in greater reproductive value (Fisher, 1930) and possibly a faster intrinsic rate of increase. Further evidence for this correlation can be found in a study of selection for the effects of different mating schemes (immediately after eclosion and delayed until age 21 days) on adult longevity (Glass, 1964).

The second factor which must be considered concerns the physiological effects of isolation (of virgins) on longevity. In terms of locomotion, for example, smaller flies (which are shorter-lived) tend to be more active than larger flies (Miller and Thomas, 1958), and neurological mutants which manifest greater physical activity also exhibit shorter adult life spans (Trout and Kaplan, 1970). In fact, it has been repeatedly demonstrated that beyond an optimal level larval crowding has an adverse impact on adult longevity (Baker *et al.*, 1983, Table 10; Sheoherbakov, 1935; Pearl and Parker, 1922b; Pearl *et al.*, 1927; Cohet and David, 1973; Lints and Lints, 1969a), and it also has unfavorable effects on fertility, viability, and developmental time (Clark and Feldman, 1981; Marks, 1982). However, it has not been determined to what extent these effects are due to restrictions in locomotion per se as opposed to alterations in media caused by depletion of nutrients, addition of waste products, or some other processes.

Another environmental "stress" which has been investigated in terms of its effects on adult longevity is the intensity and circadian cycle of light (Baker *et al.*, 1983, Table 11). In *D. melanogaster* it has been shown that permanent darkness increases imaginal longevity (Allemand *et al.*, 1973; O'Brian *et al.*, 1965), whereas constant illumination may (Erk and Samis, 1970) or may not (Allemand *et al.*, 1973) reduce the life span. Developmental time does not seem to be affected by continuous breeding and maintenance in total darkness (Northrup, 1926); increasing light intensity beyond 640 meter-candles causes an exponential decrease in imaginal longevity (Northrup, 1925).

Since various species of *Drosophila* (and related subgenera) utilize fermenting fruit as a food resource (Parsons, 1982; Starmer *et al.*, 1977; Parsons, 1981), it is not surprising that there is substantial genetic polymorphism at the alcohol dehydrogenase (ADH) locus (Grossman *et al.*, 1970). Investigations of reactions to varying levels of atmospheric and dietary alcohols reveal that there is a fluctuating decrease in resistance with age and that males are slightly hardier than females in terms of survival (Crozier and Enzmann, 1936; Crozier *et al.*, 1935). Further, in the absence of other food, there is an optimal concentration range of ethanol for both developmental time and adult longevity among a range of species and geographic subraces (Starmer *et al.*, 1977; Parsons, 1981; Parsons *et al.*, 1979). In terms of other similar experiments, adult exposure to pure oxygen shows a fairly consistent dose–response decrease in imaginal longevity (Philpott *et al.*, 1974), whereas even repeated exposure to ether does not appear to affect survival (Pearl and Parker, 1922c). Interestingly enough, there appears to be a developmental reversal of ether sensitivity and resistance between the embryonic (3–21 hours) and adult stages of the life cycle (Nakashima-Tanaka and Ogaki, 1980). Los Angeles smog and ozone both decrease adult life span in Canton-S and in hyperkinetic mutant virgin females (Trout and Hanson, 1971).

Weightlessness does not seem to affect development of *D. melanogaster* but has a negative impact on adult life span (Miquel and Philpott, 1978). Humidity (in contrast to dry air) seems to prolong survival at high temperatures (above 33°C), although adult *D. subobscura* can apparently "adapt" to dry air if development occurs in dry air (Maynard Smith, 1957). Six strains of *D. melanogaster* grown under asceptic conditions during the preimaginal phase have a 14 to 35% increased adult longevity, whereas the adult longevity of flies the entire life spans of which were asceptic, exceeded the mean duration of adult controls by 69% (Steinfeld, 1928). Finally, inbred female *D. melanogaster* deprived of 0.10 or 0.25 μl of hemolymph at 3 days after emergence exhibited reduced adult life span, as did 3-day-old hosts receiving 0.25 μl of hemolymph from 12- to 24-day-old donors (Sohndhi, 1966, 1967a). Curiously, fertility was also reduced in females deprived of 0.10 μl of hemolymph (Sondhi, 1967a) but not in females who lost 0.25 μl or who received equal volumes of hemolymph from different-aged donors (Sondhi, 1966). Early deaths were reduced when hybrid donors replaced inbred donors (Sondhi, 1965, 1967b).

III. Parental Age Effects

The effects observed in offspring of parents of varying ages can be divided into two general categories. First we shall summarize some of the investigations into germ line mutations and chromosomal aberrations. Then we shall consider differences in the life cycles of offspring produced by younger and older parents. An earlier review of this work with *Drosophila* can be found in Lints (1978).

It is relatively easy to count the number of eggs laid during a specified period of time and subsequently to count the number (and sex) of adult flies which ultimately "hatch" from those eggs. This ratio of emergences to eggs (viability) is an efficient and commonly used measure of fitness in *Drosophila*. It also provides an appropriate means of measuring the frequency of autosomal and sex-linked lethal mutations. Storage of sperm (in males or females) and of oocytes results in increased mutation rates for the former and in increased rates of nondisjunction for the latter (Wurgler, 1972). However, since gametogenesis is a continuous process in adult males and females, nondisjunction may (Tokunaga, 1970) or may not (Kelsall, 1963) increase with maternal age, while it does appear to increase with increasing paternal age (Lamy, 1949). In an earlier study, spontaneous mutations reportedly do not increase with paternal age (Olenov 1945) and aging of X-irradiated sperm does not increase the number of mutations (Harris, 1929). However, a recent study on the rate of sex-linked spontaneous recessive lethal mutations (SRLMs) in a population of individually housed males demonstrated a 24-fold increase between 35- and 58-day-old animals. In addition, the number of males producing sterile progeny increased, as did the number of sterile F_1 progeny, with advancing age (Merkin and Baker, 1982).

Mature germ cells exhibit higher mutation rates and are more susceptible to X-ray damage than immature germ cells (Harris, 1929; Kossikov, 1937), although the very first batches of sperm are highly susceptible to mutagenic influences (Lamy, 1947). Somatic crossing over has been reported not to increase with maternal aging (Brown and Welshons, 1955). The relationship between maternal age and recombination is parabolic, with a minimum between 6 and 12 days posteclosion (Bridges, 1927, 1929). (*Drosophila* males exhibit no meiotic recombination.) In fact, the variability due to crossing over seen in the genotypes of offspring produced by older and younger parents seems to involve an interactive effect between the parental germ lines (Jebrak, 1930a,b). It may also be true that older parents of either sex (30–45 days versus newly emerged) tend to produce more male than female progeny (Vassileva-Dryanovska and Gencheva, 1965).

As parental age increases, *D. melanogaster* generally show a decrease in viability (O'Brian *et al.*, 1965), in hatchability (Biemont, 1976), and in imaginal longevity (Butz and Hayden, 1962; O'Brian *et al.*, 1964; O'Brian, 1961; cf. O'Brian and Beckman, 1967) of offspring. Detrimental inbreeding effects (i.e., reduced egg hatchability and adult emergence) also have been reported to increase with parental age (Biemont, 1976), as has degree of parental–offspring resemblance (heritability) for sternopleural bristle number (Beardmore *et al.*, 1975). At 15°C, heterozygous *D. persimilis* exhibit higher daily fecundity than homozygotes (17–20 eggs/day versus 13–15) for ages 1–60 days, after which point the rates are essentially equal (days 61–110, range = 7–13 eggs/day; at 110–160 days, range = 4–5 eggs/day) (Spiess *et al.*, 1952). Furthermore, *D.*

melanogaster offspring homozygous for the second chromosome also exhibit decreased longevity (and viability) as a parental age effect, although heterozygotes do not (Marinkovic *et al.*, 1973; Andjelkovic *et al.*, 1979).

The claim that parental age effects on adult longevity of offspring in *D. melanogaster* are cumulative, selectable, and reversible (Lints, 1978; Andjelkovic *et al.*, 1979; Lints and Hoste, 1974) is not supported by studies with *D. subobscura* (Comfort, 1953; Wattiaux, 1968) or *D. pseudoobscura* (Wattiaux, 1974). The observation of cyclical (over tens of generations) "Lansing effects" on imaginal longevity in *D. melanogaster*, wherein flies consistently produced at either old or young parental ages achieve similar maxima and minima for longevity (Lints and Hoste, 1974), may be related to the increase in heritability found with increasing parental age (Beardmore, 1976). This increase—which can lead to a doubling of offspring on midparent regression—is seen only among "central phenotypes" and not with "extreme phenotypes" (Beardmore, 1976). It is possible that organisms which reach maximal and minimal longevity through parental age effects are homozygous for genes with additive effects on adult life span, whereas intermediate (optimal?) values of longevity are determined by heterozygous effects.

Such an explanation, of course, does not account for the species difference in the presence or absence of the "Lansing effect." Furthermore, a cyclical or "Lansing effect" has been reported for wing length (Delcour and Heuts, 1968) and for developmental time (Delcour, 1969) in *D. melanogaster*, but it has not been confirmed (Butz and Hayden, 1962; O'Brian, 1961). As has been suggested (Parsons, 1962), these phenomena with respect to developmental time and imaginal longevity may reflect the results of natural selection in optimizing the lengths of the phases of the life cycle. In terms of viability or hatchability, it seems well established that the age-related peak in fecundity coincides with maximal likelihood of survival of offspring to adulthood (Butz and Hayden, 1962; O'Brian, 1961; Parsons, 1962, 1964). Nevertheless, the situation is complicated by the repeated finding that the fecundity of offspring of older parents exceeds the fecundity of offspring from younger parents, whereas for viability the opposite is true (Lints and Hoste, 1977). Perhaps the "Lansing effect" is produced by a "spontaneous reequilibration mechanism" which operates through cycles of oogenesis such that the "quality" of an egg is a function of "the proportion of eggs" which have been laid previously (Lints and Hoste, 1977). However, since a proportion is a fraction of the total, it is not at all clear how such a parameter could be ascertained before the end of the reproductive period.

In summary, while there appears to be some set of processes which coordinate reproductive and survival maxima and minima, thereby producing a limited range of optimal phenotypes, the elucidation of these processes remains a major challenge of evolutionary, developmental, and gerontological biology. Some of the studies with *Drosophila* which have addressed this challenge will be considered in the next section.

IV. Development and Adult Longevity

Studies which investigate the entire life cycle of *Drosophila* have been critically reviewed in terms of their relevance to theories of aging current a decade ago (Lints, 1971). The primary conclusion of this review was "that a prolongation or a shortening of the duration of development results in an increase or a decrease in the speed of the aging process" (p. 45). In the following sections we shall discuss in some detail how the evidence of environmental and genetic manipulation leads to the conclusion that, in general, there is a positive correlation between developmental time and adult longevity in *Drosophila*. Furthermore we shall consider some of the effects of prolonged development on other variables such as fecundity, body size, and viability which have been considered relevant to evolutionary fitness. Without reiterating the results discussed earlier, we shall summarize first the reports detailing the effects of numerous stresses and second the consequences of different breeding schemes. The concept of genetic homeostasis (Lerner, 1954) is once again central to our understanding of the interrelationship between the earlier and the later phases of the life cycle.

A. ENVIRONMENTAL STUDIES

Temperature manipulations during the preimaginal period demonstrate that, in the range of 10° to 32°C, colder temperatures prolong development of the embryonic, larval, and pupal periods in *D. melanogaster, D. simulans,* and *D. subobscura* (Sondhi, 1968; Alpatov and Pearl, 1929; Loeb and Northrup, 1917; Lints and Lints, 1971b; McKenzie, 1978; Powsner, 1935; Davidson, 1944). In the same way, as reported earlier, adult longevity is extended when flies age at lower temperatures. Thus, one sees a positive correlation between developmental time and adult longevity in experiments where lower temperature increases the total life span and higher temperature decreases the total life span (Lints, 1971; Alpatov and Pearl, 1929). However, when preimaginal temperature varies (12 to 32°C) and imaginal temperature is constant at 25°C, there appears to be an optimal preimaginal temperature range (17 to 25°C) which yields maximal adult longevity (McKenzie, 1978; Cohet, 1975). Similarly there is an optimal temperature for development itself, although the fastest rate and the maximal viability may not be achieved at the same temperature (Davidson, 1944).

When only two temperatures are used, flies which are maintained at 25°C throughout the life cycle outlive flies which had developed at a colder temperature (13 or 16°C) (Sondhi, 1967c; David and Cohet, 1971; Cohet and David,

1973), although there is not complete consistency in results (Sondhi, 1968; Burcombe and Hollingsworth, 1970). In fact, for the reciprocal experiment, in which flies develop at a constant 25°C but are then subject to various temperatures as imagoes (15 to 30°C), adults in colder temperatures survive significantly longer (five to seven times) than flies at warmer temperatures (Burcombe and Hollingsworth, 1970).

There could be at least two important intervening variables in these studies, namely, fecundity and adult body size. Mean daily egg production is fairly constant when females develop within the preimaginal temperature range 15 to 25°C, with substantial reductions outside of this range (Lints and Lints, 1971b; McKenzie, 1978). Inbred flies which developed at 16°C had lower average total fecundity compared to inbreds which developed at 25°C, whereas hybrids exhibited higher average total fecundity at the lower developmental temperature (Sondhi, 1968). Given the generally positive correlation between longevity and egg laying (see earlier), it seems that developmental time does not directly influence egg production except under extreme conditions [e.g., environmental stress or consistent brother-sister mating (Hollingsworth and Maynard Smith, 1955)]. Thus, fecundity is probably not a significant variable affecting the relationship between developmental time and adult longevity. It cannot be entirely ruled out, however, since mean daily egg production is positively correlated with adult body size (Lints and Lints, 1971c) and body weight (Barker and Podger, 1970).

Flies which develop at colder temperatures, that is, more slowly (Alpatov and Pearl, 1929; Loeb and Northrup, 1917; Burcombe and Hollingsworth, 1970; Tantawy, 1961b), are larger than flies which develop more rapidly (Alpatov and Pearl, 1929; Lints and Lints, 1971b; Burcombe and Hollingsworth, 1970; Lints, 1963; Tantawy, 1961b). Flies which are underfed as larvae have smaller wing dimensions (Alpatov, 1930) and consistently take longer to develop (David *et al.*, 1971b) compared to normally fed larvae, but their adult longevities do not differ (Alpatov, 1930; David *et al.*, 1971b). *D. melanogaster* flies selected for larger body size or longer developmental time exhibit a positive correlated response between these two traits, depending on diet (Robertson, 1963, 1964). Slower feeding larvae reach their critical weight for pupation later than faster feeding larvae and eclose at larger body size than controls (Burnet *et al.*, 1977). Larval feeding behavior responds to selection for increased or decreased speed (i.e., number of cephalopharyngeal retractions per minute), even though unselected control populations seem to be buffered in this trait by epistatic and dominance interactions (Burnet *et al.*, 1977; Sewell *et al.*, 1975). Larval density is also a critical variable, since *D. melanogaster* developing at 30 eggs per vial exhibit nearly perfect negative correlations between adult size and developmental time ($r = -0.95$ to -1.00), whereas at 240 eggs per vial no significant correlations were found (Lints, 1963). At 15 and 27°C, *D. pseudoobscura* flies of larger adult body size live longer, whereas no consistent relationship was seen at 25°C (Tantawy, 1961b).

It appears that there is a measure of physiological homeostasis in *Drosphila* such that minor nutritional variation (e.g., diet lacking fructose or deficient in RNA) causes a positive correlation between body size and developmental time, whereas a low-protein diet (reduced from 5% casein to 2%) yields a negative correlation (Robertson, 1960). It would seem, then, that the distribution of body size is positively skewed, indicating a strict lower limit and a more flexible upper limit which can be attained by prolongation of the developmental period under adequate environmental conditions. Moreover, there may be a similar positive skew in the distribution of developmental times (Mayer and Baker, 1984) such that selection can only be effective in prolonging the period (Sang, 1962; also see later). The existence of at least 40 mutants which manifest increased duration of development, and none of which demonstrate development significantly more rapid than normal (Lints and Gruwez, 1972; Lindsley and Grell, 1968), reflects a positively skewed distribution of developmental times.

Increased preimaginal population density has been shown to increase developmental time and decrease body size (Powsner, 1935; Lints, 1963; Lints and Lints, 1969b); in fact, the ratio of these two variables (cube of body size divided by duration of development) is highly significantly negatively correlated with adult longevity (Lints and Soliman, 1977). Other factors which prolong development include atmospheric ethanol concentrations above 3% in the absence of other food (Parsons *et al.*, 1979), light intensity between 2500 and 7000 meter-candles (Northrup, 1925), and adaptation to media with extreme pH (i.e., pH 2–3 or pH 9–11) (de Oliveira and Condeiro, 1980). It has also been shown that prolonged development results in an increase in the amount of crossing over (Bergner, 1928), which could influence epistatic or position effects on genes that affect survival and homeostatic adjustment.

In brief, then, we can say that various environmental stresses appear to induce a kind of coupling effect such that prolonged development often results in prolonged adult longevity. However, some studies which used varying light intensity (Northrup, 1925), environmental ethanol (Parsons *et al.*, 1979), temperature (David and Cohet, 1971; David *et al.*, 1975; McKenzie, 1978), and the addition of a "gero-protector" (NDMU) to the medium (Obukhova *et al.*, 1979) report either a lack of correlation, a negative correlation, or a nonlinear relationship between development time and imaginal longevity. Our own work with a "minimal stress" environment demonstrated negligible negative correlations between these two variables (Mayer and Baker, 1984; Bergner, 1928). This result is complementary to the positive correlation between developmental time and adult longevity consistently seen under conditions of environmental perturbation.

There is some evidence for an additive component to the genetic variance of developmental time when selection occurs under "unusual" media treatments

(Robertson, 1960; de Oliveira and Condeiro, 1980; Sang, 1962). Yet a highly controlled study, in which environmental factors known to influence developmental time were kept as constant as possible, reported ineffective response to selection (Lints and Gruwez, 1972). Apparently almost one-half of the variance in duration of development can be explained by the duration of development of the previous generation (Lints and Gruwez, 1972). These results lead to the question of the effects of environmental stress and to a comparison of genetic manipulations of developmental time with the data cited earlier.

B. OTHER STUDIES

As was suggested earlier in the discussion of variation in body size, developmental time too may be asymmetrically distributed such that only selection for slower rates (longer development) can be achieved. This conclusion has been reached for *D. subobscura*, for example, in that it has been postulated that there exists a "developmental barrier" under epigenetic control (Clarke *et al.*, 1961). Successful selection for fast and slow developing *D. subobscura* (using brother–sister matings) suggested that genetic variance for this trait is associated with heterosis (Hollingsworth and Maynard Smith, 1955), implying epistasis. Similarly, selection has been effective solely to prolong development in *D. melanogaster* on normal (Sang and Clayton, 1957) and nutritionally manipulated diets (Robertson, 1960; de Oliveira and Condeiro, 1980; Sang, 1962). However, when *D. persimilis* are maintained at 15°C (with median developmental times of 40–47 days), selection in both directions has been demonstrated (Spiess and Spiess, 1964), and it was suggested that third chromosome supergenes are involved in the control of development (Spiess and Spiess, 1966).

That homozygotes are less viable, develop more slowly, and attain shorter imaginal longevities than comparable heterozygotes seems firmly established for a number of *Drosophila* species (Hiraizume and Crow, 1960; Marks, 1982; Hollingsworth and Maynard Smith, 1955; Tantawy, 1961b; Maynard Smith and Maynard Smith, 1954; Bonnier, 1961; Spiess and Schuellein, 1956; and see earlier). Homozygotes also exhibit consistently greater variability in these and other quantitative traits, a finding leading to the hypothesis that heterosis is due to superior (developmental) homeostatic buffering (Dobzhansky and Levene, 1955; Dobzhansky and Wallace, 1953) or stronger (genetic) canalization (Waddington, 1942). This issue will now be addressed; but to simplify and standardize the terminology, we use the following definitions: Heterosis means heterozygote advantage over homozygotes under similar environmental conditions (see Fig. 2); homeostasis (or homeostatic buffering) refers to superiority over a range of environments or under fluctuating environmental conditions (see Fig. 3); and canalization is demonstrated by lesser variability in a trait (see Fig. 4). Clearly these terms refer to relative differences (not absolute values), and they are

FIG. 2.   Idealized frequency distributions of any trait demonstrating heterosis for the hybrid (A) between two populations (B and C). Defining characteristics: $\bar{X}_a > \bar{X}_b$, $\bar{X}_a > \bar{X}_c$; second, third, and fourth moments of the distributions (i.e., standard deviation, skewness, and kurtosis) are approximately equal.

complementary since the first specifies genotype, the second concerns adjustment or adaptation, and the third comprises a statistical comparison of phenotypes. In other words, theoretically any trait which demonstrates variability can be analyzed in terms of heterosis, homeostasis, and canalization as defined above and depicted in Figs. 2–4.

Heterosis in *D. pseudoobscura* has been demonstrated for lifetime egg production, viability, and female adult longevity (Tantawy, 1961b). Homeostasis of heterozygotes for these traits was also exhibited at 25 and 27°C, and for fluctuating temperatures, but not at 15°C (Tantawy, 1961b). Heterozygotic canalization of female imaginal longevity, and of wing length, thorax length, and body weight was generally realized at all temperatures, with a slightly more consistent pattern as regards morphology among females than among males (Tantawy, 1961b). Heterosis with respect to karyotype (polymorphic versus monomorphic third chromosome) has been reported for mean fecundity, female and male adult longevity, and viability, but not developmental rate at 16 and 25°C (Dobzhansky *et al.*, 1964). Homeostasis at 16 and 25°C was shown by polymorphic populations with respect to male and female imaginal longevity and viability, but not for fecundity and developmental rate. Canalization (calculated from pooled standard errors) is not evident for imaginal longevity, while it is for heterozygote developmental time (calculated from Dobzhansky *et al.*, 1964).

In a series of experiments with *D. melanogaster,* heterosis was exhibited for larval rate of development (Bonnier, 1961) and for adult longevity (Ramel and Eiche, 1960), while homeostasis for larval resistance to 30°C was also reported (Bonnier, 1961). Lifetime egg production shows a heterotic effect which appears to be due primarily to higher maximum egg production and more days of egg laying for each female, rather than greater longevity among hybrids (Gowen and Johnson, 1946). Canalization for rate of development among viability mutants was seen only among the less viable strains, which nevertheless had prolonged developmental times (Bonnier and Jonsson, 1957). Canalization for male and female adult longevity was not seen when one hybrid line was compared to nine inbred lines (Gowen and Johnson, 1946).

Genetic and cytological investigations of *D. subobscura* have shown heterosis for viability, fertility, faster rate of development (Maynard Smith *et al.*, 1955; Maynard Smith and Maynard Smith, 1954), and longer imaginal life span (Maynard Smith, 1959; Clarke and Maynard Smith, 1955; Maynard Smith *et al.*, 1955) in addition to greater canalization of these traits among heterozygotes (Maynard Smith, 1959; Clarke and Maynard Smith, 1955; Maynard Smith *et al.*,

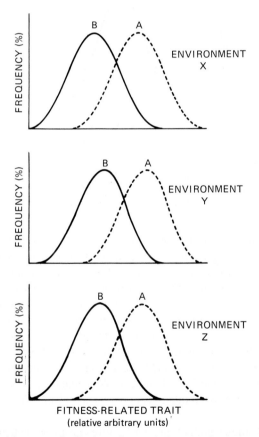

FIG. 3. Idealized frequency distributions of any trait demonstrating homeostasis in one population (A) relative to another population (B) in a range of environments (X,Y,Z). Defining characteristics: $\bar{X}_a > \bar{X}_b$; second, third, and fourth moments (standard deviation, skewness, and kurtosis) are approximately equal.

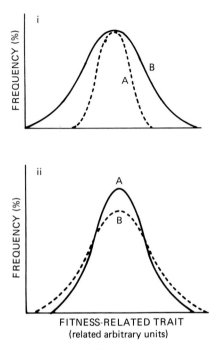

FIG. 4. Idealized frequency distributions of any trait demonstrating canalization in one population (A) relative to another population (B) as measured by the second moment [standard deviation (i)] or by the fourth moment [kurtosis (ii)]. Defining characteristics: $\bar{X}_a = \bar{X}_b$; $\sigma_a < \sigma_b$ [standard deviations (i)]; $Ku_a > Ku_b$ [kurtosis (ii)]; third moments (skewness) are approximately equal.

1955; Maynard Smith and Maynard Smith, 1954). Furthermore, in response to temperature change, heterozygotes exhibited superior homeostasis for rate of development (Maynard Smith and Maynard Smith, 1954) and adult longevity (Bowler and Hollingsworth, 1966). Whether the overall superiority of heterozygotes is due to stricter canalization such that the optimal phenotype is more likely to be produced in all environments, to wider developmental flexibility which allows a range of phenotypes to adjust to changing environments (Thoday, 1953), to greater biochemical versatility (Robertson and Reeve, 1952), to masking of deleterious recessive genes (Maynard Smith and Maynard Smith, 1954), to some form of intra- and interallelic complementation or coadaptation (Manwell and Baker, 1970), or to other synergistic and epistatic interactions remains unknown.

A sequence of studies with *D. persimilis* third chromosome hetero- and homo-karyotes at 15°C revealed the following: clear heterosis of percentage hatchability of eggs, rate of development, daily fecundity until age 60, and female adult survival, and no heterosis for percentage adult eclosion (Spiess *et al.*, 1952;

Spiess and Schuellein, 1956; Spiess, 1958). Viability exhibited heterotic effects at high egg densities (300 and 500 eggs per container) but not at lower densities (Spiess, 1958). Heterokaryotypes demonstrated narrower canalization of hatchability, percentage eclosion, and developmental rate, but not for daily fecundity (Spiess *et al.*, 1952; Spiess and Schuellein, 1956). (Adult longevity could not be assessed from the published data.) When the same stocks were selected for rapid or slow development over 22 generations, flies with longer developmental times (35 versus 32 days at 15°C) had lower daily fecundity, males had slightly reduced viability, and females were much shorter lived (Spiess and Spiess, 1964, 1966).

Attempts to select directly for increased adult longevity have not been successful (Lints *et al.*, 1979), although a pleiotropic response to selection for early versus late increase in fecundity was reported to increase imaginal longevity (Rose and Charlesworth, 1980, 1981a,b). Our own observations (Mayer and Baker, unpublished; Mayer and Baker, 1982) with two strains of *D. melanogaster* using sibling intraclass correlations, and those of others using mother–daughter correlations in *melanogaster simulis* (Tantawy and Rakha, 1961) indicate heritability of adult longevity. Furthermore, in *D. melanogaster* genetic correlations between adult longevity and a number of traits conceptually related to evolutionary fitness have shown opposite directions of association: with egg-laying rate (-0.71), with lifetime egg production ($+0.76$), with first third of life mean daily fecundity ($+0.85$), with last day of egg laying ($+0.77$), with last third of life daily fecundity ($+0.60$), with wing length ($+0.22$), with thorax length ($+0.33$), and with developmental rate ($+0.67$, -0.09 to -0.25) (Tantawy and Rakha, 1961; Giesel, 1979b; Rose and Charlesworth, 1981a; Mayer and Baker, unpublished).

In summary, it seems that there is evidence to support additive, dominance, pleiotropic, and epistatic genetic effects influencing imaginal longevity in *Drosophila*. Moreover, developmental and epigenetic factors, as well as a wide range of environmental variables, have been identified. The lack of consistent and significant responses to selection for longevity suggests the primacy of genetic homeostasis in determining this trait inasmuch as "genetic homeostasis may be the reason for all instances of evolutionary stagnation" (Mayr, 1970, p. 182). Furthermore, the repeated demonstration of heterosis, (physiological) homeostasis, and canalization of imaginal longevity supports the interpretation that a coadapted genotype evolved through selection for an optimal range of life span. Interactions among ontogenetic processes and nongenetic stresses further complicate investigation of the coadapted genotype and analysis of the genetics of aging. Nevertheless, one important point which does emerge is the necessity of conducting research under a range of experimental conditions from extreme to minimal stress (cf. Parsons, 1978b), and with an eye toward revealing the genetic determinants and phenotypic plasticity of the entire life span. Thus, one must conclude that further studies of the genetics of aging and longevity in *Drosophila* will be necessary in order to try to resolve some of the contradictory findings and explore some of the unanswered questions. Suggestions along these lines are made in the final section.

V. Future Prospects

As examples of some of the ways in which we think *Drosophila* will continue to serve as valuable models for the study of the genetics of aging, we shall briefly consider two research techniques and two substantive areas. The use of isofemale strains and the generation of genetic mosaics represent two complementary means of investigating the life span effects of genes: the first focuses on naturalistic data from wild populations, and the second relies upon developmental analysis of experimental manipulation. Neither type of endeavor has yet received widespread attention among gerontological researchers.

The substantive issues to be discussed illustrate ways in which a *Drosophila* model of aging can be (and has been) applied to other areas of biological investigation. Specifically we consider how trying to understand the mechanisms pertaining to heterosis and to aging are related, and how they in turn relate to homeostasis and canalization. As mentioned earlier, there is substantial evidence to suggest that optimal phenotypes manifest "buffered" development and a relatively narrow range of variability in longevity. Optimization of the phenotype presumably reflects the adaptive outcome of evolutionary processes, the subject of the last area we shall cover. A recent renewal of interest in life history traits and in evolutionary models of life cycle parameters points to the utility of *Drosophila* as a model system for population genetic studies in a range of biological investigations.

A. Use of Isofemale Strains

While not extensively reported in the literature on aging, isofemale strains of *Drosophila* have been used to explore the nature of genetic variation specifically in wild populations. The technique simply involves studying the descendants of individual females and using each descendant population as the unit of analysis for within- and between-group comparisons. Since female *Drosophila* can store sperm from more than one male (Milkman and Zeitler, 1974), there is significant genetic variation to be found in isofemale lines derived from wild-caught females; conversely, under controlled conditions one can establish "half-sibling populations" which share a common mother and, on average, 50% of their genetic material.

Isofemale strains are particularly valuable in assessing the ecological correlates of variations in life history traits (e.g., developmental time, egg to adult viability, imaginal longevity, fecundity) (Parsons, 1980). By sampling from different habitats, and under seasonally varying conditions, it is possible to explore more fully the nature of adaptations via changes in life cycle parameters suggested by laboratory research, (e.g., Mayer and Baker, 1984). Complementarily, by creating extreme and optimal environments in the laboratory, it is possible to begin to dissect the genetics of aging with isofemale strains (Parsons, 1978a) using, for example, diallele crosses (Parsons, 1978b). Furthermore, genetic correlations between pairs of traits such as developmental time and adult longevity can be used to distinguish between hypotheses of genetic homeostasis for a common developmental pathway (canalization) and linkage among a number of loci (e.g., a supergene complex) (Parsons, 1980).

The primary value in employing isofemale strains, then, is that relatively quick investigations of natural population variability, both within and among species, can be conducted under controlled conditions. The main drawback is that, due to sampling error, there is always the question of the generalizability of results when using these strains as "a genetic assay of a whole population" (Parsons, 1980). Parsons and his co-workers have pioneered this technique in gerontological research (Parsons, 1978a,b, 1980), and there are many promising ecological and evolutionary research possibilities which they have suggested at the molecular, biochemical, physiological, and population level. For example, the possible role of metabolic polymorphism as a mechanism in heterosis (in support of the idea of biochemical versatility) could be assessed on the assumption that wild populations manifest heterozygote advantage. In fact, this assumption with respect to aging could be tested by analyzing the biochemical variability of shorter- and longer-lived isofemale strains derived from the same locality.

B. Use of Genetic Mosaics

Drosophila genetic mosaics (gynandromorphs) can be constructed by using an unstable ring-X chromosome which is subsequently lost (with predictable frequency) during the first division of the zygote of a female embryo (Hotta and Benzer, 1970; Ikeda and Kaplan, 1970). The product of this first cell division is two daughter clones, one of which possesses the normal complement (rod-X and ring-X) and one of which is genomically identical (barring somatic mutation) except that it is X0. The former daughter clone gives rise to phenotypically female tissue, whereas the latter clone yields phenotypically male tissue. By recombining mutations or genes of interest along with markers on the rod-X chromosome, it is possible to generate mosaic phenotypes which express alleles on both X chromosomes. It is further possible to construct a developmental fate map of *Drosophila* such that the embryological origins of larval and adult tissue can be located on the surface of the blastoderm (Sturtevant, 1929; Poulson, 1950). Finally this procedure has been advanced from the analysis of developmental foci for morphological traits to the anatomical mapping of behavioral abnormalities (Hottz and Benzer, 1972).

The application of these techniques to aging research is just beginning. The drop-dead mutant is of interest because this X-linked recessive is expressed as the sudden onset of uncoordinated walking behavior followed by death in a few hours (Hotta and Benzer, 1972). Imago mutants apparently behave normally for the first few days postecolosion, after which survival decreases exponentially, with a half-life of 2 days, and the death of all mutant adults occurring before normals begin to die (Hotta and Benzer, 1972). The developmental focus of this behavior has been mapped, and results suggest that the primary site is in the brain. Since only bilateral mosaics exhibit the mutant trait, the suggestion has been made that the nonaffected region of one side of the brain can prevent the histological degeneration of the affected area on the other side (Hotta and Benzer, 1972).

A recent investigation of genetic mosaic mapping represents a specific attempt to locate anatomical and developmental foci associated with determinants of longevity (Trout and Kaplan, 1981). Using two neurological mutants, hyperkinetic[1] and shaker[5], which have been shown to exhibit reduced imaginal longevity (Trout and Kaplan, 1970), it was determined that the mutant focus was located in the ventral anterior part of the thorax, possibly in the anterior thoracic ganglion (Trout and Kaplan, 1981). Furthermore, by individually housing the mutants, the researchers were able to minimize phenotypic variation due to gene–environment interaction. However, individual housing also resulted in increased longevity of the mutants so that their life spans were reduced 18–22% of normals, as compared to a 48% reduction under conditions of 50 flies per container (Trout and Kaplan, 1970). Also mosaicism itself seems to exhibit a life-shortening effect of perhaps 9% on a genetic background which produces mean longevity phenotypes which range from 73 to 95 days (Trout and Kaplan, 1981).

As these workers point out (Trout and Kaplan, 1970, 1981), the mutant stocks which they used demonstrate reduced imaginal longevity in association with increased physical activity and metabolic rate. Thus, there is the temptation to infer the existence and location of an "aging pacemaker" which might clock the rate of living. Before such an implication is justified, however, it would seem that genetic mosaic mapping techniques must be extended to a range of life span-affecting mutations such as vestigial, female sterile (2) adipose, and several DNA repair-deficient stocks. Furthermore, based upon the strong evidence for the influence of preimaginal events on imaginal longevity, it is apparent that developmental and homeotic mutants (which exhibit developmental defects analogous to transdetermination of imaginal discs (Holliday and Pugh, 1975) should also be mapped. Finally, taking into account the overwhelming conclusion of population genetic studies that longevity is a multigenic trait, it is not clear to what extent mosaic mapping with (single) mutants will reveal answers to questions about the basic biology of (normal) aging.

C. Heterosis, Homeostasis, and Canalization

Since greater fitness is a recognized attribute of hybrid vigor, and since longevity or aging is a logical component of fitness (e.g., in terms of survival and reproductive value), it is not surprising that longevity repeatedly demonstrates heterotic effects. That many hybrids should also demonstrate canalization of longevity (see earlier) despite greater heterozygosity than inbred lines is less obvious. One general explanation for the observation of lesser phenotypic variability (for any trait) among hybrids suggests that inbreds are less well "buffered" or are more sensitive to environmental causes of variation (Thoday, 1953; Falconer, 1960). Thus, developmental homeostasis (i.e., survivability and maintenance of the phenotype through time, from birth or hatching to maturity) and physiological homeostasis (i.e., adaptability and maintenance of the phenotype at any particular time despite environmental perturbation) may represent similar processes and genetic endowments. Loss of homeostatic capacity, in fact, is often taken to reflect directly the condition of senescence (e.g., Shock, 1977; Sacher and Trucco, 1962), and has been suggested to be correlated with longevity in *Drosophila* (Giesel, 1979b; Dobzhansky, 1958).

Data cited earlier support this idea inasmuch as inbred strains appear to adapt less successfully to a range of environmental conditions, to exhibit what we have termed poorer developmental homeostasis, and what others refer to as lesser versatility (Dobzhansky, 1955) or weaker developmental plasticity (Thoday, 1953). At least three explanations which have been offered to suggest how heterosis relates to superior homeostatic adjustments are potentially testable with regard to development and aging in *Drosophila*.

The heterosis of homeostasis for aging may be due to directional dominance (Falconer, 1960), following the argument that inbreeding depression is the result of the expression of recessive alleles (Mather, 1953). If there exist polygenic systems which act to maintain homeostasis of development and aging, then one would expect directional selection to be more relevant than stabilizing selection with respect to homeostasis of longevity. This distinction is analogous to the difference in the presumed action of natural selection between viability (toward a maximal value) and chaeta number (around a central optimal value) which may be reflected in differing genetic architectures (Breese and Mather, 1960). Hence it may be possible to observe segregation of homeostasis for longevity among the F_2 of the cross between highly inbred and randomly bred lines (Vetukhiv and Beardmore, 1959; Vetukhiv, 1957). However, one might also expect a "duplicate system of interaction (i.e., epistasis) where dominance and interaction pull together'' (Breese and Mather, 1960, p. 395) to possibly mask the hypothesized segregation. Since we know that recessive lethals and semilethals will reduce survival in the homozygotes, one would need to use lines with comparable viabilities and adult longevities. Furthermore, the measurement of homeostasis would have to be made over a range of environments in order to detect the hypothesized multimodality against a background unimodal distribution (Vetukhiv, 1957).

An alternative explanation for heterosis, namely, biochemical versatility (Robertson and Reeve, 1952), may be more easily demonstrated by the use of protein separation by gel electrophoresis. The approach has been explored based on the hypothesis that complementation between proteins and between protein subunits is the biochemical basis of heterosis (Manwell and Baker, 1970). The investigation of ''structural versatility'' involves the electrophoretic analysis of the quaternary structure of hybrid proteins (Manwell and Baker, 1970) and would require comparing variability at specified loci between inbred and hybrid strains at equivalent ages. An analysis of ''temporal versatility'' involves comparing the variability in rates of metabolism of the same pathways (Manwell and Baker, 1970) at different stages of the life cycle. The latter is complicated by the unknown level of interindividual variability and might necessitate the use of extreme environmental stresses (e.g., hypoxia, atmospheric ethanol) to elicit a sufficiently wide range of physiological response. While it may be beyond present technical capabilities, such a union of molecular biology and population genetics holds great promise for the elucidation of the genetic and biochemical bases of aging. It may even be possible, with subtle but quantitative manipulations of tissue culture media, to detect biochemical differences in variability of cells obtained from inbred and hybrid donors, thereby using environmental variability as a probe rather than accepting it as uncontrollable error.

A third mechanism proposed for heterosis, not incompatible with one or the other of the above, focuses on intergenic effects of the ''coadapted genotype'' (Dobzhansky and Wallace, 1953) and on the role of genetic homeostasis (Lerner, 1954) in maintaining phenotypic stability. If a heterotic effect on longevity is due to epistasis, one would expect crosses between geographically diverse populations (interpopulation hybrids) to exhibit breakdown of the locally evolved coadapted genotype (Mather, 1943; Dobzhansky, 1955). In fact, this has been demonstrated for longevity among the F_2 generation (Vetukhiv, 1957), although it was not seen in a repeat experiment in which higher levels of fecundity were suggested as being responsible for the difference (Vetukhiv and Beardmore, 1959). Further progress in location of the epistatic factors may be revealed by crossing inbred lines from ecologically diverse habitats, lines which have been made homozygous for all chromosomes but the test. Since both developmental time and adult longevity could be measured in the same populations, differences or similarities in the genetic homeostatis properties of these two aspects of the life cycle could be ascertained. Moreover, since ''epistatic balance'' differs among different species (Mayr, 1970), and since heterosis is partially dependent on environment (Dobzhansky, 1955), ideally a range of *Drosophila* under various environmental conditions should be evaluated. In effect, this type of experimental design represents a test of the distinction between "euheterosis" and "luxuriance" (Dobzhansky, 1952) of developmental time and longevity.

While the homeostatic "buffering" of development and longevity seen among many hybrids may be a result of canalization of aging (or age-related) processes, the phenomenon of canalization might be profitably studied without reference to heterosis. In exploring the relationship between early (preimaginal) and later (adult) processes and capacities, selection for slower and faster developmental rates could be used in conjunction with environmental stresses. For example, following Waddington's experiments to increase canalization of eye size at two different temperatures (Waddington, 1960), it would be possible to assess the relationship between canalization of preimaginal development and canalization of longevity. The procedure would involve rearing two populations of a random-bred strain at, for instance, 16 and 26°C, and selecting the fastest developers at the colder temperature and the slowest developers at the warmer temperature. After a number of generations one would compare the degree of overlap in rates of development (and relative amount of change from initial mean rate at each temperature) and in adult longevity at an intermediate temperature. To the extent that the two selected populations converge in either measure and exhibit reduced variability, one could say that the phenotypes have been canalized; to the extent that individual developmental time and imaginal longevity become more strongly correlated, one can infer a "coupling process" which links the length of the two phases of the life cycle (Mayer and Baker, 1984). However, it is also possible that canalization itself can reduce the effectiveness of selection (Barclay and Gregory, 1981), in which case the means might not converge while the variances decrease.

The use of other types of stress (see earlier) may reveal different aspects of the "coupling process," although one would expect a degree of similarity inasmuch as most of the stresses used regularly increase developmental time and generally increase adult longevity. The use of stress as a probe into the nature of the range and coordination between developmental processes and aging, and the concomitant analyses of selection for canalization of the phenotypes, may represent genetic assimilation (Schaffer, 1974) of the timing of life cycle processes. This concept of genetic assimilation may be useful and relevant because it focuses on environmental and genotypic influence on two aspects of genetic adaptation: the degree of flexibility or rigidity in canalization processes, and the degree of control or reactivity of systems of canalization. Exploring the developmental plasticity of optimal phenotypes and the environmental sensitivity of optimal genotypes will bring us a lot closer to understanding the basic biology of aging. Operational definitions of optimality could include fertility, fecundity, viability, survival to age x, maximal longevity, or a combination of these.

D. LIFE HISTORY TRAITS AND EVOLUTION

Since we know that experimental manipulation of either genotypes or environments results in changes in development, and that subsequently adult longevity (or mortality or survivorship) can be affected, we think it safe to infer that natural selection could operate to determine the relative lengths of the immature and adult stages of the life span. Furthermore, there is some evidence to suggest that the interrelationships between the duration of these two stages are influenced by genetic factors. Feedforward loops seem to be positive under conditions of environmental stress (with notable exceptions) such that, for any individual, greater developmental time is associated with increased longevity; whereas feedback loops (progressing into the next generation, but still back in terms of ontogenetic stages), as demonstrated by parental age effects, appear related more to internal physiological and biochemical states without clear relationship to the lengths of life cycle stages. It is intriguing to consider the possibility that parental age effects may have been selected to favor continued reproduction by older parents since their progeny might be better adapted to major changes in environmental conditions due to greater genetic variability (Marinkovic *et al.*, 1980).

Experimental and theoretical explorations of the genetic mechanisms which may operate to produce these loops are needed. One line of research we have emphasized concerns the ranges and processes of phenotypic plasticity and genetic flexibility (Thoday, 1953). A second type of investigation might involve the exceptions to the positive relationship between developmental time and adult longevity: These merit analysis of possible ecological correlates and circumstances found among wild populations. Here the use of isofemale strains would seem to be quite pertinent.

Further exploration of the relationship between developmental time and longevity, with respect to both mean individual scores and group variances, has value in at least two contexts: The first, as considered in part above, involves the environmental and genetic manipulations of developmental time as a probe for changes in adult longevity; the second, to which we now turn, concerns the idea of life history traits as evolutionary and ecological phenomena.

While most discussions of life history traits focus on the reproductive components of fitness (for recent reviews, see Stearns, 1976, 1977; Giesel, 1976), there is always some consideration of survivorship functions or mortality rates. In such work the dependent variable is almost exclusively the intrinsic rate of population increase (the Malthusian parameter) following Fisher's development (Fisher, 1930) of the Euler, Volterra, or Lotka equations. Since the population is usually taken to be the unit of evolution and of analysis, *individual* life cycles are less frequently followed, with the result that explorations of the genetics of aging involve only aggregate properties. While there are many advantages to this population genetic approach, it is individuals which are the units of selection (at least in the neo-Darwinian paradigm) and it is individuals which age. [The aging of populations (e.g., Rossett, 1964) represents the demographic consequences of the physiological and genetic processes under consideration.] Thus, studies of life history traits which follow individual organisms offer a new range of results which may advance our understanding of the genetics of aging.

In a series of analyses of covariations of life history parameters of 20 isogenic strains of *Drosophila melanogaster* (Giesel *et al.*, 1982; Giesel, 1979a,b; Giesel and Zettler, 1980), conflicting results were obtained for genetic correlations between developmental time and adult longevity. In a study of seven strains (four isogenic, three F_1 hybrids), age of death and developmental time (the inverse of developmental rate as reported in Giesel, 1979b) were significantly and strongly negatively correlated ($r = -0.67$); whereas in a similar study with 15 strains (eight isogenic, seven F_1 hybrids), the lengths of these two phases of the life cycle were not significantly related ($r = 0.13$) (Giesel and Zettler, 1980). Most other indices of fitness, e.g., peak fecundity, larval viability, first third of life fecundity, and longevity, were positively intercorrelated, a finding which indicates that individuals or strains more "fit" in one aspect are likely to be superior in other traits as well (Giesel, 1979a,b; Giesel and Zettler, 1980). These results can be used to argue against the idea that trade-offs prevail among life history traits (Stearns, 1976, 1977; Gadgil and Bossert, 1970; Williams, 1957; Schaffer, 1974) such that one population or species is more r-selected (favoring higher rate of reproduction and shorter life span) while another is more K-selected (favoring lower rate of reproduction and longer life span) (see below and Pianka, 1970; MacArthur and Wilson, 1967). However, evolution above the level of the species may involve different types or directions of selection. Near-starvation experimental conditions and adjustment to a range of fruit-based media (Giesel and Zettler, 1980), combined with analysis of the coefficients of variation for life history traits, further suggest that superior homeostatic ability among F_1 hybrids may be attributable to genetic heterozygosity.

When this type of analysis was extended to three different temperatures (22, 25, and 28°C), interesting genotype–environment interactions emerged. For example, among outbred flies genetic correlations between developmental rate and age of death were negative at 22° but positive at 28°C (Giesel *et al.*, 1982). Moreover, full sib heritabilities (in the broad sense; i.e., the ratio of genetic to total phenotypic variance) for age of death were significantly different from zero only at the highest temperature and only for inbred flies, whereas heritabilities for development rate were statistically significant at all temperatures for both inbred and outbred flies. These results support the findings of others (see above) that have demonstrtated lack of success in experimentally selecting for longevity but a degree of success in selecting for accelerated or retarded developmental time. They also emphasize the need to explore the genetics of life history traits (especially ontogenetic and aging aspects) in a variety of environments and caution against generalizing evolutionary conclusions without considering ecological details.

Density effects on life history traits have been examined for wild-caught *Drosophila melanogaster* using the experimental technique of selective removal of larvae or adults from jars calculated to have a carrying capacity (K) of about

600 adult flies (Barclay and Gregory, 1981). Selection continued for 6 months with treatments varying in the percentage of organisms removed and in the removal intervals. Results indicated that viability and imaginal life expectancy were lowest when adults were removed, and viability was highest and imaginal life expectancy increased when larvae were removed. Nevertheless, imaginal life expectancy was highest when no organisms were removed, a finding suggesting that density-dependent selection acting on preimaginal mortality may not affect the duration of adult longevity as effectively as density-independent factors. In conjunction with results discussed previously, this supports the idea that in *Drosophila* natural selection may adjust imaginal longevity primarily by increasing or decreasing developmental time (in response to environmental changes). In other words, two sorts of processes may be involved in the evolutionary adjustment of adult longevity: the response of an organism's preimaginal developmental time, and the degree of coupling between the length of this phase and the length of the adult phase.

In this study (Barclay and Gregory, 1981), time to eclosion was shortest in the group subject to larval removal only, and longest in the group with mortality at both stages. Unlike the results with viability and adult survivorship, developmental time conformed to none of the three models tested (i.e., Schaffer, 1974; Pianka, 1970; Istock, 1967). This may have been due, in part, to the variability of temperature reported ($23 \pm 3°C$) since others have shown that results in the range 22–28°C can demonstrate significant differences. Moreover, for one of the models tested (Istock, 1967), at least, this lack of fit for time to eclosion may not be too surprising inasmuch as the model makes the assumption that for a life cycle comprising two "ecologically distinct phases . . . there does not exist any overlap among the factors which limit abundance in each phase" (p. 592). As our own work has shown (Mayer and Baker, 1984), independence of the lengths of the preimaginal and imaginal stages of the life cycle seems to occur only in the highly artificial absence of environmental stress (Giesel, 1979b; Giesel and Zettler, 1980), a condition clearly not met when density effects are being investigated.

One final recent study which explicitly tested the predictions of models of *r*- and K-selection used *Drosophila pseudoobscura* reared in uncrowded (= *r*-selected) and crowded (= *K*-selected) population cages (Taylor and Condra, 1980). After 10 months of selection, the major predictions of the theory were "weakly met" in that *r*-selected populations developed more rapidly (range, 19.08 to 20.21 days) than *K*-selected populations (range, 20.20 to 20.97 days), whereas *K*-selected populations had higher viability (82–95% versus 68–73%) and greater median adult longevity (49–66 days versus 46–53 days) than *r*-selected populations. Interestingly enough, females exhibited more significant responses in imaginal longevity than did males, which is what one would expect since females more directly represent the reproductive potential of the population. These results, however, may be species specific since a life history study of *Drosophila melanogaster* demonstrated that strains with greater intrinsic rates of increase (akin to *r*-selected) were also better able to thrive under nutrient poor or dietarily diverse conditions (equivalent to *K*-selected) (Giesel and Zettler, 1980).

While there is a clear need for replications of these types of studies, we think that when the focus of the work is on the genetics of aging, gathering fewer statistics on individual organisms might be more rewarding than generating large data sets using population aggregates. In addition to the argument that aging is a process of individual biochemical, physiological, and possibly epigenetic change, we have presented much evidence to suggest that selection may act as much on the *rates* of development and aging as on *phenotypic responses* to the many environmental and stochastic factors which determine the shape of the survivorship curve. To the extent that this is valid, analysis of survivorship data will not reveal relevant evolutionary phenomena because the same means and variances of, for example, adult mortality distributions could be exhibited by two different populations, one with a strictly negative and one with a strictly positive correlation between the lengths of the prereproductive and the reproductive stages of the life cycle. In fact, in order to devise testable predictions, life history theorists often "ignore complications of developmental plasticity and canalization" (Stearns, 1977, p. 149); yet we believe that these are the processes which may be most revealing about the genetics of aging.

One last example of this type of approach concerns an issue raised earlier, namely, the reciprocal or interacting relationships between body size and two types of fitness indices, reproduction and survival. The evolutionary implications of "allometry" between morhpological and chronological characters have recently been considered in detail (Gould, 1977). The fact that acceleration or retardation of growth processes, and of the timing of developmental events (e.g., larval stages, eclosion) are under both genetic and environmental influence (e.g., Davidson, 1944; Robertson, 1963, 1964; Church and Robertson, 1966; Burnet *et al.*, 1977; Sewell *et al.*, 1975) makes body size a useful measure and probe for studies of the rate of individual aging. Furthermore, since much is already known about the biochemical and metabolic aspects of growth regulation, tissue culture models may prove useful in elaboration of the genetic mechanisms which have been hypothesized (e.g., Kirkwood and Holliday, 1979) to time development. Yet attempts to combine knowledge of development with understanding processes of aging by manipulations of body size are rare at best. A recent analysis of optimal body size in *Drosophila melanogaster* as it relates to life history parameters does contain a consideration of larval and adult mortality rates (Roff, 1981). It raises the question of physiological as opposed to real time (i.e., degree days versus days) and suggests that intrinsic rate of population increase "is maximized within the observed range in (body) size" (p. 419) with the exception of very large body size in some Hawaian species. This is the kind of result upon which further analyses of the interrelationships among developmental time, imaginal longevity, and other life history traits can be built, using both genetic and environmental manipulation to further our understanding of the basic biology of aging within an ecological and evolutionary framework.

ACKNOWLEDGMENTS

We would like to thank Drs. F. Lints, Universite de Louvain, Louvain-la-Neuve, Belgium, and T. Johnson, University of California at Irvine, for their helpful critique of this manuscript. Special thanks go to Ms. S. Nippes, Mr. J. Eicher, and Ms. G. Kocis for preparation of this manuscript. This work was supported by an NIA/NIH Grant 2T32A00034-04-08 Fellowship to P. J. Mayer and private funding to G. T. Baker. All inquiries should be directed to G. T. Baker, Center on Aging, University of Maryland, College Park, MD 20742.

REFERENCES

Allemand, R., Cohet, Y., and David, J. (1973). *Exp. Gerontol.* **8,** 279–283.
Alpatov, W. W. (1930). *Am. Nat.* **64,** 37–55.
Alpatov, W. W., and Pearl, R. (1929). *Am. Nat.* **63,** 37–67.
Andjelkovic, M., Marinkovic, D., Tucic, N., and Tosic, M. (1979). *Am. Nat.* **114,** 915–939.
Atlan, H., Miquel, J., and Binnard, R. (1969). *J. Gerontol.* **24,** 1–4.
Baker, G. T. (1975). *Exp. Gerontol.* **10,** 231–237.
Baker, G. T. (1976). *Gerontologia* **22,** 334.
Baker, G. T. (1978). *Mech. Aging Dev.* **3,** 367–373.
Baker, G. T. (1981). *Int. Congr. Gerontol.* **2,** 125.
Baker, G. T., Jacobson, M., and Mokrynski, G. (1985). "Handbook of Cell Biology of Aging." CRC, Boca Raton, FL.
Barclay, H. J., and Gregory, P. T. (1981). *Am. Nat.* **11,** 944–961.
Barker, J. S. F., and Podger, R. N. (1970). *Ecology* **51,** 170–189.
Bartosz, G., Leyko, W., and Fried, R. (1979). *Experientia* **35,** 11–31.
Baumberger, J. P. (1914). *Ann. Entomol. Soc. Am.* **7,** 323–353.
Baxter, R. C., and Blair, H. A. (1967). *Radiat. Res.* **31,** 287–303.
Baxter, R. C., and Tuttle, L. W. (1957). *Radiat. Res.* **7,** 303.
Beardmore, J. A. (1976). *Eugen. Soc. Bull.* **8,** 39–42.
Beardmore, J. A., Lints, F., and Al-Baldawi, A. L. F. (1975). *Heredity* **34,** 71–82.
Bergner, A. D. (1928). *J. Exp. Zool.* **50,** 107–163.
Biemont, C. (1976). *Mech. Ageing Dev.* **5,** 315–324.
Bileva, D. S., Zimina, L. N., and Malinovsky, A. A. (1978). *Sov. Genet.* **14,** 848–852.
Bilewicz, S. (1953). *Folia Biol. (Krakow)* **1,** 177–194.
Birren, J., ed. (1964). "Relations of Development and Aging." Thomas, Springfield, IL.
Bonnier, G. (1961). *Genetics* **46,** 85–91.
Bonnier, G., and Jonsson, U. B. (1957). *Evolution* **11,** 271–279.
Bowler, K., and Hollingsworth, M. J. (1966). *Exp. Gerontol.* **2,** 1–8.
Bozcuk, A. N. (1972). *Exp. Gerontol.* **7,** 147–156.
Bozcuk, A. N. (1977). *Exp. Gerontol.* **23,** 414–418.
Bozcuk, A. N. (1978). *Exp. Gerontol.* **13,** 279–285.
Bozcuk, A. N. (1981). *Exp. Gerontol.* **16,** 415–427.
Breese, E. L., and Mather, K. (1960). *Heredity* **14,** 375–399.
Bridges, C. B. (1927). *J. Gen. Physiol.* **8,** 689–700.
Bridges, C. B. (1929). *Carnegie Inst. Washington Publ.* **399,** 63–89.
Brierley, J. (1938). *Biol. Bull.* **75,** 475–493.
Brncic, D., and del Solar, E. (1961). *Am. Nat.* **95,** 211–216.
Brown, S. W., and Welshons, W. (1955). *Proc. Natl. Acad. Sci. U.S.A.* **41,** 209–215.
Burcombe, J., and Hollingsworth, M. J. (1970). *Gerontologia* **16,** 172–181.

Burnet, B., Sewell, D., and Bos, M. (1977). *Genet. Res.* **30**, 149–164.

Butz, A., and Hayden, P. (1962). *Ann. Entomol. Soc. Am.* **55**, 617–618.

Byung, P. Y., Masore, E. J., Murata, I., Bertrand, H. A., and Lynd, F. T. (1982). *J. Gerontol.* **37**, 130–141.

Cannon, G. B. (1966). *Evolution* **20**, 117–131.

Church, R. B., and Robertson, F. W. (1966). *J. Exp. Zool.* **162**, 337–351.

Clark, A. G., and Feldman, M. W. (1981). *Genetics* **101**, 301–316.

Clark, A. M. (1964). *Adv. Gerontol. Res.* **1**, 207–255.

Clarke, A. M., and Gould, A. B. (1970). *Exp. Gerontol.* **5**, 157–162.

Clarke, J. M., and Maynard Smith, J. (1955). *J. Genet.* **53**, 172–180.

Clarke, J. M., and Maynard Smith, J. (1961a). *J. Exp. Biol.* **38**, 679–684.

Clarke, J. M., and Maynard Smith, J. (1961b). *Nature,* **190**, 1027–1028.

Clarke, J. M., Maynard Smith, J., and Sondhi, K. C. (1961). *Genet. Res.* **2**, 70–81.

Cohet, Y. (1973). *C.R. Hebd. Seances Acad. Sci., Ser. A* **227**, 2227–2230.

Cohet, Y. (1975). *Exp. Gerontol.* **10**, 181–184.

Cohet, Y., and David, J. (1973). *C.R. Hebd. Seances Acad. Sci., Paris* **276**, 181–184.

Comfort, A. (1953). *Nature (London)* **172**, 83–84.

Comfort, A. (1979). ''Biology of Senescence.'' Elsevier, New York.

Crozier, W. J., and Enzmann, E. V. (1936). *J. Gen. Physiol.* **20**, 595–602.

Crozier, W. J., Pincus, G., and Zahl, P. A. (1935). *J. Gen. Physiol.* **19**, 523–557.

Curtis, H. J. (1963). *Science* **141**, 686–694.

Daly, R. N., Davis, F. A., and Baker, G. T. (1979). *Gerontologist* **19**, 60.

Daly, R. N., Jacobson, M., Cunningham, E. T., Davis, F. A., and Baker, G. T. (1980). ''Neural Regulatory Mechanisms during Aging.'' pp. 209–210. Liss, New York.

David, J., and Cohet, Y. (1971). *C.R. Hebd. Seances Acad. Sci., Paris* **273**, 1028–1031.

David, J., and Cohet, Y. (1972). *D.I.S.* **48**, 120.

David, J., van Heggewege, J., and Fouillet, P. (1971a). *Exp. Gerontol.* **6**, 249–257.

David, J., Cohet, Y., and Fouillet, P. (1971b). *C.R. Soc. Biol. (Paris)* **165**, 2110–2112.

David, J., Cohet, Y., and Fouillet, P. (1975). *Exp. Gerontol.* **10**, 17–25.

Davidson, J. (1944). *J. Anim. Ecol.* **13**, 26–38.

Delcour, J. (1969). *J. Insect Physiol.* **15**, 1999–2011.

Delcour, J., and Heuts, M. J. (1968). *Exp. Gerontol.* **3**, 45–53.

De Oliveira, A. K., and Condeiro, A. R. (1980). *Heredity* **45**, 111–122.

Dingley, F., and Maynard Smith, J. (1969). *Exp. Gerontol.* **4**, 145–149.

Doane, W. W. (1960). *J. Exp. Zool.* **145**, 1–13.

Dobzhansky, T. (1952). *In* ''Heterosis'' (J. Gowen, ed.), pp. 218–223. Iowa State College Press, Ames.

Dobzhansky, T. (1955). *Cold Spring Harbor Symp. Quant. Biol.* **20**, 1–15.

Dobzhansky, T. (1958). *Ann. N. Y. Acad. Sci.* **71**, 1234–1240.

Dobzhansky, T., and Levene, H. (1955). *Genetics* **40**, 797–808.

Dobzhansky, T., and Wallace, B. (1953). *Proc. Natl. Acad. Sci. U.S.A.* **39**, 162–171.

Dobzhansky, T., Lewontin, R. C., and Pavlovskuy, O. (1964). *Heredity* **19**, 597–614.

Dolkas, C. B., Atlan, H., Dolkas, G., and Miquel, J. (1975). *Mech. Ageing Dev.* **4**, 59–69.

Economos, A. C., and Ballard, R. C. (1982). *Exp. Gerontol.* **17**, 105–114.

Erk, F. C., and Samis, H. V., Jr. (1970). *D.I.S.* **45**, 148.

Failla, G. (1958). *Proc. N.Y. Acad. Sci.* **71**, 1124–1140.

Falconer, D. S. (1960). ''Introduction to Quantitative Genetics.'' Roland Press, New York.

Fisher, R. A. (1930). ''The General Theory of Natural Selection.'' Oxford Univ. Press, Oxford.

Fleming, J. E., Leon, H. A., and Miquel, J. (1981). *Exp. Gerontol.* **16**, 287–293.

Gadgil, M., and Bossert, W. (1970). *Am. Nat.* **104**, 1–24.

Gartner, L. P. (1973). *Gerontologia* **19**, 295–302.

Giesel, J. T. (1976). *Annu. Rev. Ecol. Syst.* **7,** 57–79.

Giesel, J. T. (1979a). *Genetics* **91,** s39.

Giesel, J. T. (1979b). *Exp. Gerontol.* **14,** 323–328.

Giesel, J. T., and Zettler, E. E. (1980). *Oecologia (Berlin)* **47,** 299–302.

Giesel, J. T., Murphy, P. A., and Manlove, M. N. (1982). *Am. Nat.* **119,** 464–479.

Giess, M. C. (1980). *Gerontology* **26,** 301–310.

Giess, M. C., and Plannel, M. H. (1973). *C.R. Hebd. Seances Acad. Sci., Paris* **276,** 1029–1032.

Giess, M. C., and Planel, H. (1977). *Gerontology* **23,** 325–333.

Giess, M. C., Cazeaux, S., and Murat, M. (1980). *Exp. Gerontol.* **15,** 503–510.

Glaser, R. W. (1924). *Am. J. Trop. Med.* **4,** 85–107.

Glass, B. (1964). Pp. 185–187. American Institute of Biological Sciences, Washington, D.C.

Gonzalez, B. M. (1923). *Am. Nat.* **57,** 289–325.

Gould, A. B., and Clark, A. M. (1977). *Exp. Gerontol.* **12,** 107–112.

Gould, S. J. (1977). Belknap Press of Harvard University, Cambridge, Massachusetts.

Gowen, J. W. (1931a). *J. Gen. Physiol.* **14,** 447–461.

Gowen, J. W. (1931b). *J. Gen. Physiol.* **14,** 463–472.

Gowen, J. W., and Johnson, L. E. (1946). *Am. Nat.* **80,** 149–176.

Green, M. M. (1970). *Mutat. Res.* **10,** 353–363.

Greiff, D. (1940). *Am. Nat.* **74,** 363–376.

Grossman, A. I., Koreneva, L. G., and Ulitscaya, C. E. (1970). *Sov. Genet.* **6,** 91–96.

Hanawalt, P. C., Cooper, P. K., Ganesan, A. K., and Smith, C. A. (1977). *Annu. Rev. Biochem.* **48,** 783–836.

Harris, B. B. (1929). *J. Hered.* **20,** 299–301.

Harrison, B. J., and Holliday, R. (1967). *Nature (London),* **213,** 990–992.

Hiraizume, Y., and Crow, J. F. (1960). *Genetics* **45,** 1071–1083.

Holliday, R., and Pugh, J. E. (1975). *Science* **187,** 226–232.

Hollingsworth, M. J. (1966). *Exp. Gerontol.* **1,** 259–267.

Hollingsworth, M. J. (1967). *In* "Social and Genetic Influences on Life and Death" (T. L. Platt and A. S. Parkes, eds.), pp. 195–214. Plenum, New York.

Hollingsworth, M. J. (1968). *Nature (London)* **218,** 869–870.

Hollingsworth, M. J. (1969). *Exp. Gerontol.* **4,** 159–167.

Hollingsworth, M. J., and Burcombe, J. V. (1970). *J. Insect Physiol.* **16,** 1017–1025.

Hollingsworth, M. J., and Bowler, K. (1966). *Exp. Gerontol.* **1,** 251–258.

Hollingsworth, M. J., and Maynard Smith, J. (1955). *J. Genet.* **53,** 295–314.

Hotta, Y., and Benzer, S. (1970). *Proc. Natl. Acad. Sci. U.S.A.* **67,** 1156–1163.

Hotta, Y., and Benzer, S. (1972). *Nature (London)* **240,** 527–535.

Ikeda, K., and Kaplan, W. D. (1970). *Proc. Natl. Acad. Sci. U.S.A.* **67,** 1480–1487.

Istock, C. A. (1967). *Evolution* **21,** 592–605.

Jebrak, A. R. (1937a). *Bull. Acad. Sci. URSS,* 82–102.

Jebrak, A. R. (1937b). *Bull. Acad. Sci. URSS,* 103–120.

Kelsall, P. (1963). *Genet. Res.* **4,** 284–289.

Kidwell, J. F., and Malick, L. (1967). *J. Hered.* **58,** 169–172.

Kirkwood, T. B., and Holliday, R. (1979). *Adv. Exp. Med. Biol.* **118,** 35–46.

Kopec, S. (1928). *Br. J. Exp. Biol.* **5,** 204–211.

Kossikov, K. V. (1937). *Genetics* **22,** 213–224.

Lamb, M. J. (1964a). *In* "Radiation and Aging" (P. J. Lindop and G. A. Sacher, eds.), pp. 163–174. Taylor & Francis, London.

Lamb, M. J. (1964b). *J. Insect Physiol.* **10,** 487–497.

Lamb, M. J. (1965). *Exp. Gerontol.* **1,** 181–187.

Lamb, M. J. (1968). *Nature (London)* **220,** 808–809.

Lamb, M. J., and Maynard Smith, J. (1964). *Exp. Gerontol.* **1**, 11–20.

Lamb, M. J., and Maynard Smith, J. (1969). *Radiat. Res.* **40**, 450–464.

Lamb, M. J. (1978). *In* "The Genetics and Biology of *Drosophila*" (M. Ashburner and E. Novitski, eds.), Vol. 2e, pp. 43–104. Academic Press, New York.

Lamy, R. (1947). *J. Genet.* **48**, 223–236.

Lamy, R. (1949). *D.I.S.* **23**, 91.

Lerner, I. M. (1954). "Genetic Homeostasis." Oliver & Boyd, London.

l'Heriter, P. (1932). *C.R. Soc. Biol. (Paris)* **111**, 982–984.

Lilleland, O. (1938). *Biol. Bull.* **74**, 314–318.

Lindsley, D. L., and Grell, E. H. (1968). "Genetic Variations of *Drosophila melanogaster*." Carnegie Institution of Washington Publication.

Lints, F. A. (1963). *Nature (London)* **197**, (London) **197**, 1128–1130.

Lints, F. A. (1971). *Gerontology* **17**, 33–51.

Lints, F. A. (1978). *In* "Genetics in Ageing" (H. P. Von Hahn, ed.), Vol. 14. Karger, Basel.

Lints, F. A., and Hoste, C. (1974). *Exp. Gerontol.* **9**, 51–69.

Lints, F. A., and Hoste, C. (1977). *Evolution* **31**, 387–404.

Lints, F. A., and Soliman, M. H. (1977). *Nature (London)* **266**, 624–625.

Lints, F. A., and Lints, C. V. (1968). *Exp. Gerontol.* **3**, 341–349.

Lints, F. A., and Lints, C. V. (1969a). *Exp. Gerontol.* **4**, 231–244.

Lints, F. A., and Lints, C. V. (1969b). *Exp. Gerontol.* **4**, 213–244.

Lints, F. A., and Lints, C. V. (1971a). *Nature (London) New Biol.* **229**, 86–88.

Lints, F. A., and Lints, C. V. (1971b). *Exp. Gerontol.* **6**, 417–426.

Lints, F. A., and Lints, C. V. (1971c). *Exp. Gerontol.* **6**, 427–445.

Lints, F. A., and Gruwez, G. (1972). *Mech. Ageing Dev.* **1**, 285–297.

Lints, F. A., Stoll, J., Gruwez, G., and Lints, C. V. (1979). *Gerontology* **25**, 192–204.

Loeb, J., and Northrup, J. H. (1917). *J. Biol. Chem.* **32**, 103–121.

MacArthur, R. H., and Wilson, E. O. (1967). "The Theory of Island Biogeography." Princeton University Press, Princeton, New Jersey.

MacBean, I. T. (1970). PhD. thesis, la Trobe University, Bundoora. [Cited in Parsons, P. A. (1980). *Evol. Biol.*]

McKay, C. M., Crowell, M. F., and Maynard, A. L. (1935). *J. Nutr.* **10**, 63–79.

McKenzie, J. A. (1978). *Aust. J. Biol.* **26**, 105–112.

Manwell, C., and Baker, C. M. (1970). "Molecular Biology and the Origin of Species." University of Washington Press, Seattle.

Marinkovic, D., and Wattiaux, J. M. (1967). *Nature (London)* **216**, 170–171.

Marinkovic, D., Tucic, N., Kekic, V., and Andjelkovic, M. (1973). *Exp. Gerontol.* **8**, 199–206.

Marinkovic, D., Tucic, N., and Kekic, V. (1980). *Genetica* **52/53**, 249–262.

Marks, R. W. (1982). *Genetics* **101**, 301–316.

Massie, H. R., and Williams, T. R. (1979). *Exp. Gerontol.* **14**, 109–115.

Massie, H. R., Baird, M. B., and Piekielniak, M. J. (1976). *Exp. Gerontol.* **11**, 37–41.

Massie, H. R., Williams, T. R., and Aiello, V. R. (1981). *Gerontology* **27**, 205–206.

Massie, H. R., Williams, T. R., and Colacicco, J. R. (1981). *Mech. Ageing Dev.* **16**, 221–231.

Mather, K. (1943). *Biol. Rev.* **18**, 32–64.

Mather, K. (1953). *Heredity* **7**, 297–336.

Mayer, P. J., and Baker, G. T. (1982). *Gerontologist* **22**, 96.

Mayer, P. J., and Baker, G. T. (1984). *In* "Altered Endocrine Status during Aging" (V. J. Cristofalo, G. T. Baker, R. C. Adelman, and J. Roberts, eds.), pp. 239–244. Liss, New York.

Mayer, P. J., and Baker, G. T. (1984). *Mech. Ageing Dev.* **26**, 283–298.

Maynard Smith, J. (1957). *J. Exp. Biol.* **34**, 85–96.

Maynard Smith, J. (1958). *J. Exp. Biol.* **35**, 832–841.

Maynard Smith, J. (1959). *Genetics* **56**, 227–235.
Maynard Smith, J. (1962). *Proc. R. Soc. London Ser. B* **157**, 115–127.
Maynard Smith, J., and Maynard Smith, S. (1954). *J. Genet.* **52**, 152–164.
Maynard Smith, J., Clarke, J. M., and Hollingsworth, M. J. (1955). *Proc. R. Soc. London Ser. B* **144**, 159–171.
Mayr, E. (1970). "Populations, Species, and Evolution." Belknap Press of Harvard University, Cambridge, Massachusetts.
Merkin, S. L., and Baker, G. T. (1982). *Gerontologist* **22**, 71.
Milkman, R. D., and Zeitler, R. R. (1974). *Genetics* **78**, 1191–1193.
Mill, A. J., Davies, R. W., Thompson, S. C., Atherton, H. A., Lindop, P. J., and Hollingsowrth, M. J. (1973). *Int. J. Radiat. Biol.* **24**, 297–305.
Miller, R. S., and Thomas, J. L. (1958). *Ecology* **39**, 118–125.
Miquel, J., and Economos, A. E. (1979). *Exp. Gerontol.* **14**, 279–285.
Miquel, J., and Philpott, D. E. (1978). *Physiologist* **21**, 80.
Miquel, J., Bensch, K. G., Philpott, D. E., and Atlan, H. (1972). *Mech. Ageing Dev.* **1**, 71–97.
Miquel, J., Lundgren, P. R., Bensch, K. G., and Atlan, H. (1976). *Mech. Ageing Dev.* **5**, 347–370.
Moment, G. B. (1982). *In* (R. C. Adelman and G. S. Roth, eds.), "Testing the Theories of Aging" pp. 1–23. CRC, Boca Raton.
Mourad, A. E. (1965). *Genet. Res.* **6**, 139–146.
Nakashima-Tanaka, E., and Ogaki, M. (1980). *Jpn. J. Genet.* **55**, 145–147.
Nichols, W. W., and Murphy, D. G., eds. (1977). "Cellular Senescence and Somatic Cell Genetics: DNA Repair." Symposia Specialists, Miami.
Northrup, J. H. (1917). *J. Biol. Chem.* **32**, 123–126.
Northrup, J. H. (1925). *J. Gen. Physiol.* **9**, 81–86.
Northrup, J. H. (1926). *J. Gen. Physiol.* **9**, 763–765.
O'Brian, D. M. (1961). *Ann. Entomol. Soc. Am.* **54**, 412–416.
O'Brian, D. M. (1962). *Proc. Indiana Acad. Sci.* **72**, 344–347.
O'Brian, D. M., and Beckman, C. (1967). *Am. Zool.* **7**, 773.
O'Brian, D., Yablonsky, C., and Gillroy, C. (1964). *Am. Zool.* **4**, 331.
O'Brian, D. M., Yablonsky, C., and Gillroy, C. (1965). *Proc. Indiana Acad. Sci.* **74**, 386–392.
Obukhova, L. K., Nakaidze, N. Sh., Serebyany, A. M., Smirnov, L. D., and Akitiev, A. P. (1979). *Exp. Gerontol.* **14**, 335–341.
Ogaski, M., and Nakashima-Tanawa, E. (1966). *Mutat. Res.* **3**, 438–443.
Ohnisni, S. (1976). *Jpn. J. Genet.* **5**, 305–314.
Olenov, J. M. (1945). *Dokl. Biol. Sci.* **49**, 598–600.
Parsons, P. A. (1962). *J. Exp. Biol.* **39**, 251–260.
Parsons, P. A. (1964). *Q. Rev. Biol.* **39**, 258–275.
Parsons, P. A. (1966). *Aust. J. Biol. Sci.* **19**, 587–590.
Parsons, P. A. (1973). *Annu. Rev. Genet.* **7**, 239–265.
Parsons, P. A. (1977). *Exp. Gerontol.* **12**, 241–244.
Parsons, P. A. (1978a). *Exp. Gerontol.* **13**, 167–169.
Parsons, P. A. (1978b). *Exp. Gerontol.* **13**, 357–363.
Parsons, P. A. (1980). *In* "Evolutionary Biology" (M. K. Hecht, W. C. Steere, and B. Wallace, eds.), Vol. 13, pp. 175–217. Plenum, New York.
Parsons, P. A. (1981). *Aust. J. Zool.* **29**, 33–39.
Parsons, P. A. (1982). *In* "Evolutionary Biology" (M. K. Hecht, B. Wallace, and G. T. Prance, eds.), Vol. 14, pp. 297–350. Plenum, New York.
Parsons, P. A., Stanley, S. M., and Spence, G. E. (1979). *Aust. J. Zool.* **27**, 747–754.
Parsons, P. A., MacBean, I. T., and Lee, B. T. D. (1969). *Genetics* **61**, 211–218.
Pearl, R. (1928a). "The Rate of Living." Knopf, New York.

Pearl, R. (1928b). *Q. Rev. Biol.* **3**, 391–407.

Pearl, R., and Parker, S. L. (1922a). *Am. Nat.* **61**, 174–187.

Pearl, R., and Parker, S. L. (1922b). *Am. Nat.* **56**, 312–321.

Pearl, R., and Parker, S. L. (1922c). *Am. Nat.* **56**, 273–280.

Pearl, R., and Parker, S. L. (1924a). *Am. Nat.* **58**, 71–82.

Pearl, R., and Parker, S. L. (1924b). *Am. Nat.* **58**, 193–218.

Pearl, R., Parker, S. L., and Gonzalez, B. M. (1923). *Am. Nat.* **57**, 153–192.

Pearl, R., Miner, J. R., and Parker, S. L. (1927). *Am. Nat.* **61**, 289–318.

Philpott, D. E., Bensch, K. G., and Miquel, J. (1974). *Aerosp. Med.* **45**, 283–289.

Pianka, E. (1970). *Am. Nat.* **104**, 592–597.

Poulson, D. F. (1950). *In* "Biology of *Drosophil* " (M. Demerce, ed.), pp. 168–274. Wiley, New York.

Powsner, L. (1935). *Physiol. Zool.* **8**, 474–520.

Ramel, C., and Eiche, A. (1960). *Hereditas* **46**, 709–716.

Robertson, F. W. (1960). *Genet. Res.* **1**, 288–304.

Robertson, F. W. (1963). *Genet. Res.* **4**, 74–92.

Robertson, F. W. (1964). *Genet. Res.* **5**, 107–126.

Robertson, F. W., and Reeve, E. C. (1952). *Nature (London)* **170**, 296–716.

Rockstein, M. (1966). *In* "Perspectives in Experimental Gerontology" (N. Shock, ed.), Thomas, Springfield, Illinois.

Roff, D. (1981). *Am. Nat.* **118**, 405–422.

Rose, M., and Charlesworth, B. (1980). *Nature (London)* **287**, 141–142.

Rose, M. R., and Charlesworth, B. (1981a). *Genetics* **97**, 173–186.

Rose, M. R., and Charlesworth, B. (1981b). *Genetics* **97**, 187–196.

Rossett, E. (1964). "Aging Processes of Populations" Macmillan, New York.

Sacher, G. A. (1963). *Physiol. Zool.* **36**, 295–311.

Sacher, G. A., and Trucco, E. (1962). *Ann. N.Y. Acad. Sci.* **96**, 985–1007.

Samis, H. V., Baird, M. B., and Massie, H. R. (1974). *Science* **183**, 427–428.

Sang, J. H. (1962). *Genet. Res.* **3**, 90–109.

Sang, J. H., and Clayton, G. A. (1957). *J. Hered.* **48**, 265–269.

Schafer, W. M. (1974). *Ecology* **55**, 291–303.

Sewell, D., Burnet, B., and Connolly, K. (1975). *Genet. Res.* **24**, 163–173.

Shecherbakov, A. P. (1935). *Arch. Biol. Nauk* **38**, 651–655.

Shock, N. (1977). *In* "Handbook of the Biology of Aging" (C. E. Finch and L. Hayflick, eds.), Van Nostrand-Reinhold, Princeton, New Jersey.

Soliman, M. H., and Lints, F. A. (1976). *Gerontology* **22**, 381–410.

Sondhi, K. C. (1965). *Am. Zool.* **5**, 243–244.

Sondhi, K. C. (1966). *J. Exp. Zool.* **162**, 89–98.

Sondhi, K. C. (1967a). *Exp. Gerontol.* **2**, 233–239.

Sondhi, K. C. (1967b). *Proc. Natl. Acad. Sci. U.S.A.* **57**, 965–971.

Sondhi, K. C. (1967c). *Exp. Gerontol.* **2**, 241–248.

Sondhi, K. C. (1968). *Proc. Natl. Acad. Sci. U.S.A.* **59**, 785–791.

Spiess, E. B. (1950). *Evolution* **4**, 14–33.

Spiess, E. B. (1958). *Evolution* **12**, 234–245.

Spiess, E. B., and Schuellein, R. J. (1956). *Genetics* **41**, 501–516.

Spiess, E. B., and Spiess, L. D. (1964). *Genetics* **50**, 863–877.

Spiess, E. B., and Spiess, L. D. (1966). *Genetics* **53**, 695–708.

Spiess, E. B., Ketchel, M., and Kinne, B. P. (1952). *Evolution* **6**, 208–215.

Starmer, W. T., Hess, W. B., and Rockwood-Sloss, E. S. (1977). *Proc. Natl. Acad. Sci. U.S.A.* **74**, 387–391.

Stearns, S. C. (1976). *Q. Rev. Biol.* **51,** 3–47.
Stearns, S. C. (1977). *Annu. Rev. Ecol. Syst.* **8,** 145–171.
Steinfeld, H. M. (1928). *Univ. Calif. Publ. Zool.* **31,** 131–178.
Strehler, B. L. (1959). *Q. Rev. Biol.* **34,** 117–142.
Strehler, B. L. (1961). *J. Gerontol.* **16,** 2–12.
Strehler, B. L. (1962). *J. Gerontol.* **17,** 347–352.
Sturtevant, A. H. (1929). *Z. Wiss. Zool.* **135,** 323.
Szilard, L. (1959). *Proc. Natl. Acad. Sci. U.S.A.* **45,** 30–45.
Tantawy, A. O. (1961a). *Genetics* **46,** 227–238.
Tantawy, A. O. (1961b). *Evolution* **15,** 132–144.
Tantawy, A. O., and Rakha, F. A. (1961). *Genetics* **50,** 1349–1355.
Tantawy, A. O., and Vetukhiv, M. O. (1960). *Am. Nat.* **94,** 395–403.
Tantawy, A. O., Mourad, A. M., and Affifi, E. L. (1973). *Egypt. J. Genet. Cytol.* **2,** 244–257.
Taylor, C. E., and Condra, C. (1978). *J. Hered.* **69,** 63–64.
Taylor, C. E., and Condra, C. (1980). *Evolution* **34,** 1183–1193.
Thoday, J. M. (1953). *Symp. Soc. Exp. Biol.* **7,** 96–113.
Tokunaga, C. (1970). *Genetics* **65,** 75–94.
Trout, W. E., and Hanson, G. P. (1971). *Genetics* **68,** S 69.
Trout, W. E., and Kaplan, W. D. (1970). *Exp. Gerontol.,* **5,** 83–92.
Trout, W. E., and Kaplan, W. D. (1981). *Exp. Gerontol.* **16,** 461–474.
Unlu, H., and Bozcuk, A. N. (1979a). *Exp. Gerontol.* **14,** 117–124.
Unlu, H., and Bozcuk, A. N. (1979b). *Exp. Gerontol.* **14,** 125–132.
Van Herrewege, J. (1974). *Exp. Gerontol.* **9,** 191–198.
Vassileva-Dryanovska, O., and Gencheva, E. (1965). *C.R. Acad. Sci. Bulg.* **18,** 59–61.
Vetukhiv, M. (1957). *Evolution* **11,** 348–360.
Vetukhiv, M. O., and Beardmore, J. A. (1959). *Genetics* **44,** 759–768.
Vinberg, G. (1937). *Bull. Exp. Biol. Med.* **3,** 5–7.
Waddington, C. H. (1942). *Nature (London)* **150,** 563–565.
Waddington, C. H. (1960). *Genet. Res.* **1,** 140–150.
Waddington, C. H. (1961). *Adv. Genet.* **10,** 257–290.
Wattiaux, J. M. (1968). *Evolution* **22,** 406–421.
Wattiaux, J. M. (1974). *Exp. Gerontol.* **3,** 55–61.
Weindruch, R., and Walford, R. L. (1982). *Science* **215,** 1415–1417.
Westerman, J. M., and Parsons, P. A. (1972). *Int. J. Radiat. Biol.* **21,** 145–152.
Westerman, J. W., and Parsons, P. A. (1973). *Can. J. Genet. Cytol.* **15,** 289–298.
Williams, G. C. (1957). *Evolution* **11,** 398–411.
Winberg, G. G. (1936). *Arkh. Biol. Nauk* **39,** 657–663.
Woodhams, C. A., and Hollingsworth, M. J. (1971). *Exp. Gerontol.* **6,** 43–48.
Wurgler, F. E. (1972). *Hum. Genet.* **16,** 61–66.
Zimina, L. N., Bileva, D. J., and Malinovsky, A. A. (1977). *Sov. Genet.* **13,** 1960–1965.

Histogenesis of the Cells of the Anterior and Intermediate Lobes of Human Pituitary Glands: Immunohistochemical Studies

R. YOSHIYUKI OSAMURA AND KEIICHI WATANABE

Department of Pathology, Tokai University School of Medicine, Boseidai Isehara-city, Kanagawa, Japan

I. Introduction

Morphological studies of developing pituitary glands have been performed on various animals, including human, rat, rabbit, other vertebrates, and nonvertebrates species (Dupouy, 1980). Recent developments in immunohistochemical techniques (Nakane and Pierce, 1966) have enhanced the developmental studies of individual hormone-secreting cells of the anterior and intermediate pituitary gland (Osamura and Nakane, 1982).

Along with this technical advance in the study of morphology, many functional aspects of the pituitary gland have been elucidated. First of all, we have to emphasize the rapid progress in cDNA recombinant technique which demonstrated the larger precursor molecule for adrenocorticotropic hormone (ACTH) (Nakanishi et al., 1979). It has been shown that not only ACTH but also β-lipotropic hormone (LPH), β-endorphin, and γ-melanocyte stimulating hormone (MSH) are derived from this molecule. Second, biochemical studies on hypothalamic tropic hormones have progressed dramatically. Luteining hormone releasing hormone (LH-RH) and somatostatin are among the classic hormones with known amino acid sequences. Morphological studies on localization of these peptides in the hypothalamus have been done. Corticotropin releasing factor (CRF) and growth hormone releasing factor (GRF) are recently identified hypophysiotrophic peptides. Third, it has been shown that nonhypophyseal organs also produce the same peptides as those synthesized in the pituitary gland. ACTH and its precursor are good examples and have been shown to be produced in the hypothalamus (Osamura et al., 1982a). Some human tumors, such as lung cancers, have also been shown to secrete ACTH and its precursor.

In this article, these several aspects of morphofunctional relationships of the developing human pituitary glands will be discussed with special emphasis on the findings of immunohistochemical techniques. Nakane's peroxidase-labeled antibody method (Nakane and Pierce, 1966) was the immunohistochemical technique used at light and electron microscopic levels.

II. Adult Pituitary Gland

The adult human pituitary gland comprises (1) the anterior lobe, (2) the posterior lobe, (3) the invading anterior cells and (4) the pars tuberalis. The pituitary stalk is the nerve tissue which connects the hypothalamic infundibulum and the posterior lobe.

The anterior lobe shows five different hormone-containing cells of different distributions. ACTH-like immunoreactivity-containing cells (ACTH cells) are distributed diffusely in the anterior lobe and are more concentrated in the upper and lateral periphery. Immunohistochemically, ACTH cells are round or ovoid when they are clustered or concentrated (Fig. 1a). When these ACTH cells are present separately, they characteristically show cytoplasmic processes which terminate mostly on the capillaries. Sometimes ACTH cells form glandular structures containing colloid material in the lumen (Fig. 1b).

Prolactin (PRL) cells (Fig. 1d) are numerous in the anterior lobe and are distributed diffusely. They are characteristically flat or cup-shaped in appearance, sometimes in close relationship with gonadotrophs. But they also frequently exhibit ovoid or angular shapes in humans. Whether this difference in shape is related to any functional difference is not fully understood.

Growth hormone (GH) cells (Fig. 1d) are classically acidophilic cells and are prominent in the lateral portions of the anterior lobe which are known as the acidophilic wings. They are usually round and are clustered or present individually.

Gonadotrophs secrete two kinds of glycoprotein hormones; luteinizing hormone (LH) and follicle stimulating hormone (FSH). These glycoprotein hormones are composed of two subunits, the α- and β-subunits. The α-subunits of LH and FSH are structurally similar. The β-subunits define the different structural (antigenic) and functional characteristics of the two hormones. Therefore,

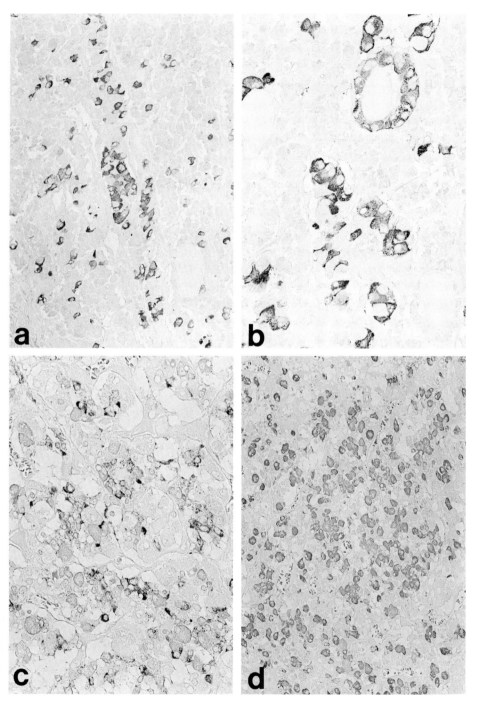

FIG. 1. Immunohistochemical appearance of ACTH cells (a,b), PRL cells (c), and GH cells (d) in the adult human anterior pituitary gland. ×300.

for the specific observations of LH and FSH, it is necessary to study the immunohistochemical localization of LH-β and FSH-β. Both LH-β and FSH-β cells are widely distributed in the anterior lobe. They show round or ovoid shapes in general. As in the rat pituitary, FSH-β cells (Fig. 2a) are more frequently seen than LH-β cells (Fig. 2b). But many gonadotrophs contain both LH-β and FSH-β. Any functional difference between the gonadotrophs which contain solely FSH-β and the ones which contain both FSH-β and LH-β is yet to be determined.

Thyroid stimulating hormone (TSH) is another glycoprotein hormone which is composed of α- and β-subunits. As for LH and FSH, it is the β-subunit which dfines both structural and functional specificities. Immunohistochemically, TSH-β cells are much fewer in number than are the other hormone-containing cells. They are scattered in the central portion of the anterior lobe and possess an angular shape.

In animals such as the rat, the pituitary gland shows a distinct bandlike intermediate lobe between the anterior and posterior lobes. However, in humans, the

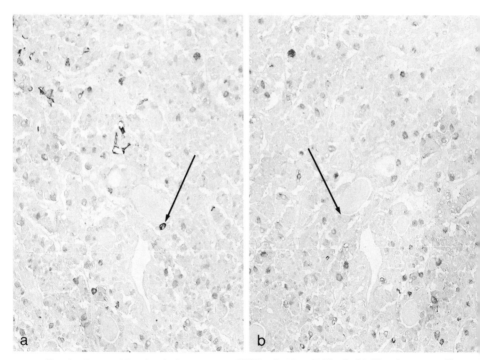

FIG. 2.   Immunohistochemical appearance of FSH cells (a) and LH cells (b). Note that some cells (long arrow) are positive for only FSH but the others contain both FSH and LH. Mirror section, ×100.

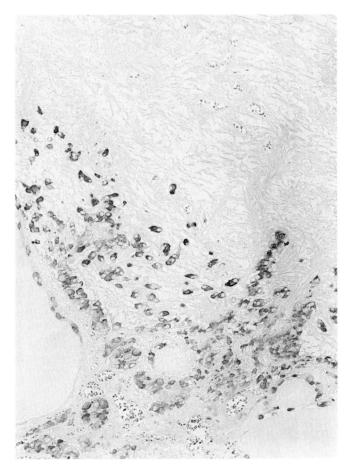

Fig. 3. All "invading anterior cells" are positive for ACTH and are embedded in glial tissue of the posterior lobe. ×150.

intermediate lobe is not distinct. At the transitional zone between the anterior and posterior lobes, many basophilic cells are seen extending into the neural lobe. These cells are designated as "invading anterior cells," and immunohistochemically most of these cells contain ACTH (Osamura *et al.*, 1978) (Fig. 3).

With the recent development of the cDNA technique, it has been known that ACTH is derived from a large precursor glycoprotein molecule from which other peptides with different functions such as β-LPH, β-endorphin, or γ-MSH are also derived (Nakanishi *et al.*, 1979). In humans, ACTH-positive cells in the anterior lobe and invading anterior cells also contain β-endorphin (Fig. 4) and γ-MSH (Osamura *et al.*, 1980, 1981; Celio *et al.*, 1980). These findings suggest

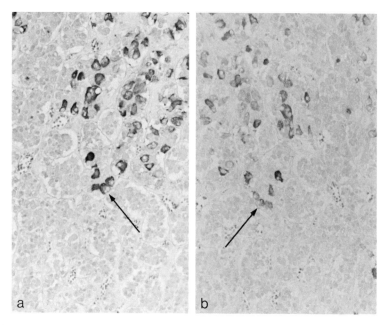

FIG. 4. The same anterior cells are immunohistochemically positive for β-endorphin (a) and ACTH (b) in the adult human pituitary gland (arrows). Mirror sections, ×150.

the production of precursor molecules by these cells. α-MSH is composed of the first 13 amino acids of ACTH and is known to be acetylated at the N-terminus. α-MSH cells are usually not seen, or are sometimes seen very occasionally in the adult human pituitary gland. When α-MSH is present, it is in the ACTH-positive cells.

The pars tuberalis is a thin structure surrounding the pituitary stalk and is composed of a few layers of anterior pituitary cells. Immunohistochemically, these cells are predominantly gonadotrophs. Most of these pars tuberalis cells contain both LH and FSH subunits (Fig. 5a). They lose the ability to product hormone when they undergo squamous metaplasia (Osamura and Watanabe, 1978).

III. Hypothalamic Tropic Hormones

It is well known that in adults production and secretion of most anterior pituitary hormones are under control of hypothalamic hypophyseotropic hormones. Among various tropic hormones, the following have known amino acid sequences; luteinizing hormone releasing hormone (LH-RH), a decapeptide; somatotropin release inhibiting factor (SRIF) (somatostatin), 27 amino acids;

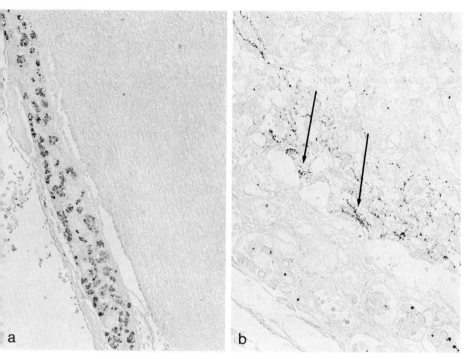

FIG. 5. The pars tuberalis of the adult human pituitary gland is mainly composed of gonado-trophs (LH is shown in a). The LH-RH nerve terminals (b) terminate near the pars tuberalis (arrows). ×300.

CRF, 42 amino acids; thyrotropin releasing factor (TRF), a tripeptide. These tropic hormones are produced in the hypothalamic neurons, enter the portal veins at the median eminence, and reach the anterior pituitary cells.

Immunohistochemically, nerve terminals containing these hypophysiotropic hormones end on the walls of portal veins. Interestingly, in humans, LH-RH nerve endings are in the vicinity of the pars tuberalis, which is mostly composed of gonadotrophs containing both LH and FSH cells (Fig. 5b).

IV. Common Peptide Production in the Pituitary Gland and the Extrahypophyseal Organs

The best example of the production of similar peptides in different organs is the production of ACTH in the hypothalamus. In humans and rats, the arcuate nucleus of the hypothalamus contains many neurons which are immunohisto-chemically positive for ACTH (Fig. 6a). These neurons are also positive for β-

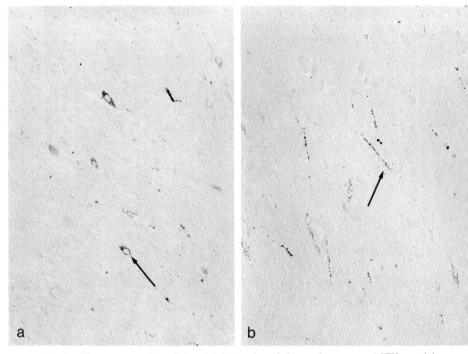

Fig. 6.   The arcuate nucleus of the adult human hypothalamus shows many ACTH-containing neurons (a; arrow) and beaded nerve fibers (b; arrow). ×150.

endorphin and γ-MSH; this finding suggests the production of a precursor molecule in the hypothalamus similar to that produced in the anterior pituitary gland. These neurons send nerve fibers to the paraventricular area and also to the periventricular thalamic nuclei (PVTN). These nerve fibers are also immunohistochemically positive for ACTH and γ-MSH and possess varicosity (Fig. 6b). Immuno-electron microscopically, nerve terminals show ACTH- and γ-MSH-positive secretory granules and synapse-like membrane structures. These features suggest that the function of these peptides in the hypothalamus is as a neurotransmitter or as a neuromodulator (Osamura *et al.*, 1982a).

V. Fetal and Developing Pituitary Gland

As in other animals, the human pituitary is considered to be derived from Rathke's pouch. During fetal life, the human pituitary gland shows two distinct structures; the anterior lobe, derived from the anterior limb of Rathke's pouch, and the intermediate lobe, derived from the posterior limb of Rathke's pouch. The latter structure is distinct during fetal life and is comparable to the intermedi-

TABLE I

IMMUNOHISTOCHEMICAL LOCALIZATION OF HORMONES IN RATHKE'S ANTERIOR LIMB OF
THE HUMAN FETAL PITUITARY GLANDS[a]

Gestational age	ACTH	β-MSH	GH	TSH	PRL	LH
5 weeks	+	−	−	−	−	−
7 weeks	+	−	−	−	−	−
11 weeks	+			−	−	−
13 weeks	+	+	+	+	+	+
14 weeks	+	+	+	+	+	+
17 weeks	+	+	+	+	+	+
19 weeks	+	+	+	+	+	+
24 weeks	+	+	+	+	+	+
Full term	+	+	+	+	+	+

[a]+, Positive staining; −, negative staining.

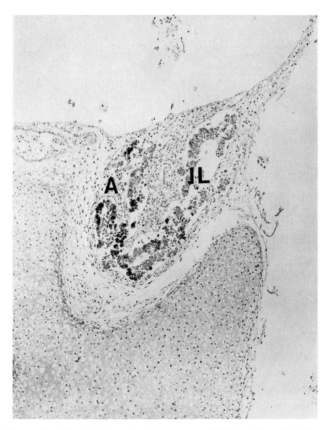

FIG. 7.   Five-week-old fetal pituitary gland shows many ACTH-positive cells in the anterior (A)
and intermediate (IL) lobes. ×60.

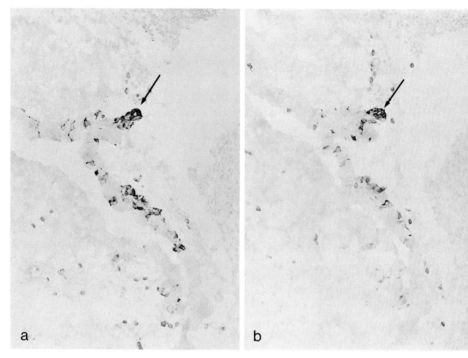

Fig. 8.   Nine-week-old fetal pituitary gland shows many ACTH-positive cells (a) which are also positive for α-MSH (b) in the anterior lobe (arrows). Serial sections, ×150.

ate lobe of other animals such as the rat. But after birth, in humans, the intermediate structure becomes more inconspicuous and in the adult its remnants are the "invading anterior cells."

During the early development of the pituitary gland, ACTH first appears immunohistochemically at 5 weeks of gestation (Table I and Fig. 7) (Osamura, 1977; Osamura and Watanabe, 1977) or at 7 weeks (Dubois *et al.*, 1973; Baker and Jaffe, 1975; Bugnon *et al.*, 1976, 1977, 1978a–c). The other hormones are not observed at 5 or 7 weeks of gestation. β-MSH is not observed at this age. Dubois *et al.* claimed that β-MSH appears some hours later than α-(17–39)-ACTH activity. Baker and Jaffe (1975) and Osamura (1977) showed β-MSH-containing cells from 13 weeks. Regarding the appearance of ACTH, the rat pituitary showed the first stainable ACTH cells in the morning of day 16 in the anteior lobe and only in the afternoon of day 17 in the intermediate lobe (Begeot *et al.*, 1979; Chatelain *et al.*, 1979a,b). α-MSH was observed in human as early as 9 weeks of gestation in both anterior and posterior limbs of Rathke's pouch. As might be anticipated, α-MSH is noted in the same cells that contain ACTH (Fig. 8). As the fetuses grow older, ACTH-containing cells increase to a great

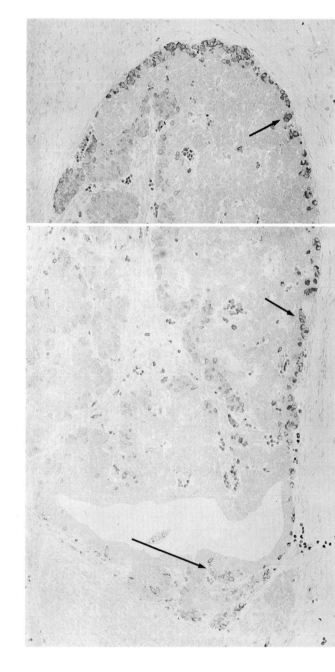

Fig. 9. ACTH-positive cells in the 12-week-old fetal pituitary gland. The anterior lobe shows the presence of many ACTH-positive cells in the periphery of the gland (short arrows) as well as in the center adjacent to irregular fibrous connective tissue. The intermediate lobe also shows many ACTH cells (long arrow), some of which are noted in the posterior nerve tissue. ×60.

extent in both anterior and intermediate lobes. In the anterior lobe, ACTH cells first proliferate at the periphery where the anterior cells are in contact with the adjacent mesenchymal cells (Fig. 9). Later, they move into the central portion of the anteior lobe. During early development, the central irregular mesenchymal island is closely related to these proliferating ACTH cells (Fig. 9). Concerning the precursor glycoprotein for ACTH, β-endorphin and γ-MSH are immunohistochemically localized in the same cells as ACTH in the fetal pituitary gland (Fig. 10) (Bugnon *et al.*, 1974, 1976b; Begeot *et al.*, 1978a–c; Osamura and Nakane, 1984; Li *et al.*, 1979).

In the intermediate lobe, only ACTH cells proliferate; and at 13, 19, and 24 weeks, in the bandlike intermediate lobe, most of the component cells contain ACTH and its precursor exclusively (Figs. 11 and 12). These investigators demonstrated the presence of ACTH and related peptides in fetal pituitary gland as early as 8 or 9 weeks. Celio (1979) demonstrated the appearance of β-endorphin immunoreactivity between the sixth and the eighth week in both anterior and posterior limbs of Rathke's pouch. At 9 weeks, ACTH was localized electron microscopically in the secretory granules as well as in the rough endo-

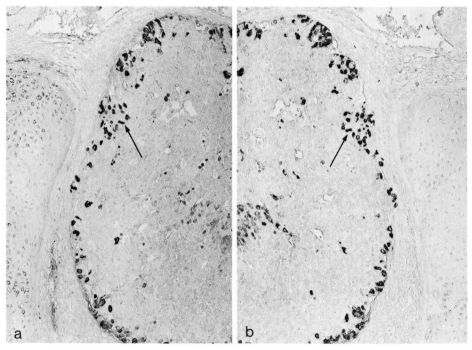

FIG. 10.   Twelve-week-old fetal anterior pituitary gland shows the presence of immunoreactivity for ACTH (a) and β-endorphin (b) in the same cells (arrows). Mirror sections, ×150.

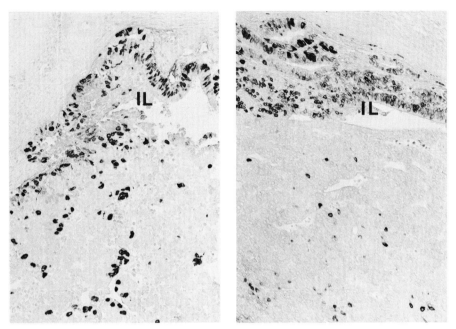

FIGS. 11 AND 12.   Development of the intermediate lobe (IL) exclusively containing ACTH in the 19-week-old (Fig. 11, left) and 24-week-old (Fig. 12, right) human fetus. ×150.

plasmic reticulum (Figs. 13 and 14). At 12 weeks, β-endorphin (Fig. 15) and LH-β (Fig. 16) were present in the cisternae of rough endoplasmic reticulum. These features are considered to be good evidence for active production of these hormones in the fetal anterior pituitary cells.

Immunohistochemical localization of α-MSH is worth discussing in further detail (Visser and Swaab, 1979). From our studies, α-MSH is first localized at 9 weeks in the fetal pituitary gland, in both the anterior and the posterior limbs of Rathke's pouch. During early fetal life, its localization in the anterior lobe increases in accordance with ACTH (Fig. 17). In later fetal life, the numbers of α-MSH cells decrease in the anterior and remain only in the intermediate lobe (Fig. 18). Still later, α-MSH positivity diminishes in both anterior and intermediate lobes. Therefore, the presence of α-MSH can be catergorized as an early fetal characteristic of hormone-secreting activity in human pituitary glands. Since our antisera against α-MSH reacts against the C-terminal position of α-MSH only after splitting from ACTH, it should be considered that the splitting off of α-MSH is fetal in its functional nature in the human pituitary gland (Osamura *et al.*, 1984).

The other hormone-producing cells, such as GH-, PRL-, LH-, and TSH-

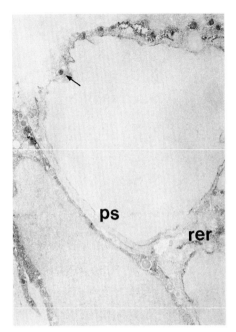 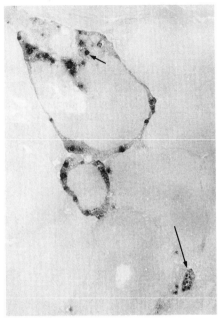

FIGS. 13 AND 14.   Immuno-electron microscopic localization of ACTH in the 9-week-old human anterior pituitary gland. ACTH is observed in the secretory granules in the cell body (short arrows) as well as in the cytoplasmic processes (long arrows). Perinuclear space (ps) and rough endoplasmic reticulum (rer) contain ACTH in the cisternae (Fig. 13, left). ×4600.

secreting cells, are observed in the anterior pituitary gland after 13 weeks of gestation (Fig. 19) (Osamura and Watanabe, 1977; Li *et al.*, 1977) (Tables I and II). These immunohistochemical studies were comparable to those in the rat fetal pituitary gland (Nakane and Setalo, 1977). The number of these hormone-producing cells increases according the gestational age. As the number of LH cells increases, they characteristically form clusters of about 5–6 cells (Fig. 20). The specific gonadotropin-containing pars tuberalis is also developed at 13 weeks of gestation (Fig. 21). Although some PRL cells or LH cells were developed in the posterior limbs of the Rathke's pouch, the ACTH cells predominate in this structure (Table II) (Osamura and Watanabe, 1977).

VI. Factors Influencing the Functional Differentiation of Anterior and Intermediate Lobes

As described earlier, the human fetal intermediate lobe, like the rat intermediate lobe, shows specific differentiation toward predominant ACTH/MSH/LPH production, although some PRL or LH cells appear in the posterior limb during early development. The question of why this structure–specific functional differentiation occurs has attracted many investigators but it has not been completely clarified. It has been suggested by various experiments, such as intrauterine encephalectomy (Daikoku *et al.*, 1973) or allografting of fetal pituitary (Gross and Baker, 1979), that pituitary cells can first differentiate without influences from the hypothalamic factors, but these factors are necessary in order to promote further differentiation. These observations have been substantiated by *in vitro* studies (Bowie *et al.*, 1978; Ishikawa *et al.*, 1977; Nemeskery *et al.*, 1976; Shiino *et al.*, 1977; Watanabe *et al.*, 1973). In the differentiation of intermediate lobe, several factors have been proposed, i.e., arginine vasopressin (AVP), corticotropin releasing factor (CRF), and aminergic supply. The effects of mesenchymal tissue have also been considered (Bugnon *et al.*, 1974; Svalander, 1974). As the ACTH/MSH/LPH differentiation can occur in the encephalectomized fetal rat pituitary and the allografted fetal rat pituitary gland as well as in human anencephalic pituitaries, hypothalamic factors may not be the sole major influence on the differentiation of the intermediate lobe.

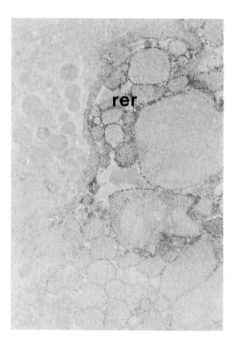 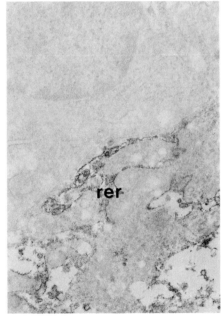

FIGS. 15 AND 16. Immuno-electron microscopic localization of β-endorphin (Fig. 15, left) and LH-β (Fig. 16, right) in the 12-week-old fetal anterior pituitary gland. Both β-endorphin and LH-β are localized in the cisternae of rough endoplasmic reticulum (rer). ×19,000.

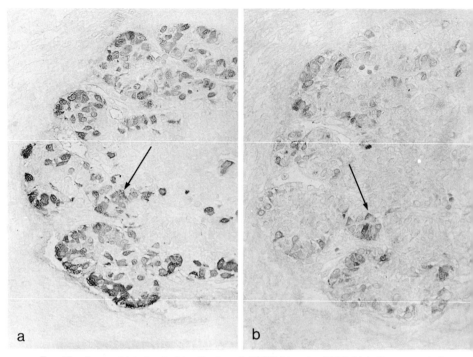

a   b

Fig. 17.   Immunohistochemical localization of ACTH (a) and α-MSH (b) in the same anterior cells of 12-week-old fetal pituitary gland (arrows). Serial sections, ×300.

In the human pituitary gland, as well as in the rat, functional differentiation, especially for ACTH, starts from the periphery of the gland both in the anterior and in the intermediate lobes. In the human anterior lobe, ACTH cells migrate into the center with the islands of connective tissue. However, the other hormone-containing cells start to appear rather sporadically in the anterior lobe and proliferate. Taken together, this evidence suggests some involvement of connective tissue in cytodifferentiation.

VII. Developmental Relationship between Hypothalamus and Pituitary

There are two primary problems concerning the developmental relationship between the hypothalamus and the pituitary: (1) differentiation of cells in both hypothalamus and pituitary toward production of the same peptide, i.e., ACTH and related peptides; (2) the relationship during fetal development between hypothalamic releasing factors and the target pituitary hormone-producing cells.

The first question, concerning the development of production of the same peptide, has been the subject of recent immunohistochemical studies. In the human brain, ACTH immunoreactivity is already noted in the primitive hypo-thalamic region of the 9-week-old fetus. In the 21-week-old fetus, neurons containing ACTH are increased and clustered in the basal hypothalamic area (Fig. 22). Development of ACTH-positive nerve fibers is minimal at this stage. It is of great interest that two separate organs of different histogenic origins should produce the same ACTH and its precursor. The functional relationship of these peptides in two different locations is yet to be determined. Schwartzberg and Nakane (1982) studied immunohistochemical localization of ACTH, β-endorphin, and 16K (γ-MSH) in developing pituitary glands and brains of rats. In their studies, pituitary glands revealed all of these antigenicities on the six-teenth day of gestation. However, in the brain, ACTH and 16K start to appear on the thirteenth day of gestation. The appearance of ACTH and 16K in the brain

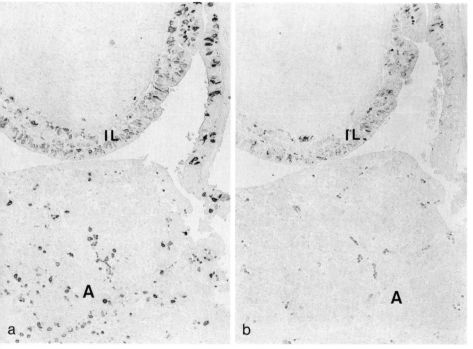

FIG. 18.   Immunohistochemical localization of ACTH (a) and α-MSH (b) in 19-week-old fetal pituitary gland. ACTH is present in the bandlike intermediate lobe (IL) as well as in many round anterior cells (A). On the other hand, α-MSH is localized exclusively in the bandlike intermediate lobe (IL). α-MSH is negative in the anterior lobe (A). Serial sections, ×150.

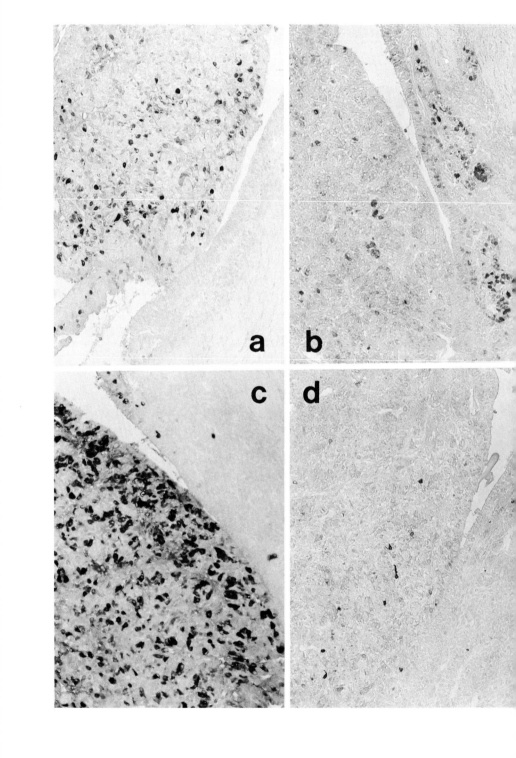

TABLE II

IMMUNOHISTOCHEMICAL LOCALIZATION OF HORMONES IN RATHKE'S POSTERIOR LIMB OF
THE HUMAN FETAL PITUITARY GLANDS[a]

Gestational age	ACTH	β-MSH	GH	TSH	PRL	LH
5 weeks	+	−	−	−	−	−
7 weeks	+	−	−	−	−	−
13 weeks	+	+	±	−	+	±
14 weeks	+	+	±	−	+	+
17 weeks	+	+	±	−	+	+
19 weeks	+	+	±	−	+	+
24 weeks	+	+	±	−	±	+

[a] +, Positive staining; ±, weakly positive staining; −, negative staining.

before their development in the pituitary may indicate active production of the precursor in the fetal brain.

For the second question, developmental studies in human have not been done extensively. In rats, Daikoku et al. (1978) reported studies on the developmental relationships between LH-RH and LH. They have suggested that the differentiation of gonadotropic cells in the pituitary gland in rats takes place earlier than that of hypothalamic gonadotropin releasing activities. That is, their immunohistochemical studies on the prenatal development of rat hypothalamic LH-RH found that, in vivo, rat LH-RH first appeared on day 20.5 of gestation. This is evidently later than the appearance of pituitary LH cells, which appear on the eighteenth day of gestation. Daikoku et al. (1981) studied the relationship between pituitary ontogenesis and the development of the portal system. Gross and Baker (1979) also suggested that pituitary functional differentiation develops independently of the hypothalamic influences.

VIII. Abnormal Development

A good example of abnormal development of the hormone-containing cells of the pituitary gland in humans is anencephaly (Allen et al., 1974; Dubois et al., 1975, 1979; Osamura, 1977; Begeot et al., 1976, 1977, 1978a–c). Anencephalic infants lack the central nervous system almost completely. A hematoma-like "area cerebrovasculata" is usually found on the open skull and is micro-

FIG. 19. Immunohistochemical appearance of GH cells (a), PRL cells (b), LH cells (c), and TSH cells (d) in 13-week-old fetal pituitary gland. Note that many anterior cells are positive for GH and LH and that some cells in the intermediate lobe are positive for PRL and LH (arrows). ×150.

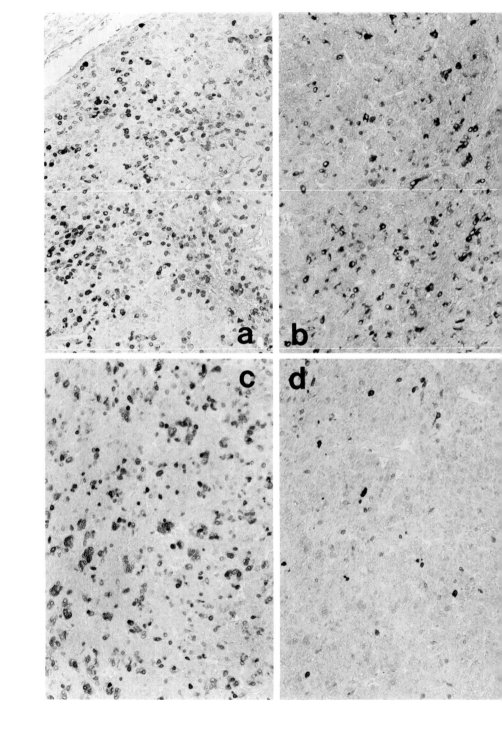

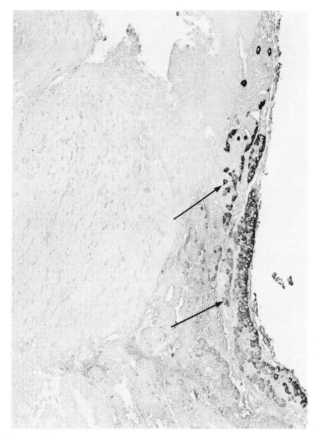

FIG. 21.   Immunohistochemical localization of LH in the human pars tuberalis of a 13-week-old fetus. Most pars tuberalis cells are positive (arrows) for LH at this fetal developmental stage. ×150.

scopically composed of vascular channels with intervening glial tissue. Usually no neurons are found. The anterior pituitary is usually found in most anencephalic cases. The posterior lobe is sometimes found and is either in direct contact with the anterior lobe or is separated from it. The anterior lobe is rather atrophic and congested with capillaries. Immunohistochemically, we have demonstrated decreased numbers of ACTH cells in the anterior lobe (Fig. 23) (Osamura, 1977). Most of the anencephalic pituitary glands lack a distinct inter-

FIG. 20.   Immunohistochemical appearance of GH cells (a), PRL cells (b), LH cells (c), and TSH cells (d) in the anterior pituitary gland of 24-week-old fetus. Note that some LH cells are clustered. ×150.

mediate lobe. But occasionally, a distinct intermediate structure with diffuse ACTH is observed in the anencephalic pituitary gland, although it appears rather atrophic compared to that of the nonanencephalic pituitary gland of corresponding gestational age (Fig. 23). It is well known that the adrenal glands of anencephalic infants show atrophy of the fetus and neonate (Osamura, 1977). This was substantiated by experiments in rats (Coffigny and Dupouy, 1978). The decrease in ACTH cells may be related to the atrophic fetal zone in anencephely. Even in the anencephalic pituitary gland, ACTH-containing cells also contain β-endorphin, a finding suggesting the production of a precursor molecule which is similar to that produced in the normal pituitary gland (Osamura et al., 1980; Dubois et al., 1979; Begeot et al., 1978a–d). The other hormone-containing cells in the anencephalic pituitary gland are similar in numbers and distribution to those in nonanencephalic pituitary glands (Osamura, 1977; Dubois et al., 1978). These observations support the view that the anterior pituitary gland can differ-

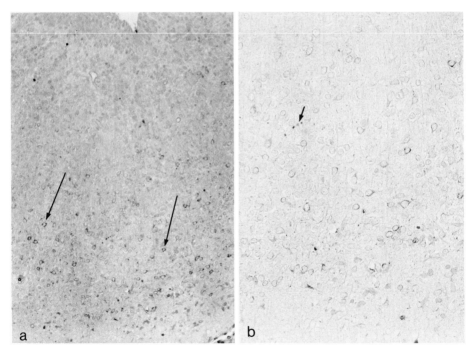

FIG. 22.   Immunohistochemical localization of ACTH in the 22-week-old fetal hypothalamus. (a) Many ACTH-positive neurons are observed in the hypothalamus (arrows). (b) The development of ACTH-positive nerve fibers are minimal at this stage (short arrow). a, ×150; b, ×300.

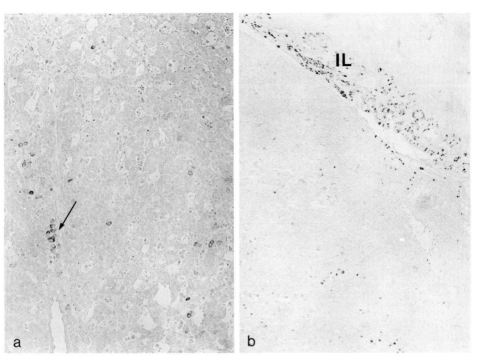

FIG. 23. Immunohistochemical localization of ACTH in the anencephalic pituitary gland. (a) The anterior pituitary gland shows markedly decreased ACTH-positive cells (arrow) compared to those found in the nonanencephalic pituitary gland. (b) Some anencephalic pituitary gland shows rather well developed intermediate lobe (IL) with diffuse ACTH immunoreactivity which is similar to but more atrophic than that in the nonanencephalic pituitary gland. a, ×150; b, ×60.

entiate functionally without influence from the central nervous system (CNS) and that it requires CNS effects to promote its acquired hormone-producing ability, especially that of ACTH cells.

Another abnormal development of the pituitary gland is represented by pituitary tissue in human ovarian teratoma. The teratoma of the ovary is characterized by the presence of histological differentiation in three directions: endoderm, ectoderm, and mesoderm. Mature components such as bronchial epithelium, gastrointestinal mucosa, skin, nerve, and cartilage are frequently seen. The anterior pituitary gland is very rare as one of the components of a benign teratoma. When the pituitary tissue occurs in teratoma, it is usually not accompanied by posterior lobe or intermediate lobe, nor are hypothalamic neurons present nearby. In this situation, the pituitary gland in ovarian teratoma can develop various hormone-containing cells that can be confirmed by immu-

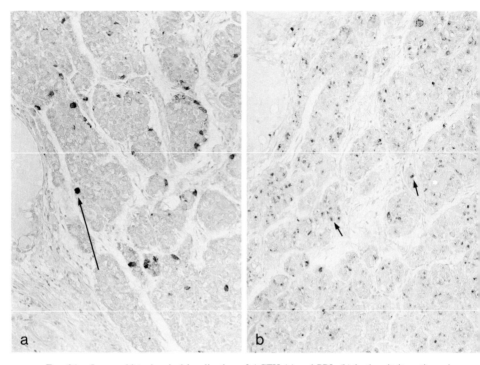

Fig. 24.   Immunohistochemical localization of ACTH (a) and PRL (b) in the pituitary tissue in ovarian cystic teratoma. Note that a few ACTH cells (long arrow) and numerous PRL cells (short arrows) are observed in this condition. ×150.

nohistochemistry, i.e., ACTH, β-endorphin, LH, TSH, GH, PRL (Fig. 24); the size and proportion of each component is not comparable to that of the normal pituitary gland. Each cell is much smaller than that in the normal gland, and no specific distribution is observed for these hormone-containing cells. Moreover, in our experience, the paucity of ACTH/endorphin cells is rather striking. These facts are further strong evidence supporting the self-differentiation of ACTH cells in the anterior pituitary. PRL cells are numerous, much more so than expected in the normal gland. The paucity of ACTH cells and numerous PRL cells may further support the influence of hypothalamic factors on the functionally committed hormone secreting anterior pituitary cells. It is also noteworthy that in this abnormal condition, no definite structures are recognizable as intermediate lobe nor are "invading anterior cells" noted. This can be easily understood from the probable absence of the development of an intact Rathke's pouch in this condition.

IX. Concluding Remarks

1. In the human fetal pituitary, ACTH-containing cells first appear immunohistochemically at 5 weeks of gestation. The other anterior pituitary hormones appear at 13 weeks of gestation.

2. In the human fetal pituitary gland, a distinct bandlike intermediate lobe differentiates predominantly toward ACTH, β-endorphin, γ-MSH, and α-MSH (ACTH-related peptides). This structure becomes indistinct in adults but remains as "invading anterior cells." The α-MSH-positive cells are at first observed in both anterior and intermediate lobes, but subsequently those in the anterior lobe disappear and eventually adult glands contain only rare α-MSH cells.

3. Immuno-electron microscopically, ACTH, β-endorphin, and LH-β are observed in the cisternae of rough endoplasmic reticulum of fetal pituitary cells, a finding which indicates active production of the hormones.

4. In abnormal development, the pituitary glands of human anencephalic infants show markedly decreased ACTH cells. Occasional anencephalic cases with a distinct intermediate lobe containing predominant ACTH differentiation may suggest that the central nervous system is not a sole factor to initiate and promote cytodifferentiation of the anterior and intermediate pituitary gland. This concept is further substantiated by the immunohistochemical findings in pituitary tissue in ovarian cystic teratomas.

ACKNOWLEDGMENTS

The authors wish to thank Dr. Paul K. Nakane (Department of Cell Biology, Tokai University) for constructive advice. The authors also wish to thank Mr. Johb Itoh (Division of Cell Biology Research Lab, Tokai University) for photographic assistance and Ms. Hiroko Toyooka (Department of Pathology, Tokai University) for technical assistance. The reading of this manuscript by Dr. John H. Bishop is also gratefully acknowledged.

REFERENCES

Allen, J. P., Greer, M. A., McGilvra, R., Castro, A., and Fisher, D. A. (1974). *J. Clin. Endocrinol. Metab.* **38,** 94.
Baker, B. L., and Jaffe, R. B. (1975). *Am. J. Anat.* **143,** 137.
Begeot, M., Chatelain, A., Dubois, M. P., Dubois, P. M., and Dupouy, J. P. (1975). *J. Physiol. (Paris)* **70,** 25B.
Begeot, M., Dubois, M. P., and Dubois, P. M. (1976). *J. Physiol. (Paris)* **72,** 8B.
Begeot, M., Dubois, M. P., and Dubois, P. M. (1977). *Neuroendocrinology* **24,** 208.
Begeot, M., Dubois, M. P., and Dubois, P. M. (1978a). *Ann. Endocrinol.* **39,** 235.

Begeot, M., Dubois, M. P., and Dubois, P. M. (1978b). *C.R. Acad. Sci. (Paris)* **286**, 213.
Begeot, M., Dubois, M. P., and Dubois, P. M. (1978c). *Cell Tissue Res.* **193**, 413.
Begeot, M., Dubois, M. P., and Dubois, P. M. (1978d). *Cell Tissue Res.* **193**, 413.
Begeot, M., Duibois, M. P., and Dubois, P. M. (1979). *J. Physiol. (Paris)* **75**, 27.
Bowie, E. P., Ishikawa, H., Shiino, M., and Rennels, E. G. (1978). *J. histochem. Cytochem.* **26**, 94.
Bugnon, C., Lenys, D., Bloch, B., and Fellman, D. (1974). *C.R. Soc. Biol.* **168**, 460.
Bugnon, C., Lenys, D., Bloch, B., and Fellmann, D. (1976a). *C.R. Soc. Biol.* **170**, 975.
Bugnon, C., Lenys, D., Bloch, B., and Fellman, D. (1976b). *J. Microsc. Biol. Cell.* **26**, 31a.
Celio, M. R. (1979). *J. Histochem. Cytochem.* **27**, 1215.
Celio, M. R., Hollt, V., Buetti, G., Pasi, A., Burgisser, E., Eberle, A., Kopp, G., Siebenmann, R., Friede, R. L., Landolt, A., Binz, H., and Zenker, W. (1980). *Adv. Biochem. Psychopharmacol.* **22**, 271.
Chatelain, A., Dupouy, J. P., and Dubois, M. P. (1979a). *Cell Tissue Res.* **196**, 409.
Chatelain, A., Dupouy, J. P., and Dubois, M. P. (1979b). *Cell Tissue Res.* **196**, 409.
Coffigny, H., and Dupouy, J. P. (1978). *Gen. Comp. Endocrinol.* **34**, 312.
Daikoku, S., Kinutani, M., and Watanabe, Y. G. (1973). *Neuroendocrinology* **11**, 284.
Daikoku, S., Kawano, H., Matsumura, H., and Saito, S. (1978). *Cell Tissue Res.* **194**, 433.
Daikoku, S., Kawano, H., Abe, K., and Yoshinaga, K. (1981). **44**, 103–116.
Dubois, P., Vargues-Regairaz, H., and Dubois, P. M. (1973). *Z. Zellforsch,* **145**, 131.
Dubois, P. M., Bethenod, M. M., Gilly, R., and Dubois, M. P. (1975). *Arch. Fr. Pediatr.* **32**, 647.
Dubois, P. M., Li, J. Y., and Begeot, M. (1976). *J. Microsc. Biol. Cell.* **26**, 11a.
Dubois, P. M., Begeot, M., Dubois, M. P., and Herbert, D. C. (1978). *Cell Tissue Res.* **191**, 249.
Dubois, P. M., Begeot, M., Paulin, C., Alizon, E., and Dubois, M. P. (1979). *J. Physiol. (Paris)* **75**, 55.
Dupouy, J. P. (1980). *Int. Rev. Cytol.* **68**, 197.
Dupouy, J. P., and Dubois, M. P. (1975). *Cell Tissue Res.* **161**, 373.
Dupouy, J. P., Chatelain, A., and Dubois, M. P. (1979). *Proc. Int. Symp. Neuroendocrinol. Regul. Mech. Serb. Acad. Sci. Arts, Belgrade* p. 219.
Gross, D. S., and Baker, B. L. (1979). *Am. J. Anat.* **154**, 1.
Ishikawa, H., Shiino, M., and Rennels, E. G. (1977). *Proc. Soc. Exp. Biol. Med.* **155**, 511.
Li, J. Y., Dubois, M. P., and Dubois, P. M. (1977). *Cell Tissue Res.* **181**, 545.
Li, J. Y., Dubois, M. P., and Dubois, P. M. (1979). *Cell Tissue Res.* **204**, 37.
Nakane, P. K. (1970). *J. Histochem. Cytochem.* **18**, 9.
Nakane, P. K. (1973). *In* "The Regulation of Mammalian Reproduction" (S. J. Segal *et al.*, eds.), pp. 79–86. Thomas. Springfield, Illinois.
Nakane, P. K., and Pierce, G. B. (1966). *J. Histochem. Cytochem.* **14**, 929.
Nakane, P. K., Setalo, G., and Mazurkiewicz, J. E. (1977). *Ann. N.Y. Acad. Sci.* **297**, 201.
Nakanishi, S., Inoue, A., Kita, T., Nakamura, M., Chang, A. C. Y., Cohen, S. N., and Numa, S. (1979). *Nature (London)* **278**, 423.
Nemeskery, A., Nemeth, A., Stealo, G., Vigh, S., and Halasz, B. (1976). *Cell Tissue Res.* **170**, 263.
Osamura, R. Y. (1977). *Acta Pathol. Jpn.* **27**, 495.
Osamura, R. Y., and Nakane, P. K. (1982). *Acta Histochem. Cytochem.* **15**, 294.
Osamura, R. Y., and Watanabe, K. (1977). *Acta Histochem. Cytochem.* **10**, 471.
Osamura, R. Y., and Watanabe, K. (1978). *Cell Tissue Res.* **194**, 513.
Osamura, R. Y., Watanabe, K., Nakai, Y., and Imura, H. (1980). *Am. J. Pathol.* **99**, 105.
Osamura, R. Y., Watanabe, K., Tanaka, I., Nakai, Y., and Imura, H. (1981). *Acta Endocrinol. (Copenhagen)* **96**, 458.

Osamura, R. Y., Komatsu, N., Watanabe, K., Nakai, Y., Tanaka, I., and Imura, H. (1982a). *Peptides* **3**, 781–787.

Osamura, R. Y., Komatsu, N., Izumi, S., Yoshimura, S., and Watanabe, K. (1982b). *J. Histochem. Cytochem.* **30**, 9.

Osamura, R. Y., Komatsu, N., Izumi, S., Toyooka, H., and Watanabe, K. (1982). *J. Histochem. Cytochem.* **30**, 572.

Osamura, R. Y., Tsutsumi, Y., and Watanabe, K. H. (1984). *J. Histochem Cytochem.* **32**, 885.

Schwartzberg, D. C., and Nakane, P. K. (1982). *Endoclinology* **110**, 855–864.

Setalo, G., and Nakane, P. K. (1972). *Anat. Rec.* **172**, 403.

Setalo, G., and Nakane, P. K. (1976). *Endocrinol. Exp.* **10**, 155.

Shiino, M., Ishikawa, H., and Rennels, E. (1977). *Cell Tissue Res.* **181**, 473.

Svalander, C. (1974). *Acta Endocrinol. Sup.* **188**, 1.

Visser, M., and Swaab, D. F. (1979). *J. Dev. Physiol.* **1**, 161–178.

Watanabe, Y. G., and Daikoku, S. (1976). *Cell Tissue Res.* **166**, 407.

Watanabe, Y. G., and Daikoku, S. (1979). *Dev. Biol.* **68**, 557.

Watanabe, Y. G., Matsumura, H., and Daikoku, S. (1973). *Z. Zellforsch.* **146**, 453.

INTERNATIONAL REVIEW OF CYTOLOGY, VOL. 95

Peroxisomes of the Kidney

SHINICHI OHNO

Department of Anatomy, Shinshu University School of Medicine, Matsumoto, Japan

I. Introduction

Microbodies were first described as newly recognized cell organelles in the proximal tubules of mouse kidneys and were thus introduced to cell biology (Rhodin, 1954). Later, the peroxisomes in mammalian cells, which had been called microbodies, received their name from the peroxidatic activity of catalase (De Duve and Baudhuin, 1966). The peroxisomes, single-membrane-bounded cytoplasmic structures, were first found in animal cells, but they are now recognized as ubiquitous cell organelles in eukaryotic cells. The peroxisomes from all animal tissues are morphologically similar, but the enzymes of peroxisomes vary, depending on the tissue (McGroarty *et al.*, 1974; Markwell *et al.*, 1976; Tolbert, 1978). It is generally accepted that they contain catalase, which functions in the detoxication of hydrogen peroxide, and several oxidative enzymes such as urate oxidase, L-α-hydroxyacid oxidase, and D-amino acid oxidase (Hruban and Rechcigl, 1969; McGroarty *et al.*, 1974; Lata *et al.*, 1977; Tolbert, 1978; Veenhuis and Wendelaar Bonga, 1979; Tolbert and Essner, 1981; Leighton and Lazo, 1982; Lord and Roberts, 1983). Although our knowledge about peroxisomes steadily increased since their discovery, their main metabolic function remained unknown. It was strongly suggested that peroxisomes were involved in lipid metabolism, as are mitochondria (Lazarow and De Duve, 1976; Osumi and Hashimoto, 1978; Lazarow, 1978a,b, 1981; Mannaerts *et al.*, 1979;

131

Debeer and Mannaerts, 1983). In addition, the identification of all the enzymes necessary for fatty acid β-oxidation in liver peroxisomes and the enhancement of their enzymes with peroxisomal proliferators provided support for the role of peroxisomes in lipid metabolism (Osumi and Hashimoto, 1979a,b, 1980; Furuta *et al.*, 1980; Miyazawa *et al.*, 1980a,b; Hashimoto, 1982). This β-oxidation system differs from the well-known mitochondrial fatty acid β-oxidation system. The existence of a fatty acid β-oxidation system in peroxisomes of animals is the biggest discovery in this field in the last decade—fatty acid β-oxidation is one of their main functions. In the view of the distribution of peroxisomes in various cell types of animals (Hruban *et al.*, 1972; Reddy and Svoboda, 1972; Robinson and Kuwabara, 1977; Psenicnik and Pipan, 1977; Goldenberg *et al.*, 1978; Eguchi *et al.*, 1979; Asano and Ashraf, 1980; Sima, 1980), it is necessary to determine whether those in other tissues contain fatty acid β-oxidation enzymes. The recent studies suggest an important involvement of peroxisomes of brown adipose tissues in lipid metabolism (Nedergaard *et al.*, 1980; Cannon *et al.*, 1982).

Despite this apparent wealth of information about lipid metabolism, we have little knowledge of other physiological roles of peroxisomes in cellular metabolism. Because it has been established that peroxisomes have a wide distribution in mammalian cells, it would be of interest to study their morphological and biochemical variations in different tissues.

The liver and kidney are main organs in animals. There has been a rapid proliferation of papers about many aspects of peroxisomes in the liver. However, there have not been as many reports about the changes of peroxisomes in renal tubular cells, because of the heterogeneity of kidney tissues and because of the difficulty of identifying the different parts of kidney tubules. It is generally accepted that there is a segmental difference in tubular functions such as electrolyte, glucose, and amino acid transport and in normally occurring protein absorptive processes. Therefore, the attempt to correlate peroxisomal functions to these segmental differences would be quite interesting.

The purposes of this article are to review the morphological and enzymatic localization of peroxisomes in the different segments of the kidney and to summarize what is known about kidney peroxisomes. Because the main metabolic function of renal peroxisomes has not yet been identified, I hope that this review will contribute to our understanding of the biological significance of peroxisomes in kidneys and provide some sorts of guide for more fruitful experimentation. Several excellent reviews on peroxisomes have already been published, covering virtually all aspects of peroxisomal structure, origin, enzymes, and possible functions (De Duve and Baudhuin, 1966; De Duve, 1969; Hruban and Rechcigl, 1969; Tolbert, 1978; Tolbert and Essner, 1981; Leighton and Lazo, 1982; Kindl, 1982; Lord and Roberts, 1983). The reader is referred to any of those reviews for

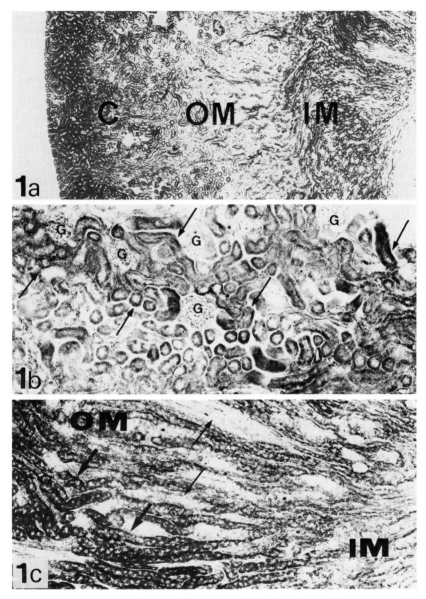

Fig. 1. Light micrographs of kidney slices (15 μm thick) of a male rat. Slices were cut with a cryostat and were incubated in the standard 3,3'-diaminobenzidine (DAB) medium for catalase enzyme histochemistry. (a) At low-power magnification, DAB reaction products can be seen throughout the slice. C, Cortex; OM, outer medulla; IM, inner medulla. ×45. (b) At high-power magnification of the cortex area, the glomeruli (G) and the proximal or distal convoluted tubules (arrows) can be identified. ×100. (c) At high-power magnification of the medulla area, the proximal or distal straight tubules (thick arrows) and collecting ducts (thin arrows) can be identified. OM, Outer medulla; IM, inner medulla. ×100.

the discussion of the biochemical properties and physiological functions of peroxisomes.

II. Normal Distribution of Peroxisomes
in the Nephron

The principal zone of the kidney can be divided into three parts: the cortex, the outer medulla, and the inner medulla (Fig. 1a). The cortex contains mainly glomeruli and the pars convoluta of both the proximal tubules and the distal tubules (Fig. 1b). The outer medulla contains no glomeruli but rather contains the collecting ducts and the pars recta of both the proximal tubules and the distal tubules (Fig. 1c). The inner medulla contains mainly thin segments of Henle's loop and collecting ducts. The structures of the nephron include a great variety of cell types, from the complex cells of the glomerulus to the relatively simple cells in the collecting ducts (Rhodin, 1958). Figure 2 indicates schematically the distribution of the various segments of the nephron. The different segments have

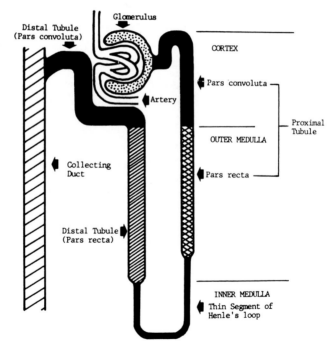

FIG. 2.   Schematic representation of various segments in the nephron and the collecting duct. The nomenclature shown in the schema will be used throughout this article.

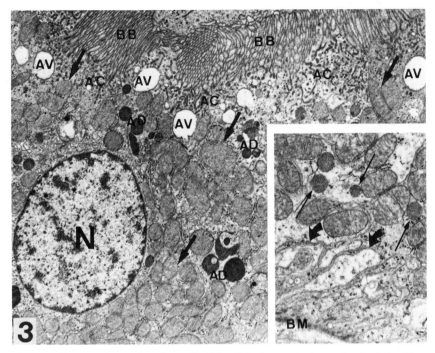

Fig. 3.   Electron micrographs of an epithelial cell in the proximal convoluted tubule. Many mitochondria (thick arrows) can be seen in this area. Other cell organelles can also be identified. N, Nucleus; BB, brush border; AC, apical canaliculi; AV, apical vacuole; AD, adsorption droplet. ×4800. Inset: At high-power magnification of the basal part of an epithelial cell, peroxisomes (thin arrows) and basal infoldings (curved arrows) can easily be identified. BM, Basement membrane. ×8300.

been studied extensively for many years, and various functions have been assigned to different segments of the nephron.

The peroxisomes can be identified morphologically in the tubular epithelial cells by electron microscopy (Fig. 3). A number of morphological variations in renal peroxisomes of rats were reported (Ericsson and Trump, 1966), but renal peroxisomes are usually small cytoplasmic organelles with a single limiting membrane and a finely granular matrix. Peroxisomes also can be visualized histochemically by incubating glutaraldehyde-fixed tissues in an alkaline medium containing 3,3′-diaminobenzidine (DAB) and hydrogen peroxide (Goldfischer, 1969; Novikoff and Goldfischer, 1969) (Fig. 4a and b). The reaction depends on the peroxidatic activity of catalase and is blocked specifically by an inhibitor, amino-1,2,4-triazole (Fig. 4c and d). In addition, potassium cyanide inhibits the mitochondrial DAB staining and enables the peroxisomes in proximal tubules to be seen more clearly (Fig. 4e and f).

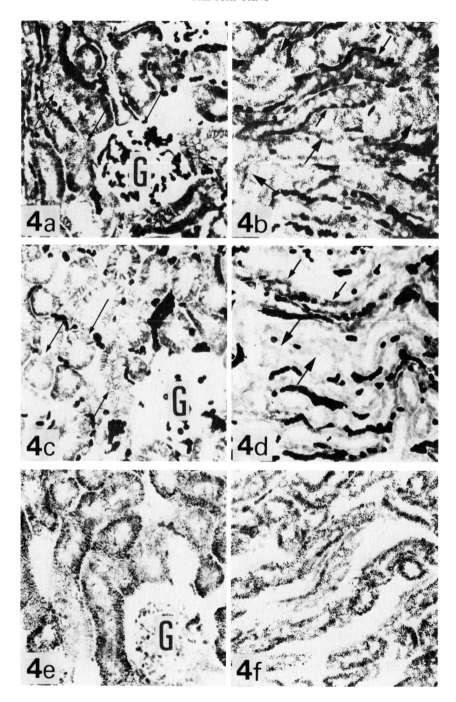

A. GLOMERULUS

The glomerulus contains abundant capillaries, which branch off from the afferent artery and come together again to form the efferent artery. The renal corpuscle consists of three types of cells: endothelial cells, epithelial cells, and mesangial cells (Fig. 5). Simple, squamous endothelial cells with elongated nuclei bulge into the capillary lumens, covering the inner surface of capillaries. Outer epithelial cells differentiate into podocytes, the foot processes of which cover the luminar side of basement membrane. The mesangial cells are localized between the basement membrane and the endothelial cells. The most outer surface of Bowman's capsule is covered by squamous epithelial cells, which are continuous with the cuboidal cells lining the proximal tubules of the nephron. The basement membrane of the glomerulus is a little thicker than that of other tissues. Functionally, the glomerulus filters small molecular proteins, lipid components, carbohydrates, salts, and vitamins through the basement membrane.

In rat kidneys all three types of cells contained microperoxisomes that can be visualized by electron microscopic enzyme histochemistry for catalase (Novikoff *et al.*, 1973). The term "microperoxisomes" was introduced for particles that lack nucleoids and have a diameter of about 0.1 μm. On the other hand, light microscopic immunostaining for catalase also revealed specific fluorescence as fine granules in some epithelial cells of Bowman's capsules in bovine kidneys (Morikawa and Harada, 1969). As mentioned earlier, microperoxisomes were

---

FIG. 4. (a, b) Light micrographs of kidney slices of a male rat; slices were incubated in the standard DAB medium. ×200. (a) Micrograph obtained from the part of cortex (shown in Fig. 1b) where the tubules mainly consist of proximal convoluted tubules. Many small peroxisomes (arrows) can be seen; the background staining is due to DAB reaction with mitochondrial cytochrome oxidase. Erythrocytes are also DAB positive. G, Glomerulus. (b) Micrograph obtained from the part of outer medulla (shown in Fig. 1c) where the tubules mainly consist of the proximal straight tubules. Many peroxisomes can be seen in the proximal straight tubules (large arrows). The distal straight tubules also contain DAB reaction products because of mitochondrial cytochrome oxidase (small arrows). (c, d) Light micrographs of kidney slices of a male rat; slices were incubated in the standard DAB medium containing aminotriazole, an inhibitor of peroxidatic activity of catalase in peroxisomes. ×200. (c) Micrograph obtained from the part of the cortex shown in Fig. 1b. No peroxisomal DAB staining appears in the proximal convoluted tubules (arrows) with the background DAB staining of mitochondrial cytochrome oxidase; cf. Fig. 4a. G, Glomerulus. (d) Micrograph obtained from the part of the outer medulla shown in Fig. 1c. No peroxisomal DAB staining appears in the proximal straight tubules (large arrows); cf. Fig. 4b. To the contrary, mitochondrial DAB staining resulting from cytochrome oxidase is also observed in the distal straight tubules (small arrows). (e, f) Light micrographs of kidney slices of a male rat; slices were incubated in the standard DAB medium containing potassium cyanide, an inhibitor of cytochrome oxidase of mitochondria. ×200. (e) Micrograph obtained from the part of the cortex shown in Fig. 1b. Many peroxisomes can be seen in the proximal convoluted tubules, which show no background DAB staining of mitochondria. G, Glomerulus. (f) Micrograph obtained from the part of the outer medulla shown in Fig. 1c. There are definitely many peroxisomes in the proximal straight tubules. The mitochondrial DAB staining is not observed in the distal straight tubules; cf. Fig. 4b and d.

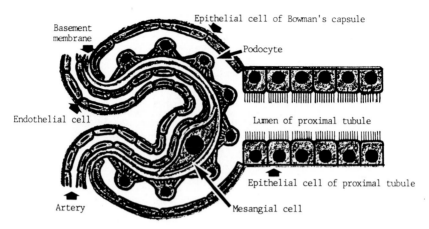

Fɪɢ. 5.   Schematic representations of the various kinds of cells in the glomerulus.

shown by electron microscopy to be localized in all three types of cells in the glomerulus. However, light microscopic immunostaining for catalase demonstrated catalase localization only in the epithelial cells and not in the other two types of cells. The exact reason for this discrepancy is unknown, but it may be due to the species difference between rats and bovines or to poor resolution of light microscopic immunostaining because of the complicated structures of the glomerulus. Therefore, immunostaining for catalase at electron microscopic levels needs to be investigated, especially in glomeruli.

B. Proximal Tubules

The apical parts of proximal tubular cells are occupied by densely packed microvilli, which are called brush borders (Fig. 3). Their basal parts are composed of basal infoldings of the cell membranes. The mitochondria of proximal tubular cells occupy large parts of the cytoplasm. Proximal tubules are grossly divided into two main parts: pars convoluta (proximal convoluted tubules) located in the cortex and pars recta (proximal straight tubules) descending into the outer medulla (Maunsbach, 1966b) (Fig. 2). In the pars convoluta, the brush border is of moderate length and the cell membrane is highly infolded. Many elongated mitochondria are oriented perpendicularly to the base of the cells and lie between the cell membranes. This part can be additionally divided into P_1 and P_2 segments (Maunsbach, 1966b). The P_1 segments are closer to the glomerulus than are the P_2 segments. In pars recta, the microvilli of the brush border are larger than those in pars convoluta. Large amounts of endoplasmic reticulum are seen in pars recta. Most mitochondria are oval rather than elongated. They are distributed in apical portions of the cytoplasm without evident orientation. In some cases, the term P_3 segment could also be defined as that part of the pars recta confined to the outer medulla (Maunsbach, 1966b). The morphological differences between the cells of the P_1 and P_2 segments are much less pronounced than those between the P_1 and P_2 segment cells and the P_3 segment cells. Therefore, the terms pars convoluta and pars recta in the proximal tubules will be used in this article. The ultrastructural differences between pars recta and pars convoluta may be correlated to the differences in their physiological activities. Some functional differences exist normally between different segments of the proximal tubules. For example, previous studies indicated that the absorption of small molecular proteins occurs to a much greater extent in pars convoluta (Katoh *et al.*, 1982).

There are more papers about the peroxisomes in the proximal tubules than about the peroxisomes in other parts of nephron. The papers about proximal tubule peroxisomes contain morphological descriptions, enzyme histochemical characteristics of peroxisomes, and immunostaining of some of the peroxisomal enzymes in various animals (Fig. 6). In these studies, peroxisomes have been studied extensively in rodents. Therefore, the peroxisomes of rodent kidneys will be described first. Peroxisomes are present not only in the tubular cells of pars

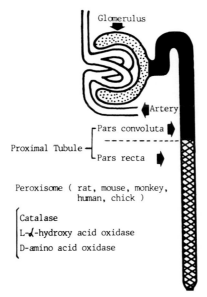

FIG. 6.   Schematic representation of the proximal tubule. The three main enzymes in peroxisomes, which are localized in the proximal tubules, are catalase, L-α-hydroxyacid oxidase, and D-amino acid oxidase.

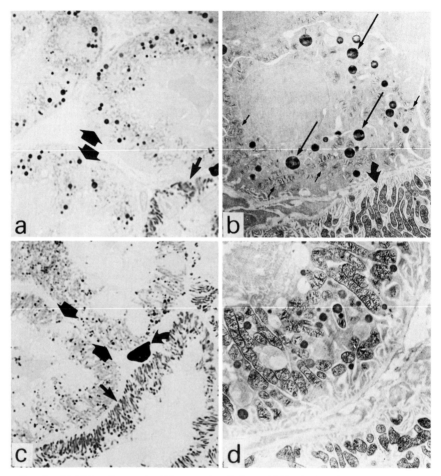

FIG. 7. (a) Light micrograph of Epon section (0.5 μm thick) of a female rat; the section was obtained from the part of outer medulla, where the tubules mainly consisted of the proximal straight tubules and distal straight tubules. Two segments of the nephron are definitely identified. There are obviously DAB-positive peroxisomes visible against the background of slight DAB staining of mitochondria in the proximal straight tubules (large arrows). There is also mitochondrial DAB staining in the distal straight tubules (small arrow). ×1250. (b) Electron micrograph of two segments in the outer medulla of a female rat. There are DAB-positive peroxisomes (large arrows) and slight mitochondrial DAB staining (small arrows) in the proximal straight tubules. Conversely, many mitochondria, which are densely stained with DAB, can be seen in the distal straight tubules (curved arrow). ×3600. (c) Light micrograph of Epon section (0.5 μm thick) of a female rat; the section was obtained from the part of cortex where the tubules mainly consisted of the proximal and distal convoluted tubules. The proximal convoluted tubules (thick arrows) with DAB-positive peroxisomes and the distal convoluted tubule (thin arrow) with only mitochondrial DAB staining are easily identified. Erythrocytes are also stained with DAB (curved arrow). ×1250. (d) Electron micrograph from the cortex. The peroxisomes and mitochondria, stained with DAB, can be identified in the proximal convoluted tubules. ×3600.

convoluta but also in the cells of pars recta, as demonstrated clearly by enzyme histochemistry for catalase (Figs. 4 and 7). At the electron microscopic level, peripheral circular profiles in peroxisomes were observed in the pars recta of rat kidneys (Ericsson and Trump, 1966). In addition, the tubular protrusions extending from the peroxisomes were described in proximal tubular cells of the rat kidneys (Maunsbach, 1966a; Ericsson and Trump, 1966). The morphology of renal peroxisomes can be changed remarkably, depending on the method of fixation (Barrett and Heidger, 1975); the tubular protrusion rods were absent in renal peroxisomes when the kidneys were fixed by perfusion method, but the circular profiles were consistently demonstrable. Another characteristic structure in peroxisomes is the marginal plate (Barrett and Heidger, 1975). It is usually located at the peroxisomal periphery and consists of a relatively straight, thickened region that sometimes shows periodic substructures. The functional significance of those structures remains obscure.

It is generally accepted that urate oxidase is present in the hepatic peroxisomes of some species; it constitutes the nucleoid or crystalline core of the peroxisomes (Lata et al., 1977). In contrast to the liver, the rat kidney lacks urate oxidase, even though most renal peroxisomes contain amorphous faint central or paracentral substructures resembling nucleoids (Svoboda et al., 1967). It was shown that the cores in the center of renal peroxisomal matrix do not oxidize DAB (Beard and Novikoff, 1969) (Fig. 8). It has also been suggested that the lack of DAB reaction product in the center of peroxisomes is not due to limited penetration of DAB into the peroxisomes, but rather to the localization of some enzymes

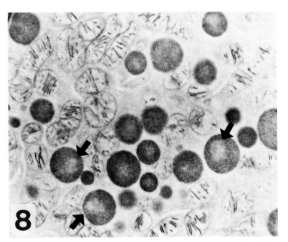

Fig. 8.   Electron micrograph of DAB-positive peroxisomes in an epithelial cell of the proximal straight tubules. The central or paracentral cores in some peroxisomes (arrows) are less reactive for catalase in DAB medium than are the peripheral regions. ×11,500.

except catalase. The difference in appearance between the hepatic and renal peroxisomes of the rat might reflect the difference in enzyme compositions. The peroxisomal membrane may play an important role in the peroxisomal function by controlling the flow of various substrates into and out of the peroxisomal matrix. It has been proposed that peroxisomal enzymes shuttle between the inside of the peroxisomes and the cytoplasm (Robbi and Lazarow, 1978; Goldman and Blobel, 1978; Furuta *et al.*, 1982; Lazarow *et al.*, 1982), but the actual mechanism of membrane transport remains unknown. Therefore, a mechanism of posttranslational transfer of peroxisomal proteins from the cytoplasm into the peroxisomal matrix through the peroxisomal membrane would be a most interesting subject to pursue (Furuta *et al.*, 1982). From the viewpoint of morphology, the freeze–fracture technique is one of the most useful methods for investigating the composition of membranes. There has been only one freeze–fracture study done on peroxisomal membranes, and it was performed in mouse liver cells treated with hypolipidemic drugs, which increase the number of peroxisomes (Reddy *et al.*, 1974b). On the other hand, in the proximal tubules of the normal rat kidney, there is a distinct group of large peroxisomes with an angular shape and inclusions which have been identified in freeze–fracture replicas (Kalmbach and Fahimi, 1978). As in the case of hepatic peroxisomes, freeze-fractured replicas of renal peroxisomes reveal more particles on the protoplasmic face than on the extracellular face of the membranes. However, more experiments will be needed to clarify the significance of the asymmetric localization of the intramembranous particles.

Although there are many papers about biochemical analyses of peroxisomal enzymes in the liver, there are only a few reports of biochemical analyses of the renal peroxisomes, maybe because of the heterogeneity of kidney tissues. It has been shown that rat kidneys have peroxisomes containing catalase, D-amino acid oxidase and L-α-hydroxyacid oxidase (De Duve, 1969; Tolbert, 1978). The reactions catalyzed by these enzymes are linked by either the generation or the utilization of hydrogen peroxide. In the heterogeneous tissues, the study of histochemical characteristics of peroxisomes plays an important role in elucidating their enzymatic and functional properties. Catalase is widely distributed in peroxisomes of different tissues. Therefore, the use of catalase for enzyme histochemistry has the most general application as a marker enzyme for peroxisomes. DAB reaction products specific for peroxisomes were obtained in the proximal tubules of the rat nephron (Goldfischer, 1969) (Figs. 4 and 7). In electron micrographs the DAB reaction products are limited to the matrix of peroxisomes, and the central or paracentral cores remain unstained (Beard and Novikoff, 1969) (Fig. 8). Although pars recta has an abundance of large peroxisomes with high levels of catalase, their mitochondria are smaller and apparently have considerably lower levels of cytochrome oxidase than do those of pars convoluta (Ohno *et al.*, 1982) (Fig. 9). It was reported that the mitochondria in

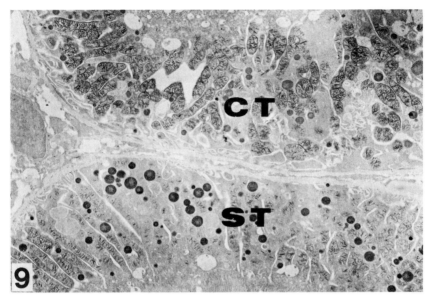

Fɪɢ. 9.   Electron micrograph of the boundary between the cortex and the outer medulla (see Fig. 1a). Two kinds of proximal tubules are visible: straight tubules (ST) and convoluted tubules (CT). There is a difference in the DAB staining patterns of the peroxisomes and mitochondria in the two parts. ×3600.

the pars recta had low levels of succinate dehydrogenase and $NADH_2$-cytochrome c reductase activity (Beard and Novikoff, 1969). This finding suggests that the epithelial cells utilize a different mode of oxidative metabolism. We propose that the epithelial cells in pars recta possess to a large extent an extramitochondrial oxidation in which the peroxisome plays an important role. The data strongly suggest that the combined mitochondrial and peroxisomal metabolism could be an important pathway for maintaining the energy level necessary for absorptive and active transport in cells in the proximal tubules.

There are extensive studies on the peroxisomes of the adult animal kidneys, but less numerous data about peroxisomes during embryogenesis. To gain knowledge of the function of renal peroxisomes, the investigation of morphogenesis of peroxisomes in developing kidneys is needed. Essner, in his study on peroxisomes in developing kidneys, used enzyme histochemistry for catalase to follow the peroxisomes in chicks (Essner, 1970). Peroxisomes were present in proximal tubules, but absent in distal tubules. They appeared to increase in number during development. Later, a few papers were published about mouse kidney peroxisomes during development (Goeckermann and Vigil, 1975; Pipan and Psenicnik, 1975). The proximal tubule is the last segment of the mammalian nephron to differentiate. The nephron apparently becomes functional following the formation of the brush borders in the proximal tubules. Biochemical analysis of catalase and D-amino acid oxidase was performed on mouse kidneys from 17 days prenatal to adulthood (Goeckermann and Vigil, 1975). Postnatal development of the metanephric kidney was found to be accompanied by a rapid increase in both activity and number of peroxisomes in the proximal tubules. The increase in the number of peroxisomes during differentiation of the renal proximal tubules is of particular importance when compared with data on mitochondria and lysosomes. Since there is such a dramatic postnatal increase in peroxisomes over mitochondria and lysosomes, it is likely that peroxisomal development relates directly to the onset of functional activities after birth within the forming nephron. The microperoxisomes were widely distributed among the tissues and were generally smaller than the nucleoid containing peroxisomes. They are also found in the proximal tubules of mouse kidneys during development (Pipan and Psenicnik, 1975), where they may represent the progenitors of the large peroxisomes. The formation of the basal infoldings in the proximal tubules of newborn mice is in relation to the increasing number and size of microperoxisomes. Therefore, it is supposed that the formation of microperoxisomes is correlated with the functional differentiation of mouse kidneys.

We presently know little about the metabolic role of L-α-hydroxyacid oxidase in rat kidneys. The enzyme oxidizes a number of L-α-hydroxyacid substrates to the corresponding keto acids, with the formation of hydrogen peroxide. The oxidases were isolated from mammalian livers and kidneys as two distinct isozymes with different substrate specificities (McGroarty et al., 1974; Hand, 1979). Biochemically, it was reported that the enzyme in rat kidneys is located in peroxisomes and the soluble fraction (Nakano et al., 1969). Allen et al. (1965) developed the specific histochemical staining procedure for L-α-hydroxyacid oxidase, based on the ability of the enzyme to transfer electrons to appropriate tetrazolium compounds. The reaction products were localized mainly in pars recta of proximal tubules. The patterns of histochemical staining were subsequently achieved by Beard and Novikoff (1969). The peroxisomes are larger and more reactive in the cells of the pars recta than in the cells of the pars convoluta. The identical staining patterns of peroxisomes by L-α-hydroxyacid oxidase and catalase may eliminate the possibility that renal peroxisomes are heterogeneous with regard to those two enzyme activities. The tetrazolium method for L-α-hydroxyacid oxidase yields the reproducible staining for light microscopy, but has not been suitable for electron microscopy. The paper was published to describe an alternate histochemical method for the light and electron microscopic demonstration, based on the use of ferricyanide as an artificial electron acceptor (Shnitka and Talibi, 1971). The staining patterns with the ferricyanide method are compared with those obtained with the tetrazolium technique developed by Allen et al. At the light microscopic level, similar staining patterns of rat peroxisomes were obtained in the proximal tubules with both procedures. At an ultrastructural level, the electron-opaque cupric ferrocyanide reaction products for L-α-hydroxyacid oxidase were deposited throughout the matrix in heavily stained preparations, but they were restricted to the outer margin of the matrix and to the nucleoid in lightly stained specimens. On the other hand, the activity of L-α-hydroxyacid oxidase was measured in microdissected segments of the rat nephron by using a microassay for hydrogen peroxide (Le Hir and Dubach, 1981). Maximum activity is found in the pars recta of the proximal tubules, where the density of peroxisomes is the highest. Enzyme histochemistry has been used to show peroxisomes strongly reacting to L-α-hydroxyacid oxidase in pars convoluta of kidneys fixed in glutaraldehyde and incubated in cerium chrolide medium containing α-hydroxyvalerate or α-hydroxybutyrate (Arnold and Holtzman, 1980).

The activity of D-amino acid oxidase was measured in microdissected segments of the nephron of rat by using a microassay for hydrogen peroxide (Le Hir and Dubach, 1981). The activity of D-amino acid oxidase has a distribution similar to that of L-α-hydroxyacid oxidase along the nephron. Maximum activity is found in the pars recta of proximal tubules. The postnatal changes of D-amino acid oxidase in different parts of the rat kidney were described biochemically (Chan et al., 1979). D-Amino acid oxidase activity was measured in glomeruli, proximal tubules, distal tubules, and the thin segments of Henle's loop. The specific activity was detectable in proximal tubules at birth and was found to increase slowly at an early stage of development. Enzyme histochemically, the portions of proximal tubular cells of rat kidneys showed the reaction products for D-amino acid oxidase (Hand, 1979; Arnold et al., 1979). The staining pattern is similar to that of catalase reaction products. It also has been reported that restricted sodium uptake increases the activity of catalase and D-amino acid oxidase in rat kidneys (Morimoto et al., 1978; Morimoto and Abe, 1983).

Next, the localization of some enzymes for fatty acid β-oxidation in normal kidneys will be described (Fig. 10). It was reported that the specific immunostaining for fatty acyl-CoA oxidase was observed as fine granules throughout the cytoplasm of proximal epithelial cells of rat kidneys by light microscopy (Yokota and Fahimi, 1982). At the electron microscopic level, the immunostained products were homogeneously distributed in the peroxisomal matrix. It is additionally confirmed by enzyme assay in microdissected nephrons that this enzyme is much more active in the proximal tubules than in the other segments (Le Hir and Dubach, 1982). On the other hand, the heat-labile enoyl-CoA hydratase was also detected in the peroxisomal matrix of proximal tubular cells of mice (Lalwani et al., 1981; Reddy et al., 1982) and rats (Bendayan et al., 1983), but was absent in the distal tubular cells. Its distribution in the proximal tubules was identical to those of D-amino acid oxidase, L-α-hydroxyacid oxidase, and catalase. The absence of heat-labile enoyl-CoA hydratase in the distal tubules is consistent with previous reports of no peroxisome except for microperoxisomes. Conversely, the heat-stable enoyl-CoA hydratase from mitochondria is present in both proximal and distal tubules (Bendayan *et al.*, 1983). Electron microscopic immunostaining demonstrated that the heat-stable enzyme was localized in mitochondria and the heat-labile enzyme was in peroxisomal matrix of rat kidneys (Bendayan *et al.*, 1983). By enzyme assay in microdissected nephrons, 3-hydroxyacyl-CoA dehydrogenase activity was seen to be distributed similarly in cortical proximal and distal tubules (Le Hir and Dubach, 1982). This result suggests that fatty acid chain shortening in the proximal tubules occurs by β-oxidation in peroxisomes and that the resultant acyl-CoA or acetyl-CoA could be further oxidized in mitochondria. Therefore, the peroxisomal β-oxidation in lipid metabolism is one of the important functions in this segment of the nephron.

Mouse kidney peroxisomes had the same distribution as found in the rat nephron (Pipan and Psenicnik, 1975; Goeckermann and Vigil, 1975; Lalwani *et al.*, 1981). Peroxisomes in mouse kidneys were without internal structures, although peroxisomes in rat kidneys often contained noncrystalline cores. Microperoxisomes were also identified in the cells of proximal tubules of mouse kidneys. In acatalasemic mice, peroxisomal staining for catalase with DAB medium was confined to proximal tubular cells and was stronger in cells of the pars recta than in cells of the pars convoluta (Goldfischer and Essner, 1970; Goldfischer *et al.*, 1973a). However, the destruction of catalase was much faster than in normal mice.

Experiments were undertaken to examine the peroxisomes in the proximal tubules of rhesus monkey kidneys (Tisher *et al.*, 1968, 1969). It was shown that the renal peroxisomes in the proximal tubules contained nucleoids with crystalline structures. However, uricase activity was not demonstrable in total homogenate of rhesus monkey kidney. It was therefore concluded that no correlation existed between the presence of nucleoids and the existence of uricase in the rhesus monkey kidneys. Such a lack of correlation was confirmed by the fact that renal peroxisomes of rats exhibited dense cores without urate oxidase activity (Beard and Novikoff, 1969).

C. Thin Segments of Henle's Loop

The epithelial cells in thin segments of Henle's loop are different from those in the proximal tubules. The number of microvilli decreases and the mitochondria are less abundant and shorter. Basal infoldings are rare and sometimes absent. The height of the cells becomes more shallow and the cells are of a definite squamous types. The organization of the cells suggests that they might function like ordinary capillary endothelial cells. It is believed that the thin segments are concerned with passive osmotic dialysis of the tubular urine before it enters the distal tubules.

In the thin segments of Henle's loop of the rats, a small number of micro-

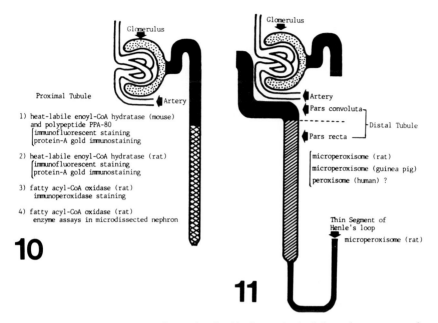

FIG. 10. Peroxisomal enzymes that are localized in the proximal tubules and are necessary for lipid metabolism.
FIG. 11. Schematic representation of microperoxisomes in the thin segment of Henle's loop and the distal tubule.

peroxisomes which resemble the peroxisomes of the proximal tubules in some respects are found (Chang *et al.*, 1971; Novikoff *et al.*, 1973) (Fig. 11).

D. DISTAL TUBULES

The basal parts of epithelial cells in distal tubules display basal infoldings similar to those found in proximal tubules. The basal infoldings are narrower, deeper, and more abundant in pars convoluta than in pars recta. In the first part of pars recta, the epithelial cells are cuboidal and characterized by a rather clear cytoplasm, resembling those in thin segments of Henle's loop. However, as the neighborhood of the glomerulus is approached, the cells become more columnar and the mitochondria increase in number and length. There is a complete lack of true brush borders, but a few small microvilli.

Enzyme histochemically, Allen and Beard (1965) first demonstrated the localization of L-α-hydroxyacid oxidase in basal portions of epithelial cells of the rat distal tubules. However, later, this enzyme was found to be localized in proximal tubules. Light microscopic enzyme histochemistry showed that the distal tubules lack the DAB reaction products for catalase. However, with electron microscopy, DAB-positive microperoxisomes were observed in the distal tubule of rats (Chang *et al.*, 1971) and humans (Roels and Goldfischer, 1979) (Fig. 11).

The kidney of the guinea pig is strikingly different from that of the rat in histochemical reactions (Novikoff *et al.*, 1972). In the guinea pig kidney, the pars convoluta in distal tubules has a population of cells with large numbers of microperoxisomes visible by light microscopy. With electron microscopy, DAB-positive microperoxisomes are also seen in the pars recta; but they are few in number and smaller than those in the pars convoluta.

III. Normal Distribution of Peroxisomes in the Collecting Duct

The collecting ducts are not considered to belong to the nephron. The cells are mainly of two types, light cells and dark cells. Close to the point where the distal tubules connect with the arched collecting tubules, the light cells are rare and the dark cells are abundant. However, distally in the collecting ducts, the light cells predominate. Small DAB-positive granules were also seen in the collecting ducts of guinea pig kidneys (Novikoff *et al.*, 1973) and human kidneys (Roels and

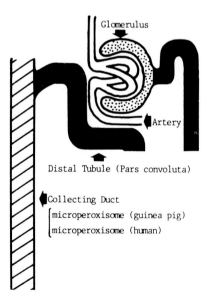

FIG. 12.   Schematic representation of microperoxisomes in the collecting duct.

Goldfischer, 1979) (Fig. 12). It was demonstrated by electron microscopy that they were the microperoxisomes.

IV. Experimental and Pathological Alteration of Peroxisomes in the Nephron

It seems important to investigate the role of peroxisomes under experimental or pathological conditions. It is generally accepted that the effect of hypolipidemic drugs on peroxisomes is a suitable model for studying the biological behavior of peroxisomes. The proliferation of peroxisomes in rat liver cells induced by these drugs has been described by many authors (Svoboda and Azarnoff, 1966; Reddy, 1974; Reddy et al., 1974b, 1978; Reddy and Krishnakantha, 1975; Leighton et al., 1975; Kolde et al., 1976; Goldenberg et al., 1976; Stäubli et al., 1977). However, little has been reported on the effects of hypolipidemic drugs on renal peroxisomes. In an early report by Svoboda in 1967, it was shown that clofibrate caused a slight increase in the number of peroxisomes, especially in proximal tubular epithelial cells of male rats (Svoboda et al., 1967). In the kidney, the degree of increase in peroxisomes was not so remarkable as in the liver. Feeding of acetylsalicylic acid to male rats results in an increase in the number and size of renal peroxisomes (Hruban et al., 1966). Hypolipidemic drugs (methyl clofenapate, BR-931, Wy14643, and fenofibrate) induced the proliferation of peroxisomes in epithelial cells in the proximal tubules of mouse kidney (Lalwani et al., 1981; Reddy et al., 1982). The studies with RMI 14514 was added to the increasing evidence for the heterogeneity of peroxisomes, not only in morphological alterations but also in their enzymatic responses (Svoboda, 1978). It has also been reported that dietary clofibrate treatment resulted in significant increases in palmitoyl-CoA oxidase in kidneys of albino mice (Small et al., 1981). Immunofluorescent staining of polypeptide PPA-80 and heat-labile enoyl-CoA hydratase was observed in the proximal tubular cells (Lalwani et al., 1981). The distribution of these two proteins is identical. In the normal kidneys, the fluorescence was less intense in the pars convoluta than in the pars recta. The glomeruli and the distal tubules showed no fluorescent immunostaining in normal mice. In hypolipidemic drug-treated mice, the proximal tubules showed the increased intensity of cytoplasmic fluorescence with anti-PPA-80 and anti-enoyl-CoA hydratase antibodies (Lalwani et al., 1981). This study provided visual evidence for the localization and induction of these enzymes by hypolipidemic drugs in the kidney. Preliminary electron microscopic immunostaining with the protein A–gold complex technique demonstrated that the hepatic heat-labile enoyl-CoA hydratase was localized in the peroxisomal matrix of the liver (Lalwani et al., 1981). However, no significant change in the activity of heat-stable mitochondrial enoyl-CoA hydratase was observed in kidney cortex. These data suggest that peroxisomes are important constituents in the proximal tubular cells of mouse kidney and that the kidney functions depend on peroxisomal enzymes, especially in lipid metabolism.

The effects of the hypolipidemic agent DEHP on peroxisomes in rat kidneys are interesting. It has been reported that DEHP increases the peroxisomal number and size (Ohno *et al.*, 1981) (Figs. 13 and 14) and the peroxisomal fatty acyl-CoA oxidase in the liver (Moody and Reddy, 1978; Osumi and Hashimoto, 1978). All the enzymes necessary for β-oxidation were identified in DEHP-treated rats (Miyazawa *et al.*, 1980a). The effects of DEHP were studied on renal tubular epithelial cells (Ohno *et al.*, 1982). The response to DEHP is not similar to that induced in liver cells by the same drug. Peroxisomal proliferation occurred at low levels of dosage in a short time (Figs. 15 and 16). The difference in the peroxisomal number between the pars recta and the pars convoluta was emphasized (Fig. 17). The peroxisomes in the pars recta are larger than those in the pars convoluta by high-voltage electron microscopic morphometry (Ohno *et al.*, 1978a; Ohno, 1980a,b) (Figs. 18, 19 and 20). In addition, it was demonstrated that DEHP induced smaller peroxisomes in proximal pars convoluta and recta, peroxisomes different from those of normal rats (Figs. 18, 19, and 20).

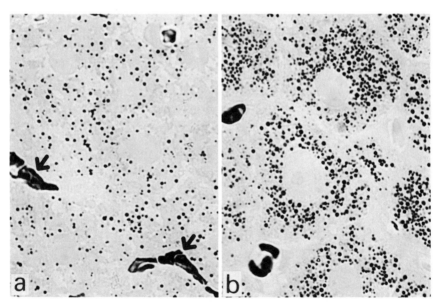

Fig. 13.   (a) Light micrograph of peroxisomes in the hepatocytes of a control male rat. Note that the peroxisomes are strongly stained by DAB. Several erythrocytes are also stained (arrows). ×1300. (b) Light micrograph of peroxisomes in the hepatocytes of an experimental male rat at 14 days during DEHP administration. Many large DAB-positive peroxisomes can be seen. ×1300.

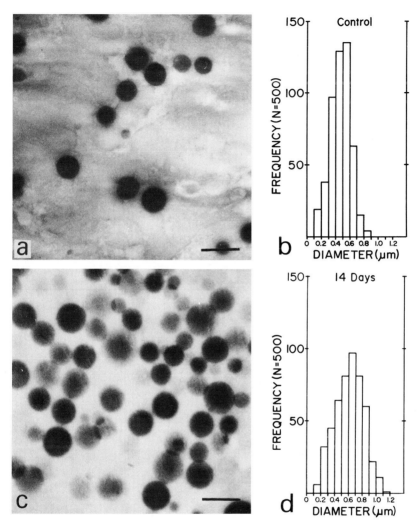

FIG. 14. (a) Electron micrograph of an Epon section (0.5 μm thick) of a control male rat; high-voltage electron microscopy at an accelerating voltage of 200 kV was used to obtain this micrograph. Bar represents 1.0 μm. ×10,600. (b) A histogram showing the size distribution of 500 peroxisomal diameters obtained by high-voltage electron microscopic morphometry. The limiting range is 0.1 μm. Classes are composed of $0 \leq x < 0.1$, $0.1 \leq x < 0.2$, . . . , $1.1 \leq x < 1.2$ μm. Control rats before DEHP administration. Mean ± SD, 0.46±0.14 μm. (c) Electron micrograph showing many round peroxisomes in the hepatocytes at 14 days during DEHP administration on the 0.5 μm thick section. Almost all peroxisomes are larger and less electron dense than those of control rat livers; cf. Fig. 14a. Bar represents 1.0 μm. ×10,600. (d) A histogram showing the size distribution of peroxisomal diameters at 14 days during DEHP administration. Mean ± SD, 0.60 ± 0.20 μm.

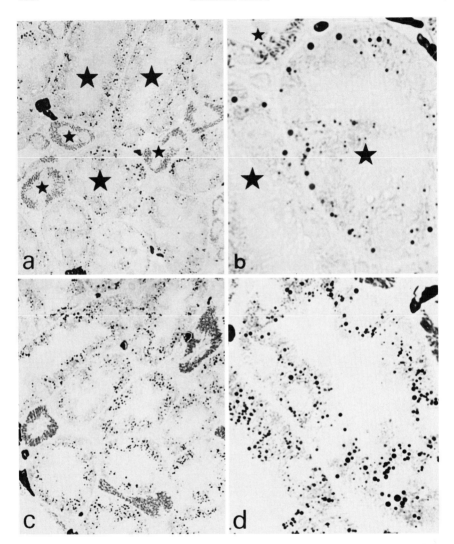

FIG. 15.   (a, b) Light micrographs of Epon sections (0.5 μm thick) of a control female rat before DEHP administration; sections were obtained from the part of outer medulla (shown in Fig. 1c). (a) Two segments of the nephron are definitely visible. At low-power magnification, DAB-positive peroxisomes are visible in the proximal straight tubules (large stars) and DAB staining of mitochondria is visible in the distal straight tubules (small stars). Erythrocytes are also stained with DAB. ×500. (b) At high-power magnification, obvious DAB-positive peroxisomes against the background of slight DAB staining of mitochondria are visible in the proximal straight tubules (large stars). Mitochondrial DAB staining can also be seen in the distal straight tubules (small stars). ×1250. (c, d) Light micrograph of Epon sections (0.5 μm thick) of an experimental female rat administered 1% DEHP for 1 week; sections were obtained from the part of the outer medulla (shown in Fig. 1c). (c) More peroxisomes are visible in the proximal straight tubules than in control female rats; cf. Fig. 15a. ×500. (d) At high-power magnification, many more peroxisomes are visible; cf. Fig. 15b. ×1250.

development of peroxisomes in regenerating cells of the pars recta of proximal tubules was studied by light and electron microscopic histochemistry in rats given a single intraperitoneal injection of D-serine (Reddy et al., 1976). Peroxisomes are abundant in the pars recta of the proximal tubules. Therefore, it is paradoxical that the cells rich in D-serine amino acid oxidase are susceptible to the injection of serine. The development of peroxisomes, which appeared to be closely related to endocytotic vacuoles in the regenerating cells, suggests that they may be essential to the renal function.

In the proximal tubular cells of riboflavin-deficient mice, glycogen particles were observed in the matrix of the peroxisomes (Kobayashi and Yamamoto, 1978). Those ultrastructural changes are restricted to the pars recta in proximal tubules. However, the occurrence of peroxisomes containing glycogen particles is very infrequent. It is, therefore, doubtful that the peroxisomes play a significant role in glycogen metabolism in the animal cells and that the enzymes participating in glycogen synthesis are components of the peroxisomes. Another possibility cannot be excluded that in some pathological conditions new kinds of enzymes are induced in the peroxisomes. However, there are no biochemical data to support this possibility of glycogen synthesis in peroxisomes. During the development of riboflavin deficiency, vacuoles were observed in tubular epithelia (Kobayashi et al., 1980). As the size of the vacuoles derived from peroxisomes increases, both the electron density of the matrix and reactivity to DAB decrease. It is known that distribution of riboflavin in the kidney is much higher in the cortex than in the medulla (Hara, 1958). The rate of riboflavin uptake is also much higher in proximal tubules than in any other parts of the tubules (Chin, 1968). These biochemical data may reflect the fact that structural changes in riboflavin-deficient kidneys are confined to the proximal tubules.

There were peroxisomes in the proximal tubules of human kidneys (Roels and Goldfischer, 1979). Enzyme histochemical staining of catalase showed that the number of peroxisomes was lower in the pars recta than in the pars convoluta, thus differing from rats in this regard. Some peroxisomes contain marginal plates. The cerebrohepatorenal syndrome (Zellweger's disease) is a rare familial disease, manifested by severe hypotonia, central nervous system abnormalities, cirrhosis, and renal and skeletal malformations (Goldfischer et al., 1973a,b). No structures resembling peroxisomes could be found in renal proximal tubules

---

FIG. 21.   Electron micrographs of epithelial cells in the proximal (a, b) and distal (c) tubules of experimental female rats, which were treated with 2% DEHP. (a) The number of peroxisomes is increased by the administration of 2% DEHP for 1 week (arrows). ×9300. Inset: DAB reaction products for catalase. ×7500. (b) The ultrastructural changes of mitochondria can be seen after administration of 2% DEHP for 4 weeks (long, thin arrows). Peroxisomes can be also identified (short arrows). Secondary lysosomes are predominant (curved arrow). ×10,600. Inset: DAB reaction products for catalase. ×7500. (c) The ultrastructural changes of mitochondria in the distal tubules can be seen by the administration of 2% DEHP for 4 weeks (arrows). ×7500.

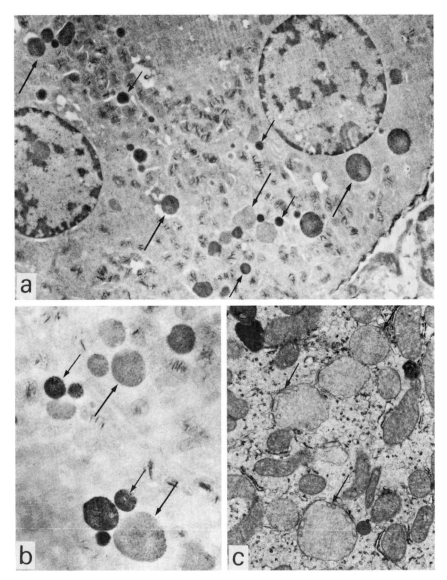

FIG. 22. Electron micrographs of an epithelial cell in the proximal straight tubules of a male rat treated with 2% DEHP for 3 days. (a) On the basis of size and the electron density, the DAB reaction products for catalase reveal two different types of peroxisomes. One type is small and electron dense (small arrows) and the other type is large and less electron dense (large arrows). Ultrathin section stained with uranyl acetate and lead citrate. ×6000. (b) Unstained ultrathin section of DAB reaction products confirms two types of peroxisomes in the identical cell. ×10,500. (c) Ultrastructure of an epithelial cell on ultrathin section; section was stained with uranyl acetate and lead citrate. Large peroxisomes containing peripheral circular structures (arrows) can easily be identified. ×10,500.

(Goldfisher *et al.*, 1973b). This observation was further confirmed by incubating glutaraldehyde-fixed kidney tissues in a standard histochemical medium with DAB for catalase.

V. Conclusion

A difference in the main metabolic role of peroxisomes of various animal tissues might exist, even though peroxisomes are cell organelles with components always synthesized and assembled by the same process. More experiments are needed to clarify all the functions of peroxisomes in animals. In this article, I have reviewed both early and recent investigations of peroxisomes of kidneys, but it was impossible to mention all the papers about peroxisomes. Fortunately, the reader can refer to more detailed reviews of peroxisomes that have already been published. The present review on kidney peroxisomes indicates the kind of information that may contribute to the elucidation of peroxisomal functions in the future.

ACKNOWLEDGMENT

The author expresses his appreciation to Professor T. Nagata, Department of Anatomy, Shinshu University School of Medicine, for his valuable advice and critical reading of this review and to Miss. N. Yoshizato and Miss M. Mitobe for their skillful techniques in preparing the schema.

REFERENCES

Allen, J. M., and Beard, M. E. (1965). *Science* **149,** 1507–1509.
Allen, J. M., Beard, M. E., and Kleinbergs, S. (1965). *J. Exp. Zool.* **160,** 329–344.
Arnold, G., and Holtzman, E. (1980). *J. Histochem. Cytochem.* **28,** 1025–1028.
Arnold, G., Liscum, L., and Holtzman, E. (1979). *J. Histochem. Cytochem.* **27,** 735–745.
Asano, G., and Ashraf, M. (1980). *Virchows Arch. B Cell Pathol.* **34,** 205–212.
Barrett, J. M., and Heidger, P. M., Jr. (1975). *Cell Tissue Res.* **157,** 283–305.
Beard, M. E., and Novikoff, A. B. (1969). *J. Cell Biol.* **42,** 501–518.
Bendayan, M., Reddy, M. K., Hashimoto, T., and Reddy, J. K. (1983). *J. Histochem. Cytochem.* **31,** 509–516.
Cannon, B., Alexson, S., and Nedergaard, J. (1982). *Ann. N.Y. Acad. Sci.* **386,** 40–57.
Chan, A. W. K., Perry, S. G., Burch, H. B., Fagioli, S., Alvey, T. R., and Lowry, O. H. (1979). *J. Histochem. Cytochem.* **27,** 751–755.
Chang, C., Schiller, B., and Goldfischer, S. (1971). *J. Histochem. Cytochem.* **19,** 56–62.
Chin, S. (1968). *J. Vitaminol.* **38,** 283–292.
Debeer, L. J., and Mannaerts, G. P. (1983). *Diabete Metab.* **9,** 134–140.
De Duve, C. (1969). *Ann. N.Y. Acad. Sci.* **168,** 369–381.
De Duve, C., and Baudhuin, P. (1966). *Physiol. Rev.* **46,** 323–357.

Eguchi, M., Sannes, P. L., and Spicer, S. S. (1979). *Am. J. Pathol.* **95**, 281–294.

Ericsson, J. L. E., and Trump, B. E. (1966). *Lab. Invest.* **15**, 1610–1633.

Essner, E. (1970). *J. Histochem. Cytochem.* **18**, 80–92.

Furuta, S., Miyazawa, S., Osumi, T., Hashimoto, T., and Ui, N. (1980). *J. Biochem.* **88**, 1059–1070.

Furuta, S., Miyazawa, S., and Hashimoto, T. (1982). *J. Biochem.* **92**, 319–326.

Goeckermann, J. A., and Vigil, E. (1975). *J. Histochem. Cytochem.* **23**, 957–973.

Goldenberg, H., Hüttinger, M., Kampfer, P., Kramar, R., and Pavelka, M. (1976). *Histochemistry* **46**, 189–196.

Goldenberg, H., Hüttinger, M., Kollner, U., Kramar, R., and Pavelka, M. (1978). *Histochemistry* **56**, 253–264.

Goldfischer, S. (1969). *J. Histochem. Cytochem.* **17**, 681–685.

Goldfischer, S., and Essner, E. (1970). *J. Histochem. Cytochem.* **18**, 482–489.

Goldfischer, S., Johnson, A. B., Essner, E., Moore, C., and Ritch, R. H. (1973a). *J. Histochem. Cytochem.* **21**, 972–977.

Goldfischer, S., Moore, C. L., Johnson, A. B., Spiro, A. J., Valsamis, M. P., Wisniewski, H. K., Ritch, R. H., Norton, W. T., Rapin, I., and Gartner, L. M. (1973b). *Science* **182**, 62–64.

Goldman, B. M., and Blobel, G. (1978). *Proc. Natl. Acad. Sci. U.S.A.* **75**, 5066–5070.

Hand, A. (1979). *J. Histochem. Cytochem.* **27**, 1367–1370.

Hara, I. (1958). *Teishin Igaku* **10**, 1–20.

Hashimoto, T. (1982). *Ann. N.Y. Acad. Sci.* **386**, 5–12.

Hruban, Z., and Rechcigl, M., Jr. (1969). *Int. Rev. Cytol. Suppl.* **1.**

Hurban, Z., Swift, H., and Slesers, A. (1966). *Lab. Invest.* **15**, 1884–1901.

Hruban, Z., Vigil, E. L., Slesers, A., and Hopkins, E. (1972). *Lab. Invest.* **27**, 184–191.

Kalmbach, P., and Fahimi, H. D. (1978). *Cell Biol. Int. Rep.* **2**, 389–396.

Katoh, M., Kanai, M., Kameko, M., Ohno, S., Fujii, Y., and Nagata, T. (1982). *Acta Histochem. Cytochem.* **15**, 68–75.

Kindl, H. (1982). *Int. Rev. Cytol.* **80**, 193–229.

Kobayashi, K., and Yamamoto, T. (1978). *J. Histochem. Cytochem.* **26**, 434–440.

Kobayashi, K., Yamamoto, T., and Omae, T. (1980). *Virchows Arch. B Cell Pathol.* **34**, 99–109.

Kolde, G., Roessner, A., and Themann, H. (1976). *Virchows Arch. B Cell Pathol.* **22**, 73–87.

Lalwani, N. D., Reddy, M. K., Mangkornkanok-Mark, M., and Reddy, J. K. (1981). *Biochem. J.* **198**, 177–186.

Lata, G. F., Mamrak, F., Bloch, P., and Baker, B. (1977). *J. Supramol. Struct.* **7**, 419–434.

Lavin, P., and Koss, L. G. (1971). *Am. J. Pathol.* **62**, 169–180.

Lazarow, P., and De Duve, C. (1976). *Proc. Natl. Acad. Sci. U.S.A.* **73**, 2043–2046.

Lazarow, P. B. (1978a). *J. Biol. Chem.* **253**, 1522–1528.

Lazarow, P. B. (1978b). *Int. Conf. Atherosclerosis* pp. 15–17.

Lazarow, P. B. (1981). *Arch. Biochem. Biophys.* **206**, 342–345.

Lazarow, P. B., Robbi, M., Fujiki, Y., and Wong, L. (1982). *Ann. N.Y. Acad. Sci.* **386**, 285–298.

Le Hir, M., and Dubach, U. C. (1981). *FEBS Lett.* **127**, 250–252.

Le Hir, M., and Dubach, U. C. (1982). *J. Histochem. Cytochem.* **30**, 441–444.

Leighton, F., and Lazo, O. (1982). *Arch. Biol. Med. Exp.* **15**, 447–456.

Leighton, F., Coloma, L., and Koenig, C. (1975). *J. Cell Biol.* **67**, 281–309.

Lord, J. M., and Roberts, L. M. (1983). *Int. Rev. Cytol. Suppl.* **15**, 115–156.

McGroarty, E., Hsieh, B., Wied, D. M., Gee, R., and Tolbert, N. E. (1974). *Arch. Biochem. Biophys.* **161**, 194–210.

Mannaerts, G., Debeer, L. J., Thomas, J., and De Schepper, P. J. (1979). *J. Biol. Chem.* **254**, 4585–4595.

Markwell, M. A. K., Tolbert, N. E., and Bieber, L. L. (1976). *Arch. Biochem. Biophys.* **176,** 479–488.

Maunsbach, A. B. (1966a). *J. Ultrastruct. Res.* **16,** 197–238.

Maunsbach, A. B. (1966b). *J. Ultrastruct. Res.* **16,** 239–258.

Miyazawa, S., Furuta, S., Osumi, T., and Hashimoto, T. (1980a). *Biochim. Biophys. Acta* **630,** 367–374.

Miyazawa, S., Osumi, T., and Hashimoto, T. (1980b). *Eur. J. Biochem.* **103,** 589–596.

Moody, D. E., and Reddy, J. K. (1978). *Toxicol. Appl. Pharmacol.* **45,** 497–504.

Morikawa, S., and Harada, T. (1969). *J. Histochem. Cytochem.* **17,** 30–35.

Morimoto, S., and Abe, R. (1983). *Chem. Pharmacol. Bull.* **31,** 2917–2919.

Morimoto, S., Matsumura, Y., Abe, R., and Furuhara, A. (1978). *Jpn. J. Pharmacol.* **28,** 793–796.

Nakano, M., Saga, M., and Tsutsumi, Y. (1969). *Biochim. Biophys. Acta* **185,** 19–30.

Nedergaard, J., Alexson, S., and Cannon, B. (1980). *Am. J. Physiol.* **239,** C208–C216.

Novikoff, A. B., and Goldfischer, S. (1969). *J. Histochem. Cytochem.* **17,** 675–680.

Novikoff, A. B., Novikoff, P. M., Davis, C., and Quintana, N. (1972). *J. Histochem. Cytochem.* **20,** 1006–1023.

Novikoff, A. B., Novikoff, P. M., Davis, C., and Quintana, N. (1973). *J. Histochem. Cytochem.* **21,** 737–755.

Ohno, S. (1980a). *J. Electron Microsc.* **29,** 98–105.

Ohno, S. (1980b). *J. Electron Microsc.* **29,** 230–235.

Ohno, S., Yoshida, K., Murata, F., and Nagata, T. (1978a). *Proc. Int. Congr. Electron Microsc., 9th* **2,** 14–15.

Ohno, S., Murata, F., Yoshida, K., Tei, I., and Nagata, T. (1978b). *J. Clin. Electron Microsc.* **11,** 841–842.

Ohno, S., Yamabayashi, S., Fujii, Y., Kawahara, I., Murata, F., and Nagata, T. (1979). *J. Clin. Electron Microsc.* **12,** 621–622.

Ohno, S., Ohtake, N., Fujii, Y., Yamabayashi, S., Usuda, N., and Nagata, T. (1981). *Acta Histochem. Cytochem.* **14,** 126–142.

Ohno, S., Fujii, Y., Usuda, N., Murata, F., and Nagata, T. (1982). *Acta Histochem. Cytochem.* **15,** 40–57.

Osumi, T., and Hashimoto, T. (1978). *J. Biochem.* **83,** 1361–1365.

Osumi, T., and Hashimoto, T. (1979a). *Biochem. Biophys. Res. Commun.* **89,** 580–584.

Osumi, T., and Hashimoto, T. (1979b). *Biochem. Biophys. Acta* **574,** 258–267.

Osumi, T., and Hashimoto, T. (1980). *Arch. Biochem. Biophys.* **203,** 372–383.

Pipan, N., and Psenicnik, M. (1975). *Histochemistry* **44,** 13–21.

Psenicnik, M., and Pipan, N. (1977). *Virchows Arch. B Cell Pathol.* **25,** 161–169.

Reddy, J. K. (1974). *Am. J. Pathol.* **75,** 103–118.

Reddy, J. K., and Krishnakantha, T. P. (1975). *Science* **190,** 787–789.

Reddy, J. K., and Svoboda, D. (1972). *Lab. Invest.* **26,** 657–665.

Reddy, J. K., Azarnoff, D. L., Svoboda, D. J., and Prasad, J. D. (1974a). **61,** 344–358.

Reddy, J. K., Tewari, J. P., Svoboda, D. J., and Malhotra, S. K. (1974b). *Lab. Invest.* **31,** 268–275.

Reddy, J. K., Rao, M. S., Moody, D. E., and Qureshi, S. A. (1976). *J. Histochem. Cytochem.* **24,** 1239–1248.

Reddy, J. K., Azarnoff, D. L., and Sirtori, C. R. (1978). *Arch. Int. Pharmacodyn.* **234,** 4–14.

Reddy, J. K., Warren, J. R., Reddy, M. K., and Lalwani, N. D. (1982). *Ann. N.Y. Acad. Sci.* **386,** 81–110.

Rhodin, J. (1954). Doctoral Thesis, Karolinska Institute, Stockholm.

Rhodin, J. (1958). *Am. J. Med.* **24,** 661–675.

Robbi, M., and Lazarow, P. B. (1978). *Proc. Natl. Acad. Sci. U.S.A.* **75**, 4344–4348.

Robinson, W. G., Jr., and Kuwabara, T. (1977). *Invest. Ophthalmol. Visual Sci.* **16**, 1110–1117.

Roels, F., and Goldfischer, S. (1979). *J. Histochem. Cytochem.* **27**, 1471–1477.

Shnitka, T. K., and Talibi, G. G. (1971). *Histochemistry* **27**, 137–158.

Sima, A. A. F. (1980). *Acta Neuropathol.* **51**, 113–117.

Small, G. M., Hoching, T. J., Sturdee, A. P., Burdett, K., and Connock, M. J. (1981). *Life Sci.* **28**, 1875–1882.

Stäubli, W., Schweizer, W., Suter, J., and Weibel, E. R. (1977). *J. Cell Biol.* **74**, 665–689.

Svoboda, D. J. (1978). *J. Cell Biol.* **78**, 810–822.

Svoboda, D. J., and Azarnoff, D. L. (1966). *J. Cell Biol.* **27**, 442–450.

Svoboda, D. J., Grady, H., and Azarnoff, D. (1967). *J. Cell Biol.* **35**, 127–152.

Tisher, C. C., Finkel, R. M., Rosen, S., and Kendig, E. M. (1968). *Lab. Invest.* **19**, 1–6.

Tisher, C. C., Rosen, S., and Osborne, G. B. (1969). *Am. J. Pathol.* **56**, 469–517.

Tolbert, N. E. (1978). *In* "Method in Enzymology" (S. Fleischer and L. Packer, eds.), Vol. 52, pp. 493–505. Academic Press, New York.

Tolbert, N. E., and Essner, E. (1981). *J. Cell Biol.* **91**, 271s–283s.

Veenhuis, M., and Wendelaar Bonga, S. E. (1979). *Histochem. J.* **11**, 561–572.

Yokota, S., and Fahimi, H. D. (1982). *Ann. N.Y. Acad. Sci.* **386**, 491–494.

INTERNATIONAL REVIEW OF CYTOLOGY, VOL. 95

Enzyme Cytochemistry

M. Borgers and A. Verheyen

*Laboratory of Cell Biology, Janssen Pharmaceutica Research Laboratories,
Beerse, Belgium*

I. Introduction

This article is written at a time when cytochemical assessments of enzyme activities with classic methodology are being replaced or compared with completely new ways of detection. The majority of methods have made use of the catalytic activity of enzymes on substrates and few have been based on the antigenicity of the enzymes or on reactions with radiolabeled enzyme inhibitors. We are about to enter an era where immunocytochemistry of enzymes will take over the conventional enzyme–substrate catalytic approach.

The need for a new methodology emerges at a time when many classic methods have not yet been fully explored. This need for a new methodology is principally related to basic shortcomings in the existent methodology, such as inadequate validation criteria to reproduce and interpret results. Enzyme cytochemistry at the electron microscopic level is still a new subdiscipline of cell biology research that exploded, so to speak, during the early sixties after the introduction of the enzyme-friendly glutaraldehyde (Sabatini *et al.*, 1963).

The last decade, however, has not shown the expected progression of the early explosion of conventional enzyme cytochemistry. Whether this is due to an initial overestimation of its relevancy, an underestimation of its difficulty, the lack of coordinated efforts between the qualitative and quantitative disciplines, or to one of many other reasons, falls beyond the scope of this article.

From the early days of explorative research, some 25 years ago, ultrastructural cytochemistry has been encumbered with basic difficulties in understanding the relevancy of the observations. One of the main causes of these uncertainties is the lack of knowledge about the underlying chemistry of the reaction (Holt, 1980). Not only the morphologist and the biochemist who critically evaluated the cytochemist's work, but the cytochemist himself became well aware of the problems which issue from the assessment of enzyme activities through visualization procedures. In contrast to biochemistry and in part also to light microscopic (LM) histochemistry, cytochemistry of enzymes is largely a qualitative discipline. Quantitative approaches at the electron microscopic (EM) level most often result in a negative cost–benefit balance, and in this respect enzyme cytochemistry will continuously be in need of support from other quantitative disciplines, such as biochemistry.

The localization of enzymes at the EM level has proved to be a major contribution to the knowledge of structure and function of many subcellular entities. Although much has been achieved over the last two decades, there are still many areas of research where cytochemistry remains largely unexplored. Indeed, there is a lot of truth in what Professor Galjaard said during a discussion on the validation of cytochemical methods: "In the histochemical journals I often read about fantastic methods for enzymes which so far seem to be of little or no medical or biological importance. I see relatively little work on enzymes that could be applied to fundamental problems in genetics and cell biology, which could take us much further ahead" (Galjaard, 1980). Obviously, a lot of work is devoted to a number of enzymes which are ubiquitously present in many organs of all higher species, but for which the exact role escapes us completely. Nonspecific alkaline phosphatase is one example. The importance to medical and cell biological research of this enzyme, albeit limited to its use as a marker of subcellular organelles in a variety of pathophysiological conditions, is unquestionable. The main emphasis of Professor Galjaard's words should, however, be put on the vast number of virgin fields in enzyme cytochemistry, "virgin" simply because no methods have been available to explore them.

The aim of this article is to summarize the data on most of the enzymes for which adequate visualization methodology exists at the ultrastructural level, to consider some general validation criteria of methodology, and to emphasize recent innovations and prospects for future research. We hope that the thread that runs through our way of thinking will be taken as a plea for multidisciplinary work in cell biology research. If one has to locate cytochemistry in such a scheme, it should fulfill the particularly challenging role of bringing morphology and biochemistry closer together, i.e., a subdiscipline functioning as a bridge.

II. Validation of Enzyme Cytochemistry

Before summarizing a number of validation criteria, we should stress that these aspects must not be regarded as generally applicable standard conditions, but that they merely represent some guidelines for those who want to initiate an enzyme cytochemical program and cannot afford to spend a lot of time making methods work. Besides the most practical and time-saving hint "go and pick the brain of your well-informed neighbor cytochemist," there are a number of points which have to be kept in mind before starting cytochemical experiments.

B. USEFUL VERSUS USELESS CYTOCHEMISTRY

Although this distinction can most often only be made "post hoc," many localization attempts reported in the literature were not relevant to the heart of the problem. In general one can state that enzyme cytochemistry is only indicated when there is a good chance that a straightforward answer can be given.

The usefulness of cytochemical investments has been proved beyond any doubt in areas where classic morphology failed or only provided incomplete infomation. Examples of areas in which cytochemistry of enzymes has played a leading role within an interdisciplinary assessment are the following:

1. The identification of uptake, secretory, and metabolic routes; sites of ion transport activity, assembly and disassembly sites of cell components and metabolites.

2. The differentiation and dedifferentiation of cells; characterization of the precancerous state; pharmacological and toxicological profile of drugs; elucidation of the mechanisms of drug action.

3. The identification of the origin of cells and of subcellular organelles with the use of marker enzymes. Some enzymes are uniformly present in a number of cell types and can therefore be usefully employed as markers of cells during development and differentiation of tissues and metaplasia. A typical example for the metaplastic situation is the stereotype reaction of an arterial blood vessel wall to physical or chemical aggression, i.e., the development of an intimal thickening, populated by cells of medial smooth muscle-, endothelial-, or blood-borne origin. For example, the assessment of purine nucleoside phosphorylase, a cytosol enzyme that is present in endothelial and not in smooth muscle cells, established the participation of the endothelial cells in the formation of the intimal thickening (Borgers *et al.*, 1973b).

4. The elucidation of the function of subcellular organelles and the functional interrelationships that exist between different organelles, e.g., Golgi-apparatus–Golgi-derived vesicles—secretory granules–microtubules—plasma membrane (for illustration, see Fig. 1).

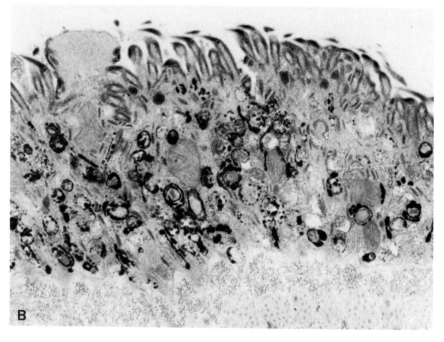

5. The processes of cell degeneration and regeneration.

6. The assessment of functional changes in relation to structural alterations of subcellular organelles in a variety of pathophysiological conditions. Enzyme cytochemistry has actively contributed to the understanding of the underlying pathology, e.g., myopathic disorders, immunodeficiency syndromes, and precancerous states. Therefore, its aid in diagnosis, prognosis, and therapy management may be of great value.

7. The "quality control" aspect of enzyme cytochemistry for quantitative determination in biochemistry is not only of extreme value, but often an absolute necessity. Extrapolations from one organ or species to another may be hazardous due to the tremendous variations that exist between organs and species with regards to the subcellular distribution of enzymes. Verification by cytochemical means of whether a so-called common marker for a subcellular organelle is applicable to the tissue under investigation is therefore warranted. This is well illustrated by a number of observations reporting extralysosomal sites of a so-called lysosome marker enzyme, i.e., acid phosphatase. The same appears to be true for plasma membrane markers such as $5'$-nucleotidase, alkaline phosphatase, and even Na^+, K^+-ATPase. In some cell types these enzymes are distributed in other organelles or label a specialized portion of the plasma membrane only.

8. The validation of cell and tissue culture systems. Enzyme cytochemistry is one of the measures to assess the functional behavior of the isolated system in relation to the intact organ.

This short series of examples shows in which areas of fundamental and applied research cytochemistry can contribute to resolve a cell biological problem, either on its own or, most frequently, in combination with other disciplines. Too often, however, enzyme cytochemical attempts are not worth the investment of energy, cost, and time. The statement by J. A. Firth, "The localization of undefined ATPase is of little or no value" (Firth, 1978), illustrates one of many examples of what can be called useless cytochemistry, and definitely exposes a major weakness of current enzyme cytochemistry: the lack of proper control criteria to disclose the desired specific activity. There are no generally applicable rules for developing a method of working with a well-delineated set of available validation criteria. Modifications and adaptations of published methodology are often

---

FIG. 1. (A) Untreated *Hymenolepis nana*. Activity with *p*-nitrophenylphosphate at pH 7. A strong phosphatase activity is seen on the microtrichous surface of the anucleated zone of the tegument. ×20,200. (B) *Hymenolepis nana* after antihelminthic treatment of the host. Activity with *p*-nitrophenyl phosphate at pH 7. Many reactive vesicles are observed in the anucleated zone, whereas the microtrichous surface is devoid of reaction product. This drug-induced alteration in enzyme localization is due to a block in transport of the enzyme from the site of synthesis to the outer surface of the microtriches. ×28,900.

required for a particular organ or species, but such changes are often made without proper knowledge of the enzymology and chemistry of the reaction and therefore may give rise to faulty interpretations (Holt, 1980). The classic drawbacks and pitfalls in cytochemistry have not or have only partly been solved during the last decade, and the main uncertainty concerns the interpretation of the distribution patterns obtained: That is, is the surviving portion of the activity randomly distributed or has a selection of the site with the highest activity taken place? Obviously, with this degree of uncertainty the information that can be obtained by cytochemistry alone is limited, and therefore one has to rely on noncytological assessments. This does not mean, however, that biochemical and cytochemical results should match completely before one can derive relevant conclusions. Very often, even with the best controls at hand, there may be a basic disagreement between results obtained with complementary disciplines.

B. VALIDATION OF CYTOCHEMICAL METHODS

1. *Preparation of Tissues and Cells*

All procedures that aim at localizing enzyme activities are faced with a compromise between the preservation of subcellular structure and the preservation of the enzyme activities at their original "*in vivo*" site of activity. In order to yield reproducible results, the optimal balance between preserved or preservable enzyme activity and the applied visualization procedure should be sought. Initially the enzymatic activity has to be uniformly preserved or, in other words, inactivated to the same extent in all parts of the tissue. The best way to achieve such uniformity is by perfusion fixation. Purified glutaraldehyde and the paraformaldehyde–glutaraldehyde mixtures are most popular and lend themselves very well to the demonstration of most enzyme activities. The concentration of the fixative and the time and temperature of fixation have to be adapted to each individual enzyme or group of enzymes. The idea that enzyme activity should be preserved as much as possible and therefore fixation should be kept to a minimum is incorrect for many enzymes. In practice, the converse appears to be true: Some enzyme activities must be inactivated to a major extent in order to meet the requirements of relatively low trapping efficiency of the capture agent in the incubation medium (*vide infra*).

Inactivation up to 95% by the fixative and components of the incubation medium is sometimes required to obtain reproducible localization of enzymes in which activity is concentrated in a specialized area, e.g., alkaline phosphatase in the brush borders of small intestinal cells and proximal tubular cells of the kidney. Not infrequently, completely negative pictures result from nearly complete preservation of activity in the tissue. Even for more fixative-sensitive enzymes such as glucose-6-phosphatase, there is no such 2-minute fixation barrier that cannot be surpassed in order to obtain a reaction product.

In general practice, it is easier to fix thoroughly (at least 5 minutes of perfusion fixation with 2% purified glutaraldehyde at 4°C) and adapt the appropriate conditions for each enzyme during the incubation step. However, when enzyme activity is present only in weak amounts, inactivation through fixation should be minimal.

Other conditions of fixation that may drastically influence the final outcome are the buffer and pH of the fixative. This aspect is practically unexplored in most of the commonly employed localization methods. In a recent review on 5′-nucleotidase in lymphocytes, Uusitalo reported that the enzyme activity was totally inhibited by 0.25% glutaraldehyde buffered to pH 7.2 with Na-cacodylate, whereas reproducible results were obtained after a 60-minute fixation in 1% glutaraldehyde in Tris-maleate buffer at pH 6 (Uusitalo, 1981). Biochemical measurements of the enzyme activities after various fixation procedures is often the only meaningful way to control and establish optimal working conditions for cytochemical assessments.

After fixation, the decision has to be made whether the incubation will be performed on small blocks of tissue, on thick frozen sections, or on slices prepared by tissue chopper or Vibratome. Although determined largely by the enzyme(s) to be investigated, the use of blocks is usually a wrong choice while frozen section is most advantageous in practical terms. Besides the uniformity in section thickness, which can be produced with a freezing microtome, the freezing effect markedly enhances penetration of components of the incubation media in the individual cells within the 30 to 40 μm thick section. This effect appeared to be important, not only in tissue but in isolated cells as well, especially with some phosphatase assessments at alkaline and neutral pH. Acid media by themselves usually disrupt membrane permeability sufficiently to allow uniform permeation of the media components. Although the structural preservation is usually superior in chopped and Vibratome sections, there often remain penetration problems resulting in an inhomogeneous distribution of the reaction products.

2. Incubation

Specific criteria to validate incubation conditions will be dealt with in the descriptions of the individual enzymes. This section is therefore restricted to some generally applicable aspects related to the preparation of incubation solutions and incubation procedures.

The success of a procedure depends on its reliability and practicality. Criteria for these factors are interrelated and are concerned with efficiency, resolution, reproducibility, and specificity of the method. An adequate incubation medium is a medium that matches the degree of enzyme activity in the section; in other words, its trapping efficiency has to be optimized for each tissue.

Optimizing the composition of a medium is not necessarily synonymous with establishing the maximum rate of the enzymatic reaction. The factors involved are largely determined by the enzyme under investigation, namely, its degree of activity in the tissue to be examined and the methods available. The limitations of most media are trapping efficiency and stability, especially in phosphatase cytochemistry. Media that are based on the capture of the split products of the enzyme substrates by heavy metals have a limited trapping efficiency, which makes them prone to easy diffusion and artificial deposition or washout of the reaction product. Owing to this low efficiency, the inactivation of the enzyme reaction by capture agents, such as lead ions, or by the use of nonoptimal enzyme substrates often represents an advantage rather than a disadvantage. On the other hand, increasing the efficiency of the capture reaction by changing the composition of the medium is the alternative way to optimize the cytochemical reaction (De Jong, 1982).

The other problem that represents a burden to many cytochemists is the instability of media. Many recent modifications of existent methods were primarily aimed at making more stable solutions through the introduction of buffers which complexed the capture agent more firmly or prevented the substrate from spontaneous decomposition (Mayahara et al., 1967, 1980). In many cases such attempts resulted in more practicable media; in others the sensitivity of the media diminished to such an extent that adequate capture of the enzymatic split product was lost. Therefore, the ''threshold'' stability of a medium is probably the most important aspect in determining its suitability for cytochemical work. The latter factor is also the main determinant for resolution and reproducibility.

Other aspects to be considered on an individual basis are the type of buffer, pH, concentrations and order of mixing of the different components of a medium, and length and temperature of incubation. To control for this variety of factors, recent attempts with model systems to study the effects of the composition of the medium on the trapping of enzymatic split products have led to considerable improvements of cytochemical media (De Jong, 1982). The large majority of media in hydrolase cytochemistry use heavy metals as capture agents. Lead ions are often considered detrimental for enzyme activities, e.g., ATPase. Moreover, lead is reported to induce spontaneous splitting of substrates or to form complexes with substrates (see later). In spite of these drawbacks, it has been shown conclusively that when lead ions are properly handled, i.e., by labile binding to an appropriate buffer prior to the addition of the other components, lead remains a most valuable capture agent in hydrolase cytochemistry (Hugon and Borgers, 1969b; Borgers et al., 1971a; Mayahara et al., 1980). Therefore, the enzyme activities, otherwise inactivated by lead ions, are spared and substrates are protected by loose coupling of the lead ions. Binding the lead ions too firmly, on the other hand, which is possible by increasing the buffer concentration, will result in inefficient trapping and may give rise to false negative results.

3. Controls

Control of the specificity of the reaction is one of the great limitations of today's enzyme cytochemistry. Too often the only control reaction performed consists in the omission of the substrate, which has, of course, only very limited value. Inhibitors of the enzymatic reaction are useful provided that they inhibit almost completely the biochemically detectable activity, are only inhibitory for the enzyme under investigation, and do not interact at all with any of the components of the medium. Inhibitors which do not fulfill these criteria are of little or no value, because some substrates, e.g., nucleoside phosphates, can be split by a number of different enzymes. Illustrative in this respect is the reaction with thiamine pyrophosphate, which in rat liver is split at neutral pH by thiamine pyrophosphatase (Golgi apparatus), nucleoside diphosphatase (endoplasmic reticulum), polyphosphatase (plasma membrane), alkaline phosphatase (bile canaliculi), and acid phosphatase (lysosomes) (Borgers and Thoné, 1976).

From the above example, it appears that one should take into account the possible interference of nonspecific acid and alkaline phosphatases when studying the distribution of specific phosphatases at neutral pH. On the other hand, the so-called nonspecific phosphatase substrates may act as substrates for specific enzymes, e.g., glucose-6-phosphatase in rat liver and kidney (Borgers and Thoné, 1976). An important point which has to be considered when interference of other enzymes is likely to occur is the competition of these enzymes for the substrate. In an organ rich in competitive nonspecific hydrolase activity, the hydrolytic site of the specific enzyme is revealed only after proper inhibition of the competitive enzyme(s).

C. INTERPRETATION

There is usually a close correlation between the esthetic beauty or "cleanness" of a preparation and the accuracy of the information—both qualitative and quantitative—obtained from it (Fahimi, 1980). Cytological criteria were recently reviewed by Stoward (1980) and Fahimi (1980) on both light and electron microscopic enzyme cytochemistry. These criteria include the following: (1) sections should look "clean"; (2) the final reaction product should be localized in or on the subcellular site of the enzyme; (3) there should be no diffusion of the enzyme or of the final reaction product. These interrelated criteria would indeed represent the ideal situation if we knew where an enzyme activity ought to be. Here Goethe's saying from 1819 is totally applicable: "Man erblickt nur wass man schon weiss und versteht"—"One only sees what one already knows and understands." Biochemical assessment, such as fractionation of subcellular organelles, is one of the leads the cytochemist can rely upon, although biochemistry on its own has its limitations and does not always reveal the truth.

Generally, a clean picture indicates that diffusion from a particular organelle did not take place. It does not, however, exclude the possibility that a "stable" site of activity has been selected. The "beautiful picture syndrome" remains a heavy burden on the cytochemists' shoulders. To date, there has never been a cytochemical assessment that has been free of problems with interpretation, although this does not imply that the investments did not pay off. Resolution of the enzymatic reaction product is a critical factor for interpretation and largely depends on the structural preservation of the tissue and well-controlled incubation and postincubation conditions using validated procedures.

III. Distribution of Enzymes

A. HYDROLASES

1. Phosphohydrolases

In 1939 Gömöri and Takamatsu independently described for the first time the visualization of alkaline phosphatase activity using the so-called metal salt technique. These investigators used calcium to trap phosphate liberated by the enzymatic reaction, a procedure resulting in the precipitation of calcium phosphate at the enzymatic site. Two years later Gömöri (1941) reported on the use of lead as a trapping agent in the localization of acid phosphatase. This lead–salt methodology described later by Gömöri (1950, 1952) has led to extensive research on the visualization of enzyme activities at both the light and electron microscopic level and on the evaluation of enzyme cytochemistry directed to the localization of molecular processes in cells.

Sheldon et al. (1955) made the first attempt to localize enzymatic activity at the ultrastructural level using lead as a trapping agent whereas Brandes et al. (1956) used the calcium salt method. Since then the original Gömöri technique was modified extensively in order to overcome problems with fixation, penetration of the components of the incubation media and composition of the incubation media. The most important modifications in revealing enzymatic activities were worked out in the late fifties and sixties (Wachstein and Meisel, 1956, 1957; Essner et al., 1958; Barrnett and Palade, 1959; Kaplan and Novikoff, 1959; Lehrer and Ornstein, 1959; Novikoff, 1959; Luft, 1961; Holt and Hicks, 1961a, b; Novikoff and Goldfisher, 1961; Barka and Anderson, 1962; Sabatini et al., 1962, 1963; Tice and Barnett, 1962; Goldfisher et al., 1964; Karnovski, 1964; Karnovski and Roots, 1964; Lewis and Shute, 1964, 1966, 1969; Goldfisher, 1965; Hugon and Borgers, 1966; M. L. Seligman et al., 1966; A. M. Seligman et al., 1966; Mayahara et al., 1967; Hugon et al., 1970; Reik et al., 1970). A large number of additional modifications of the original cytochemical techniques appeared over the years. These will be described in the sections dealing with the individual phosphohydrolases.

    a. *Acid Phosphatase.* Biochemical studies performed by de Duve and co-workers indicated that acid phosphatase (ACPase; EC 3.1.3.2) could be localized in a distinct subcellular structure (de Duve, 1969). Histochemical and particularly cytochemical work further indicated that this enzyme was predominantly associated with a membrane-bounded organelle (Daems *et al.*, 1972) which de Duve called "lysosome." ACPase is therefore considered as the marker enzyme for this organelle (Novikoff, 1976). The accuracy of the definition of ACPase as a marker enzyme for lysosomes has been questioned, since considerable ACPase activity was found localized at various extralysosomal sites in different organs. This will be discussed further on.

    As previously described, the demonstration of ACPase, first developed by Gömöri for light microscopy in 1952, was thereafter modified for electron microscopy by Holt and Hicks (1961a, b) and Barka and Anderson (1962). The most widely used substrates for this enzyme were β-glycerophosphate (Gömöri, 1952; Holt and Hicks, 1961b; Barka and Anderson, 1962), cytidine 5'-monophosphate (Novikoff, 1963) and *p*-nitrophenyl phosphate (Butterworth, 1971; Luppa *et al.*, 1972; Miyayama *et al.*, 1975; Ryder and Bowen, 1975). ACPase cytochemistry was also performed with other substrates such as uridine-5'-monophosphate (Lazarus *et al.*, 1966), α-naphthyl phosphate (Etherton and Botham, 1970), naphthol AS BI phosphoric acid (Livingston *et al.*, 1969; Katayama *et al.*, 1972), phosphorylcholine (Seligman *et al.*, 1975), inorganic trimetaphosphate (Doty *et al.*, 1977), and pyridoxal-5-phosphate (Spater *et al.*, 1978) in order to improve detection of enzyme activity or to disclose specific localization sites.

    Other changes in the incubation medium have been reported throughout the years. Barka and Anderson (1962) used a Tris-maleate buffer, Luppa *et al.*, (1972) a succinate buffer, and Weissenfels (1967) a cacodylate buffer. Acetate buffer was required for demonstration of ACPase in the granules of rabbit basophils (Komiyama and Spicer, 1974). Ericsson and Trump (1965) emphasized the importance of the buffer to substrate ratio and the purity of the substrate β-glycerophosphate for obtaining good localization with the Gömöri technique. Others modified the Barka and Anderson (1962) medium by addition of dimethylsulfoxide (Brunk and Ericsson, 1972). Poux (1970) adapted a special technique of prolonged incubation at low temperature for the enzyme localization in root meristematic cells and added lower concentrations of sucrose to the incubation medium without harmful effects.

    Recently the trapping agent was also changed. Veenhuis *et al.* (1980b) used cerium chloride to produce precipitation of cerium phosphate which, in the electron microscope, appears as very fine granular electron-dense deposits allowing a more accurate localization of the site of enzyme activity. Such fine granular deposits were also found with aluminum (nitrate) as a trapping agent (Berry *et al.*, 1982).

The preceding discussion describes the large variations in methodology used to localize ACPase. This makes it extremely difficult to compare the results from different laboratories, especially when the method is given simply as "after Gömöri (1952)" (Waters and Butcher, 1980). Moreover, with the heavy-metal ion methods an uncertainty remains about the efficiency with which the primary product is trapped so that under suboptimal conditions one can find artifactual precipitation (e.g., staining of nuclei) or no staining at all. Since variables in tissue sections such as enzymatic activity and permeability are difficult to control and the results of the reactions are difficult to quantify, artificial model systems were applied to characterize optimal incubation conditions (reviewed by De Jong, 1982).

As previously described, cytochemically detectable ACPase is predominantly localized in subcellular organelles (of animal and plant tissues) which are characterized morphologically as dense bodies, the lysosomes. It has been used to study autophagy, autolysis, and cell death; in processes which occurred naturally such as in the planarian *Polycelis tenuis* Ijima (Bowen and Ryder, 1975); pathology (Dingle and Fell, 1969; Dingle, 1973); and pharmacology and chemotherapy (Raymackers and Hugon, 1973; Borgers and De Nollin, 1975; and others).

The primary lysosomes (which are not yet fused with other subcellular organelles to form secondary lysosomes) were found to originate from the Golgi complex. This Golgi complex is the predominant extralysosomal localization site for ACPase. Based on studies of dorsal root ganglion neurons, Novikoff (1964) proposed that the Golgi-associated ACPase activity was present in a specialized region of smooth endoplasmic reticulum at the inner face of the Golgi apparatus. The acronym GERL was given to this ACPase smooth membrane system to indicate its origin from the *E*ndoplasmic *R*eticulum and its apparent function in *L*ysosome formation.

Since the work of Novikoff (1964), the study of the structural characteristics of the GERL system has led to a large number of studies in different types of cells using a combination of morphological, cytochemical, and functional criteria (reviewed by Hand, 1980). The cytochemistry included, besides ACPase, the localization of thiamine pyrophosphatase and nucleoside diphosphatase (see later). These studies have shown that acid hydrolase activity and the formation of lysosomes, considered characteristic of GERL, is not a consistent property in all cells. It appeared further that GERL and Golgi cisternae of certain cells undergo significant changes in their cytochemical and structural properties in response to specific alterations in cellular activity. ACPase is also detected in multivesicular bodies present in different types of cells (Hugon and Borgers, 1969a; Ma and Biempica, 1971; Malassiné, 1976; Serrano *et al.*, 1976; Jaeken and Thinès-

Sempoux, 1978). According to Jaeken and Thinès-Sempoux (1978), the multi-vesicular bodies may be involved in plasma membrane retrieval.

In fungi, ACPase has been localized in the vacuolar system, which may be considered therefore as the digestive site of yeast cells (Bowers and Korn, 1973; De Nollin *et al.*, 1975). Other investigators have found activity on the cell wall and plasmalemma of yeast cells (Bauer and Sigarlakie, 1973; Linnemans *et al.*, 1977; Rainina *et al.*, 1979). The discrepancy between these findings may be attributed to the different experimental methods used.

Extralysosomal localization of ACPase activities have been further described in different organs. Most of the extralysosomal activities were found with aryl substrates such as naphthol phosphate, which stains the plasmalemma and the basal infoldings of the tubular cells in the mouse kidney (Maggi *et al.*, 1966; Sasaki and Fishman, 1973); *p*-nitrophenyl phosphate, which stains the endoplasmic reticulum, the brush border, the basal infoldings, and the plasmalemma of the tubular cells in the mouse kidney (Miyayama *et al.*, 1974, 1975); and phosphorylcholine, which stains nonlysosomal organelles in the rat prostate (Seligman *et al.*, 1975; Serrano *et al.*, 1976). With β-glycerophosphate, extralysosomal ACPase activity was seen in the wall of growing coronary collateral vessels after hydrocortisone treatment and was associated with the endoplasmic reticulum of endothelial cells, modified smooth muscle cells and adventitial mesenchymal cells (Borgers *et al.*, 1973c). The nuclear envelope and differentiated endoplasmic reticulum was also stained in the notochordal cells of chick embryos (Kayahara, 1982) and spermatids of the domestic fowl (Gunawardana *et al.*, 1982). Seiden (1973), Christie and Stoward (1977) and Trout *et al.* (1979) showed activity in the sarcoplasmic reticulum of skeletal muscle tissue. Ono (1979) and Ono and Satoh (1981) found ACPase present on the lateral plasma membrane of small intestinal absorptive cells of adult and neonatal rats, respectively. Reaction product was seen in the cytosol of central cells in the submandibular gland of the cat (β-glycerophosphate and *p*-nitrophenyl phosphate as substrates) (Harrison *et al.*, 1979). These cells showed no clear signs of degeneration, unlike thymic lymphocytes containing cytosolic ACPase in the mouse thymus (Bowen and Lewis, 1980). Mitochondrial staining was reported in rabbit submandibular glands (Kyriacou and Garrett, 1980).

The occurrence of nonlysosomal staining with incubation media used to reveal ACPase activity has been extensively studied by comparing enzyme activities in rat liver and kidney after incubation in the presence of either β-glycerophosphate, *p*-nitrophenyl phosphate, or phenyl phosphate at various pHs and by using specific inhibitors (Borgers and Thonè, 1976). It was concluded that with these substrates the possible interference of specific phosphatases and of nonspecific alkaline phosphatase has to be considered in the search for extralysosomal sites of ACPase. True extralysosomal ACPase is most probably confined to the outer surface of the brush border of the intestinal cells in several invertebrates: the nematode *Ascaris suum* (Borgers *et al.*, 1970), the trematodes *Schistosoma* sp., *Haematoloechus medioplexus*, and *Fasciola hepatica* (Bogitsh and Shannon, 1971; Bogitsh *et al.*, 1968; A. Verheyen, personal observations), and the insect *Triatoma infestans* (Guitierrez and Burgos, 1978). For *Ascaris suum* and *Fasciola hepatica*, it was found that the activity could be inhibited by sodium fluoride and was not due to the interfering action of alkaline phosphatase since this enzyme was not demonstrated at alkaline pH (Borgers *et al.*, 1970; A. Verheyen, personal observations). In most of the investigated invertebrate species, ACPase was also found in subcellular structures which were morphologically defined as secretory granules. It is believed that, at least in helminths, ACPase is transported (probably together with other secretory products) in these secretory granules to the outer surface of the intestinal cells where it may serve in the extracellular digestion of nutrients (Bogitsh and Shannon, 1971; Borgers *et al.*, 1975a; A. Verheyen, personal observations).

b. *Alkaline Phosphatase.* The ultrastructural localization of alkaline phosphatase (AlPase; EC 3.1.3.1) on the microvillar surface of intestinal epithelium was first described by Brandes *et al.* (1956) using the calcium salt method of Gömöri. Clark (1961) also used the calcium–lead variant of the Gömöri method. However the conversion of calcium phosphate into lead phosphate was an important source of diffusion. Several other techniques and modifications were afterward reported. A direct lead method was described by Mölbert *et al.* (1960a,b), but the method of tissue preparation and the low pH of the incubation medium did not provide accurate localization. Better results were obtained by Reale (1962) and Chase (1963) using frozen sections. Hugon and Borgers (1966) developed a direct lead salt method at pH 9 with lead nitrate and Tris-maleate buffer. This, together with the Mayahara technique (1967), is widely used to localize AlPase.

The Mayahara technique is derived from the Tranzer medium (1965) in which lead citrate is added as capturing agent and Mg^{2+} used as an activator. The Seligman cadmium capture method (Seligman *et al.*, 1970), modified from the method of Mizutani and Barnett (1965) uses di (dicyclohexylammonium) naphthyl thiophosphate as substrate. However, the most frequently used substrates for AlPase detection were β-glycerophosphate, *p*-nitrophenyl phosphate, and, to a lesser extent also, α-naphthol phosphate. These substrates were also adopted to localize ACPase. In later studies (Vengesa and Hopfer, 1979a,b; Healy and Dinsdale, 1979), strontium chloride was added to the incubation medium according to the method of Ernst (1972b). The precipitated strontium phosphate was converted afterward to lead phosphate (with lead nitrate) for visualization in the electron microscope. Several of the reported methods have been compared (Leonard and Provenza, 1972; Doty, 1980), studies indicating that the techniques of Hugon and Borgers (1966) and Mayahara *et al.* (1967)

were most reliable in localizing AlPase. It was concluded that the Mayahara solution, as modified by Yoshiki and Kurahashi (1971), is the most stable.

In most tissues the activity of AlPase is confined to the plasma membranes of different types of cells. Enzymatic activity has been described on the external or internal side of the lipid bilayer. However, the actual permeability to lead ions of the fixed and frozen sectioned tissue is poorly understood and different fixation processes may change the position of the precipitate on the membranes. One should, therefore, be extremely cautious before asserting that the precipitate has a very definite localization on one of the membrane leaflets.

It appeared from biochemical studies that specific inhibitors exist for different organ-specific isoenzymes of AlPase (reviewed by Fishman, 1974; Van Belle, 1972, 1976). These drugs are uncompetitive inhibitors and are stereospecific. Several of these inhibitors were tried out successfully in cytochemical experiments performed on different types of tissues and cells (Hugon and Borgers, 1966; Borgers, 1973; Lin et al., 1976; Benham et al., 1977; Wilson et al., 1977; Borgers et al., 1978a; Healy and Dinsdale, 1979; Vengesa and Hopfer, 1979a, b; Sugimura and Mizutani, 1979b; Doty, 1980; and others). The most frequently used inhibitors were L-phenylalanine, L-homoarginine, and levamisole (L-tetramisole) and its analogue L-p-bromotetramisole. The first compound inhibits the intestinal-type or heat-stable placental AlPase, the latter three the liver-type enzyme, L-homoarginine being less potent and more substrate specific than levamisole and L-p-bromotetramisole. Other less specific inhibitors used in cytochemical experiments were aminophyllin, theophyllin, ethylenediaminetetraacetic acid (EDTA), L-cysteine and glycine.

Since the first attempt to localize AlPase ultrastructurally in the mouse small intestine by Brandes et al. (1956), many studies with improved localization techniques have been performed on the intestinal tissue in different stages of development. These studies demonstrated that the activity was present on the brush border, on the Golgi apparatus, on dense bodies, on smooth membrane profiles, and also in the lateral plasma membranes (Hugon and Borgers, 1966, 1967, 1968a,b, 1969a; Brown and Millington, 1968; Leonard and Provenza, 1972; Borgers, 1973; Van Dongen et al., 1977; Healy and Dinsdale, 1979; Vengesa and Hopfer, 1979a, b; Houdry and Hugon, 1979; Daufa et al., 1980). All these reactive sites could be inhibited by L-phenylalanine, including the activity in the dense bodies which were also reactive to ACPase. The enzyme activity present on the microvilli most likely occurs via the cascade of events which include synthesis in the rough endoplasmic reticulum, packaging and transformation in the Golgi fields, and transportation to the apical plasma membrane (Hugon and Borgers, 1968a; Houdry and Hugon, 1979). It is thought that the activity in smooth membranous profiles, particularly present at the apical side of the absorptive cells, could be engulfed during a pinocytic process. These reactive vesicular profiles may then enter a catabolic pathway whereby the enzyme is finally degraded, thus localizing activity in the dense bodies which likely represent lysosomes (Hugon and Borgers, 1968b, 1969a; Healy and Dinsdale, 1979).

In fetal mouse, AlPase in the reactive structures appeared to increase rapidly with the differentiation of the duodenal cells (Hugon and Borgers, 1969b). In the adult stage AlPase is not present in crypt cells but becomes apparent after the cells have migrated onto the villus (Van Dongen et al., 1977). These authors have suggested, based on recovery experiments after irradiation, that during cell maturation normal values for AlPase activity are only attained after a 10 to 12-hour period of maturation in a nonproliferative state and only after the cells have migrated onto the functional villus compartment. The cells situated near the tip of the villus, in the process of being extruded, show a tremendous decrease of enzymatic activity, a finding which suggests that the enzymatic synthesis stopped before the desquamation of the cells (Hugon and Borgers, 1968a).

L-Phenylalanine-sensitive AlPase was also found on the plasma membrane, in the Golgi fields, and in some granules of HeLa cells (Hugon et al., 1967; Lin et al., 1976; Vorbrodt and Borun, 1979). It seemed, however, that the sensitivity of the HeLa cell AlPase activity was not limited to L-phenylalanine alone because the cells used by Vorbrodt and Borun (1979) were influenced by both L-phenylalanine and levamisole. It therefore appeared that the AlPase content depended on the cell line of the examined HeLa cells. Due to the sensitivity to both inhibitors, Vorbrodt and Borun claimed that at least two isoenzymes existed in their HeLa cell line. They also recognized a difference in intensity of the AlPase activity according to the cell-cycle phase of the cells. AlPase has been localized on the syncytiotrophoblasts of the human (Hulstaert et al., 1973; Martin et al., 1974) and feline (Malassiné, 1980) placenta. The enzyme was sensitive to L-phenylalanine as well as to levamisole (Malassiné, 1980).

Alterations in surface enzymes and other structural components have been shown to occur during tumor induction (Emmelot, 1973). Focal loss of AlPase has been shown to occur in chemically induced bladder hyperplasia in rats (Kunze and Schauer, 1971; Stiller and Rauscher, 1971; Kunze et al., 1975) and mice (Highman et al., 1975) and has been proposed as a marker of preneoplastic change. Therefore, several cytochemical studies were performed to investigate this phenomenon further (Wilson et al., 1977; Benham et al., 1977; Wilson and Hodges, 1979; Kumagae et al., 1981; Harrison and Auger, 1982). These studies showed that abnormal enzymatic differentiation can occur according to the type of investigated neoplastic tissue and that the response to selective inhibitors (particularly L-phenylalanine, levamisole, and L-p-bromotetramisole) may vary in relation to the site of reaction product and the cell type, but these differences could not be related to the neoplastically transformed state.

Biochemical and cytochemical studies on the distribution of nonspecific AlPase in human polymorphonuclear leukocytes (PMN) are conflicting. Bainton et *al.* (1971) claimed that in bone marrow cells AlPase is confined to the specific granules. In contrast, West *et al.* (1974), Bretz and Baggiolini (1974), and Spitznagel *et al.* (1974) found AlPase to be concentrated in a subcellular fraction that was clearly distinct from that containing specific granules. Bretz and Baggiolini (1974) suggested that the AlPase-rich fraction probably consisted largely of plasmalemma fragments. This was confirmed in cytochemical experiments by Borgers *et al.* (1978a). They found staining of the plasma membrane, of the membrane of endocytic vacuoles, and of some vesicular structures of the PMN. It was further found that the demonstration of the activity depended on the preparatory procedure employed for PMN isolation. A strongly increased activity was observed in PMN from cancer patients, and additional staining was seen in atypical vesicles and sometimes in the Golgi apparatus. Using the Mayahara technique, Rustin *et al.* (1979) and Wilson *et al.* (1981a) detected also a strong activity in irregular-shaped, often tubular structures (Fig. 2). The activity in this unique cytoplasmic vesicle population termed "phosphasomes" and on the plasma membrane was found to change during pregnancy and in patients with chronic granulocytic leukemia (Wilson *et al.*, 1981a).

AlPase phosphatase activity has also been localized on the plasma membrane and in some intracellular structures of rat neutrophilic and eosinophilic leukocytes (Williams *et al.*, 1978, 1979), on the plasma membrane and in the specific granules of guinea pig neutrophils (Borgers *et al.*, 1978a), and in vacuolated neutrophils of the catfish (Garavini *et al.*, 1981), but not in mature chicken granular leukocytes (Daimon and Caxton-Martins, 1977). The PMN AlPase activity was completely inhibited by levamisole or its analogue, a finding indicating its liver-type origin. Apart from the previously described cellular sites, levamisole and L-*p*-bromotetramisole-sensitive AlPase activity has also been confined to the bile canaliculi of the liver, the brush border, apical vacuoles, and Golgi apparatus of the cells of the proximal convoluted tubules of the kidney, the apical plasma membranes, cytoplasmic granules, and Golgi apparatus of bronchiolar Clara cells and of type II alveolar pneumocytes, the capillary endothelium in several tissues, and some other sites (see Borgers, 1973; Borgers and Thonè, 1976).

The localization of AlPase activity is also described in several other tissues and cells including yeast cells (De Nollin *et al.*, 1975; Quiviger *et al.*, 1978), Anthazoa (Tiffon and Hugon, 1977), heart tissue (Müller *et al.*, 1971), skeletal muscle (Borgers *et al.*, 1975b), lymph nodes (Masubuchi, 1972), salivary glands (Garrett and Harrison, 1970), brain tissue (Ovtscharoff, 1973; Sugimura and Mizutani, 1979a,b), and bone tissue (Göthlin and Ericsson, 1973; Salomon, 1974).

The wide distribution of AlPase throughout the tissues of particularly vertebrate species, the marked variations of its activity in blood and tissues in disease states, and the ease with which its activity can be detected and measured, have

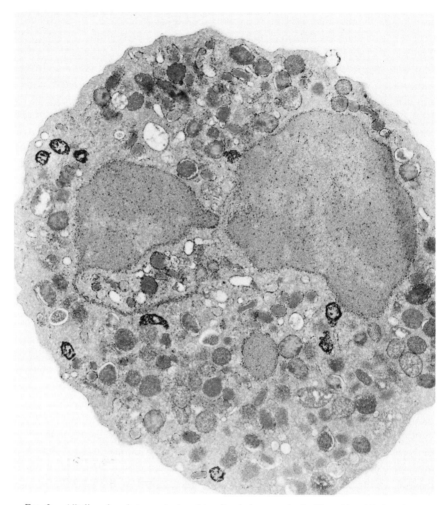

FIG. 2. Alkaline phosphatase cytochemistry. Lead citrate method with pyridoxal 5-phosphate on substrates. Polymorphonuclear leukocyte incubated for 40 minutes at 37°C for alkaline phosphatase activity. Heavy deposits of reaction product can be seen in some granules (phosphasomes). No reaction can be seen at the plasma membrane, in the endoplasmic reticulum, or in specific or azurophil granules. ×20,250. (Courtesy of Dr. P. D. Wilson, Dept. of Medicine, University of Colorado Health Service Center, Denver, CO.)

made this enzyme a favorite object of study for biochemists, chemical pa-thologists, and histo- and cytochemists (Moss, 1974). In spite of the efforts of many scientists over a space of more than 50 years and the great accumulation of knowledge that has resulted, the role of AlPase in physiological processes still remains to be elucidated. The membrane localization and association of this enzyme strongly suggests its involvement in membrane function. It is, however, not known how. This is best expressed by Fishman (1974) in his review on the perspectives on AlPase isoenzymes: "Is the enzyme a structural component of specialized membrane systems? Is it functional in membrane sites? Does specific inhibition of membrane AlPase have consequences for transport of ions or phosphate or metabolism of fat? Does hormonal enhancement of activity reflect the physical state of the microvilli of absorbing cells and does it modify physiologic transport? What in cancer? Since these questions are put on paper no real progress has been made in disclosing its physiologic role."

c. *Nucleoside Phosphatases.* A striking observation which emerged from a study performed on a large number of cell types, mostly by light microscopy, was the marked difference in substrate specificities among the nucleoside phosphatases in plasma membranes (Novikoff *et al.*, 1962; reviewed by Goldfisher *et al.*, 1964). The enzymes which were localized in the bile canaliculi or in the endothelium of most capillaries were able to hydrolyze all nucleoside phosphates whereas those at the base of renal tubule cells were specific for triphosphates. These results were later confirmed in a large number of cytochemical studies using different cytochemical techniques.

Many of these studies were performed with the incubation medium of Wachstein and Meisel (1957). The usefulness of this medium in the localization of membrane phosphatases was debated in the late sixties by a number of investigators (Moses *et al.*, 1966; Moses and Rosenthal, 1968; Rosenthal *et al.*, 1966; Ganote *et al.*, 1969; Tice, 1969). They claimed that the membrane staining after the Wachstein and Meisel procedure was better explained by lead-catalyzed hydrolysis of adenosine triphosphates and other nucleoside phosphates than by enzymatic activity. Novikoff (1967) argued with them and mentioned a number of facts supporting the thesis that the Wachstein and Meisel technique does not lead to artifacts.

Other authors have also revised the technique for nucleoside phosphatases and have gathered data in support of a reliable visualization of true enzymatic activity with this method. The pros and cons were compiled by Hugon (1973) in a review concerning the lead salt methods. From this debate data related to the incubation medium have emerged which modify the original Wachstein and Meisel technique (Otero-Vilardebó *et al.*, 1963; Farquhar and Palade, 1966; Marchesi and Palade, 1967; Campbell, 1968; Hündgen, 1968; Morita *et al.*, 1969; Guth and Samaha, 1970; Csuka and Sugar, 1971; Borgers *et al.*, 1971a; Koenig and Vial, 1973; Mahrle and Orfanos, 1975b; Russo and Wells, 1977; Cutler *et al.*, 1978; Mayahara *et al.*, 1980; Cushieri *et al.*, 1982; and others). Ernst (1972a,b) prepared a new incubation medium to localize the ouabain-sensitive transport adenosine triphosphatase (ATPase) using strontium chloride as a capturing agent. Veenhuis *et al.* (1980b) performed cytochemical studies with cerium chloride as a metal salt. More recently autoradiograph and immunocytochemical methods were applied (see following).

i. Adenosine triphosphatases. Since the various cytochemical approaches to the localization of the different adenosine triphosphatases (ATPases; EC 3.6.1.3) have been excellently reviewed by Firth (1978, 1980) and by Ernst and Hootman (1981), we shall refer to these reviews for a more detailed description on the relevance of the published cytochemical methods.

As indicated by Firth (1980), ATPases are a collection of different families of enzymes, these families being linked only by the fact that they metabolize the same substrate. However, not all ATP-hydrolyzing enzymes are regarded as ATPases. There is a large group of nonspecific phosphatases for which ATP is only one of a wide range of possible substrates, the most important being, from the cytochemist's point of view, AlPase. It is therefore important to include inhibitors of nonspecific phosphatases when attempts are made to demonstrate specific phosphatases such as ATPase, especially in tissues or organs that are rich in nonspecific phosphatases (Borgers and Thoné, 1976). Firth (1978) classified the specific ATPases in three broad groups: proton-translocating ATPases, other ion-transporting ATPases, and cytoplasmic ATPases, the latter associated with contractile systems.

Proton-Translocating ATPase. Enzymes of this class are present on the inner mitochondrial membrane of eukaryotic cells, the grana membranes of chloroplasts, and the plasma membranes of bacteria. These enzymes are concerned with the synthesis of ATP and therefore run in reverse. The establishment of a proton gradient across the different membrane compartments plays a decisive role in the phosphorylation process (coupling of respiration and phosphorylation). Any rupture or leakiness short-circuits the proton gradient and drives the enzyme reaction in the direction of ATP breakdown. This is important for the cytochemists since leakage and uncoupling is necessary for sustained enzyme activity.

Mitochondrial ATPase has been described in a large number of studies using the media of Padykula and Herman (1955) and Wachstein and Meisel (1957) (Wachstein *et al.*, 1962; Lazarus and Barden, 1962; Otero-Vilardebó *et al.*, 1963; Essner *et al.*, 1965; Rechard and Kokko, 1967; Grossman and Heitkamp, 1968; Ogawa and Mayahara, 1969; Abel, 1969; Ahrens and Weissenfels, 1969; Borgers *et al.*, 1971a; Felix and Remien, 1971; Legrand, 1973; Hájos *et al.*, 1974; Watanabe *et al.*, 1978; Verheyen *et al.*, 1979; Cronshaw, 1980). Except for some studies describing mitochondrial ATPase in the intracristal spaces, most authors localized the enzyme activity in the mitochondrial matrix. The enzyme activity could be inhibited by adding *p*-chloromercuribenzoate and more specifically by adding oligomycin to the incubation media. A stimulation was found after incubating the tissues in the presence of the uncoupler 2,4-dinitrophenol. Verheyen *et al.* (1979) also reported an increase in mitochondrial ATPase activity in some tissues of the liver fluke *Fasciola hepatica* after *in vivo* treatment of the host with the antihelminthic closantel, a compound which is reported to disturb the mitochondrial phosphorylation in this worm species (Van den Bossche *et al.*, 1979).

Recently a plasma membrane proton-translocating ATPase has been described in the gastric mucosa (Sachs *et al.*, 1977). It is not yet apparent whether this can be localized by modification of existing methods.

Other Ion-Transporting ATPases. The enzymes which belong to this class of ATPases and which are investigated by cytochemical means are Na^+,K^+-ATPase, Ca^{2+}-ATPase, and carbonate-ATPase. Unlike proton-translocating ATPase, these enzymes normally run in the direction of ATP hydrolysis using the derived energy for active ion transport. These enzymes appear to be dependent on sulfhydryl groups for continued activity and are therefore inhibited by *p*-chloromercuribenzoate, which destroys the sulfhydryl groups. Mg^{2+} seems to be required for activity by all members of this group. For Na^+,K^+-ATPase (extensively reviewed by Ernst and Hootman, 1981) it is well established that this enzyme provides the catalytic machinery for coupling the energy released by ATP hydrolysis to the exchange of Na^+ and K^+ across plasmalemmal surfaces against their respective concentration gradients and thus plays a key role in the maintenance and regulation of the internal milieu of eukaryotic cells. In order to localize Na^+,K^+-ATPase, many modifications of the original Wachstein and Meisel technique have been utilized (Abel, 1969; Forbes and Sperelakis, 1972; Russo and Wells, 1977; Nakagaki *et al.*, 1978; Threadgold and Brennan, 1978). However, because of this enzyme's extreme sensitivity to lead and the absence of specific inhibitors of Mg^{2+}-ATPase activity (see later), such approaches have little value. Therefore, results obtained by this technique, even when carefully performed as in the studies of Tervo *et al.* (1977) and Palva *et al.* (1978), must be interpreted with caution.

The search for more appropriate methods for localizing Na^+, K^+-ATPase has led to the development of a new methodological approach which has been most successful and widely accepted (Ernst, 1972a, b). The principle of the strontium capture method is to use the second (phosphorylation) step of the Na^+,K^+-ATPase system, thus avoiding overlap with mitochondrial and cytoplasmic contractile ATPase, which have different reaction mechanisms. The investigators adapted *p*-nitrophenyl phosphate as substrate, hence the enzyme is also called K^+-nitrophenylphosphatase. The strontium as capturing ion in the incubation medium should result in significantly less enzyme inhibition in comparison with lead. The contrast of the reaction product can subsequently be enhanced by conversion into a lead salt. It is important that the reaction product is found on the cytoplasmic surface of the plasma membrane. This finding seems biochemically appropriate and is the reverse of the normal findings with Wachstein-Meisel methods.

Further criteria for valid action of the Na^+,K^+-ATPase method are given by Ernst and Hootman (1981). Since the description of the technique by Ernst, it has been used in a number of studies searching for the localization of the transport enzyme in the avian salt gland, the rat cornea, the rat and human gastric mucosa, the ferret, guinea pig, and cat placenta, the mammary tissue of cow, sheep, and guinea pig, the rat liver, the rat cerebral cortex, the rat colon, the guinea pig myocardium, and the fish electric organ (Leuenberger and Novikoff, 1974; Ernst, 1975; Rubin and Aliasgharpour, 1976; Wakely, 1976; Johnson and Wooding, 1978; Blitzer and Boyer, 1978; Broderson et al., 1978; Vengesa and Hopfer, 1979b; Firth et al., 1979; Malassiné, 1980; Asano et al., 1980; Denizot, 1982a).

A new one-step method introduced by Mayahara et al. (1980) also used p-nitrophenyl phosphate as substrate, but it used lead citrate as the capturing agent and dimethylsulfoxide as activator. With this method, ouabain-sensitive K^+-nitrophenylphosphatase could be reliably localized in the adult and developing rat kidney (Mayahara et al., 1980, 1982). This variation seems to provide a valid alternative technique for the localization of Na^+,K^+-ATPase, its advantage being one of slightly greater methodological simplicity.

Mazurkiewicz et al. (1978) reported an alternate method by exploiting the pharmacological specificity of ouabain for Na^+, K^+-ATPase. They employed a heme peptide derivation of ouabain in which the peroxidatic activity could be exploited to localize binding sites of the altered glycoside to avian tissue slices at the electron microscopic level.

Another inhibitor method applied to localize this transport enzyme is the labeled inhibitor method using tritiated ouabain. The technique was introduced and developed by Stirling (1972, 1976) and has been performed on a wide variety of epithelial tissues (see Ernst and Mills, 1980; Ernst and Hootman, 1981). It was concluded that the demonstration of Na^+,K^+-ATPase by this technique indicates that sodium pumps are distributed uniformly along plasmalemmal surfaces and are restricted to the basolateral interface of reabsorption and secretory epithelia despite the opposing polarity of net transepithelial electrolyte transport. The main disadvantage of the latter method is that the resolution of the method effectively limits its use to the light microscopic level.

Kyte (1974, 1976a,b) introduced a technique using ferritin-labeled antibodies; Wood et al. (1977) substituted ferritin for horseradish peroxidase; and Schwartz et al. (1980, 1981) employed the peroxidase–antiperoxidase method. These immunocytochemical techniques for localizing Na^+,K^+-ATPase are characterized by excellent resolution and high sensitivity, but the main problems appear to be the technical complexity of the methods and the fact that the demonstration of immunological activity does not necessarily mean that catalytic activity exists at the same site.

Anion-transporting ATPases are poorly understood elements in the membrane transport complex. ATPase stimulated by HCO_3^- have been described biochemically in microsome preparations from gastric mucosa, proximal tubules, salivary gland, and pancreas; on the outer mitochondrial membrane; and in the erythrocyte membrane (see Firth, 1978). The enzyme is dependent on Mg^{2+}, Na^+, and K^+ as well as HCO_3^-. It differs from Na^+,K^+-ATPase in that it is not inhibited by either Ca^{2+} or ouabain. This enzyme has been cytochemically localized at the apical border of the cells lining the intralobular ducts and of the centroacinar cells in dog pancreas tissue (Koenig et al., 1976). The enzyme activity was increased with HCO_3^-, depressed by SCN^- and OCN^- and completely abolished by CN^-.

In normal physiological situations, divalent cation-transporting ATPases are concerned with the transport of Ca^{2+} and Mg^{2+}. Sarcoplasmic reticular Ca^{2+}-transporting ATPase should function in Ca^{2+} reuptake into the lumen of the sarcoplasmic reticulum following fiber contraction. Cytochemical studies of this enzyme have largely used variants of the Wachstein-Meisel technique. Localization of the enzyme was readily achieved but demonstration of specificity was less convincing (Firth, 1978).

Very recently Jorgensen et al. (1982a,b) demonstrated the presence of Ca^{2+}, Mg^{2+}-ATPase in the sarcoplasmic reticulum of the adult rat papillary and skeletal muscle by an immunoferritin-labeling technique. They found that the enzyme was antigenically unrelated to the Ca^{2+},Mg^{2+}-ATPase of the sarcolemma.

Membrane ATPases dependent on divalent ions have been described in plasma membrane locations using modifications of the Wachstein-Meisel medium (North, 1966; Campbell, 1968; Hoff, 1969; Ferrans et al., 1969; Backwinkel et al., 1971, 1973; Toth et al., 1972; Gerzeli and Cucchi, 1975; Mahrle and Orfanos, 1975a; Koenig et al., 1976; Firth and Bock, 1976; Sosa et al., 1978; Cutler et al., 1978; Seibel et al., 1979; Vorbrodt and Borun, 1979; Idé and Saito, 1980; Ando et al., 1981; Spater et al., 1981; Fox and Studzinski, 1982; Hall et al., 1982; Denizot, 1982b; Cushieri et al., 1982; Kobayashi et al., 1982). In these studies, enzyme activity was attributed either to Mg^{2+}- or Mg^{2+},Ca^{2+}-ATPase activity. It appeared difficult to give clear criteria for cytochemical identification of these enzymes because of the lack of inhibitors of high specificity. It also appeared that the ion dependence of these enzymes is a criterion which needs to be used cautiously (Firth, 1978). The specific localization of divalent ion-dependent ATPases of the plasma membrane seems to be the area most in need of development. The value of the traditional Wachstein-Meisel methods appears in this context to be very limited, and progress will depend on the introduction of more specific techniques (Firth, 1980).

Cytoplasmic ATPases. These enzymes presumably represent a very heterogeneous group associated with filamentous and other nonmembranous structures in the cytoplasmic matrix. Ultrastructurally, the most satisfactory technique for myosin-ATPase employs lead citrate, cysteine and Ca^{2+} at pH 5. Under these conditions, myofibrillar reaction with appropriate ion dependence and inhibitor responses can be obtained (Somogyi and Sotonyi, 1969). The enzyme is stimulated by Ca^{2+} but inhibited by Mg^{2+} and is partially sensitive to sulfhydryl reagents but not to ouabain or oligomycin (Firth, 1978).

Wachstein-Meisel procedures often give reactions at microtubules and related structures, reactions which can be ascribed to ATPase as has been assayed biochemically for the microtubule-associated proteins. The demonstration of this enzyme cytochemically, at least with the limits of sensitivity and resolution imposed by the cytochemical methods currently available (Firth, 1978), may be of little value.

ii. Nucleoside diphosphatase. Nucleoside diphosphatase (NDPase; EC 3.6.1.6) is a membrane-bound enzyme that is thought to exhibit substrate specificity for inosine diphosphate, uridine diphosphate, and guanine diphosphate. Adenosine diphosphatase (ADPase) has also been associated with nonnucleoside diphosphatase enzymes (Goff, 1980). Cytochemical localization of activity sites are frequently revealed by modifications of the Wachstein-Meisel technique (1957), particularly that of Novikoff and Goldfischer (1961). Other slight modifications of the Wachstein-Meisel medium are described by Borgers *et al.* (1971a) and Smith and Peters (1980). Recently, the cerium method of Veenhuis *et al.* (1980a,b) has been used as an ultrastructural cytochemical probe for NDPase (Robinson and Karnovsky, 1982). In all the studies, Mg^{2+} (or sometimes Mn^{2+}) was added to the incubation medium as activator.

Enzyme activity has consistently been localized in the Golgi cisternae of a wide variety of tissue cells (reviewed by Goldfischer *et al.*, 1964; Ferrans *et al.*, 1969; Borgers *et al.*, 1971b; Hündgen, 1972; Yokoyama, 1974; Hand and Oliver, 1977; Hirsimäki and Reunanen, 1980; Bogitsh, 1982; Vorbrodt and Wisniewsky, 1982). Its activity was found particularly in the trans aspect of the Golgi stacks. Available biochemical evidence, limited to subfractions of hepatocyte Golgi fields, confirms the existence of chemical and enzymatic heterogeneity between the various Golgi elements (Bergeron *et al.*, 1973). NDPase has further been considered as a marker enzyme for the endoplasmic reticulum in several cell types (Novikoff, 1976). The distribution in the endoplasmic reticulum of different cell types has been reviewed by Goldfischer *et al.* (1964) and has in addition been described by Ferrans *et al.* (1969), Borgers *et al.* (1971a), Hündgen (1972), Hirsimäki and Reunanen (1980), and Vorbrodt and Wisniewski (1982). NDPase has also been confined to the outer surface of the cell membrane of intimal, medial, and adventitial cells of canine coronary blood vessels (Borgers *et al.*, 1971a), of microglial cells, endothelial cells of microvessels, pericytes and smooth muscle cells of arterioles in the central nervous system (Vorbrodt and Wisniewski, 1982), and human neutrophils (Wilson *et al.*, 1981b). In the latter cells, it was additionally localized in some specific granules.

Experiments on onion root tips demonstrated reaction product in Golgi cisternae and associated vesicles, the rough endoplasmic reticulum, the outer surface of the cell membrane, the intact contents of secreted cell wall material, and vacuoles (Goff, 1973). Enzyme activity is described in the cytoplasmic vacuoles of *Candida albicans* (De Nollin *et al.*, 1975) and *Entamoeba histolytica* (Kobayashi *et al.*, 1982).

The function of NDPase has been correlated with conjugation reactions such as those involved in polysaccharide synthesis and secretion (Novikoff *et al.*, 1962; Dauwalder *et al.*, 1969; Kessel *et al.*, 1969; Goff, 1973). It could play an important role in inhibiting platelet aggregation in neutrophils (Smith and Peters, 1980). The true metabolic function of the enzyme remains, however, a matter of controversy.

iii. Nucleoside monophosphatase (5'-nucleotidase). 5'-Nucleotidase (EC 3.1.3.5) is reported to be a reliable marker enzyme of cell surface membranes (Emmelot *et al.*, 1964; Reid, 1967; Bodansky and Schwartz, 1968; Song *et al.*, 1969; Song and Ray, 1970; Bosmann and Pike, 1971; De Vries, 1976). Since the enzyme is localized on the extracellular side of the plasma membrane, it has been defined as an "ectoenzyme" (De Pierre and Karnovsky, 1973, 1974a,b; Trams and Lauter, 1974). The enzyme has, however, also been associated with the membranes of the endoplasmic reticulum (Widnell and Unkeless, 1968; Widnell, 1972; Magnusson *et al.*, 1974), the nuclear fraction (Israel and Franchon-Mastour, 1970; Zentgraff *et al.*, 1971), and the Golgi complex (Farquhar *et al.*, 1974).

Ultrastructurally, the enzyme has been localized using modifications of the Wachstein-Meisel technique (Borgers *et al.*, 1971a; Widnell, 1972; Uusitalo and Karnovsky, 1977a,b). Uusitalo and Karnovsky (1977a,b) suggested fixation at low pH to prevent inactivation of enzyme activity in lymphocytes. The optimal conditions for the cytochemical localization of 5'-nucleotidase in these cells has recently been reviewed (Uusitalo, 1981). Activators used were Mg^{2+} and Mn^{2+}; inhibition experiments were performed by adding Ca^{2+} to the incubation medium (Borgers *et al.*, 1971a) or by replacing the substrate 5'-adenosine monophosphate by the competitive inhibitors 2'-adenosine monophosphate (Farquhar *et al.*, 1974) or adenosine-5'-*O*-thiomonophosphate (Blok *et al.*, 1982). Since 5'-adenosine monophosphate is a very good substrate for nonspecific AlPase at neutral pH, it is recommended that control incubations be performed including specific AlPase inhibitors.

Since the first localization of 5'-nucleotidase at the electron microscopic level by Essner *et al.* (1958), the enzyme activity has been demonstrated on the surface membranes of rat liver cells (Farquhar *et al.*, 1974), human prostate (Mao *et al.*, 1966), adventitial and perivascular mesenchymal cells of canine coronary vessels (Borgers *et al.*, 1971a,b), liver cells in culture (Charbonne *et al.*, 1974), rat kidney proximal tubules (Leung and Babai, 1974), developing murine esophagus (Klaushofer *et al.*, 1974), the central vacuole of *Candida albicans* (De Nollin *et al.*, 1975); in the stratum intermedium and ameloblasts of murine dental tissue (Gartner *et al.*, 1978), acinar cells of rat salivary glands, (Yamashina and Kawai, 1979) brain tissue (Suran, 1974; Bernstein *et al.*, 1978; Kreutzberg *et al.*, 1978; Marani, 1982), and lymphocytes (Monneron, 1974; Misra *et al.*, 1974, 1975; Uusitalo and Karnovsky, 1977a, b; Dornand *et al.*, 1978; Uusitalo, 1981). Blok *et al.* (1982) localized 5'-nucleotidase in mouse peritoneal macrophages with cerium chloride as trapping agent. Enzyme histochemical tests on the activity of 5'-nucleotidase have been utilized in the diagnosis of malignant lesions. This has been confirmed ultrastructurally in chemically induced squamous cell carcinomas (Magnusson *et al.*, 1974) and bladder tumors (Wilson and Hodges, 1979) in the rat, a finding indicating that it may be a more suitable marker for transformation than AlPase. However, no difference in enzyme activity was found between adenomatous goiter and normal thyroid in man (Mizukami *et al.*, 1982).

Functionally, 5'-nucleotidase has been involved in transport processes (Klaushofer and Pavelka, 1974; Gartner *et al.*, 1978), in cellular growth rates (Hardonk and Koudstaal, 1968a,b), and in the synthesis of fibrous proteins and calcification (Gibson and Fullmer, 1967). It has also been proposed to be a key enzyme in the metabolic regulation of coronary blood flow by generating adenosine, a potential vasodilator (Berne, 1963; Katory and Berne, 1966; Rubio and Berne, 1969; Borgers *et al.*, 1971b). The presence of the enzyme on the plasma membrane of some populations of lymphocytes might be implicated with the production of adenosine to help in the migration of the cells (Uusitalo and Karnovsky, 1977a). It has been proposed that the enzyme plays a role in intercellular regulatory mechanisms, possibly by generating nucleosides which may in turn affect cyclic nucleotide levels (Uusitalo, 1981). In brain tissue it may be connected with certain membrane transport processes (Israel and Franchon-Mastour, 1970), catabolism of nucleic acids and/or NADP (Hardonk, 1968; Hardonk and Koudstaal, 1968a; Galabov *et al.*, 1969), and it may participate in the process of neurotransmission (Burnstock *et al.*, 1970; Ozeki and Sato, 1970; Kluge *et al.*, 1975; Phillis and Kostopoulos, 1975; Hedqvist and Fredholm, 1976; Bernstein *et al.*, 1978; Kreutzberg *et al.*, 1978; Schubert *et al.*, 1979).

d. *Glucose-6-Phosphatase.*   Glucose-6-phosphatase (G-6-Pase; EC 3.1.3.9) has been described as a multifunctional enzyme (Cohn *et al.*, 1969; Nordlie, 1974) which is present in all mammalian organs capable of releasing glucose in the bloodstream, except in cases of glycogen storage disease (Pearse, 1972). The enzyme is a characteristic constituent of the endoplasmic reticulum (de Duve *et al.*, 1949; Hers *et al.*, 1951), where it releases its product on the internal side of the membranes. It is uncertain whether G-6-Pase is a transmembrane protein that binds glucose 6-phosphate (G-6-P) on the cytoplasmic side and releases glucose and phosphate on the cisternal side (Stetten and Burnett, 1967; Goldsmith and

Stetten, 1979) or faces the external side exclusively and is aided by a specific G-6-Pase transporter (Arion et al., 1975; Ballas and Arion, 1977).

Tice and Barnett (1962) first applied the medium of Wachstein and Meisel (1957) to localize the enzyme ultrastructurally. From the modifications of the original Wachstein and Meisel technique described later on, the modifications of Hugon et al. (1970) and Leskes et al. (1971) have often been used. More recently Veenhuis et al. (1980b) and Robinson and Karnovsky (1982) also localized G-6-Pase with a cerium-based method. The enzyme has been reported to be very sensitive to aldehyde fixation (Allen 1961; Tice and Barnett, 1962; Sabatini et al., 1963), therefore Benner et al. (1979) used native cryostat sections fixed with glutaraldehyde through semipermeable membranes to retain increased enzyme activity. Goldfischer et al. (1964), however, found that some of the enzyme activity survives a 2-hour fixation in 5% glutaraldehyde. Most studies have used G-6-P as substrate, but it appears that p-nitrophenyl phosphate and phenyl phosphate, unlike β-glycerophosphate, can also be hydrolyzed by G-6-Pase (Borgers and Thoné, 1976). These conclusions were derived from experiments on tissues preincubated in sodium acetate buffer at pH 5 preceding the incubation in the appropriate standard medium. These conditions are deleterious for G-6-Pase only (Hugon et al., 1970). Cytochemically, G-6-Pase activity has been confined to the endoplasmic reticulum and the nuclear envelope in a number of tissues and cells. The reaction product after incubation with G-6-Pase at neutral pH present on the brush border membranes of the proximal tubule cells of the rat kidney and of murine intestinal cells was attributed to nonspecific AlPase (Borgers, 1973; Hugon et al., 1973).

The large majority of G-6-Pase cytochemical studies have been performed on liver cells (Tice and Barnett, 1962; Goldfischer et al., 1964; Ericsson, 1966; Leskes et al., 1971; Farquhar et al., 1974; Hand and Hassell, 1976; Benner et al., 1979; Shio and Lazarow, 1981) and small intestinal cells, the latter in different developmental stages and under different experimental conditions (Hugon et al., 1971, 1973; Ménard et al., 1974; Chabot et al., 1978; Calvert et al., 1979; Ménard, 1980). In one of these studies, Hugon et al. (1973) indicated that stimulation of G-6-Pase activity, obtained after fructose feeding, was accompanied by proliferation of endoplasmic reticulum and that the increase in enzymatic activity preceded this proliferation. The enzyme also has been demonstrated in the different cells constituting the coronary blood vessels (Borgers et al., 1971a), in the cells of the rat adrenal cortex (Penasse and Frühling, 1973), in rat choroid plexus epithelial cells (Masuzawa et al., 1981), and in astrocytes of the rat cerebral cortex (Al-Ali and Robinson, 1982). Daimon and Gotoh (1982) localized G-6-Pase activity in the dense tubular system of murine platelets, thereby providing new cytochemical evidence to support the hypothesis that the dense tubular system of the platelets originates from the endoplasmic reticulum of the megakaryocyte.

e. *Thiamine Pyrophosphatase.* Thiamine pyrophosphatase (TPPase; EC 3.6.1.1) is the most widely used cytochemical marker enzyme for the Golgi apparatus (Novikoff, 1976; Hand, 1980), where it is believed to be involved in secretory and metabolic activities of carbohydrates (Tohyama *et al.,* 1972; Kim *et al.,* 1976). The original method of Novikoff and Goldfischer (1961) or slight modifications were used almost exclusively to localize activity of this particular enzyme. The group of Ogawa described tissue incubations with the lead citrate method (Ogawa *et al.,* 1967).

Most studies which aimed at demonstrating TPPase were performed in conjunction with ACPase assessments (see earlier) in order to investigate the functional differentiation between the Golgi apparatus itself and the GERL system (see reviews by Novikoff, 1976; Novikoff and Novikoff, 1977; and Hand, 1980). TPPase activity was usually found in one to three saccules at the trans side of the Golgi fields in endocrine cells (insulinoma, β cells of the pancreas, thyroid epithelial cells, luteal cells, cells of adrenal medulla and cortex, hypothalamic neurosecretory cells, pituitary gland cells), exocrine cells (acinar cells of the pancreas, lacrimal gland cells, salivary gland cells, choroid plexus epithelial cells, gastric chief and parietal cells), liver and kidney cells, different cells of canine coronary blood vessels, cardiac myocytes, astrocytes, neurons, small intestinal epithelial cells, lymphocytes, cells of the germinal epithelium of the testis, vas deferens cells, gastrodermal cells of *Schistosoma mansoni,* and so on (see references in reviews of Novikoff, 1976; Novikoff and Novikoff, 1977; Hand, 1980; Goldfischer *et al.,* 1964; Friend and Farquhar, 1967; Ferrans *et al.,* 1969; Borgers *et al.,* 1971a; Ma and Biempica, 1971; Hündgen, 1972; Raymackers and Hugon, 1973; Griffith and Bondareff, 1973; Farquhar *et al.,* 1974; Yokoyama, 1974; Malassiné, 1976; Borgers and Thoné, 1976; Kim *et al.,* 1976; Novikoff *et al.,* 1978; Dabholkar and Ogawa, 1976, 1978; Harrison *et al.,* 1979; Fujita and Okamoto, 1979; Sawano and Fujita, 1981; Masuzawa *et al.,* 1981; Pino *et al.,* 1981; Grossi *et al.,* 1982; Bogitsh, 1982; Al-Ali and Robinson, 1982; Gunawardana *et al.,* 1982). In acinar cells of stimulated sublingual glands of the rat, TPPase could also be demonstrated at the cis side of the Golgi complex, a finding indicating that the detectability of this enzyme activity (and also of other enzymes) may be related to cellular secretory activity (Kim *et al.,* 1976). A decrease in enzyme activity was seen in nerve cells of thiamine- and vitamin E-deficient rats (Dabholkar and Ogawa, 1976, 1978), a finding which may indicate a decreased rate of carbohydrate metabolism.

Pino *et al.* (1981) reported that the phagosomes in Kupffer cells may receive material packaged by the Golgi apparatus as well as by the GERL since immediately after latex administration TPPase was detectable in these phagosomes before ACPase could be demonstrated. TPPase activity has further been localized in presynaptic vesicles in axonal terminals of the brain, a finding suggesting that these vesicles could be derived from membranes of the Golgi complex (Griffith and Bondareff, 1973). True TPPase activity has been shown to be present on the plasma membrane of tanycytes and microglia in the central nervous tissue of the rat (Luppa *et al.*, 1976; Murabe and Sano, 1981).

After incubation of tissues in the TPPase medium, reaction product has been localized by several authors, not only in the Golgi fields, but also on plasma membranes and in the endoplasmic reticulum and nuclear envelope. Comparable results were obtained by Borgers and Thoné (1976) in liver and kidney tissues. These observations led to the conclusion that at least five different enzymes could be responsible for producing the precipitate when TPP was used as substrate at neutral pH, i.e., NDPase (endoplasmic reticulum); AlPase (plasma membrane, lysosomal structures and Golgi apparatus); ACPase (lysosomes and Golgi vesicles); polyphosphatase (plasma membrane); and TPPase (Golgi apparatus). TPPase, therefore, appears to be one of the most "unspecific" substrates currently used in phosphatase cytochemistry.

2. *Esterases*

Esterases are often divided into three groups: nonspecific esterases, cholinesterases, and lipases. We shall also consider here the nucleotide phosphodiesterases.

a. *Nonspecific Esterases and Cholinesterases.* Most of the knowledge about the cytochemical localization of esterases (EC 3.1.1) has been compiled by Friedenberg and Seligman (1972) (cholinesterases) and by Shnitka (1974) and von Deimling and Böcking (1976) (particularly the other nonspecific esterases). We refer the reader, therefore, to these reviews for detailed information about the properties, the current methodology, and the subcellular localization of the esterases; an extensive list of references related to this matter can also be found therein. Within the group of esterase enzymes, great attention has been paid to the localization of cholinesterases.

Reviews by Shnitka (1974) and von Deimling and Böcking (1976) have summarized the methods for demonstrating esterases that have been introduced over the years (using a large number of substrates and reagents) since the first electron microscopic demonstration of esterase by Lehrer and Ornstein (1959) and Barnett and Palade (1959).

Currently used substrates react predominantly in the endoplasmic reticulum, nuclear envelope, lysosomal structures, and sometimes the Golgi region. Esterase activity associated with lipid droplets has been demonstrated with quinoline derivatives, *p*-nitrophenylthiol esters and Tween 80 as substrates. Esterase activity using 8-hydroxyquinoline esters as substrate is found in all subcellular compartments in which esterase has been localized, but they differ from all other substrates in that they demonstrate activity in the mitochondrial matrix of cells (von Deimling and Böcking, 1976; Böcking *et al.*, 1976a,b; Böcking and Riede, 1979).

The major sites of surfactant-associated esterases are the lamellar bodies of the type II alveolar pneumocytes (Vatter *et al.*, 1968; O'Hare *et al.*, 1971; Hitchcock-O'Hare *et al.*, 1976; Douglas and Hitchcock, 1979). Nonspecific esterase also has been found on the outer surface of the plasma membrane in human lung macrophages (Jaubert *et al.*, 1978), in macrophages and different blood cells in guinea pig bone marrow and peritoneal exudates, and in human peripheral blood cells (Monahan *et al.*, 1981). Reaction product was also observed on different plasma membranes of tissue cells, in pinocytic vesicles of endothelial cells, in cytoplasmic-vesicle structures and non-membrane-bound cytoplasmic granules of different blood cells and macrophages, and on basement membranes (Yokota, 1974; von Deimling and Böcking, 1976; Böcking *et al.*, 1976a,b; Douglas and Hitchcock, 1979; Payne *et al.*, 1980; Monahan *et al.*, 1981).

Two substrates have been used for cholinesterase localization: acetylthiocholine iodide (to demonstrate specific cholinesterase, EC 3.1.1.7) and butyrylthiocholine iodide (to demonstrate nonspecific cholinesterase, EC 3.1.1.8). Specific inhibitors for both enzymes can be included in the incubation medium: bis-(4-trimethylammoniumphenyl)pentan-3-one diiodide (inhibits specific cholinesterase) and tetraisopropylpyrophosphoramide (inhibits nonspecific cholinesterase) (Friedenberg and Seligman, 1972). Such inhibition is also achieved by *in vivo* injection of both former inhibitors (Davis and Koelle, 1978). Eserine sulfate inhibits both enzymes.

Most cytochemical studies aimed at localizing cholinesterases are based on the methods of Koelle and Friedenwald (1949), Lehrer and Ornstein (1959), Crévier and Bélanger (1955) and M. L. Seligman *et al.* (1966) and were further improved by Karnovsky and Roots (1964), Lewis and Shute (1966), Kasa and Csillik (1966), Brzin *et al.* (1966, 1967), Kokko *et al.* (1969), Mednick *et al.* (1971), Rash and Ellisman (1974), Tsuji (1974), Brzin and Pucihar (1976), Golder *et al.* (1977), and Gautron (1982). The methods of Karnovsky and Roots (1964) and Lewis and Shute (1966) or modifications of these techniques are frequently employed. Comparisons of the different methods are described by Tsuji (1974), Friedenberg and Seligman (1972), Klinar and Brzin (1977), and Sehgal *et al.* (1981). Kinetic studies on an artificial system have been performed by Malpiece *et al.* (1981). Salpeter *et al.* (1978) described the distribution of acetylcholinesterase by autoradiography.

As described for the other nonspecific esterases, the cholinesterases have been localized in the endoplasmic reticulum, nuclear envelope, and sometimes the Golgi apparatus of different types of cells: myocardium and skeletal muscle, *in vivo* as well as in culture, Friedenberg and Seligman, 1972; Taylor, 1976; Sawyer *et al.*, 1976; Golder *et al.*, 1978; small intestinal smooth muscle, Majcen and Brzin, 1979; liver, Satler *et al.*, 1974; granule-containing cells of glomus-like bodies, Papka, 1975; pars intermedia of the hypophysis, Bäck *et al.*, 1976; capillary endothelium, Panula and Rechardt, 1978, 1979; Liesi *et al.*, 1980;

neurons, Lewis and Shute, 1966; Kim, 1976; Ciani *et al.*, 1978; Panula and
Rechardt, 1979; Liesi *et al.*, 1980; Gautron, 1982). The main activity, however,
concerned the nervous tissue. In the neuromuscular junction of vertebrates and
invertebrates, cholinesterase activity has been confined to the synaptic clefts and
to the surface of the axonal plasma membrane outside the synaptic areas (Lehrer
and Ornstein, 1959; Lewis and Shute, 1966; Friedenberg and Seligman, 1972;
Rash and Ellisman, 1974; Gilloteaux, 1978; McMahan *et al.*, 1978; Schober and
Thomas, 1978; Czubaj, 1979; Sketelj and Brzin, 1979; Sehgal *et al.*, 1981;
Gautron, 1982). The cholinesterases in the synaptic clefts should be present on
the postsynaptic plasma membrane but have also been associated with the basal
lamina (Rash and Ellisman, 1974; McMahan *et al.*, 1978; Sketelj and Brzin,
1979). Reaction product is also found between the axonal plasma membrane and
Schwann cells, and (or) in the synaptic clefts of nerves innervating pancreas α
and β cells (Esterhuizen *et al.*, 1968), arterioles (Ausprunk *et al.*, 1973), vas
deferens and atrial cells (Chiba, 1973), granule-containing cells of glomus-like
bodies (Papka, 1975), cornea (Tervo, 1976), compound eye of the honeybee
(Kral and Schneider, 1981), and around lobster giant axons (Holtzman *et al.*,
1970).

Besides their presence in neuronal subcellular organelles (see earlier), the
cholinesterases are also demonstrated on axonal plasma membranes and in synaptic spaces of central nervous tissue (Lewis and Shute, 1966; Pannese *et al.*,
1974; Broderson *et al.*, 1974; Klinar and Brzin, 1977; Davis and Koelle, 1978).
A positive reaction for cholinesterase was seen in membrane-bound granules of
amphidial, esophageal, and excretory glands of nematodes (McLaren *et al.*,
1974).

No technique for esterase cytochemistry can be regarded as ideal, nor do
different procedures give entirely comparable staining results. The development
of new substrates that are hydrolyzed more selectively than those known is an
area that requires further development. The application of specific antibodies,
which will depend upon further advances in the isolation and purification of the
individual organ esterases (von Deimling and Böcking, 1976) is another approach. These statements are still valid today.

b. *Lipases.* Various modifications of the Gomori method (1945) utilizing
calcium as capturing agent, with and without lead substitution, were employed to
detect lipase activity (EC 3.1.1.3) at the ultrastructural level in the acinar cells of
the mouse pancreas (membranes of zymogen granules, endoplasmic reticulum,
nuclear envelope, Golgi fields, and the glandular lumen of the acinar cells)
(Nagata and Murata, 1972). Nagata (1974) discussed the problems with methodology, the distribution of the activity, and the specificity of the reaction. Using
the Nagata technique, phospholipase A, lysophospholipase, and lipase activities
were localized cytochemically in the Clara cells of the rat bronchiole (Yoneda,
1978) and lipase activity was localized in germinating spores of plants (Carrapio

and Pais, 1983). A cytochemical procedure based on the original Gömöri technique (1945) has been described to detect phospholipase A and lysophospholipase in developing buds and in the cell membranes and walls of yeast cells (Pugh and Cawson, 1975).

The differentiation of lipase from nonspecific esterases can be accomplished by utilizing specific substrates, inhibitors, and activators (Shnitka, 1974; Nagata, 1974).

c. *Nucleotide Phosphodiesterase.* The enzymes demonstrated ultrastructurally are cyclic 3':5'-nucleotide phosphodiesterase (EC 3.1.4.17) and 5'-nucleotide phosphodiesterase (EC 3.1.4.1, phosphodiesterase I).

Cyclic 3':5'-nucleotide phosphodiesterase should be involved in controlling the concentration of cyclic 3':5'-adenosine monophosphate (cAMP) or cyclic 3':5'-guanine monophosphate (cGMP) in a wide variety of eukaryotic and prokaryotic cells through their degradation. The basis of the cytochemical procedure is to convert 5'-AMP (or 5'-GMP), generated from cAMP (or cGMP) by cyclic 3':5'-nucleotide phosphodiesterase, to adenosine (or guanine) with an excess of exogenously added 5'-nucleotidase and to precipitate the newly formed inorganic phosphate with lead ions. Florendo *et al.* (1971) first introduced this technique using a two-step method; Kalderon and Ravanshenas (1974) used a one-step procedure. The venom of *Ophiophagus hannah* was the source of exogenous 5'-nucleotidase (Sugimura and Mizutani, 1978) and gave superior morphological preservation over that of *Crotalus atrox* taken by Florendo *et al.* (1971) and Kalderon and Ravanshenas (1974). Enzyme activity localizations, based on both formerly cited methods, have been described in brain tissue (Florendo *et al.*, 1971; Sugimura and Mizutani, 1978), thyroid cells (Kalderon and Ravanshenas, 1974) and thyroid cell membranes (Kalderon *et al.*, 1980), renal medulla (Florendo *et al.*, 1978), submaxillary gland (Kalderon, 1977), the neuromuscular junction and skeletal muscle of the newt (Pardoz and Lentz, 1976), different tissues of invertebrates (Duma and Moraczewski, 1980; Benedeczky and Rozsa, 1981b), and *Dictyostelium* (Farnham, 1975).

Control reactions were necessary to discriminate between cyclic 3':5'-nucleotide phosphodiesterase and endogenous 5'-nucleotidase. Theophylline and imidazole were used as the specific enzyme inhibitor and activator, respectively. However, theophylline did not appear to be an appropriate inhibitor for the enzyme in the planarian *Dugesia lugubris* (O. Schmidt) (Duma and Moraczewsky, 1980) and in the slime mold (Farnham, 1975). Duma and Moraczewsky (1980) further discussed problems in cytochemical localization of cyclic 3':5'-nucleotide phosphodiesterase.

5'-Nucleotide phosphodiesterase (or 5'-exonuclease) represents a group of nucleases that can hydrolyze the bond of a phosphodiester of a nucleotide and liberate a 5'-nucleotide. The function of this enzyme obviously lies in the degradation of DNA or of RNA and is, therefore, related to the regulation of DNA and RNA synthesis. The method of enzyme localization is based on the indigogenic principle. Enzyme activity has been primarily associated with the endoplasmic reticulum, the nuclear envelope, and the Golgi apparatus. For a more detailed description on the methodology and distribution of 5'-nucleotide phosphodiesterase, we refer readers to the review of Tsou (1975).

3. Sulfatases

Of the sulfatases, only arylsulfatases or arylsulfate sulfohydrolases (EC 3.1.6.1) have been demonstrated ultrastructurally. A detailed description of the methodology used for the localization of these enzymes has been compiled by Hopsu-Havu and Helminen (1974). This review indicated that the most reliable methods were based on the techniques of Goldfischer (1965) and Hopsu et al. (1965, 1967) which used the heavy metals lead and barium as capturing agents. When considering the substrate specificity and other enzymatic characteristics of arylsulfatases, one would expect that arylsulfatases A and B are primarily demonstrated by the preceding methods (Hopsu-Havu and Helminen, 1974). Most studies performed after 1974 to localize arylsulfatase activities adopted one of these techniques. One study reports an alternative method utilizing the synthetic substrate 4-nitro-1, 2-benzenediol mono(hydrogen sulfate) to form osmium black at the site of copper capture (Hanker et al., 1975).

Arylsulfatase activity has been localized in the lysosomes of many different tissues (see references in Hopsu-Havu and Helminen, 1974; Nichols and Bainton, 1973; Lockshin and Beaulaton, 1974; Hofstein et al., 1975; Hanker et al., 1975; Bentfeld and Bainton, 1975; Nichols, 1976; Jones and Fox, 1976; Meda, 1978; Decker and Wildenthal, 1978a, b; Paavola, 1978a, b). Enzyme activity has also, but less consistently, been described in Golgi cisternae and GERL and occasionally in the endoplasmic reticulum and nuclear envelope (Bainton and Farquhar, 1968, 1970; Bainton et al., 1971; Nichols et al., 1971; Hofstein et al., 1975; Bentfeld and Bainton, 1975; Nichols, 1976; Maxwell, 1978). Other sites of activity include the azurophilic granules in human developing neutrophils (Bainton et al., 1971), the primary and specific granules of duck eosinophils (Maxwell, 1978), and the α-granules of rabbit blood platelets (Murata et al., 1975).

4. Glycosidases

Cellulase (EC 3.2.1.4) is a multienzyme complex which brings about the complete degradation of cellulose to monosaccharide residues. The monosaccharide end product (glucose) can be made to reduce cupric salts to cuprous oxide precipitate, which can be visualized with the electron microscope. This method and the problems encountered have been presented by Bal (1974).

5. *Proteinases*

Since proteinases have extremely strict substrate specificity (Neurath and Walsh, 1976; Kolata, 1977), the cytochemical investigation of these enzymes requires specific (synthetic) substrates (Smith and Dean, 1979). Many specific proteinase substrates, using the principle of active site modeling, have been synthesized. Cytochemical studies to detect aminopeptidase A, B, and M; γ-glutamyl transpeptidase; endopeptidase I and II; membrane-associated endopeptidase I, II, and IV; trypsin; and chymotrypsin are performed using the 4-methoxy-2-naphthylamine substrates; ester proteinases are detected with N-acetyl-L-methionine-1-naphthyl ester as substrate (Gossrau, 1981; Lojda, 1981). The cited enzymes include membrane-bound proteinases, lysosomal proteinases, and cytosol peptidases, which have been demonstrated in different kinds of organs and cells in normal and pathological conditions(see Smith and Dean, 1975; Gossrau, 1981; Lojda, 1981; Kugler, 1982). Most cytochemical procedures used are based on the method of Smith and van Frank (1975). We refer the reader to the former studies for details about the existing methodology and localizations of the indicated proteinases.

The thiol ester N-t-Boc-L-alanine-p-nitrothiophenol ester is synthesized and applied in another technique as an ultrastructural cytochemical substrate for the intracellular demonstration of elastase-like enzymes in human neutrophils. Incubation of fixed cells with this substrate in the presence of gold ions generates electron-dense deposits of gold p-nitrothiophenolate in the nuclear membrane, endoplasmic reticulum, Golgi complex, mitochondria, and granules (Clark *et al.*, 1980a,b). The deposition of reaction product can be prevented with specific chemical inactivators of neutrophil elastase.

Immunocytochemistry has been adapted to localize lysosomal cathepsin D (and B) (Decker *et al.*, 1980; Poole and Mort, 1981; Simonis *et al.*, 1982).

B. OXIDOREDUCTASES

Dehydrogenations provide most of the energy for aerobic and particularly anaerobic cells and are involved in oxidation reactions of metabolically important compounds. These dehydrogenation reactions are catalyzed by the oxidoreductases. Based on the different methods used to localize these enzymes cytochemically, it is possible to discern two groups of enzymes: those revealed by the diaminobenzidine procedure (catalase, peroxidase, cytochrome oxidase/cytochrome c system, cytochrome c peroxidase) and those demonstrated by other techniques (many oxidases and dehydrogenases).

Since Graham and Karnovsky (1966) introduced 3′,3-diaminobenzidine (DAB) into the field of histo- and cytochemistry, this reagent has been used extensively in a large number of studies. It has been used to demonstrate tracer hemoproteins and endogenous enzymes (hemoproteins); it has been used widely in immunocytochemistry and in localization studies of cellular glycoproteins; and it was adopted in methods based on nonenzymatic DAB oxidation (reviews by Essner, 1974; Litwin, 1979). The methodology for localizing hemoproteins with the DAB procedure has appeared as one of the most versatile cytochemical methods available and has been regarded as specific under strictly defined conditions.

1. Catalase and Peroxidase

Catalase (EC 1.11.1.6) has been shown to be a marker enzyme for perox-isomes (microbodies) while peroxidases (EC 1.11.1.7) have been located in several other subcellular organelles. Since both enzymes can be demonstrated by the DAB procedure and since 3-amino-1,2,4-triazole and 2,6-dichlorophenolin-dophenol (which are considered to be specific inhibitors of catalase) are also inhibitory to several peroxidases (see Roels et al., 1975), it appeared necessary to modify the currently used techniques (Novikoff and Goldfischer, 1968, 1969; Fahimi, 1968, 1969; Hirai, 1969; Novikoff and Novikoff, 1972; Novikoff et al., 1972; see reviews of Essner, 1974; Litwin, 1979, for more details on the meth-odology) in order to obtain appropriate experimental conditions to discriminate between both enzymes which are often present in the same tissues and cells. This problem is comprehensively investigated by Roels and co-workers (Roels and Wisse, 1973; Roels et al., 1974a,b, 1975) and by the group of Herzog and Fahimi (Herzog and Fahimi, 1974, 1976; Fahimi et al., 1976; Fahimi, 1979; LeHir et al., 1979; Angermüller and Fahimi, 1981). From these studies it be-came obvious that discrimination between catalase and peroxidase depended on aldehyde fixation and temperature, pH and H_2O_2 concentrations of the incuba-tion medium. Observations indicated that there is no single optimal condition for the enzyme localization; rather the fixation and incubation conditions should be modified according to the type of study and the nature of the material to be investigated. Peroxidase has been found to be sensitive to aldehyde fixation and should have its optimal staining reaction in the neutral pH range, while aldehyde fixation is a prerequisite for the demonstration of peroxidatic activity of catalase with an optimal pH around 10. A high-temperature procedure has been reported to demonstrate human hepatic and renal peroxisomes (Roels and Goldfischer, 1979).

As previously mentioned, catalase activity has been confined to peroxisomes. Its activity is shown in different vertebrate (particularly liver and kidney cells) and invertebrate tissues (see references in Essner, 1974; Litwin, 1979; Reddy et al., 1975, 1976; Herzog and Fahimi, 1975; Regh et al., 1975; Barrett and Heidger, 1975; Goldenberg et al., 1975a, 1976; Hand, 1976; Hanna et al., 1976; Veenhuis and Wendelaar Bonga, 1977; Yokota and Fahimi, 1978) and has been described in plant cells, mainly yeasts (see Essner, 1974; Silverberg, 1975; De

Nollin et al., 1975; Osumi et al., 1975; De Nollin and Borgers, 1976; Osumi and Sato, 1978). The activity in yeast cells differed according to the applied growth medium and disappeared after antifungal treatment (De Nollin et al. 1975; De Nollin and Borgers, 1976).

In 1972 Novikoff and Novikoff described a small, DAB-positive subcellular organelle characterized by numerous slender membrane continuities with endoplasmic reticulum, absence of nucleoids and moderately opaque matrix which they designated "microperoxisomes," a term which has been questioned by Böck (1973a,b). Such DAB-positive organelles are reported in a large variety of tissue cells (see references in Hruban and Reckcigl, 1969; Böck, 1973a; Essner, 1974; Leuenberger and Novikoff, 1975; Masters and Holmes, 1977; Litwin, 1979; Tolbert, 1981; Pipan and Psenicnik, 1975; De Bruyn et al., 1975; Fomina et al., 1975; Böck et al., 1975; Goldenberg et al., 1975b; Hicks and Fahimi, 1977; Mooradian and Cutler, 1978; King, 1982). Besides the presence of peroxidatic activity of catalase, biochemical studies have also shown that α-hydroxy acid and D-amino acid oxidase were present in the DAB-positive organelles of rat preputial gland and bovine adrenal cortex, a finding indicating that these structures may be peroxisomal systems. Hence, these organelles can be called true (micro) peroxisomes. Whether the DAB-positive organelles in all the other cell types are peroxisomal in nature remains to be determined.

Extraperoxisomal, cytosolic localization of catalase is verified cytochemically in liver parenchymal cells of sheep, rhesus monkey, and guinea pig (Roels, 1976; Roels et al., 1977), in duct cells of murine salivary glands (Hanker et al., 1977b), and in the epidermal cells of Tubifex tubifex Müll. (Fischer and Horváth, 1977). Peroxidatic activity of catalase should also be present in specific granules of human peripheral blood leukocytes (Nishismura et al., 1976) and in secondary granules of rat blood monocytes (Van der Rhee et al., 1977). Some immunocytochemical techniques were performed to localize catalase activity (Yokota and Nagata, 1974; Yokota and Fahimi, 1981; Iozzo et al., 1982; Bendayan and Reddy, 1982; Bendayan and Zollinger, 1983).

Different endogenous peroxidases have been detected cytochemically which can, to some extent, be distinguished on the basis of their responses to different inhibitors: potassium cyanide, sodium azide, excess hydrogen peroxide, 3-amino-1,2,4-triazole. The results of the inhibitor studies are difficult to interpret (Essner, 1974; Litwin, 1979).

In rat liver, endogenous peroxidase has been used as a marker for the identification of Kupffer cells since the endoplasmic reticulum and nuclear envelope can be stained in only this sinusoidal cell type (Widmann et al., 1972; Wisse, 1974; Pino and Bankston, 1979). It appeared, however, that in the mouse liver, besides the Kupffer cells, half of the sinusoidal endothelial cells showed a weak to moderate peroxidase activity in the indicated subcellular organelles so that peroxidase cytochemistry in this species should be used in conjunction with other methods (Stöhr et al., 1978).

The localization of peroxidase activity has further been studied in mononuclear phagocytes of different mammalian species including several types of tissue macrophages (other than Kupffer cells), exudate and resident peritoneal macrophages, and differentiating bone marrow and mature blood monocytes (see Daems et al., 1975; Nichols and Bainton, 1975; Schlüns and Graf, 1976; Bodel et al., 1977; Van der Rhee et al., 1977; Ogawa et al., 1978). According to the type of tissue, the species, and the developmental stage, activity was present (or not) in the endoplasmic reticulum, nuclear envelope, Golgi apparatus, and (or) cytoplasmic granules. The different distribution of peroxidase in monocytes compared with its localization in tissue macrophages has been cited as evidence that the blood monocyte is not a direct precursor of the macrophages (Daems et al., 1975; Widmann and Fahimi, 1975). However, the appearance of peroxidase activity within the endoplasmic reticulum of blood monocytes after surface adherence in vitro suggests that blood monocytes may be the precursors of such cells (Bodel et al., 1977). There is also cytochemical evidence against the transformation of preexisting endothelial cells into Kupffer cells (Pino and Bankston, 1979).

Cytochemical peroxidase reactions in hematology have been extensively studied. In developing polymorphonuclear blood cells, (myelo)peroxidase activity is described in the endoplasmic reticulum, the nuclear envelope, and the Golgi fields. During maturation, peroxidase activity becomes confined to specific granules in neutrophils, eosinophils, basophils, and monocytes and disappears from the sites indicated in the premature forms (Baehner et al., 1969; Bainton and Farquhar, 1970; Ackerman and Clark, 1971; Maldonado and Pierre, 1975; Roels et al., 1975; Daimon and Caxton-Martins, 1977; Van der Rhee et al., 1977; Maxwell, 1978; and reviews by Breton-Gorius 1980; and Karnovsky et al., 1981). Platelet peroxidase is revealed in the dense tubular system which is derived from the endoplasmic reticulum of megakaryocytes (see Litwin, 1979; Breton-Gorius, 1980).

The detection of different peroxidases by ultrastructural cytochemistry has provided significant contributions to the knowledge of normal and aberrant hematopoietic cell maturation and, together with the cytochemistry of other oxidative enzymes, insight into the phagocytic process (Breton-Gorius, 1980; Karnovsky et al., 1981). In organs secreting peroxidase, the reactivity was found in the endoplasmic reticulum, the nuclear envelope, the Golgi fields, secretory granules, and occasionally other sites (Tice and Wollman, 1972; Herzog, 1973, 1979; Tice, 1974; Essner, 1974; Garrett and Kidd, 1976; Giorgi and Deri, 1976; Anderson and Burnett, 1979; Litwin, 1979; Sugimoto et al., 1983). Speculations about the function of the peroxidases has been related to the specific organs.

Peroxidase appeared to be present in "microbodies" of *Trypanosoma cruzi* (Docampo *et al.*, 1976).

2. *Cytochrome Oxidase/Cytochrome c System and Cytochrome c Peroxidase*

Incubation of tissues in the Graham and Karnovsky (1966) medium not only visualizes simultaneously peroxidase and catalase activity but often reveals staining of the compartment between the inner and outer membrane and in the intracristal space of mitochondria. The latter activity has been attributed to cytochrome oxidase activity. A (specific) DAB method for the demonstration of cytochrome oxidase has been developed by Seligman *et al.* (1968) wherein exogenous cytochrome *c* was added to enhance mitochondrial staining and exogenous catalase is introduced to destroy all possible traces of peroxide. Novikoff and Goldfischer (1969) elicited mitochondrial staining in the presence of H_2O_2. The technique of Seligman and co-workers, or modifications thereof, was used frequently in later studies (Essner, 1974; Hanker, 1975; Litwin, 1979). Inhibition was achieved with potassium and sodium cyanide, sodium fluoride, and sodium azide; the reaction was insensitive to 3-amino-1,2,4-triazole. Recently, Angermüller and Fahimi (1981) described a method for exclusive localization of cytochrome oxidase in rat liver mitochondria.

The mechanism of mitochondrial DAB oxidation has long been the subject of serious controversy. The reaction is thought either to be due to peroxidatic activity of mitochondria, to reflect the presence of cytochrome or cytochromes, or to result from the activity of the cytochrome oxidase/cytochrome *c* system (see Essner, 1974; Liwin, 1979). From the different experimental data described in the literature, Litwin (1979) concluded that DAB *localizes* cytochrome *c* and *demonstrates* cytochrome oxidase. Anderson *et al.* (1975) concluded that the intensity of the cytochemical reaction depended on the oxidation state of mitochondrial membranes, availability and concentration of the electron receptors, solubility of substrates, inhibition of the enzyme and/or oxidoreduction reaction, effect of fixation, and a possible solubility of the reaction product in unfixed tissue. Cytochrome oxidase has been demonstrated in a variety of animal tissues, in plants, and also in isolated mitochondria (referenced in Essner, 1974; Hanker, 1975; Litwin, 1979; and described by Teranishi *et al.*, 1974; Osumi *et al.*, 1974, 1975; Silverberg and Sawa, 1974; Roels *et al.*, 1975; Hersey *et al.*, 1975; De Nollin *et al.*, 1975, 1977; Vorisek and Volfova, 1975; Fomina *et al.*, 1975; Maxwell *et al.*, 1975; Krupa and Bogitsh, 1975; De Nollin and Borgers, 1976; Wiseman, *et al.*, 1977; Somogyi *et al.*, 1978; Marinos, 1978; Sannes *et al.*, 1979; Al-Ali and Robinson, 1979b, 1982; Hoshino and Shannon, 1979; Angermüller and Fahimi, 1981; Itoiz *et al.*, 1982). Some of these studies mentioned changes in cytochrome oxidase activities related to experimental conditions or mutation. Perotti and Anderson (1980) and Perotti *et al.* (1983) obtained semiquantitative information of the total oxidative activity of cardiac muscle and pancreas from cytochrome oxidase cytochemistry.

The oxidation of DAB in mitochondria of yeast cells under specified incubation conditions has been attributed by some authors to cytochrome c peroxidase activity (Hoffman et al., 1970; Todd and Vigil, 1972; De Nollin et al., 1975, 1977; De Nollin and Borgers, 1976). Its activity decreased significantly after antifungal treatment (De Nollin and Borgers, 1976; De Nollin et al., 1977).

3. Oxidases and Dehydrogenases

In the late sixties two techniques were introduced to localize oxidases and dehydrogenases ultrastructurally: the tetrazolium salt technique and the ferricyanide method. Both methods are extensively described in a review by Hanker (1975).

The formation of osmiophilic formazans by the reduction of a variety of tetrazolium salts is reported (as referenced, among others, by Hanker, 1975) in the demonstration of lactate dehydrogenase (EC 1.1.1.27) (Al-Ali and Robinson, 1979a; Deimann et al., 1981), succinate dehydrogenase (EC 1.3.99.1) (Athanassious et al., 1982), glucose-6-phosphate dehydrogenase (EC 1.1.1.49) Sakharova et al., 1979), NADPH dehydrogenase (EC 1.6.99.1) (Van Noorden and Tas, 1982), NADH dehydrogenase (diaphorase) (EC 1.6.99.3) (Al-Ali and Robinson, 1979a; Van Noorden and Tas, 1982), nitrate reductase (EC 1.6.6.1) (Vaughn and Duke, 1981), and monoamine oxidase (EC 1.4.3.4) (Shannon et al., 1974, 1976; Lowe et al., 1975; Yoo and Oreland, 1976; Müller and Da Laga, 1977; Shannon, 1978). The low electron density of the formazan reaction product renders the technique less useful for electron microscopy (Beard and Novikoff, 1969; Hand, 1979). Recently improved contrast in the cytochemistry of dehydrogenases has been achieved in unosmicated preparations by scanning transmission electron microscopy (Deimann et al., 1981).

Ogawa et al. (1966, 1968) and Kerpel-Fronius and Hajós (1968) reported ferricyanide to be a substitute for tetrazolium salts on the basis of the principle developed by Karnovsky and Roots (1964). The primary reaction product formed at the sites of enzyme activity (copper ferrocyanide, also called Hatchett's brown) can then be amplified by DAB and OsO_4 treatment (Hanker et al., 1973). The ferricyanide method has been used particularly to demonstrate different dehydrogenases (Hanker, 1975; see also Hanker, 1975 for additional references on methodology and localizations) such as lactate dehydrogenase (Coleman et al., 1976; Hanker et al., 1977a; Sasaki, 1979), succinate dehydrogenase (Bell, 1979; Schuurhuis et al., 1980), glucose-6-phosphate dehydrogenase (Benkoël et al., 1976; Bara, 1979), NADPH dehydrogenase (Benkoël et al., 1976; Hanker et al., 1977a; Bara, 1979), malate dehydrogenase (EC 1.1.1.37), 3-hydroxybutyrate dehydrogenase (EC 1.1.1.30) (Bara, 1979), L-α-glycerophosphate dehydrogenase (EC 1.1.99.5), β-hydroxysteroid dehydrogenase (EC 1.1.1.51) (Benkoël *et al.*, 1976), 3β-hydroxysteroid dehydrogenase (EC 1.1.1.145) (Berchtold, 1977, 1978; Bara, 1979), 11β-hydroxysteroid dehydrogenase (EC 1.1.1.146) (Bara, 1979). It has been used to localize monoamine oxidase (Yoo and Oreland, 1976), glycollate oxidase (EC 1.1.3.1) (Gruber and Frederick, 1977), L-α-hydroxyacid oxidase (EC 1.1.3.15) (Hand, 1975, 1976), and malate synthase (EC 4.1.3.2) (Trelease, 1975).

Since the oxidases and dehydrogenases are considered to be particularly susceptible to fixation, most cytochemical studies are performed on slightly fixed or unfixed tissues (Hanker 1975; Berchtold, 1977; Al-Ali and Robinson, 1979a; and others). Appropriate substrates and inhibitors are used according to the enzyme to be detected.

A major difficulty in coenzyme-linked dehydrogenase localization, particularly at the ultrastructural level, results from the fact that the final reaction products localize NADPH oxidase ("diaphorase") activity instead of the actual dehydrogenase activity to be studied. This nonspecific reaction is called the "nothing dehydrogenase" reaction (Berchtold, 1979). Therefore, exogenous electron carriers are usually applied. More details about the role of exogenous electron carriers in NAD(P)-dependent dehydrogenase cytochemistry can be found in the work by Van Noorden and Tas (1982).

Depending on the enzyme localized, activity is mostly indicated to be present in (micro)peroxisomes and in mitochondrial outer membranes and cristae. In some studies, activity is also associated with the endoplasmic reticulum, the nuclear envelope, plasma membranes, membranes of cytoplasmic vacuoles, and the hyaloplasm.

In 1975, Briggs *et al.* introduced a cerium chloride technique to localize NADH oxidase on the surface and on the phagosomes of human polymorphonuclear leukocytes (neutrophils). The procedure is based on the formation of an electron-dense precipitate during incubation with cerous ions and in the presence of aminotriazole to inhibit endogenous catalase. The cerous ions form an insoluble compound with the H_2O_2 generated by the oxidase, presumably cerium perhydroxide. In addition to NADH oxidase, D-amino acid oxidase and aldehyde oxidase have been confined to the outer cell surface and (or) phagosomes and vesicles. This localization is not only found in human polymorphonuclear leukocytes but also in the phagocytosing cells of other mammalian species. These results, which are compiled in the review by Karnovsky *et al.* (1981), show that the production of H_2O_2 on the plasmalemma and plasmalemma-derived structures (phagosomes or vesicles) in stimulated neutrophils may be a general phenomenon and occurs following particulate as well as nonparticulate stimulation of the respiratory burst. It should be realized, however, that the cytochemical methods utilized in these studies detect the end product of an enzymatic reaction

(H_2O_2) and not the site of the enzyme itself (Karnovsky *et al.*, 1981). The exact sites can presumably be revealed by immunocytochemistry.

The cerium reaction also appeared to be applicable to the localization of intracellular oxidase activity in yeast microbodies (L-α-hydroxyacid oxidase; methanol oxidase, EC 1.1.3.13; D-amino acid oxidase, EC 1.4.3.3) (Veenhuis *et al.*, 1976) and in yeast mitochondria and central vacuoles (NADH oxidase) (DeNollin and Borgers, 1976; Borgers *et al.*, 1977). The technique has also been successfully applied in the ultrastructural detection of one or more of the H_2O_2-producing oxidases (L-α-hydroxyacid oxidase, D-amino acid oxidase, urate oxidase) present in peroxisomes and microperoxisomes in different kinds of animal and plant cells (Arnold *et al.*, 1977, 1979; Veenhuis and Wendelaar Bonga, 1977, 1979; Hand, 1979; Arnold and Holtzman, 1980; Vaughn *et al.*, 1982), NADH oxidase in phagocytic vacuolar membranes of human platelets (Del Principe *et al.*, 1980), NAD(P)H oxidase on the apical plasma membrane of isolated thyroid follicles (Björkman *et al.*, 1981), and monoamine oxidase in mitochondria and some other sites of myocardial and endothelial cells of rat heart (Fujimoto *et al.*, 1982). Tyrosinase (EC 1.10.3.1) is involved in the process of melanogenesis in a wide range of melanin-producing cells. Its activity is localized cytochemically by the dihydroxyphenylalanine (DOPA) reaction and has been found in the Golgi apparatus, in smooth-surface vesicles or tubules associated with the Golgi complex, and in developing melanosomes. Comments on enzyme properties, cytochemical procedure, and localizations are described by Eppig (1974).

In plant tissue, phenoloxidases take part in reactions involved in wall thickening, electron transport and resistance to infections. One has tried to adapt the DOPA-method (used to localize tyrosinase) in order to detect phenol oxidases cytochemically. It resulted in precipitate formation in thylakoids of tobacco leaves and of potatoes. The phenol oxidase cytochemistry is reviewed by Czaninski and Catesson (1974). An immunoadsorption method has been reported to show the presence of NADPH-cytochrome *P*-450 reductase (EC 1.6.2.4.) in rat liver Golgi membranes (Ito and Palade, 1978).

C. TRANSFERASES

1. *Carbamoyltransferases*

Ornithine carbamoyltransferase (EC 2.1.3.3) is mostly confined to the liver of ureotelic animals. The principle of the ultrastructural detection is identical to that of the phosphatases and has been worked out by Mizutani (1967, 1968). Appropriate fixation appeared to be a prerequisite for the localization of specific enzyme activity in the mitochondrial matrix of hepatocytes (Mizutani, 1967, 1968;

Mizutani and Fujita, 1968b,c, 1979). According to the experimental conditions used, nonspecific enzyme activity was found in lysosomes, in the brush border of the proximal tubules of the kidney, and in the endoplasmic reticulum and nuclear envelope of hepatocytes, neurons, and renal epithelium (Mizutani, 1968, 1979; Mizutani and Fujita, 1968a–c). The nonspecific activities were respectively attributed to ACPase, AlPase, and acylphosphatase (EC 3.6.1.7) (Mizutani, 1979).

2. Acyltransferases

The acyltransferases catalyze the transfer reaction of the acyl CoA group from CoA to an acceptor molecule. Since the only difference between acyl CoA and free CoA is the presence of a free SH group in the latter molecule, the cytochemical capture reagent for acyltransferases must be based on this SH group. The intrinsic properties of the free SH groups have led to two cytochemical techniques: a direct technique based on mercaptide formation with cadmium or lanthanum and an indirect technique based on the oxidation of free CoA including the copper, the uranyl, and the manganous ferrocyanide method (Higgins and Barnett, 1970, 1971). The kinetics of these different techniques as well as the specific procedures for carnitine acyltransferase, monoglyceride acyltransferase, and α-glycerophosphate acyltransferase are discussed by Higgins (1974).

The cytochemistry of acyltransferases have contributed significantly to the understanding of the organization of the cell in lipid metabolism. Acyltransferase activities have been detected in the endoplasmic reticulum, Golgi fields, the intracristal space, and the space between inner and outer membranes of mitochondria and have been connected with photosynthetic membranes, envelope, and pyrenoid tubules of *Chlamydomonas* chloroplasts (see references in Higgins, 1974; and Bonilla *et al.*, 1975; Kerényi *et al.*, 1975; Michaels *et al.*, 1983).

3. Purine Nucleoside Phosphorylase

Purine nucleoside phosphorylase (PNPase; EC 2.4.2.1) catalyzes the reversible reaction purine nucleoside + phosphate ↔ purine base + α-ribose 1-phosphate. A cytochemical method has been developed on the basis of the reversibility of the above reaction by Rubio *et al.* (1972) and has been further discussed by Rubio (1974). High concentrations of hypoxanthine and ribose 1-phosphate in the incubation solution drives the reaction backward toward inosine and phosphate. The liberated phosphate is then captured by a heavy metal (lead) as in the classic Gömöri reaction. PNPase has been localized in the hyaloplasm and nuclei of endothelial cells and pericytes of guinea pig myocardium (Rubio *et al.*, 1972). No activity was seen in myocardial cells and vascular smooth muscle cells. Borgers *et al.* (1972) used a slightly modified technique and found enzyme activity in the cytosol, not the nucleus, of endothelial cells, adventitial fibroblasts, and fibrocytes and in the axonal cytoplasm of nerves in the dog heart. A uniform enzyme reaction was also present in circulating neutrophils, basophils, monocytes, platelets, and part of the lymphocyte population, whereas eosinophils and erythrocytes lacked activity (Borgers et al., 1972). Using this enzyme as a specific and differential marker of endothelial and some blood-borne cells, it appeared possible to obtain information about the origin of the subendothelial cells in the intima of developing coronary collaterals (Borgers et al., 1973a, b). A possible relationship of PNPase with particular subpopulations of lymphocytes of various mammalian species has been suggested (Borgers et al., 1977; Borgers and Thoné, 1978) and could be of value in the differentiation of the B and T cell origins in lymphoproliferative disorders (Borgers et al., 1978).

4. Glycogen Phosphorylase

Glycogen phosphorylase (EC 2.4.1.1), a key enzyme in the degradation of glycogen in animal tissues, has been localized by precipitating the phosphate ions, liberated by the enzyme from glucose 1-phosphate, with ferrous ions according to a method introduced by Lindberg and Palkama (1974). Enzyme activity is found to be associated with the endoplasmic reticulum membranes and with glycogen particles. The method has been further improved by Lindberg and Palkama (1977). Poor results were obtained earlier by Hori (1966) and Personne and Anderson (1970), who used lead to capture the released phosphate.

5. Nucleotidyltransferases

The ultrastructural demonstration of NAD pyrophosphorylase (adenosine triphosphate:nicotinamide mononucleotide adenylyltransferase, EC 2.7.7.1) activity in isolated rat and mouse liver nuclei (nucleolus, interchromatin granules, and coiled bodies) can be demonstrated on the basis of pyrophosphate precipitation in media containing lead or manganese ions. Knowledge about its localization is compiled by Unger and Buchwalow (1975).

6. Creatine Kinase

Mitochondrial and sarcoplasmic creatine phosphokinase (EC 2.7.3.2) is localized ultrastructurally using a Nitro Blue Tetrazolium salt method as well as by immunocytochemistry. These techniques have been described by Farrell and Baba (1974).

D. LYASES AND LIGASES

1. Adenylate Cyclase

Based on extensive biochemical work, cyclic 3':5' adenosine monophosphate (cAMP), which is formed by the catalytic action of adenylate cyclase (EC 4.6.1.1), is now recognized as the intracellular mediator (second messenger) for the effect of a large number of hormones. Cytochemical studies were used to reveal the specific cellular locations of the adenylate cyclase activity and to study the differences in hormone responsiveness between the various cells constituting particular tissues. The first cytochemical procedure, based on the technique of Wachstein and Meisel (1957), was described by Reik *et al.* (1970). The substrate used by these authors (ATP) could, however, also be hydrolyzed by a variety of specific and nonspecific enzymes other than adenylate cyclase, so that Howell and Whitfield (1972) and Wagner and co-workers (1972) introduced the more specific substrate 5′-adenylylimidodiphosphate. This substrate is now commonly used in recent cytochemical studies using modifications of the original technique.

As for other phosphatases, the lead capture technique, adopted to localize adenylate cyclase activity has been criticized (Lemay and Jarett, 1975; Kempen *et al.*, 1978). The latter reports gave rise to comments by Kvinnsland (1979), Cutler and Christian (1980), and Cutler (1983), who evaluated the efficacy of the procedures by biochemical and cytochemical means. They came to the conclusion that the lead capture procedure appears to be valid. Incubations with strontium and cobalt as capture agents were introduced by Cutler (1983) and yielded promising results. These studies, together with the work of Wagner and Bitensky (1974) extend the information available about the methodology and application of the techniques.

Cutler (1983) also reviewed the literature and included a listing of tissues examined cytochemically for adenylate cyclase activity. Additional reports concerning adenylate cyclase cytochemistry are those of Joó and Tóth (1975). Mahrle and Orfanos (1975a), Trandaburu (1976), Conway-Jones and Rothman (1978), Greene and Pratt (1979), Rostomian and Abramian (1980), Boyadjieva-Michailova *et al.* (1980), Rostomian *et al.* (1981), Benedeczky and Rózsa (1981a), Moraczewsky and Duma (1981), Buchwalow *et al.* (1981), Mizukami *et al.* (1982), and Zajic and Schacht (1983). From these studies it appears that adenylate cyclase is predominantly associated with the plasma membrane. Reaction product is in some studies seen at the outer surface of the plasma membrane, whereas the catalytic side is believed to be present at the cytoplasmic side (see Tse *et al.*, 1978). This discrepancy is not explained. Activity has occasionally been described in the endoplasmic reticulum, nuclear envelope, and Golgi vesicles (Slezak and Geller, 1979; Revis, 1979; Moraczewsky and Duma, 1981; Buchwalow *et al.*, 1981). Precipitation is rarely observed in mitochondria, in centrioles, and on the surface of lipid droplets (Moraczewsky and Duma, 1981; Buchwalow *et al.*, 1981). Platelets contained adenylate cyclase mainly in the dense tubular and open canalicular system (Cutler *et al.*, 1978, 1981). Stimulation of enzyme activity has been achieved in appropriate tissues with isoproterenol, NaF, glucagon, prostaglandin E_1, secretin, thyroid stimulating hormone, estrogens, and gonadotropic hormones. The most frequently used inhibitors were alloxan, 9-(tetrahydro-2-furyl)adenine, oxalacetic acid, and *p*-chloromercuribenzoic acid (Cutler *et al.*, 1981; Mizukami *et al.*, 1982). Guanylate cyclase (EC 4.6.1.2) activity has been localized on plasma membranes by Tse *et al.* (1978), Boyadjieva-Michailova *et al.* (1980), and Kang *et al.* (1982). Enzyme activity in the pancreatic islet cells can be stimulated by acetylcholine (Tse *et al.*, 1978).

2. Carbonic Anhydrase

Carbonic anhydrase (EC 4.2.1.1) is a zinc protein enzyme that catalyzes the hydration of carbon dioxide or the dehydration of carbonic acid. It is important in the regulation of acid–base homeostasis and salt and water transport by epithelia. The ultrastructural localization of the enzyme activity is currently based on the cobalt sulfide method of Hansson (1967), reviewed by Cassidy and Lightfoot (1974) and Rosen (1974) and described by Sugai and co-workers (Sugai and Ito, 1980a,b; Sugai *et al.*, 1981). In these studies, much information also can be obtained about the Hansson method and its modifications, the localization in different tissue cells, specificity of the reaction product, enzyme properties, specific inhibitors, and so on. Enzyme activity was present in the hyaloplasm of several cell types, sometimes associated with different kinds of subcellular organelles.

More recently, immunocytochemical techniques were used to detect carbonic anhydrase (Roussel *et al.*, 1979; Langley *et al.*, 1980; Sato *et al.*, 1980; Anderson *et al.*, 1982), particularly to overcome the controversy regarding the specificity of the cobalt trapping reaction (for references, see previously cited studies). In these reports the (immune) precipitate seemed to be confined to the cytosol and cytosolic surfaces of intracellular membranes. In the study of Anderson *et al.* (1982), the Hansson cobalt salt method has been compared with immunocytochemical localization of carbonic anhydrase, a finding indicating discrepancies between the two techniques.

3. Carboxylases

Two carboxylases are localized cytochemically: acetyl CoA carboxylase (EC 6.4.1.2) and phosphoenol pyruvate carboxylase (EC 4.1.1.31). The sites of both enzyme activities are visualized by the Gömöri-type lead precipitation technique.

The method to detect acetyl CoA carboxylase (the enzyme catalyzes the synthesis of malonyl CoA) has been developed by Yates *et al.* (1969) and is reviewed in detail by Higgins and Yates (1974). Lead phosphate precipitate is found to be associated with the cytoplasmic side of the rough endoplasmic reticulum in rat hepatocytes; in the mammary glands of hamsters and mice, reaction product is additionally noted in the Golgi fields and associated vacuoles (Higgins and Yates, 1974). Enzyme activity is also confined to the membranes of the endoplasmic reticulum and their derivatives in cells of an ascomycetous fungus, activity seen by using a slight modification of the technique of Yates *et al.* (Vorisek and Lojda, 1979). A new cytochemical method has been elaborated for the ultrastructural detection of phospholenol pyruvate carboxylase in an ascomycetous fungus (Vorisek *et al.*, 1980). Enzyme activity is localized in vacuoles, particularly in spherosomes (lipid globules), and less frequently in membranous vesicles.

IV. Perspectives of Future Research

Methodology based on either entirely new principles or major modifications for several enzymes or groups of enzymes have recently been introduced. The immunocytochemical approach for the detection of enzyme activities at the EM level is probably the technique with the most promising future. However, few examples are available as yet, e.g., taurine synthetizing enzyme (Lin and Wu, 1982), cathepsin D (Simonis *et al.*, 1982), phosphohydrolases (Lietz *et al.*, 1974; Reggio *et al.*, 1982), tyroxine hydroxylase (Pickel *et al.*, 1983), α-mannosidase (Zanetta *et al.*, 1983), enoyl CoA hydratase (Bendayan and Reddy, 1982; Bendayan *et al.*, 1983), catalase, and carbamoyl phosphate synthetase (Bendayan and Zöllinger, 1983; Knecht *et al.*, 1979).

The limiting factors in these new techniques, so far, have been twofold: the availability of specific antibodies and the poor penetration of the antibody–marker complex in structurally well-preserved tissue. However, it is expected that the number of monoclonal antibodies against enzymes will be growing fast. Coupling of antibodies to markers such as ferritin or colloidal gold particles of very small size (5 nm) (De Mey, 1983; De Mey *et al.*, 1981; Bendayan, 1982) no longer poses a problem and the use of non-resin-embedded tissue (Wolosewick, 1980) can largely solve the currently existing permeation problems.

The great advantage of immunoenzymology is that, if the aforementioned technicalities can be mastered, there is no other methodological problem that hampers the visualization of enzymes, so far inaccessible with the currently available techniques. A disadvantage, of course, is that this approach only tells us where the enzyme is located but gives no clues as to its activity.

A different type of enzymological visualization has been introduced by Bendayan (1981) and consists of localizing enzyme substrates. The purified enzyme is coupled to colloidal gold particles. The first approaches in this area were applied to DNA and RNA distribution.

A new promising innovation concerns the introduction of cerium ($CeCl_3$) as visualization metal (Fig. 3). First introduced in oxidase cytochemistry (Briggs *et al.*, 1975), cerium appears to give consistently reproducible results of high quality in phosphatase cytochemistry, such as alkaline and acid phosphatases, TPPase, NDPase, 5′-nucleotidase, G-6-Pase, and FDPase (Veenhuis *et al.*,

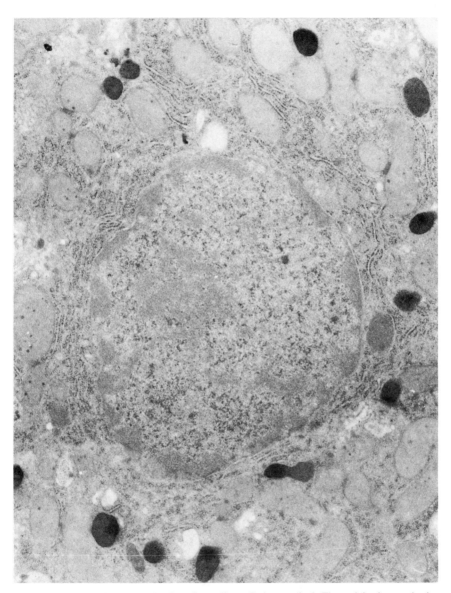

FIG. 3. Urate oxidase cytochemistry in rat liver. Cerium method. The activity is seen in the peroxisomes. ×22,400. (Courtesy Dr. M. Veenhuis, Dept. of Electron Microscopy, Biological Center, University of Groningen, The Netherlands.)

1980a,b; Robinson and Karnovsky, 1982; Hulstaert *et al.*, 1983). The only apparent drawback is its limitation to EM cytochemistry, because the phosphate salt of cerium or the cerium hydroperoxide is not, or only weakly, visible at the LM level. This excludes "stain" quantification.

Another interesting innovative field is represented by combined assessment of enzyme activities and nonenzymatic visualization of subcellular components such as carbohydrates, lipids, proteins, ions, and radiolabeled precursor substances. Examples are the localization of purine nucleoside phosphorylase and ACPase in lymphocyte subsets combined with labeling of immunoglobulins or monoclonal antibodies at the surface membrane (Borgers *et al.*, 1977, 1978).

The search for natural substrates for enzymes remains a necessity if we are to learn more about the exact role of some enzymes. Indeed, many substrates are artificial. Recently Wilson *et al.* (1983) detected a new organelle in PMNs containing strong AlPase activity (Fig. 2). The activity was found to be strongly enhanced when pyridoxal 5-phosphate was used, the latter being proposed as one of the physiological substrates of the enzyme. This would not only lead to higher or more consistently detectable activity, but, more important, could contribute to the better understanding of its physiological or pathophysiological meaning. Further progress in cytochemical characterization of enzymes depends on the exploration of existent methodology, both at the level of enzyme preservation and handling of detection media, the recent work of Uusitalo (1981) and De Jong (1982) being remarkable examples of the dormant potential in "old" methodology. It is to be hoped that these new outlooks will conveniently fulfill the urgent need for methods to visualize enzymes, hitherto not assessed, which could contribute enormously to the understanding of many unknown cell biological processes. Enzyme cytochemistry still has a long way to go, but no doubt, in its functioning as a bridge between biochemistry and morphology, it has a promising future.

REFERENCES

Abel, J. H., Jr. (1969). *J. Histochem. Cytochem.* **17**, 570–584.
Ackerman, G. A., and Clark, M. A. (1971). *Z. Zellforsch.* **117**, 463–475.
Ahrens, R., and Weissenfels, M. (1969). *Histochemie* **19**, 248–254.
Al-Ali, S. A., and Robinson, N. (1979a). *Histochemistry* **61**, 307–318.
Al-Ali, S. Y., and Robinson, N. (1979b). *J. Histochem. Cytochem.* **27**, 1261–1266.
Al-Ali, S. Y. A., and Robinson, N. (1982). *Histochem. J.* **14**, 311–321.
Allen, J. M. (1961). *J. Histochem. Cytochem.* **9**, 681–689.
Anderson, R. E., Gay, C. V., and Schraer, H. (1982). *J. Histochem. Cytochem.* **30**, 1335–1345.
Anderson, W. A., and Burnett, C. (1979). *J. Histochem. Cytochem.* **27**, 1363–1364.
Anderson, W. A., Bara, G., and Seligman, A. M. (1975). *J. Histochem. Cytochem.* **23**, 13–20.
Ando, T., Fujimoto, K., Mayahara, H., Miyajima, H., and Ogawa, K. (1981). *Acta Histochem. Cytochem.* **14**, 705–726.

Angermüller, S., and Fahimi, H. D. (1981). *Histochemistry* **71**, 33–44.

Arion, W. J., Wallin, B. K., Lange, A. J., and Ballas, L. M. (1975). *Mol. Cell. Biochem.* **6**, 75–83.

Arnold G., and Holtzman, E. (1980). *J. Histochem. Cytochem.* **28**, 1025–1028.

Arnold, G., Liscum, L., and Holtzman, E. (1977). *J. Cell Biol.* **75**, 202a.

Arnold, G., Liscum, L., and Holtzman, E. (1979). *J. Histochem. Cytochem.* **27**, 735–745.

Asano, G., Ashraf, M., and Schwartz, A. (1980). *J. Mol. Cell. Cardiol.* **12**, 257–266.

Athanassious, R., Klyne, M. A., and Ali, M. A. (1982). *Mikroskopie* **39**, 125–131.

Ausprunk, D. H., Berman, H. J., and McNary, W. F. (1973). *Am. J. Anat.* **137**, 31–45.

Backwinkel, K.-P., Schmitt, G., and Themann, H. (1971). *Virchows Arch. Abt. B Zellpathol.* **7**, 90–98.

Backwinkel, K.-P., Schmitt, G., Themann, H., and Haus, W. H. (1973). *Arzneimittelforschung (Drug Res.)* **23**, 198–201.

Bäck, N., Rechardt, L., and Pertanen, S. (1976). *Histochemistry* **46**, 121–130.

Baehner, R. L., Karnovsky, M. J., and Karnovsky, M. L. (1969). *J. Clin. Invest.* **48**, 187–192.

Bainton, D. F., and Farquhar, M. G. (1968). *J. Cell Biol.* **39**, 299–317.

Bainton, D. F., and Farquhar, M. G. (1970). *J. Cell Biol.* **45**, 54–73.

Bainton, D. F., Ullyot, J. L., and Farquhar, M. G. (1971). *J. Exp. Med.* **134**, 907–934.

Bal, A. K. (1974). In "Electron Microscopy of Enzymes. Principles and Methods" (M. A. Hayat, ed.), Vol. III, pp. 68–76. Van Nostrand-Reinhold, Princeton, New Jersey.

Ballas, L. M., and Arion, W. J. (1977). *J. Biol. Chem.* **252**, 8512–8518.

Bara, G. (1979). *Histochem. J.* **11**, 51–71.

Barka, T., and Anderson, P. J. (1962). *J. Histochem. Cytochem.* **10**, 741–753.

Barrett, J. M., and Heidger, P. M., Jr., (1975). *Cell Tissue Res.* **157**, 283–305.

Barrnett, R., and Palade, G. (1959). *J. Biophys. Biochem. Cytol.* **6**, 163–170.

Bauer, H., and Sigarlakie, E. (1973). *J. Microsc.* **99**, 205–218.

Beard, M. E., and Novikoff, A. B. (1969). *J. Cell Biol.* **42**, 501–518.

Bell, P. R. (1979). *Histochemistry* **62**, 85–91.

Bendayan M. (1981). *Histochem. J.* **13**, 699–708.

Bendayan, M. (1982). *J. Histochem. Cytochem.* **30**, 81–85.

Bendayan, M., and Reddy, J. K. (1982). *Lab Invest.* **47**, 364–369.

Bendayan, M., and Zöllinger, M. (1983). *J. Histochem. Cytochem.* **31**, 101–109.

Bendayan, M., Reddy, M. K., Hashimoto, T., and Reddy, J. K. (1983). *J. Histochem. Cytochem.* **31**, 509–516.

Benedeczky, I., and Rózsa, K. S. (1981a). *Histochemistry* **70**, 179–188.

Benedeczky, I., and Rózsa, K. S. (1981b). *Histochemistry* **70**, 189–197.

Benham, F., Cottell, D. C., Franks, L. M., and Wilson, P. D. (1977). *J. Histochem. Cytochem.* **25**, 266–274.

Benkoël, L., Chamlian, A., Barrat, E., and Laffargue, P. (1976). *J. Histochem. Cytochem.* **24**, 1194–1203.

Benner, U., Hacker, H. J., and Bannasch, P. (1979). *Histochemistry* **65**, 41–47.

Bentfeld, M. E., and Bainton, D. F. (1975). *J. Clin. Invest.* **56**, 1635–1649.

Berchtold, J.-P. (1977). *Histochemistry* **50**, 175–190.

Berchtold, J.-P. (1978). *Cell Tissue Res.* **188**, 143–148.

Berchtold, J.-P. (1979). *Histochemistry* **63**, 173–180.

Bergeron, J. J. M., Ehrenreich, J. H., Siekevitz, P., and Palade, G. E. (1973). *J. Cell Biol.* **59**, 73–88.

Berne, R. (1963) *Am. J. Physiol.* **204**, 317–322.

Bernstein, H.-G., Weiss, J., and Luppa, H. (1978). *Histochemistry* **55**, 261–267.

Berry, J. P., Hourdry, J., Sternberg, M., and Galle, P. (1982). *J. Histochem. Cytochem.*, **30**, 86–90.

Björkman, U., Ekholm, R., and Denef, J.-F. (1981). *J. Ultrastruct. Res.* **74**, 105–115.
Blitzer, B. L., and Boyer, J. L. (1978). *J. Clin. Invest.* **62**, 1104–1108.
Blok, J., Onderwater, J. J. M., de Water, R., and Ginsel, L. A. (1982). *Histochemistry* **75**, 437–443.
Bodansky, O., and Schwartz, M. K. (1968). *In* "Advance in Clinical Chemistry" (O. Bodansky and C. P. Stewart, eds.), Vol. 2, pp. 277–328. Academic Press, New York.
Bodel, P. T., Nichols, B. A., and Bainton, D. F. (1977). *J. Exp. Med.* **145**, 264–274.
Böck, P. (1973a). *Z. Zellforsch.* **144**, 539–547.
Böck, P. (1973b). *Z. Anat. Entwicklungsgesch.* **141**, 265–273.
Böck, P., Goldenberg, H., Hüttinger, M., Kolar, M., and Kramar, R. (1975). *Exp. Cell Res.* **90**, 15–19.
Böcking, A., and Riede, U. N. (1979). *J. Histochem. Cytochem.* **27**, 967–974.
Böcking, A., Hansert, J., and von Deimling, O. (1976a). *Histochemistry* **46**, 177–188.
Böcking, A., Grossarth, C., and von Deimling, O. (1976b). *Histochemistry* **50**, 65–76.
Bogitsh, B. J. (1982). *Exp. Parasitol.* **53**, 57–67.
Bogitsh, B. J., and Shannon, W. A. Jr. (1971). *Exp. Parasitol.* **29**, 337–347.
Bogitsh, B. J., Davis, D. A., and Nunnally, D. A. (1968). *Exp. Parasitol.* **23**, 303–308.
Bonilla, E., Schotland, D. L., DiMauro, S., and Aldover, B. (1975). *J. Ultrastruct. Res.* **51**, 404–408.
Borgers, M. (1973). *J. Histochem. Cytochem.* **21**, 812–824.
Borgers, M., and De Nollin, S. (1975). *J. Parasitol.* **61**, 110–122.
Borgers, M., and Thoné, F. (1976). *Histochem. J.* **8**, 301–317.
Borgers, M., and Thoné, F. (1978). *Histochem. J.* **10**, 721–730.
Borgers, M., Vanden Bossche, H., and Schaper, J. (1970). *J. Histochem. Cytochem.* **18**, 519–521.
Borgers, M., Schaper, J., and Schaper, W. (1971a). *J. Histochem. Cytochem.* **19**, 526–539.
Borgers, M., Schaper, J., and Schaper, W. (1971b). *J. Mol. Cell. Cardiol.* **3**, 287–296.
Borgers, M., Schaper, J., and Schaper, W. (1972). *J. Histochem. Cytochem.* **20**, 1041–1048.
Borgers, M., Schaper, J., and Schaper, W. (1973a). *Bibl. Anat.* **12**, 124–130.
Borgers, M., Schaper, J., and Schaper, W. (1973b). *Virchows Arch. Abt. A Pathol. Anat.* **358**, 281–294.
Borgers, M., Schaper, J., Xhonneux, R., and Schaper, W. (1973c). *Virchows Arch. Abt A Pathol. Anat.* **361**, 283–297.
Borgers, M., De Nollin, S., De Brabander, M., and Thienpont, D. (1975a). *Am. J. Vet. Res.* **36**, 1153–1166.
Borgers, M., De Nollin, S., and Thoné, F. (1975b). *Histochemistry* **43**, 257–267.
Borgers, M., Verhaegen, H., De Brabander, M., Thoné, F., Van Reempts, J., and Geuens, G. (1977). *J. Immunol. Methods* **16**, 101–110.
Borgers, M., Thoné, F., De Cree, J., and De Cock, W. (1978a). *Histochem. J.* **10**, 31–43.
Borgers, M., Verhaegen, H., De Brabander, M., De Cree, J., De Cock, W., Thoné, F., and Geuens, G. (1978b). *Blood* **52**, 886–895.
Bosmann, H. B., and Pike, G. Z. (1971). *Biochim. Biophys. Acta* **227**, 402–407.
Bowen, I. D., and Lewis, G. H. J. (1980). *Histochemistry* **65**, 173–179.
Bowen, I. D., and Ryder, T. A. (1975). *Histochem. J.* **8**, 319–329.
Bowers, B., and Korn, E. D. (1973). *J. Cell Biol.* **59**, 784–791.
Boyadjieva-Michailova, A. G., Staneva, L. L., and Denkova, R. T. T. (1980). *Eur. Congr. Electron Microsc. Found. 7th*, Leiden **2**, 304–305.
Brandes, D., Zetterqvist, W., and Sheldon, H. (1956). *Nature (London)* **177**, 382–383.
Breton-Gorius, J. (1980). *Histochem. J.* **12**, 127–137.
Bretz, U., and Baggiolini, M. (1974). *J. Cell Biol.* **63**, 251–269.
Briggs, R. T., Drath, D. B., Karnovsky, M. L., and Karnovsky, M. J. (1975). *J. Cell Biol.* **67**, 566–586.

Broderson, S. H., Westrum, L. E., and Sutton, A. E. (1974). *Histochemistry* **40**, 13–23.
Broderson, S. H., Patton, D. L., and Stahl, W. L. (1978). *J. Cell Biol.* **77**, R13–R17.
Brown, A., and Millington, P. (1968). *Histochemie* **12**, 83–94.
Brunk, U. T., and Ericsson, J. L. E. (1972). *Histochem. J.* **4**, 349–363.
Brzin, M., and Pucihar, S. (1976). *Histochemistry* **48**, 283–292.
Brzin, M., Tennyson, V. M., and Duffy, P. E. (1966). *J. Cell Biol.* **31**, 215–242.
Brzin, M., Tennyson, V. M., and Duffy, P. E. (1967). *Int. J. Neuropharmacol.* **6**, 265–272.
Buchwalow, I. B., Kopiov, O. V., and Schulze, W. (1981). *Histochemistry* **72**, 625–634.
Burnstock, G., Campbell, G., Satchell, D. G., and Smythe, A. (1970). *Br. J. Pharmacol.* **40**, 668–688.
Butterworth, J. (1971). *Histochem. J.* **3**, 477–487.
Calvert, R., Malka, D., and Ménard, D. (1979). *Histochemistry* **63**, 209–220.
Campbell, W. G. (1968). *Lab. Invest.* **18**, 304–316.
Carrapio, F., and Pais, M. S. S. (1983). *Eur. J. Cell Biol.* **30**, 42–46.
Cassidy, M. M., and Lightfoot, F. G. (1974). *In* "Electron Microscopy of Enzymes. Principles and Methods" (M. A. Hayat, ed.), Vol. III, pp. 77–108. Van Nostrand-Reinhold, Princeton, New Jersey.
Chabot, J.-G., Ménard, D., and Hugon, J. S. (1978). *Histochemistry* **57**, 33–45.
Charbonne, F., Perissel, B., Chessebeuf, M., and Bazerolle, O. (1974). *Ann. Histochim.* **19**, 27–33.
Chase, W. (1963). *J. Histochem. Cytochem.* **11**, 96–101.
Chiba, T. (1973). *Anat. Rec.* **176**, 35–48.
Christie, K. M., and Stoward, P. J. (1977). *J. Ultrastruct Res.* **58**, 219–234.
Ciani, F., Contestabile, A., and Villani, L. (1978). *Histochemistry* **59**, 81–95.
Clark, J. M., Aiken, B. M., Vaughan, D. W., and Kagan, H. M. (1980a). *J. Histochem. Cytochem.* **28**, 90–92.
Clark, J. M., Vaughan, D. W., Aiken, B. M., and Kagan, H. M. (1980b). *J. Cell Biol.* **84**, 102–119.
Clark, S. L. (1961). *Am. J. Anat.* **109**, 57–83.
Cohn, R., Herman, R., and Zakim, D. (1969). *Am. J. Clin. Nutr.* **22**, 1204–1210.
Coleman, R. A., Ramp, W. K., Toverud, S. U., and Hanker, J. S. (1976). *Histochem. J.* **8**, 543–558.
Conway-Jones, P. B., and Rothman, A. H. (1978). *Exp. Parasitol.* **46**, 152–156.
Crévier, M., and Bélanger, L. F. (1955). *Science* **122**, 556.
Cronshaw, J. (1980). *J. Histochem. Cytochem.* **28**, 375–377.
Csuka, O., and Sugár, J. (1971). *Cancer* **27**, 422–426.
Cushieri, A., Mughal, S., and Kharbat, B. A. (1982). *Histochem. J.* **14**, 593–607.
Cutler, L., Rodan, G., and Feinstein, M. B. (1978). *Biochim. Biophys. Acta* **542**, 357–371.
Cutler, L. S. (1983). *J. Histochem. Cytochem.* **31**, 85–93.
Cutler, L. S., and Christian, C. P. (1980). *J. Histochem. Cytochem.* **28**, 62–65.
Cutler, L. S., Feinstein, M. B., Rodan, G. A., and Christian, C. P. (1981). *Histochem. J.* **13**, 547–554.
Czaninski, Y., and Catesson, A.-M. (1974). *In* "Electron Microscopy of Enzymes. Principles and Methods" (M. A. Hayat ed.), Vol. II, pp. 66–78. Van Nostrand-Reinhold, Princeton, New Jersey.
Czubaj, A. (1979). *Histochemistry* **61**, 189–198.
Dabholkar, A. S., and Ogawa, K. (1976). *Acta Histochem. Cytochem.* **9**, 214–226.
Dabholkar, A. S., and Ogawa, K. (1978). *Acta Histochem. Cytochem.* **11**, 52–63.
Daems, W. Th., Wisse, E., and Brederoo, P. (1972). *In* "Lysosomes. A Laboratory Handbook" (J. T. Dingle, ed.), pp. 150–199. North-Holland Publ., Amsterdam.
Daems, W. T., Wisse, P., Brederoo, P., and Emeis, J. J. (1975). *In* "Mononuclear Phagocytes in Immunity, Infection and Pathology" (R. van Furth, ed.), pp. 57–77. Blackwell, Oxford.

Daimon, T., and Caxton-Martins, A. (1977). *J. Anat.* **123**, 553–562.

Daimon, T., and Gotoh, Y. (1982). *Histochemistry* **76**, 189–196.

Daua, M., Hourdry, J., Hugon, J. S., and Ménard, D. (1980). *Histochemistry* **70**, 33–42.

Dauwalder, M., Whaley, W. G., and Kephart, J. E. (1969). *J. Cell Sci.* **4**, 455–497.

Davis, R., and Koelle, G. B. (1978). *J. Cell Biol.* **78**, 785–809.

De Bruyn, P. P. H., Michelson, S., and Becker, R. P. (1975). *J. Ultrastruct. Res.* **53**, 133–151.

Decker, R. S., and Wildenthal, K. (1978a). *Am. J. Pathol.* **92**, 1–22.

Decker, R. S., and Wildenthal, K. (1978b). *Lab. Invest.* **38**, 662–673.

Decker, R. S., Decker, M. L., and Poole, A. R. (1980). *J. Histochem. Cytochem.* **28**, 231–237.

De Duve, C. (1969). *In* "Lysosomes in Biology and Pathology" (J. T. Dingle and H. B. Fell, eds.), Vol. 1, pp. 1–40. North-Holland Publ., Amsterdam.

De Duve, C., Berthet, J., Hers, H. G., and Dupret, L. (1949). *Bull. Soc. Chim. Biol. (Paris)* **31**, 1242–1253.

Deimann, W., Freeman, R., and Fahimi, H. D. (1981). *J. Histochem. Cytochem.* **29**, 678–681.

De Jong, A. S. H. (1982). *Histochem. J.* **14**, 1–33.

Del Principe, D., Mancuso, G., Menichelli, A., Gabriotti, M., Cosmi, E. V., and Gherardi, G. (1980). *Biol. Cell.* **38**, 135–140.

De Mey, J. (1983). *In* "Immunochemistry" (J. L. Polak and S. Van Noorden, eds.), pp. 82–112. Wright, Bristol.

De Mey, J., Moeremans, M., Geuens, G., Nuydens, R., and De Brabander, M. (1981). *Cell Biol. Int. Rep.* **5**, 889–899.

Denizot, J.-P. (1982a). *Histochemistry* **74**, 213–221.

Denizot, J.-P. (1982b). *Histochem. J.* **14**, 239–255.

De Nollin, S., and Borgers, M. (1976). *Mykosen* **19**, 317–328.

De Nollin, S., Thoné, F., and Borgers, M. (1975). *J. Histochem. Cytochem.* **23**, 758–765.

De Nollin, S., Van Belle, H., Goossens, F., Thoné, F., and Borgers, M. (1977). *Antimicrob. Agents Chemother.* **11**, 500–513.

De Pierre, J., and Karnovsky, M. L. (1973). *J. Cell Biol.* **56**, 275–303.

De Pierre, J. W., and Karnovsky, M. L. (1974a). *J. Biol. Chem.* **249**, 7111–7120.

De Pierre, J. W., and Karnovsky, M. L. (1974b). *J. Biol. Chem.* **249**, 7121–7129.

De Vries, G. H. (1976). *Neurosci. Lett.* **3**, 117–122.

Dingle, J. T. (1973). *In* "Lysosomes in Biology and Pathology," Vol. 3. North-Holland Publ., Amsterdam.

Dingle, J. T., and Fell, H. B. (1969) *In* "Lysosomes in Biology and Pathology," Vol. 2. North-Holland Publ., Amsterdam.

Docampo, R., de Boiso, J. F., Boveris, A., and Stoppani, A. O. M. (1976). *Experientia* **32**, 972–975.

Dornand, J., Bonnafous, J.-C., and Mani, J.-C (1978). *Eur. J. Biochem.* **87**, 459–465.

Doty, S. B. (1980). *J. Histochem. Cytochem.* **28**, 66–68.

Doty, S. B., Smith, C. E., Hand, A. R., and Oliver, C. (1977). *J. Histochem. Cytochem.* **25**, 1381–1384.

Douglas, W. H. J., and Hitchcock, K. R. (1979). *J. Histochem. Cytochem.* **27**, 852–856.

Duma, A., and Moraczewski, J. (1980). *Histochemistry* **66**, 211–220.

Emmelot, P. (1973). *Eur. J. Cancer* **9**, 319–333.

Emmelot, P., Bos, C. S., Bennedetti, E. I., and Rümke, P. H. (1964). *Biochim. Biophys. Acta* **90**, 126–145.

Eppig, J. J., Jr. (1974). *In* "Electron Microscopy of Enzymes. Principles and Methods" (M. A. Hayat, ed.), Vol II, pp. 79–89. Van Nostrand-Reinhold, Princeton, New Jersey.

Ericsson, J. (1966). *J. Histochem. Cytochem.* **14**, 361–362.

Ericsson, J. L. E., and Trump, B. F. (1965). *Histochemie* **4**, 470–487.

Ernst, S. A. (1972a). *J. Histochem. Cytochem.* **20**, 13–22.

Ernst, S. A. (1972b). *J. Histochem. Cytochem.* **20**, 23–38.

Ernst, S. A. (1975). *J. Cell Biol.* **66**, 586–608.

Ernst, S. A., and Hootman, S. R. (1981). *Histochem. J.* **13**, 397–418.

Ernst, S. A., and Mills, J. W. (1980). *J. Histochem. Cytochem.* **28**, 72–77.

Essner, E. (1974). *In* "Electron Microscopy of Enzymes. Principles and Methods" (M. A. Hayat, ed.), Vol. II, pp. 1–33. Van Nostrand-Reinhold, Princeton, New Jersey.

Essner, E., Novikoff, A. B., and Masek, B. (1958). *J. Biophys. Biochem. Cytol.* **4**, 711–716.

Essner, E., Foch, J., and Fabrizio, P. (1965). *J. Histochem. Cytochem.* **13**, 647–656.

Esterhuizen, A. C., Spriggs, T. L. B., and Lever, J. D. (1968). *Diabetes* **17**, 33–36.

Etherton, J. E., and Botham, C. M. (1970). *Histochem. J.* **2**, 507–519.

Fahimi, H. D. (1968). *J. Histochem. Cytochem.* **16**, 547–550.

Fahimi, H. D. (1969). *J. Cell Biol.* **43**, 275–288.

Fahimi, H. D. (1979). *Histochem. Cytochem.* **27**, 1365–1366.

Fahimi (1980). *In* "Trends in Enzyme Histochemistry and Cytochemistry," pp. 33–47. Ciba Found. Symposium Publ. Excerpta Medica, Amsterdam.

Fahimi, H. D., Gray, B. A., and Herzog, V. K. (1976). *Lab. Invest.* **34**, 192–201.

Farnham. C. J. M. (1975). *Exp. Cell Res.* **91**, 36–46.

Farquhar, M. G., and Palade, G. E. (1966). *J. Cell Biol.* **30**, 359–379.

Farquhar, M. G., Bergeron, J. J. M., and Palade, G. E. (1974). *J. Cell Biol.* **60**, 8–25.

Farrell, E. C., and Baba, N. (1974). *In* "Electron Microscopy of Enzymes. Principles and Methods" (M. A. Hayat, ed.), Vol. III, pp. 135–152. van Nostrand-Reinhold, Princeton, New Jersey.

Felix, W., and Remien, J. (1971). *Z. Ges. Exp. Med.* **156**, 139–150.

Ferrans, V. J., Hibbs, R. G., and Buja, L. M. (1969). *Am. J. Anat.* **125**, 47–86.

Firth, J. A. (1978). *Histochem. J.* **10**, 253–269.

Firth, J. A. (1980). *J. Histochem. Cytochem.* **28**, 69–71.

Firth, J. A., and Bock, R. (1976). *Histochemistry* **47**, 145–157.

Firth, J. A., Farr, A., and Koppel, H. (1979). *Histochemistry* **61**, 157–165.

Fischer, E., and Horváth, I. (1977). *Histochemistry* **54**, 259–271.

Fishman, W. H. (1974). *Am. J. Med.* **56**, 617–650.

Florendo, N. T., Barrnett, R. J., and Greengard, P. (1971). *Science* **173**, 745–748.

Florendo, N. T., Pitcock, J. A., and Muirhead, E. E. (1978). *J. Histochem. Cytochem.* **26**, 441–451.

Fomina, W. A., Rogovine, V.V., Piruzyan, L. A., Muravieff, R. A., and Podovinnikova, E. A. (1975). *Experientia* **31**, 1030–1031.

Forbes, M. S., and Sperelakis, N. (1972). *Z. Zellforsch.* **134**, 1–11.

Fox, N., and Studzinski, G. P. (1982). *J. Histochem. Cytochem.* **30**, 364–370.

Friedenberg, R. M., and Seligman, A. M. (1972). *J. Histochem. Cytochem.* **20**, 771–792.

Friend, D. S., and Farquhar, M. G. (1967). *J. Cell Biol.* **35**, 357–376.

Fujimoto, T., Inomata, K., and Ogawa, K. (1982). *Histochem. J.* **14**, 87–98.

Fujita, H., and Okamoto, H. (1979). *Histochemistry* **64**, 287–295.

Galabov, J. G., Davidoff, M., and Manolov, M. S. (1969). *Anat. Anz. Ergaebungsh.* **125**, 713–719.

Galjaard (1980). *In* "Trends in Enzyme Histochemistry and Cytochemistry," pp. 53–65. Ciba Found. Symposium Publ. Excerpta Medica, Amsterdam.

Ganote, Ch., Rosenthal, A., Moses, H., and Tice, L. (1969). *J. Histochem. Cytochem.* **17**, 641–650.

Garavini, C., Martelli, P., and Borelli, B. (1981). *Histochemistry* **72**, 75–81.

Garrett, J. R., and Harrison, J. D. (1970). *Histochemie* **24**, 214–229.

Garrett, J. R., and Kidd, A. (1976). *Histochem. J.* **8**, 532–538.

Gartner, L. P., Seibel, W., Hiatt, J. L., and Provenza, D. V. (1978). *Histochem. J.* **10**, 115–122.

216   M. BORGERS AND A. VERHEYEN

Gautron, J. (1982). *Histochemistry* **76**, 469–478.
Gerzeli, G., and Cucchi, M. L. (1975). *Virchows Arch. Abt. A Pathol. Anat. Histol.* **365**, 201–212.
Gibson, W., and Fullmer, H. (1967). *Periodonctics* **5**, 226–232.
Gilloteaux, J. (1978). *Histochemistry* **55**, 209–224.
Giorgi, F., and Deri, P. (1976). *Histochemistry* **48**, 325–334.
Gömöri, G. (1939). *Proc. Soc. Exp. Biol. Med.* **42**, 23–26.
Gömöri, G. (1941). *Arch. Pathol.* **32**, 188–199.
Gömöri, G. (1945). *Proc. Soc. Exp. Biol. Med.* **58**, 362–364.
Gömöri, G. (1950). *Stain Technol.* **25**, 81–85.
Gömöri, G. (1952). "Microscopic Histochemistry, Principles and Practice." Univ. of Chicago Press, Chicago.
Göthlin, G., and Ericsson, J. L. E. (1973). *Histochemie* **36**, 225–236.
Goff, C. W. (1973). *Protoplasma* **78**, 397–416.
Goff, C. W. (1980). *J. Histochem. Cytochem.* **28**, 372–374.
Goldenberg, H., Hüttinger, M., Böck, P., and Kramar, R. (1975a) *Histochemistry* **44**, 47–56.
Goldenberg, H., Hüttinger, M., Ludwig, R., Kramar, R., and Böck, P. (1975b). *Exp. Cell Res.* **93**, 438–442.
Goldenberg, H., Hüttinger, M., Kampfer, P., Kramar, R., and Pavelka, M. (1976). *Histochemistry* **46**, 189–206.
Golder, T. K., Nieberg, P. S., and Wilson, B. W. (1977). *J. Histochem. Cytochem.* **25**, 376–383.
Golder, T. K., Nieberg, P. S., and Wilson, B. W. (1978) *J. Histochem. Cytochem.* **26**, 719–728.
Goldfischer, S. (1965). *J. Histochem. Cytochem.* **13**, 520–523.
Goldfischer, S., Essner, E., and Novikoff, A. B. (1964). *J. Histochem. Cytochem.* **12**, 72–95.
Goldsmith, P. K., and Stetten, M. R. (1979). *Biochim. Biophys. Acta* **583**, 133–147.
Gossrau, R. (1981). *J. Histochem. Cytochem.* **29**, 464–480.
Graham, R. C., and Karnovsky, M. J. (1966). *J. Histochem. Cytochem.* **14**, 291–302.
Greene, R. M., and Pratt, R. M. (1979). *J. Histochem. Cytochem.* **27**, 924–931.
Griffith, D. L., and Bondareff, W. (1973). *Am. J. Anat.* **136**, 549–556.
Grossi, C. E., Cadoni, A., Zicca, A., Leprini, A., and Ferrarini, M. (1982). *Blood* **59**, 277–283.
Grossman, I. W., and Heitkamp, D. H. (1968). *J. Histochem. Cytochem.* **16**, 645–653.
Gruber, P. J., and Frederick, S. E. (1977). *Planta* **135**, 45–49.
Guitierrez, L. S., and Burgos, M. H. (1978). *J. Ultrastruct. Res.* **63**, 244–251.
Gunawardana, V. K., Mayahara, H., and Ogawa, K. (1982). *Histochemistry* **74**, 157–169.
Guth, L., and Samaha, F. J. (1970). *Exp. Neurol.* **25**, 365–367.
Hájos, F., Sótonyi, P., Kerpel-Fronius, S., Somogyi, E., and Budjosó, G. (1974). *Histochemistry* **40**, 89–95.
Hall, J. L., Kinney, A. J., Drymott, A., Thorpe, J. R., and Brummell, D. A. (1982). *Histochem. J.* **14**, 323–331.
Hand, A. R. (1975). *Histochemistry* **41**, 195–206.
Hand, A. R. (1976). *J. Histochem. Cytochem.* **24**, 915–925.
Hand, A. R. (1979). *J. Histochem. Cytochem.* **27**, 1367–1370.
Hand, A. R. (1980). *J. Histochem. Cytochem.* **28**, 82–86.
Hand, A. R., and Hassell, J. R. (1976). *J. Histochem. Cytochem.* **24**, 1000–1011.
Hand, A. R., and Oliver, C. (1977). *Histochem. J.* **9**, 375–392.
Hanker, J. S. (1975). In "Electron Microscopy of Enzymes. Principles and Methods" (M. A. Hayat, ed.), Vol. IV, pp. 1–139. Van Nostrand-Reinhold, Princeton, New Jersey.
Hanker, J. S., Kusyk, C. J., Bloom, F. E., and Pearse, A. G. E. (1973). *Histochemie* **33**, 205–230.
Hanker, J. S., Thornburg, L. P., Yates, P. E., and Romanovicz, D. K. (1975). *Histochemistry* **41**, 207–225.

Hanker, J. S., Coleman, R. A., Carson, K. A., and Pearse, A. G. E. (1977a). *Acta Histochem. Cytochem.* **10,** 380–386.

Hanker, J. S., Preece, J. W., Jefferson Burkes, E., Jr., and Romanovicz, D. K. (1977b). *Histochem. J.* **9,** 711–728.

Hanna, C. H., Hopkins, T. A., and Buck, J. (1976). *J. Ultrastruct. Res.* **57,** 150–162.

Hansson, H. P. J. (1967). *Histochemie* **11,** 112–128.

Hardonk, M. J. (1968). *Histochemie* **12,** 1–17.

Hardonk, M. J., and Koudstaal, J. (1968a). *Histochemie* **12,** 18–28.

Hardonk, M. J., and Koudstaal, J. (1968b). *Histochemie* **15,** 290–299.

Harrison, J. D., and Auger, D. W. (1982). *Histochem. J.* **14,** 703–711.

Harrison, J. D., Borgers, M., and Thoné, F. (1979). *Histochem. J.* **11,** 311–320.

Healy, P. J., and Dinsdale, D. (1979). *Histochem. J.* **11,** 289–298.

Hedqvist, P., and Fredholm, B. P. (1976). *Arch. Pharmacol.* **293,** 217–223.

Hers, H. G., Berthet, J., Berthet, L., and de Duve, C. (1951). *Bull. Soc. Chim. Biol. (Paris)* **33,** 21–41.

Hersey, S. S., Simon, T. W., and Baste, C. (1975). *J. Histochem. Cytochem.* **13,** 271–282.

Herzog, V. (1973). *Acta Histochem. Suppl.* **13,** 203–206.

Herzog, V. (1979). *J. Histochem. Cytochem.* **27,** 1360–1362.

Herzog, V., and Fahimi, H. D. (1974). *J. Cell Biol.* **60,** 303–311.

Herzog, V., and Fahimi, H. D. (1975). *J. Mol. Cell. Cardiol.* **8,** 271–281.

Herzog, V., and Fahimi, H. D. (1976). *Histochemistry* **46,** 273–286.

Hicks, L., and Fahimi, H. D. (1977). *Cell Tissue Res.* **175,** 467–481.

Higgins, J. A. (1974). *In* "Electron Microscopy of Enzymes. Principles and Methods" (M. A. Hayat, ed.), Vol. 2, pp. 34–85. Van Nostrand-Reinhold, Princeton, New Jersey.

Higgins, J. A., and Barrnett, R. J. (1970). *J. Cell Sci.* **6,** 29–51.

Higgins, J. A., and Barrnett, R. J. (1971). *J. Cell Biol.* **50,** 102-120.

Higgins, J. A., and Yates, R. D. (1974). *In* "Electron Microscopy of Enzymes. Principles and Methods" (M. A. Hayat, ed.), Vol. III, pp. 153–165. Van Nostrand-Reinhold, Princeton, New Jersey.

Highman, B., Frith, C., and Littlefield, N. (1975). *J. Natl. Cancer Inst.* **54,** 257–261.

Hirai, K.-I. (1969). *J. Histochem. Cytochem.* **17,** 585–590

Hirsimäki, P., and Reunanen, H. (1980). *Histochemistry* **67,** 139–153.

Hitchcock-O'Hare, K., Meymaris, E., Bonaccorso, J., and Vanburen, S. B. (1976). *J. Histochem. Cytochem.* **24,** 487–507.

Hoff, H. F. (1969). *Histochemie* **18,** 210–216.

Hoffman, H.-P., Szabo, A., and Avers, C. J. (1970). *J. Bacteriol.* **104,** 581–584.

Hofstein, S., Gennaro, D. E., Weissmann, G., Hirsch, J., Streuli, F., and Fox, A. C. (1975). *Am. J. Pathol.* **79,** 193–200.

Holt, S. (1980). *In* "Trends in Enzyme-Histochemistry and Cytochemistry," pp. 53–65. Ciba Found. Symposium Publ. Excerpta Medica, Amsterdam.

Holt, S. J., and Hicks, R. M. (1961a). *J. Biophys. Biochem. Cytol.* **11,** 31–45.

Holt, S. J., and Hicks, R. M. (1961b). *J. Biophys. Biochem. Cytol.* **11,** 47–66.

Holtzman, E., Freeman, A. R., and Kashner, L. A. (1970). *J. Cell Biol.* **44,** 438–445.

Hopsu, V. K., Arstila, A. V., and Glenner, G. G. (1965). *Ann. Med. Exp. Biol. Fenn.* **43,** 114–116.

Hopsu-Havu, V. K., and Helminen, H. (1974). *In* "Electron Microscopy of Enzymes. Principles and Methods" (M. A. Hayat ed.), Vol II, pp. 90–109. Van Nostrand-Reinhold, Princeton, New Jersey.

Hopsu-Havu, V. K., Arstila, A. V., Helminen, H. J., and Kalimo, H. O. (1967). *Histochemie* **8,** 54–64.

Hori, S. H. (1966). *Stain Technol.* **41**, 91–95.

Hoshino, Y., and Shannon, W. A. (1979). *Acta Histochem. Cytochem.* **12**, 206–212.

Houdry, J., and Hugon, J. S. (1979). *Histochemistry* **63**, 181–190.

Howell, S. L., and Whitfield, M. (1972). *J. Histochem. Cytochem.* **20**, 873–879.

Hruban, Z., and Rechcigl, M. (1969). *Int. Rev. Cytol. Suppl.* **1**, 1–296.

Hündgen, M. (1968). *Histochemie* **15**, 46–61.

Hündgen, M. (1972). *Acta Histochem.* **12**, 291–295.

Hugon, J. S. (1973). *In* "Electron Microscopy and Cytochemistry" (E. Wisse, W. Th. Daems, I. Molenaar, and P. van Duijn, eds.), pp. 29–50. North-Holland Publ., Amsterdam.

Hugon, J., and Borgers, M. (1966). *J. Histochem. Cytochem.* **14**, 629–640.

Hugon, J., and Borgers, M. (1967). *Exp. Cell Res.* **45**, 698–702.

Hugon, J., and Borgers, M. (1968a). *Histochemie* **12**, 42–66.

Hugon, J., and Borgers, M. (1968b). *Gastroenterology* **55**, 608–618.

Hugon, J. S., and Borgers, M. (1969a). *Acta Histochem.* **34**, 349–359.

Hugon, J., and Borgers, M. (1969b). *Histochemie* **19**, 13–30.

Hugon, J., Borgers, M., and Loni, M. C. (1967). *J. Histochem. Cytochem.* **15**, 417–418.

Hugon, J. S., Borgers, M., and Maestracci, D. (1970). *J. Histochem. Cytochem.* **18**, 361–364.

Hugon, J. S., Maestracci, D., and Ménard, D. (1971). *J. Histochem. Cytochem.* **19**, 515–525.

Hugon, J. S., Maestracci, D., and Ménard, D. (1973). *J. Histochem. Cytochem.* **21**, 426–440.

Hulstaert, C. E., Torringa, J. I., Koudstaal, J., Hardonk, M. J., and Molenaar, I. (1973). *Gynecol. Invest.* **4**, 24–30.

Hulstaert, C. E., Kalicharan, D., and Hardonk, M. J. (1983). *Histochemistry* **78**, 71–79.

Idé, C., and Saito, T. (1980). *Histochemistry* **65**, 83–92.

Iozzo, R. V., MacDonald, G. H., and Wight, T. N. (1982). *J. Histochem. Cytochem.* **30**, 697–701.

Israel, M., and Franchon-Mastour, P. (1970). *Arch. Anat. Microsc. Morphol. Exp.* **59**, 382–392.

Ito, A., and Palade, G. E. (1978). *J. Cell Biol.* **79**, 590–597.

Itoiz, M. E., De Rey, B. M., and Cabrini, R. L. (1982). *Histochem. J.* **14**, 205–213.

Jaeken, L., and Thinès-Sempoux, D. (1978). *Cell Biol. Int. Rep.* **2**, 515–524.

Jaubert, F., Monnet, J. P., Danel, C., Chretien, J., and Nezelot, C. (1978). *Histochemistry* **59**, 141–147.

Johnson, M. P., and Wooding, F. B. P. (1978). *Histochem. J.* **10**, 171–183.

Jones, C. J. P., and Fox, H. (1976). *J. Pathol.* **119**, 91–99.

Joó, F., and Tóth, I. (1975). *Naturwissenschaften* **62**, 397–398.

Jorgensen, A. O., Shen, A. C.-Y., MacLennan, D. H., and Tokuyasu, K. T. (1982a). *J. Cell Biol.* **92**, 409–416.

Jorgensen, A. O., Shen, A. C.-Y., Daly, P., and MacLennan, D. H. (1982b). *J. Cell Biol.* **93**, 883–892.

Kalderon, A. E. (1977). *In* "Electron Microscopy of Enzymes. Principles and Methods" (M. A. Hayat, ed.), Vol. V, pp. 1–25. Van Nostrand-Reinhold, Princeton, New Jersey.

Kalderon, A. E., and Ravanshenas, S. F. (1974). *Histochemistry* **39**, 229–242.

Kalderon, A. E., Dobbs, J. W., and Greenberg, M. L. (1980). *Histochemistry* **65**, 277–289.

Kang, Y.-H., Sahai, A., Criss, W. E., and West, W. L. (1982). *J. Histochem. Cytochem.* **30**, 331–342.

Kaplan, S., and Novikoff, A. B. (1959). *J. Histochem. Cytochem.* **7**, 295.

Karnovski, M. J. (1964). *J. Cell Biol.* **23**, 217–232.

Karnovski, M. J., and Roots, L. (1964). *J. Histochem. Cytochem.* **12**, 219–221.

Karnovsky, M. L., Robinson, J. M., Briggs, R. T., and Karnovsky, M. L. (1981). *Histochem. J.* **13**, 1–22.

Kasa, P., and Csillik, B. (1966). *Neurochemistry* **13**, 1345–1349.

Katayama, I., Li, C. Y., and Yam, L. T. (1972). *Am. J. Pathol.* **69**, 471–482.

Katory, M. D., and Berne, R. M. (1969). *Circ. Res.* **19**, 420–425.
Kayahara, T. (1982). *Histochem. J.* **14**, 347–360.
Kempen, H. J. M., de Pont, J. J. H. H. M., Bonting, S. L., and Stadhouders, A. M. (1978). *J. Histochem. Cytochem.* **26**, 298–312.
Kerényi, N. A., Sótonyi, P., and Somogyi, E. (1975). *Histochemistry* **46**, 77–80.
Kerpel-Fronius, S., and Hajós, F. (1968). *Histochemie* **14**, 343–351.
Kessel, R. G., Panje, W. R., and Decker, M. L. (1969). *J. Ultrastruct. Res.* **27**, 319–329.
Kim, S. K., Han, S. S., and Nasjleti, C. E. (1976). *Histochemie* **47**, 89–99.
Kim. S. U. (1976). *Histochemistry* **48**, 205–217.
King, B. F. (1982). *Histochemistry* **74**, 115–121.
Klaushofer, K., and Pavelka, M. (1975). *Histochemistry* **43**, 373–385.
Klaushofer, K., Böck, P., and Miller, M. (1974). *Histochemistry* **39**, 41–55.
Klinar, B., and Brzin, M. (1977). *Histochemistry* **50**, 313–318.
Kluge, H., Zahlten, W., Hartmann, W., Wieczorek, V., and Ring, U. (1975). *Acta Biol. Med. Germ.* **34**, 27–36.
Knecht E., Hernandez, F., Wallace, R., and Grisola, S. (1979). *J. Histochem. Cytochem.* **27**, 978–981.
Kobayashi, S., Takeuchi, T., Asami, K., and Fujiwara, T. (1982). *Exp. Parasitol.* **54**, 202–212.
Koelle, G. B., and Friedenwald, J. S. (1949). *Proc. Soc. Exp. Biol. Med.* **70**, 617–622.
Koenig, C. S., and Vial, J. D. (1973). *Histochem. J.* **5**, 503–518.
Koenig, C. S., Santelices, L. C., and Vial, J. D. (1976). *J. Histochem. Cytochem.* **24**, 1065–1075.
Kokko, A., Mautner, H. G., and Barnett, R. J. (1969). *J. Histochem. Cytochem.* **17**, 625–640.
Kolata, G. B. (1977). *Science* **198**, 596–598.
Komiyama, A., and Spicer, S. S. (1974). *J. Histochem. Cytochem.* **22**, 1092–1104.
Kral, K., and Schneider, L. (1981). *Cell Tissue Res.* **221**, 351–359.
Kreutzberg, G. W., Barron, K. D., and Schubert, P. (1978). *Brain Res.* **158**, 247–257.
Krupa, P. L., and Bogitsh, B. J. (1975). *Exp. Parasitol.* **37**, 147–156.
Kugler, P. (1982). *Histochemistry* **74**, 199–212.
Kumagae, Y., Sasajima, K., Hashimato, M., Numajiri, H., Tokunaga, Z., Tanaka, N., Shirota, A., and Asano, G. (1981). *Histochem. J.* **13**, 57–62.
Kunze, E., and Schauer, A. (1971). *Z. Krebsforsch.* **75**, 146–160.
Kunze, E., Schauer, A., and Krüsmann, G. (1975). *Z. Krebsforsch.* **84**, 143–160.
Kvinnsland, S. (1979). *Histochem. J.* **11**, 669–684.
Kyriacou, K., and Garrett, J. R. (1980). *Histochem. J.* **12**, 609–614.
Kyte, J. (1974). *J. Biol. Chem.* **249**, 3652–3660.
Kyte, J. (1976a). *J. Cell Biol.* **68**, 287–303.
Kyte, J. (1976b). *J. Cell Biol.* **68**, 304–318.
Langley, O. K., Ghandour, M. S., Vincendon, G., and Gombos, G. (1980). *Histochem. J.* **12**, 473–483.
Lazarus, S. G., Volk, B. W., and Barden, H. (1966). *J. Histochem. Cytochem.* **14**, 233–246.
Lazarus, S. S., and Barden, H. (1962). *J. Histochem. Cytochem.* **10**, 285–293.
LeHir, M., Herzog, V., and Fahimi, H. D. (1979). *Histochemistry* **64**, 51–66.
Legrand, B. (1973). *C. R. Soc. Biol.* **167**, 1820–1823.
Lehrer, G. M., and Ornstein, L. (1959). *J. Biophys. Biochem. Cytol.* **6**, 399–406.
Lemay, A., and Jarett, L. (1975). *J. Cell Biol.* **65**, 39–50.
Leonard, E. P., and Provenza, D. V. (1972). *Histochemie* **30**, 1–12.
Leskes, A., Siekevitz, P., and Palade, G. E. (1971). *J. Cell Biol.* **45**, 264–287.
Leuenberger, P. M., and Novikoff, A. B. (1974). *J. Cell Biol.* **60**, 721–731.
Leuenberger, P. M., and Novikoff, A. B. (1975). *J. Cell Biol.* **65**, 324–334.
Leung, T.-K., and Babai, F. (1974). *J. Microsc.* **21**, 111–118.

220 M. BORGERS AND A. VERHEYEN

Lewis, P. R., and Shute, C. C. D. (1964). *J. Physiol. (London)* **175**, 5–7P.
Lewis, P. R., and Shute, C. C. D. (1966). *J. Cell Sci.* **1**, 381–390.
Lewis, P. R., and Shute, C. C. D. (1969). *J. Microsc.* **89**, 181–193.
Liesi, P., Panula, P., and Rechardt, L. (1980). *Histochemistry* **70**, 7–18.
Lietz, H., Böcker, W., and Gröblinghoff M. (1974). *Histochemistry* **42**, 181–191.
Lin, C. T., and Wu, J. Y. (1982). *J. Cell Biol.* **95**, 16a.
Lin, C. W., Sasaki, M., Orcutt, M. L., Miyayama, H., and Singer, R. M. (1976). *J. Histochem. Cytochem.* **24**, 659–667.
Lindberg, L.-A., and Palkama, A. (1974). *Histochemistry* **38**, 285–296.
Lindberg, L.-A., and Palkama, A. (1977). *Histochem. J.* **9**, 277–284.
Linnemans, W. A. M., Boer, P., and Elbers, P. F. (1977). *J. Bacteriol.* **131**, 638–644.
Litwin, J. A. (1979). *Folia Histochem. Cytochem.* **17**, 3–28.
Livingston, D. C., Coombs, M. M., Franks, L. M., Maggi, V., and Gahan, P. B. (1969). *Histochemie* **18**, 48–60.
Lockshin, R. A., and Beaulaton, J. (1974). *J. Ultrastruct. Res.* **46**, 43–62.
Lojda, Z. (1981). *J. Histochem. Cytochem.* **29**, 481–493.
Lowe, M. C., Reichenbach, D. D., and Horita, A. (1975). *J. Pharmacol. Exp. Ther.* **194**, 522–536.
Luft, J. H. (1961). *J. Biophys. Biochem. Cytol.* **9**, 409–414.
Luppa, H., Weiss, J., and Martin, G. (1972). *Acta Histochem.* **43**, 184–188.
Luppa, H., Weiss, J., and Bernstein, H.-G. (1976). *Histochemistry* **49**, 309–313.
Ma, M. H., and Biempica, L. (1971). *Am. J. Pathol.* **62**, 353–390.
McLaren, D. J., Burt, J. S., and Ogilvie, B. M. (1974). *Int. J. Parasitol.* **4**, 39–46.
McMahan, U. J., Sanes, J. R., and Marshall, L. M. (1978). *Nature (London)* **271**, 172–174.
Maggi, V., Franks, L. M., and Carbonell, A. W. (1966). *Histochemie* **6**, 305.
Magnusson, B. C., Heyden, G., and Svennson, S. E. (1974). *Histochemistry* **42**, 1–8.
Mahrle, G., and Orfanos, C. E. (1975a). *Br. J. Dermatol.* **93**, 495–507.
Mahrle, G., and Orfanos, C. E. (1975b). *Br. J. Dermatol.* **91**, 529–540.
Majcen, Z., and Brzin, M. (1979). *Histochemistry* **63**, 295–302.
Malassiné, A. (1976). *Histochemistry* **47**, 191–205.
Malassiné, A. (1980). *Histochemistry* **65**, 239–248.
Maldonado, J. E., and Pierre, R. V. (1975). *Mayo Clin. Proc.* **50**, 573–587.
Malpiece, Y., Sharan, M., Barbotin, J.-N., Personne, P., and Thomas, D. (1981). *J. Histochem. Cytochem.* **29**, 633–643.
Mao, P., Nakao, K., and Angrist, A. (1966). *Lab. Invest.* **15**, 422–434.
Marani, E. (1982). Thesis, University of Leiden.
Marchesi, V. T., and Palade, G. E. (1967). *J. Cell Biol.* **35**, 385–404.
Marinos, E. (1978). *J. Histochem. Cytochem.* **26**, 658–662.
Martin, B. J., Spicer, S. S., and Smythe, N. M. (1974). *Anat. Rec.* **178**, 769–786.
Masters, C., and Holmes, R. (1977). *Physiol. Rev.* **57**, 816–882.
Masubuchi, S. (1972). *Acta Pathol. Jpn.* **22**, 107–130.
Masuzawa, T., Shimabukuro, H., Sato, F., and Saito, T. (1981). *Histochemistry* **72**, 489–498.
Maxwell, D. P., Maxwell, M. D., Hänssler, G., Armentrout, V. N., Murray, G. M., and Hoch, H. C. (1975). *Planta* **124**, 109–123.
Maxwell, M. H. (1978). *Histochem. J.* **10**, 63–77.
Mayahara, H., Hirano, H., Saito, T., and Ogawa, K. (1967). *Histochemie* **11**, 88–96.
Mayahara, H., Fujimoto, K., Ando, T., and Ogawa, K. (1980). *Histochemistry* **67**, 125–138.
Mayahara, H., Ando, T., Ishikawa, Y., and Ogawa, K. (1982). *Acta Histochem. Cytochem.* **15**, 421–438.
Mazurkiewicz, J. E., Hossler, F. E., and Barrnett, R. J. (1978). *J. Histochem. Cytochem.* **26**, 1042–1052.

Meda, P. (1978). *Diabetologia* **14**, 305–310.

Mednick, M. L., Petrali, J. P., Thomas, N. C., Sternberger, L. A., Plapinger, R. E., Davis, D. A., Wasserkrug, H. L., and Seligman, A. M. (1971). *J. Histochem. Cytochem.* **19**, 155–160.

Ménard, D. (1980). *Histochemistry* **67**, 53–64.

Ménard, D., Penasse, W., Drochmans, P., and Hugon, J. S. (1974). *Histochemistry* **38**, 229–239.

Michaels, A. S., Jelsema, C. L., and Barrnett, R. J. (1983). *J. Ultrastruct. Res.* **82**, 35–51.

Misra, D. N., Gill, T. J., III, and Estes, L. W. (1974). *Biochim. Biophys. Acta* **352**, 455–461.

Misra, D. N., Ladoulis, C. T., Estes, L. W., and Gill, T. J. III (1975). *Biochemistry* **14**, 3014–3024.

Miyayama, H., Sasaki, M., and Fishman, W. H. (1974). *J. Histochem. Cytochem.* **22**, 287–288.

Miyayama, H., Solomon, R., Sasaki, M., Lin, C. W., and Fishman, W. H. (1975). *J. Histochem. Cytochem.* **23**, 439–451.

Mizukami, Y., Matsubara, F., and Matsukawa, S. (1982). *Histochemistry* **74**, 9–19.

Mizutani, A. (1967). *J. Histochem. Cytochem.* **15**, 603.

Mizutani, A. (1968). *J. Histochem. Cytochem.* **16**, 172–180.

Mizutani, A., and Barrnett, R. J. (1965). *Nature (London)* **206**, 1001–1003.

Mizutani, A. (1979). *Acta Histochem. Cytochem.* **12**, 157–164.

Mizutani, A., and Fujita, H. (1968a). *J. Histochem. Cytochem.* **16**, 546–547.

Mizutani, A., and Fujita, H. (1968b). *Acta Histochem. Cytochem.* **1**, 79–94.

Mizutani, A., and Fujita, H. (1968c). *Bull. Chest Dis. Res. Inst. Kyoto Univ.* **2**, 1–10.

Mölbert, R. G., Duspiva, F., and von Deimling, O. H. (1960a). *J. Biophys. Biochem. Cytol.* **7**, 387–390.

Mölbert, R. G., Duspiva, F., and von Deimling, O. H. (1960b) *Histochemie* **2**, 5–22.

Monahan, R. A., Dvorak, H. F., and Dvorak, A. M. (1981). *Blood* **58**, 1089–1099.

Monneron, A. (1974). *J. Histochem. Cytochem.* **22**, 1128–1134.

Mooradian, B. A., and Cutler, L. S. (1978). *J. Histochem. Cytochem.* **26**, 989–999.

Moraczewsky, J., and Duma, A. (1981). *Histochemistry* **71**, 301–311.

Morita, M., Sugimoto, J., and Tashiko, U. (1969). *Jpn. J. Pharmacol.* **19**, 613–618.

Moses, H., Rosenthal, A., Beaver, D., and Schuffman, S. (1966). *J. Histochem. Cytochem.* **14**, 702–710.

Moses, H. L., and Rosenthal, A. S. (1968). *J. Histochem. Cytochem.* **16**, 530–539.

Moss, D. W. (1974). *Histochem. J.* **6**, 353–360.

Müller, E., Van Noorden, S., and Pearse, A. G. E. (1971). *J. Mol. Cell. Cardiol.* **3**, 209–212.

Müller, J., and Da Laga, C. (1977). *J. Histochem. Cytochem.* **25**, 337–348.

Murabe, Y., and Sano, Y. (1981). *Histochemistry* **71**, 45–52.

Murata, F., Nagata, T., and Spicer, S. S. (1975). *Histochemistry* **44**, 307–312 (1975).

Nagata, T. (1974). *In* "Electronmicroscopy of Enzymes. Principles and Methods" (M. A. Hayat ed.), Vol. II, pp. 132–148. Van Nostrand-Reinhold, Princeton, New Jersey.

Nagata, T., and Murata, F. (1972). *Histochemie* **29**, 8–15.

Nakagaki, I., Goto, T., Sasaki, S., and Imai, Y. (1978). *J. Histochem. Cytochem.* **26**, 835–845.

Neurath, H., and Walsh, K. A. (1976). *Proc. Natl. Acad. Sci. U.S.A.* **73**, 3825–3832.

Nichols, B. A. (1976). *J. Exp. Med.* **144**, 920–932.

Nichols, B. A., and Bainton, D. F. (1973). *Lab. Invest.* **29**, 27–40.

Nichols, B. A., and Bainton, D. F. (1975). *In* "Mononuclear Phagocytes in Immunity, Infection and Pathology" (R. van Furth, ed.), pp. 17–55. Blackwell, Oxford.

Nichols, B. A., Bainton, D. F., and Farquhar, M. G. (1971). *J. Cell Biol.* **50**, 498–515.

Nishimura, E. T., Whest, G. M., and Yang, H.-Y. (1976). *Lab Invest.* **34**, 60–68.

Nordlie, R. C. (1974). *Curr. Top. Cell. Regul.* **8**, 33–117.

North, R. J. (1966). *J. Ultrastruct. Res.* **16**, 83–95.

Novikoff, A. B. (1959). *J. Biophys. Biochem. Cytol.* **6**, 136–138.

Novikoff, A. B. (1963). *Ciba Found. Symp. Lysosomes* pp. 36–73.

Novikoff, A. B. (1964). *Biol. Bull.* **127**, 359.

Novikoff, A. B. (1967). *J. Histochem. Cytochem.* **15**, 353–354.

Novikoff, A. B. (1976). *Proc. Natl. Acad. Sci. U.S.A.* **73**, 2781–2787.

Novikoff, A., and Goldfisher, S. (1961). *Proc. Natl. Acad. Sci. U.S.A.* **47**, 802–810.

Novikoff, A. B., and Goldfischer, S. (1968). *J. Histochem. Cytochem.* **16**, 507.

Novikoff, A. B., and Goldfischer, S. (1969). *J. Histochem. Cytochem.* **17**, 657–680.

Novikoff, A. B., and Novikoff, P. M. (1977). *Histochem. J.* **9**, 525–551.

Novikoff, A. B., Essner, E., Goldfischer, S., and Heus, M. (1962). *Symp. Int. Soc. Cell Biol.* **1**, 149–192.

Novikoff, A. B., Novikoff, P. M., Davis, C., and Quintana, N. (1972). *J. Histochem. Cytochem.* **20**, 1006–1023.

Novikoff, A. B., Quintana, N., and Mori, M. (1978). *J. Histochem. Cytochem.* **26**, 83–93.

Novikoff, P. M., and Novikoff, A. B. (1972). *J. Cell Biol.* **53**, 532–560.

Ogawa, K., and Mayahara, H. (1969). *J. Histochem. Cytochem.* **17**, 487–490.

Ogawa, K., Saito, T., and Mayahara, H. (1966). *In* "Electron Microscopy, 1966" (R. Uyeda, ed.), Vol. II, pp. 105. Maruzen, Tokyo.

Ogawa, K., Saito, T., Hirano, H., and Mayahara, H. (1967). *Acta Anat. Nippon.* **42**, 40.

Ogawa, K., Saito, T., and Mayahara, H. (1968). *J. Histochem. Cytochem.* **16**, 45–47.

Ogawa, T., Koerten, H. K., and Daems, W. Th. (1978). *Cell Tissue Res.* **188**, 361–373.

O'Hare, K. H., Reiss, O. K., and Vatter, A. E. (1971). *J. Histochem. Cytochem.* **19**, 97–123.

Ono, K. (1979). *Histochemistry* **62**, 113–124.

Ono, K., and Satoh, Y. (1981). *Histochemistry* **71**, 501–512.

Osumi, M., and Sato, M. (1978). *J. Electron Microsc.* **27**, 127–136.

Osumi, M., Miwa, N., Teranishi, Y., Tanaka, A., and Fukui, S. (1974). *Arch. Microbiol.* **99**, 181–201.

Osumi, M., Fukuzumi, F., Teranishi, Y., Tanaka, A., and Fukui, S. (1975). *Arch. Microbiol.* **103**, 1–11.

Otero-Vilardebó, L. R., Lane, N., and Godman, G. C. (1963). *J. Cell Biol.* **19**, 647–652.

Ovtscharoff, W. (1973). *Histochemie* **37**, 93–95.

Ozeki, M., and Sato, M. (1970). *Comp. Biochem. Physiol.* **32**, 203–209.

Paavola, L. G. (1978a). *J. Cell Biol.* **79**, 45–58.

Paavola, L. G. (1978b). *J. Cell Biol.* **79**, 59–73.

Padykula, H. A., and Herman, E. (1955). *J. Histochem. Cytochem.* **6**, 61–71.

Palva, M., Tervo, T., and Plakama, A. (1978). *Cell. Mol. Biol.* **23**, 33–41.

Pannese, E., Luciano, L., Iwato, S., and Reale, E. (1974). *Histochemistry* **39**, 1–13.

Panula, P., and Rechardt, L. (1978). *Histochemistry* **55**, 49–54.

Panula, P., and Rechardt, L. (1979) *Histochemistry* **64**, 35–50.

Papka, R. E. (1975). *Cell Tissue Res.* **162**. 185–194.

Pardoz, G. J., and Lentz, T. L. (1976). *Brain Res.* **107**, 355–364.

Payne, B. C., Kim, H., Pangalis, G. A., Rothman, A., and Rappaport, H. (1980). *Histochem. J.* **12**, 71–86.

Pearse, A. G. E. (1972). *In* "Histochemistry. Theoretical and Applied," Vol. 1, 3rd Ed., pp. 535–536. Churchill Livingstone, Edinburgh.

Penasse, W., and Frühling, J. (1973). *Histochemie* **34**, 117–126.

Perotti, M. E., and Anderson, W. A. (1980). *Eur. Congr. Electron Microsc. Found., 7th, Leiden* **2**, 310–311.

Perotti, M. E., Anderson, W. A., and Swift, H. (1983). *J. Histochem. Cytochem.* **31**, 351–365.

Personne, P., and Anderson, W. (1970). *J. Cell Biol.* **44**, 20–28.

Phillis, J. W., and Kostopoulos, G. K. (1975). *Life Sci.* **17**, 1085–1094.

Pickel, V., Joh, T. H., and Reis, D. H. (1975). *Brain Res.* **85**, 295–300.

Pino, R. M., and Bankston, P. W. (1979). *J. Histochem. Cytochem.* **27**, 643–652.

Pino, R. M., Pino, L. C., and Bankston, P. W. (1981). *J. Histochem. Cytochem.* **29**, 1061–1070.

Pipan, N., and Psenicnik, M. (1975). *Histochemistry* **44**, 13–21.

Poole, A. R., and Mort, J. S. (1981). *J. Histochem. Cytochem.* **29**, 494–500.

Poux, N. (1970). *J. Microsc.* **9**, 407–434.

Pugh, D., and Cawson, R. A. (1975). *Sabouraudia* **13**, 110–115.

Quiviger, B., de Chastellier, C., and Ryter, A. (1978). *J. Ultrastruct. Res.* **62**, 228–236.

Rainina, E. I., Zubatov, A. G., Buchwalow, I. B., and Luzikov, V. N. (1979). *Histochem. J.* **11**, 299–310.

Rash, J. E., and Ellisman, M. H. (1974). *J. Cell Biol.* **63**, 567–586.

Raymackers, E., and Hugon, J. S. (1973). *Histochemie* **34**, 65–76.

Reale, E. (1962). *Exp. Cell Res.* **26**, 210–211.

Rechard, L, and Kokko, A. (1967). *Histochemie* **10**, 278–286.

Reddy, J. K., Krishnakantha, T. P., and Rao, M. S. (1975). *Virchows Arch. B Cell Pathol.* **17**, 295–306.

Reddy, J. K., Rao, M. S., Moody, D. E., and Qureshi, S. A. (1976). *J. Histochem. Cytochem.* **24**, 1239–1248.

Reggio, H., Harms, E., Bainton, D., Condrier, E., and Lonvard, D. (1982). *J. Cell Biol.* **95**, 413a.

Regh, J. E., Montali, R. J., and Szymkowiak, M. E. (1975). *Vet. Pathol.* **12**, 186–195.

Reid, E. (1967). *In* "Enzyme Cytology" (D. B. Roodyn, ed.), pp. 321–406. Academic Press, New York.

Reik, L., Petzold, G. L., Higgins, J. A., Greengard, P., and Barrnett, R. J. (1970). *Science* **168**, 382–384.

Revis, N. W. (1979). *J. Histochem. Cytochem.* **27**, 1322–1326.

Robinson, J. M., and Karnovsky, M. J. (1982). *J. Cell Biol.* **95**, 462a.

Roels, F. (1976). *J. Histochem. Cytochem.* **24**, 713–724.

Roels, F., and Goldfischer, S. (1979). *J. Histochem. Cytochem.* **27**, 1471–1477.

Roels, F., and Wisse, E. (1973). *C. R. Acad. Sci. (Paris) Ser. D* **276**, 391–393.

Roels, F., Wisse, E., De Prest, B., and Van der Meulen, J. (1974a). *Histochemistry* **6**, 91–92.

Roels, F., Wisse, E., De Prest, B., and Van der Meulen, J. (1974b). *In* "Electron Microscopy and Cytochemistry" (E. Wisse, W. Th. Daems, I. Molenaar, and P. van Duijn, eds.), pp. 115–118. North-Holland Publ. Amsterdam.

Roels, F., Wisse, E., De Prest, B., and Van der Meulen, J. (1975). *Histochemistry* **41**, 281–312.

Roels, F., De Coster, W., and Goldfischer, S. (1977). *J. Histochem. Cytochem.* **25**, 157–160.

Rosen, S. (1974). *In* "Electron Microscopy of Enzymes. Principles and Methods" (M. A. Hayat, ed.), Vol. III, pp. 109–134. Van Nostrand-Reinhold, Princeton, New Jersey.

Rosenthal, A., Moses, H., Beaver, D., and Schuffman, S. (1966). *J. Histochem. Cytochem.* **14**, 698–701.

Rostomian, M. A., and Abramian, K. S. (1980). *Eur. Congr. Electron Microsc. Found., 7th,* Leiden **2**, 302–303.

Rostomian, M. A., Abramian, K. S., and Hajos, F. (1981). *Histochemistry* **70**, 167–171.

Roussel, G., Delaunoy, J.-P., Nussbaum, J.-L., and Mandel, P. (1979). *Brain Res.* **160**, 47–55.

Rubin, W., and Aliasgharpour, A. A. (1976). *Anat. Rec.* **184**, 251–264.

Rubio, R. (1974). *In* "Electron Microscopy of Enzymes. Principles and Methods" (M. A. Hayat, ed.), Vol. 3, pp. 54–67. Van Nostrand-Reinhold, Princeton, New Jersey.

Rubio, R., and Berne, R. M. (1969). *Circ. Res.* **25**, 407–415.

Rubio, V. R., Wiedmeier, T., and Berne, R. M. (1972). *Am. J. Physiol.* **222**, 550–555.

Russo, J., and Wells, P. (1977). *J. Histochem. Cytochem.* **25**, 135–148.

Rustin, G. J. S., Wilson, P. D., and Peters, T. J. (1979). *J. Cell Sci.* **36**, 401–412.

Ryder, T. A., and Bowen, I. D. (1975). *J. Histochem. Cytochem.* **23,** 235–237.

Sabatini, D. D., Bensch, K., and Barrnett, R. J. (1962). *Anat. Rec.* **142,** 274.

Sabatini, D. D., Bensch, K., and Barrnett, R. J. (1963). *J. Cell Biol.* **17,** 19–58.

Sachs, G., Spenney, J. G., and Rehm, W. S. (1977). *Int. Rev. Physiol.* **12,** 127–171.

Sakharova, A. V., Salimova, N. B., and Sakharov, D. A. (1979). *Neuroscience* **4,** 1173–1177.

Salomon, C. D. (1974). *Calcium Tissue Res.* **15,** 201–212.

Salpeter, M. M., Rogers, A. W., Kasprzak, H., and McHenry, F. A. (1978). *J. Cell Biol.* **78,** 274–285.

Sannes, P. L., Katsuyama, T., and Spicer, S. G. (1979). *J. Histochem. Cytochem.* **27,** 873–877.

Sasaki, F. (1979). *Acta Histochem. Cytochem.* **12,** 7–19.

Sasaki, M., and Fishman, W. H. (1973). *J. Histochem. Cytochem.* **21,** 653–660.

Satler, J. J., Predan, S., and Brzin, M. (1974). *Histochemistry* **39.** 65–70.

Sato, A., Spicer, S. S., and Tashian, R. E. (1980). *Histochem. J.* **12,** 651–659.

Sawano, F., and Fujita, H. (1981). *Histochemistry* **71,** 335–348.

Sawyer, H. R., Golder, T. K., Nieberg, P. S., and Wilson, B. W. (1976). *J. Histochem. Cytochem.* **24,** 969–978.

Schlüns, J., and Graf, R. (1976). *Histochemistry* **48,** 219–232.

Schober, R., and Thomas E. (1978). *Cell Tissue Res.* **186,** 39–52.

Schubert, P., Komp, W., and Kreutzberg, G. W. (1979). *Brain Res.* **168,** 419–424.

Schuurhuis, G. J., Dijk, F., Hardonk, M. J., and Molenaar, I. (1980). *Eur. Cong. Electron Microsc. Found., 7th, Leiden* **2,** 314–315.

Schwartz, M., Seigel, G. J., Chen, N., and Agranoff, B. W. (1980). *J. Neurochem.* **34,** 1745–1752.

Schwartz, M., Ernst, S. A., Siegel, G. J., and Agranoff, B. W. (1981). *J. Neurochem.* **36,** 107–115.

Sehgal, S. S., Tewari, J. P., and Malhotra, S. K. (1981). *Cytobios* **30,** 69–82.

Seibel, W., Gartner, L. P., Hiatt, J. L., and Provenza, D. V. (1979). *Histochem. J.* **11,** 435–445.

Seiden, D. (1973). *Z. Zellforsch.* **144,** 467–473.

Seligman, A. M., Ueno, H., Wasserkrug, H. L., and Hanker, J. S. (1966). *Ann. Histochem.* **11,** 115–129.

Seligman, A. M., Karnovsky, M. J., Wasserkrug, H. L., and Hanker, J. S. (1968). *J. Cell Biol.* **38,** 1–14.

Seligman, A. M., Kawashima, T., Ueno, H., Katzoff, L., and Hanker, J. S. (1970). *Acta Histochem. Cytochem.* **3,** 29–40.

Seligman, A. M., Shannon, W. H., Sternberger, N. J., Serrano, J. A., Paul, B. D., Wasserkrug, H. L., and Serrano, A. A. (1975). *J. Histochem. Cytochem.* **23,** 322.

Seligman, M. L., Ueno, H., Hanker, J. S., Kramer, S. P., Wasserkrug, J., and Seligman, A. M. (1966). *Exp. Mol. Pathol. Suppl.* **3,** 21–35.

Serrano, J. A., Shannon, W. A., Jr., Sternberger, N. S., Wasserkrug, H. L., Serrano, A. A., and Seligman, A. M. (1976). *J. Histochem. Cytochem.* **24,** 1046–1056.

Shannon, W. A. (1978). *J. Histochem. Cytochem.* **26,** 202–204.

Shannon, W. A., Wasserkrug, H. L., and Seligman, A. M. (1974). *J. Histochem. Cytochem.* **22,** 170–182.

Shannon, W. A., Wasserkrug, H. L., Plapinger, R. E., and Seligman, A. M. (1976). *J. Histochem. Cytochem.* **24,** 527–539.

Sheldon, H., Zetterqvist, W., and Brandes, D. (1955). *Exp. Cell Res.* **9,** 592–596.

Shio, H., and Lazarow, P. B. (1981). *J. Histochem. Cytochem.* **29,** 1263–1272.

Shnitka, T. K. (1974). *In* "Electron Microscopy of Enzymes. Principles and Methods" (M. A. Hayat, ed.), Vol. III, pp. 1–53. Van Nostrand-Reinhold, Princeton, New Jersey.

Silverberg, B. A. (1975). *Protoplasma* **83,** 269–295.

Silverberg, B. A., and Sawa, T. (1974). *Protoplasma* **81,** 177–188.

Simonis, S., Snyder, D. S., Uzman, B. G., and Whitaker J. N. (1982). *J. Cell Biol.* **95,** 439a.

Sketelj, J., and Brzin, M. (1979). *Histochemistry* **61**, 239–248.

Slezak, J., and Geller, S. A. (1979). *J. Histochem. Cytochem.* **27**, 774–781.

Smith, G. P., and Peters, T. J. (1980). *Cell Biol. Int. Rep.* **4**, 747.

Smith, R. E., and Dean, P. N. (1979). *J. Histochem. Cytochem.* **27**, 1499–1504.

Smith, R. E., and van Frank, R. M. (1975). *In* "Lysosomes in Biology and Pathology" (J. T. Dingle and R. T. Dean, eds.), Vol. IV, pp. 193–249. American Elsevier, New York.

Somogyi, E., and Sotonyi, P. (1969). *Acta Histochem.* **34**, 70–85.

Somogyi, E., Sotonyi, P., and Nemes, A. (1978). *Arzneimittelforsch.* **28**, 2070–2075.

Song, C. S., and Ray, T. K. (1970). *Biochim. Biophys. Acta* **196**, 1–9.

Song, C. S., Kappers, A., and Bodansky, O. (1969). *Ann. N.Y. Acad. Sci.* **166**, 565–573.

Sosa, A., Gonzales-Angulo, A., Calzada, L., and Alva, S. (1978). *Experientia* **34**, 175–177.

Spater, H. W., Novikoff, A. B., Spater, S. H., and Quintana, N. (1978). *J. Histochem. Cytochem.* **26**, 809–821.

Spater, H. W., Schnitzer, J. A., Quintana, N., Spater, S. H., and Novikoff, A. B. (1981). *J. Histochem. Cytochem.* **29**, 693–702.

Spitznagel, J. K., Dalldorf, F. G., Leffell, M. S., Fold, J. D., Welsh, I.R.H., Cooney, M. H., and Martin, L. E. (1974). *Lab. Invest.* **30**, 774–785.

Stetten, M. R., and Burnett, F. F. (1967). *Biochim. Biophys. Acta* **139**, 138–147.

Stiller, D., and Rauscher, H. (1971). *Exp. Pathol.* **5**, 255–258.

Stirling, C. E. (1972). *J. Cell Biol.* **53**, 704–714.

Stirling, C. E. (1976). *J. Microsc.* **106**, 145–157.

Stöhr, G., Deimann, W., and Fahimi, H. D. (1978). *J. Histochem. Cytochem.* **26**, 406–411.

Stoward (1980). *In* "Trends in Enzyme Histochemistry and Cytochemistry," pp. 11–31. Ciba Found. Symposium Publ. Excerpta Medica, Amsterdam.

Sugai, N., and Ito, S. (1980a). *J. Histochem. Cytochem.* **28**, 511–525.

Sugai, N., and Ito, S. (1980b). *J. Histochem. Cytochem.* **28**, 563–569.

Sugai, N., Ninomiya, Y., and Oosaki, T. (1981). *Histochemistry* **72**, 415–424.

Sugimoto, K., Ichikawa, Y., and Nakamura, I. (1983). *Cell Tissue Res.* **230**, 451–461.

Sugimura, K., and Mizutani, A. (1978). *Histochemistry* **55**, 97–105.

Sugimura, K., and Mizutani, A. (1979a). *Histochemistry* **61**, 123–129.

Sugimura, K., and Mizutani, A. (1979b). *Histochemistry* **61**, 131–137.

Suran, A. A. (1974). *J. Histochem. Cytochem.* **22**, 802–811.

Takamatsu, H. (1939). *Trans. Soc. Pathol. Jpn.* **29**, 492–498.

Taylor, I. M. (1976). *Histochemistry* **47**, 239–246.

Teranishi, Y., Kawamoto, S., Tanaka, A., Osumi, M., and Fukui, S. (1974). *Agric. Biol. Chem.* **38**, 1221–1225.

Tervo, T. (1976). *Histochemistry* **47**, 133–143.

Tervo, T., Palva, M., and Plakama, A. (1977). *Cell Tissue Res.* **176**, 431–443.

Threadgold, L. T., and Brennan, G. (1978). *Exp. Parasitol.* **46**, 300–316.

Tice, L. W. (1969). *J. Histochem. Cytochem.* **17**, 85–94.

Tice, L. W. (1974). *Endocrinology* **95**, 421–433.

Tice, L. W., and Barrnett, R. J. (1962). *J. Histochem. Cytochem.* **10**, 754–762.

Tice, L. W., and Wollman, S. H. (1972). *Lab. Invest.* **26**, 63–73.

Tiffon, Y., and Hugon, J. S. (1977). *Histochemistry* **54**, 289–297.

Todd, M. M., and Vigil, E. L. (1972). *J. Histochem. Cytochem.* **20**, 344–349.

Tohyama, M., Akai, F., Sakumoto, T., and Maeda, T. (1972). *Ann. Histochim.* **17**, 203–214.

Tolbert, N. E. (1981). *Annu. Rev. Biochem.* **50**, 133–157.

Tóth, J., Csuka, O., and Sugár, J. (1972). *Virchows Arch. Abt. B Zellpathol.* **12**, 84–90.

Trams, E. G., and Lauter, C. J. (1974). *Biochim. Biophys. Acta* **345**, 180–197.

Trandaburu, T. (1976). *Histochemistry* **48**, 1–6.

Tranzer, J. P. (1965). *J. Microsc.* **4**, 409–412.

Trelease, R. N. (1975). In "Electron Microscopy of Enzymes. Principles and Methods" (M. A. Hayat, ed.), Vol. IV, pp. 157–176. Van Nostrand-Reinhold, Princeton, New Jersey.

Trout, J. J., Stauber, W. T., and Schottelius, B. A. (1979). Histochem. J. 11, 223–230.

Tse, J. S. T., Shibayama, Y., and Lin, B. J. (1978). Histochemistry 58, 297–305.

Tsou, K. C. (1975). In "Electron Microscopy of Enzymes. Principles and Methods" (M. A. Hayat, ed.), Vol. IV, pp. 141–156. Van Nostrand-Reinhold, Princeton, New Jersey.

Tsuji, S. (1974). Histochemistry 42, 99–110.

Unger, E., and Buchwalow, I. B. (1975). In "Electron Microscopy of Enzymes. Principles and Methods" (M. A. Hayat, ed.), Vol. 4, pp. 202–216. Van Nostrand-Reinhold, Princeton, New Jersey.

Uusitalo, R. J. (1981). Histochem. J. 13, 525–534.

Uusitalo, R. J., and Karnovsky, M. J. (1977a). J. Histochem. Cytochem. 25, 87–96.

Uusitalo, R. J., and Karnovsky, M. S. (1977b). J. Histochem. Cytochem. 25, 97–103.

Van Belle, H. (1972). Biochim. Biophys. Acta 289, 158–168.

Van Belle, H. (1976). Gen. Pharmacol. 7, 53–58.

Vanden Bossche, H., Verhoeven, H., Vanparijs, O., Lauwers, H., and Thienpont, D., (1979). Arch. Int. Physiol. Biochim. 87, 851–852.

Van der Rhee, H. J., de Winter, C. P. M., and Daems, W. Th. (1977). Cell Tissue Res. 185, 1–16.

Van Dongen, J. M., Kooyman, J., Visser, W. J., Holt, S. J., and Galjaard, H. (1977). Histochem. J. 9, 61–75.

Van Noorden, C. J. F., and Tas, J. (1982). J. Histochem. Cytochem. 30, 12–20.

Vatter, A. E., Reiss, O. K., Newman, J. K., Lindquist, K., and Groeneboer, E. (1968). J. Cell Biol. 38, 80–98.

Vaughn, K. C., and Duke, S. O. (1981). Histochemistry 72, 191–198.

Vaughn, K. C., Duke, S. O., Duke, S. H., and Henson, C. A. (1982). Histochemistry 74, 309–318.

Vennhuis, M., and Wendelaar Bonga, S. D. (1977). Histochem. J. 9, 171–181.

Veenhuis, M., and Wendelaar Bonga, S. D. (1979). Histochem. J. 11, 561–572.

Veenhuis, M., Van Dijken, J. P., and Harder, N. (1976). Arch. Microbiol. 111, 123–135.

Veenhuis, M., Van Dijken, J. P., and Harder, W. (1980a). Microbiol. Lett. 9, 285–292.

Veenhuis, M., Flik, G., and Wendelaar Bonga, S. E. (1980b). Eur. Congr. Electron Microsc. Found., 7th, Leiden 2, 284–285.

Vengesa, P. B., and Hopfer, U. (1979a). Histochem. J. 11, 289–298.

Vengesa, P. B., and Hopfer, U. (1979b). J. Histochem. Cytochem. 27, 1231–1235.

Verheyen, A., Borgers, M., Vanden Bossche, H., Vanparijs, O., Lauwers, H., and Thienpont, D. (1979). Biol. Cell. 35, 36a.

Von Deimling, O., and Böcking, A. (1976). Histochem. J. 8, 215–252.

Vorbrodt, A., and Borun, T. W. (1979). J. Histochem. Cytochem. 27, 1596–1603.

Vorbrodt, A. W., and Wisniewski, H. M. (1982). J. Histochem. Cytochem. 30, 418–424.

Vorisek, J., and Lojda, Z. (1979). Histochemistry 65, 59–65.

Vorisek, J., and Volfova, O. (1975). FEBS Lett. 52, 246–250.

Vorisek, J., Sajdl, P., and Lojda, Z. (1980). Histochemistry 67, 257–265.

Wachstein, M., and Meisel, E. (1956). J. Histochem. Cytochem. 4, 592.

Wachstein, M., and Meisel, E. (1957). Am. J. Clin. Pathol. 27, 13–23.

Wachstein, M., Bradshow, M., and Ortiz, J. M. (1962). J. Histochem. Cytochem. 10, 63–74.

Wagner, R. C., and Bitensky, M. W. (1974). In "Electron Microscopy of Enzymes. Principles and Methods" (M. A. Hayat, ed.), Vol. II, pp. 110–131. Van Nostrand-Reinhold, Princeton, New Jersey.

Wagner, R. C., Keiner, P., Barnett, R. J., and Bitensky, M. (1972). Proc. Natl. Acad. Sci. U.S.A. 69, 3175–3179.

Wakely, J. (1976). Histochem. J. 8, 351–356.

Watanabe, K., Sasaki, F., and Khan, M. A. (1978). *Histochemistry* **55**, 293–305.

Waters, S. E., and Butcher, R. G. (1980). *Histochem. J.* **12**, 191–200.

Weissenfels, N. (1967). *Histochemie* **9**, 189–202.

West, B. C., Rosenthal, A. S., Gelb, N. A., and Kimball, H. R. (1974). *Am. J. Pathol.* **77**, 41–66.

Widmann, J. J., and Fahimi, H. D. (1975). *Am. J. Pathol.* **80**, 349–366.

Widmann, J. J., Cotran, R. S., and Fahimi, H. D. (1972). *J. Cell Biol.* **52**, 159–170.

Widnell, C. C. (1972). *J. Cell Biol.* **52**, 542–558.

Widnell, C. C., and Unkeless, J. C. (1968). *Proc. Natl. Acad. Sci. U.S.A.* **61**, 1050–1052.

Williams, D. M., Linder, J. E., Hill, M. W., and Gillett, R. (1978). *J. Histochem. Cytochem.* **26**, 862–864.

Williams, D. M., Gillett, R., and Linder, J. E. (1979). *J. Histochem. Cytochem.* **27**, 665–675.

Wilson, P. D., and Hodges, G. M. (1979). *J. Histochem. Cytochem.* **27**, 1236–1246.

Wilson, P. D., Benham, F., and Franks, L. M. (1977). *Cell Biol. Int. Rep.* **1**, 229–238.

Wilson, P. D., Rustin, G. J. S., and Peters, T. J. (1981a). *Histochem. J.* **13**, 31–43.

Wilson, P. D., Rustin, G. J. S., Smith, G. P., and Peters, T. J. (1981b). *Histochem. J.* **13**, 73–84.

Wilson, P. D., Smith, G. P., and Peters, T. J. (1983). *Histochem. J.* **15**, 257–264.

Wiseman, A., Gillham, N. W., and Boynton, J. E. (1977). *J. Cell Biol.* **73**, 56–77.

Wisse, E. (1974). *J. Ultrastruct. Res.* **46**, 393–426.

Wolosewick, J. J. (1980). *J. Cell Biol.* **86**, 675–681.

Wood, J. G., Jean, D. H., Whitaker, J. N., McLaughlin, B. J., and Albers, R. W. (1977). *J. Neurocytol.* **6**, 571–581.

Yamashina, S., and Kawai, K. (1979). *Histochemistry* **60**, 255–263.

Yates, R. D., Higgins, J. A., and Barrnett, R. J. (1969). *J. Histochem. Cytochem.* **17**, 379–385.

Yokayama, M. (1974). *J. Electron Microsc.* **23**, 285–293.

Yokota, R. (1974). *Acta Histochem. Cytochem.* **7**, 217–230.

Yokota, S., and Fahimi, H. D. (1978). *Histochem. J.* **10**, 469–487.

Yokota, S., and Fahimi, D. (1981). *J. Histochem. Cytochem.* **29**, 805–812.

Yokota, S., and Nagata, T. (1974). *Histochemistry* **40**, 165–174.

Yoneda, K. (1978). *Am. J. Pathol.* **93**, 745–752.

Yoo, B. Y., and Oreland, L. (1976). *Histochemistry* **46**, 131–137.

Yoshiki, S., and Kurahashi, Y. (1971). *Arch. Oral Biol.* **16**, 1143–1154.

Zajic, G., and Schacht, J. (1983). *J. Histochem. Cytochem.* **31**, 25–28.

Zanetta, J. P., Roussel, G., Donternwill, M., and Vincendon, G. (1983). *J. Neurochem.* **40**, 202–208.

Zentgraff, H., Deumling, B., Jarasch, E. P., and Franke, W. W. (1971). *J. Biol. Chem.* **246**, 2989–2995.

INTERNATIONAL REVIEW OF CYTOLOGY, VOL. 95

Cell Position and Cell Interactions in Expression of Fetal Phenotype of Hepatocyte

A. S. GLEIBERMAN AND G. I. ABELEV

Laboratory of Tumor Immunochemistry, Cancer Research Center, Moscow, USSR

I. Introduction

The dependence of cell phenotype on its position in the tissue structure seems to be especially pronounced in the definitive liver plate. Most hepatic enzymes, revealed histochemically, produce well-expressed gradients along the central vein–portal tract axis. The gradients are typical, not only for the enzyme level in the liver lobule, but also for the order of cell involvements in the process of enzyme induction with the corresponding substrates, or the synthesis of the acute-phase proteins under stress conditions.

It should be emphasized that the "cell phenotype–cell position" dependency is expressed in the liver, so to say, in an immediate form. The gradients are not due to a specific distribution of putative hepatocyte subpopulations or to their clonal heterogeneity. They are formed, most probably, in a potentially homogeneous cell population. This makes liver tissue essentially different in its organization from lymphoid tissue; the latter is divided into genetically stable and noninterconvertible subpopulations and clones, which are not firmly bound to spatial positions.

The gradients in the liver lobule are not obviously related to the stage of maturation of the hepatocytes in their different parts, as, for instance, is the case with the differentiating cells in the intestinal crypt.

229

It is completely unknown how the hepatocyte "feels" its position in the liver lobule, and how it determines, according to this position, its phenotype.

The structural control of the cell phenotype is not limited to the characters of the mature, completely differentiated hepatocyte, it was shown that synthesis of liver-specific embryonic proteins, such as α-fetoprotein (AFP) or γ-glutamyl transpeptidase (GGT), is also controlled by cell interactions in the developing liver. The ability to synthesize AFP is fully retained in the mature, entirely differentiated hepatocyte, but it is reversibly repressed therein. The "topography" of such repression in the postnatal liver correlates clearly with the formation of the liver plates. The destruction of the plates by hepatotoxins or surgery results in the reappearance of AFP-synthesizing cells only in the destroyed areas.

These observations showed that the ability to synthesize a characteristic embryo-specific protein such as AFP is not only related to an early stage of hepatocyte development but is also controlled by a factor that is dependent, in one way or another, on the tissue structure. Hence, we have suggested that the expression of embryonic or adult phenotype by the hepatocyte is determined by whether the latter enters a certain tissue structure or remains relatively autonomous. In the first case, the "mature" phenotype is expressed; in the second the embryonic one.

In parallel with the studies on AFP regulation in the liver, an investigation of its synthesis in the yolk sac endoderm demonstrated very clearly the role of cell interactions in that process.

The possible role of cell interactions in the expression of the other embryo-specific protein, GGT, has been investigated far less. However, there are occasional observations suggesting such a role in the control of this protein also.

AFP and GGT can be considered as "direct embryonic markers" of the hepatocyte. But there exists in the liver a peculiar group of proteins, such as ligandin and A-protein, which are maximally and homogeneously expressed in the immature liver cell population but form well-expressed gradients in the adult liver lobule. In this case substitution of the immature phenotype by the adult one manifests itself in the capacity to construct a gradient. It is reasonable to discuss in this article the hepatocyte features characterizing this group.

Finally, during liver development, substitution of the acinary structures by the trabecular ones takes places, i.e., there is a formation of one-cell-thick liver plates. Simultaneously there occurs quite specific redistribution of certain antigens in the hepatocyte membrane. Localization of these antigens on the surface of the hepatocyte is firmly bound to the type of the structure—embryonic or adult—to which they belong. This group of antigens is also within the scope of our analysis.

Hence, in this article we shall consider the three aforementioned groups of characters: true embryonic markers and those macromolecules that are redistributed during liver ontogenesis. The role of cell interactions in the control of their expression is the primary focus on our discussion. The analysis of this role in AFP expression will be more thorough than the analyses of other markers since this protein is within our field of investigation. We also shall discuss the cell interaction control of AFP in the yolk sac, because this system is directly related to its synthesis in the liver.

II. AFP in the Yolk Sac Endoderm

Detailed immunohistochemical observation of AFP in the normal development of murine embryos showed that AFP appeared in the egg-cylinder stage on the seventh day p.c. (Engelhardt et al., 1973, 1974; Dziadek and Adamson, 1978). In this stage, AFP is localized exclusively in the visceral endoderm and mainly in its embryonic part. Later on, synthesis of AFP spreads into the extraembryonic part of the visceral endoderm.

AFP was also found in the blood of patients with teratocarcinoma (Abelev et al., 1967; Masopust et al., 1968). All AFP-positive samples of teratocarcinoma contain structures corresponding to the yolk sac visceral endoderm. It is true for human primary teratocarcinomas and for mouse and rat primary and transplantable ones (Engelhardt et al., 1973, 1974; Teilum et al., 1975; Teilum, 1976; Damjanov and Sell, 1977; Suurmejer et al., 1983). All these findings served as the biological basis of AFP application in teratocarcinoma immunodiagnostics (see Abelev, 1974; Abelev and Elgort, 1982).

The immunomorphological data were supported by experiments with isolated inner cell mass (ICM: epiblast of early murine embryos) and with aggregates of embryonal carcinoma cells (ECC; stem cells of teratocarcinoma, equivalent in their developmental potencies to the ICM both in vivo and in vitro) (e.g., Mintz and Illmensee, 1975; Martin, 1981).

Aggregates of ECC are able to differentiate either spontaneously or after treatment with different inductors. As a rule, the first step of differentiation of floating aggregates of ECC is a formation of the endoderm layer on their free surfaces. These structures are called embryoid bodies. Embryoid bodies may be covered either with parietal endoderm or with visceral endoderm. Synthesis of AFP was found only in the case of visceral endoderm formation (see Martin, 1975; Solter and Damjanov, 1979; Hogan et al., 1983).

A close connection between the synthesis of AFP and the formation of the visceral endoderm in normal development of mouse embryo was demonstrated in excellent experiments by Dziadek (1979). She carried out three subsequent rounds of "immunosurgery" accompanied by immunohistochemical observations of AFP on in vitro-cultivated early murine embryos.

Immunosurgery is a method that enables the experimenter to kill the outer cell layer of an unimplanted embryo or of floating embryoid bodies by complement-dependent cytotoxic antisera without damaging inner cells (Solter and Knowles, 1975).

Dziadek showed that on the surface of intact murine embryos isolated in the morula stage and cultivated *in vitro* without attachment an AFP-negative layer consisting of trophoectodermal cells was formed. The first round of immunosurgery led to the replacement of trophoectoderm by an AFP-negative endoderm on the surface of ICM. This endoderm resembled the parietal one. Prolonged cultivation of these embryos resulted in the appearance of single AFP-positive cells in the outer cell layer. The second round of immunosurgery was carried out 1 day after the first round and resulted in formation of a strong AFP-positive cell layer resembling the visceral endoderm. The third round of immunosurgery did not result in regeneration of the outer layer.

Besides establishing an association between AFP and visceral endoderm, these experiments showed that the precursors of visceral and parietal endoderm seem to be separated from ICM and are exposed on its surface in sequence and at different times. The development of each type of the endoderm is possible only on the free surface of ICM.

Hence, synthesis of AFP in early embryogenesis is due to formation of the visceral endoderm.

The first steps of development, such as formation of trophoectoderm and endoderm, may be considered in terms of positional information. Indeed, the trophoblast is developed from the outer cells of the early murine embryo and the embryoblast is formed from the inner ones (Graham, 1971; Hillmann *et al.*, 1972). At the same time, all the cells of the embryo in these stages are totipotent, and their fates are dependent only on their location in the embryo.

The formation of endoderm also is characterized by topographic patterns and is connected with free surfaces of aggregates of polypotent embryonic cells.

However, there is some evidence that endoderm formation can be discussed in terms of local cell-to-cell interactions rather than in terms of positional information. This evidence was obtained on murine nullipotent teratocarcinoma F9.

As a rule, murine teratocarcinomas have no trophoectodermal derivatives, and embryoid bodies are covered with endoderm, parietal or visceral. Immunosurgery leads, for embryoid bodies, to regeneration of the same type of the provisore tissue. All differentiated structures found in teratocarcinomas originate from the ECC. However, ECC from various lines of transplantable teratocarcinomas are known to be different in their developmental potencies. In some cases, teratocarcinomas (the so-called nullipotent teratocarcinomas) lose the ability to form any differentiated structures and are composed of the ECC only.

F9 is the most well known mouse nullipotent teratocarcinoma (Bernstine *et al.*, 1973). F9 cells cannot form spontaneously any differentiating structures, both *in vivo* and *in vitro*. However, some years ago Strickland and Mahdavi

(1978) reported that treatment of the F9 cells with retinoic acid causes their differentiation into endodermal cells. Further observations demonstrated that combination of retinoic acid with cyclic AFP results in parietal endoderm formation (Strickland *et al.*, 1980). Treatment of cultures with retinoic acid alone and high cell density cause visceral endoderm formation accompanied by AFP synthesis (Hogan *et al.*, 1981). The development of visceral endoderm from F9 cells took place both in suspension culture, when embryoid bodies were formed, and in monolayer culture.

The dependency of visceral endoderm formation on cell density means, as suggested by the authors, that this process is regulated through cell-to-cell interactions.

As shown by the experiments of Dziadek (1978), not only is development of the visceral endoderm dependent on cell-to-cell interactions, but expression of AFP in this endoderm also is controlled by contact with the surrounding tissues. In a series of isolation–recombination experiments, she found that the extra embryonic part of visceral endoderm isolated from a 6-day-old mouse embryo begins to synthesize AFP at the same time that embryonal visceral endoderm does, although *in situ* the latter tissue starts to produce AFP a little earlier. Recombination of different regions of visceral endoderm with some other embryonic tissues showed that the contact with the extraembryonic ectoderm reversibly inhibited AFP synthesis both in embryonal and in extraembryonic visceral endoderm. In a 6- to 7-day-old mouse embryo, close contact between extraembryonic visceral endoderm and extraembryonic ectoderm occurs. It seems that this provides an explanation for the lag period in AFP synthesis in extraembryonic visceral endoderm. The lag continues up to the time of spreading of mesoderm into the extraembryonic part of the embryo, a movement which causes separation of extraembryonic ectoderm and visceral endoderm.

A correlation between the appearance of AFP and a change of other markers in developing endoderm is a particular interest. AFP is not an ultimate serum protein produced by visceral endoderm. In the yolk sac of the human embryo, synthesis of transferrin and albumin (besides AFP) was found (Gitlin and Boesman, 1967; Gitlin *et al.*, 1972). Synthesis of AFP and transferrin without albumin was found in 11- to 13-day-old murine yolk sac (Janzen *et al.*, 1982).

Interestingly, Adamson (1982) found synthesis of transferrin in 6-day-old murine visceral endoderm, i.e., earlier than the time at which synthesis of AFP was established.

It seems that the expression of AFP synthesis is an element of the united program of endoderm development dependent on the cell-to-cell interactions and characterized by strict topographic patterns. This process takes place on the free surface of aggregates of polypotent embryonic cells and is related to formation of inner and outer metabolic compartments (Ducibella *et al.*, 1975). Cell interactions determine both "permission" to transcribe the block of serum protein genes, including the AFP gene, (realized when visceral endoderm is differentiated) and regulation of the activity of the "permitted" gene.

III. The Liver

A. Structure and Morphophysiological Gradients

In ontogenesis the liver substitues for the yolk sac in hemopoiesis and serum protein production. The liver is related in its histogenesis to the yolk sac because it originates from the intestinal diverticulum. The intestinal endoderm is, in its turn, derived from the visceral endoderm (see Elias, 1955). The adult mammalian liver consists of layers one cell thick (liver plates) and formed the so-called muralium (Elias and Sherrick, 1969; Jones and Schmucker, 1977).

The blood supply in the liver creates a clear-cut gradient, i.e., the arterial blood comes to the liver parenchyma from the triads and goes out through the central veins (Rappoport, 1958, 1963, 1973).

In accordance with portocentrolobular gradient of blood supply, one can detect in the liver parenchyma morphological and morphogenetic gradients. Thus, the morphometric assay of hepatocytes in the adult rat reveals that the degree of development of rough endoplasmic reticulum (RER) forms a gradient from the triads to the central veins (Jones and Schmucker, 1977; Schmucker et al., 1978). This finding indicates that the periportal hepatocytes are most active in the synthesis of secreted (plasma) proteins. Besides, the periportal hepatocytes in their features are "younger" than the centrolubular ones, in liver regeneration after partial hepatectomy, the triad areas appear to be the "proliferative centers" of the liver parenchyma. In the triad areas, the first mitoses are seen and from there they extend wavelike along the liver tissue (Bucher and Malt, 1971).

Conversely, the processes of detoxication and excretion are localized around the central veins.

Formation of the definitive liver structure is also organized in accordance with portocentrolobular gradients. The fading of proliferative activity and DNA synthesis in hepatocytes of early postnatal rat liver starts in the central vein areas and then extends toward the triads. In parallel, the first binucleated cells arise near the central veins and subsequently in the rest of the parenchyma (LeBouton and Marchand, 1970; LeBouton, 1974a,b, 1976). These processes lead to the establishment in the liver tissue of the ploidy gradient as well as the oppositely directed gradient of the hepatocyte proliferative potencies. As is well known, these two features are inversely related (see Brodsky and Uryvaeva, 1977).

A number of different enzymatic markers of distinct physiological functions are distributed in the liver according to well-expressed gradients: canalicular

ATPase, glucose-6-phosphatase, glucose-6-phosphate dehydrogenase, and succinate dehydrogenase display higher activity in the periportal area, whereas
alkaline RNase, epoxide hydratase, and some other enzymes are more active in
the centrolobular areas (Desmet, 1963; Wachstein, 1963; Kalengai and Desmet,
1975; Schwartz, 1978; Bentley et al., 1979).

For the carcinogen-binding proteins, ligandin and A-protein, the transition
from homogeneous to graded localization could be considered to be a transition
from immature to adult-type differentiation (Bannikov et al., 1977; Guelstein et
al., 1980; Karavanova et al., 1980). In the liver of adult rats, one can observe
reciprocal gradients of these two proteins. The maximal level of ligandin is
detected in the centrolobular areas, whereas that of A-protein is detected in the
periportal regions.

Ligandin and A-protein can first be seen in hepatocytes of 15- to 16-day-old
rat fetuses. They could be detected in the same cells and are homogeneously
distributed in the liver parenchyma. The heterogeneity in localization of these
proteins appears in postnatal life by the fifteenth to the eighteenth day after birth.
By that time definitive reciprocal gradients of both proteins have been established. We believe that the establishment of these gradients is related to the
formation of the liver plates. It is clearly demonstrated by this system that every
hepatocyte is able to synthesize both proteins but that their expression is strictly
related to the hepatocyte position in the definitive liver plate (Fig. 1).

The system of the cytochrome P-450 monooxidases is very close to the system
just described. These oxidases can be induced in any hepatocyte, but the inducibility is subordinated to a well-expressed centrolobular–portal gradient. It was
clearly shown for that component of the system that is induced by phenobarbital
(Fig. 2). Depending on the dose of the "inducer" and time after the treatment,
induction of the enzyme is maximal near the central veins and, finally, extends to
the entire liver parenchyma. When the introduction of phenobarbital ceases, the
level of cytochrome gradually drops, starting from the portal area. A similar
situation was observed when aroclore 1254 and methylcholanthrene were used as
inducers (Baron et al., 1978; Kolyada, 1981; Kolyada et al., 1982).

The above components of the cytochrome P-450 system are actually missing
in the intact liver and only injection of their respective substrates results in the
appearance of their gradients in the liver parenchyma. Thus, the gradient of
inducibility for these enzymes most probably exists in the liver plate.

At the same time, the liver tissue displays without induction a form (or forms)
of P-450 cytochrome characterized by similar graded distribution with the maximum near the central veins.

These forms are, for instance, responsible for metabolism of CCl_4, which
results in the death of the cells metabolizing this compound and formation of
centrolobular necroses (see Schultze et al., 1973).

Thus, the cytochrome P-450 system presents a very demonstrative example of

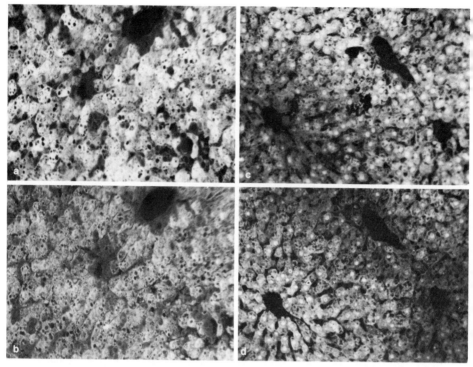

Fig. 1.   A-protein and ligandin in the liver of newborn and adult rats. In newborn rats A-protein (a) and ligandin (b) have overlapping and homogeneous distributions. In the serial sections in the adult liver, reciprocal gradients of A-protein (c) and ligandin (d) are clearly seen. Indirect immunofluorescence. (Courtesy of Drs. T. A. Tshypysheva, G. A. Bannikov, and I. D. Karavanova.)

equipotential cells that create a phenotypically diverse system, depending on their position in the liver lobule. It is necessary to emphasize that such gradients are typical only for the definitively organized adult organ.

B. Synthesis of Plasma Proteins in the Liver

Polyfunctionality of the liver in the synthesis of a wide variety of plasma proteins leads one to expect mosaicism in its tissue structure, clonal organization, with each individual clone displaying the ability to synthesize only one individual protein. An alternative view considers the hepatocyte to be a polyfunctional cell, the activity of which is subordinated to its position in the tissue structure. First findings on localization of albumin and fibrinogen revealed that 10–15% of the hepatocytes in the human liver were homogeneously stained for

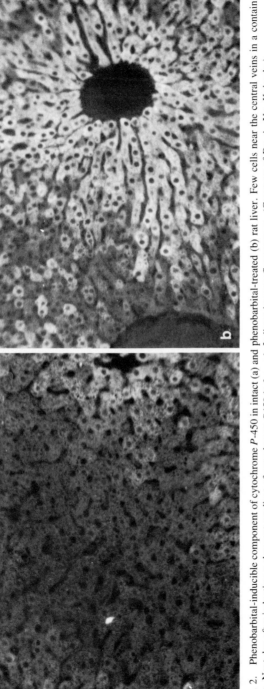

FIG. 2. Phenobarbital-inducible component of cytochrome P-450 in intact (a) and phenobarbital-treated (b) rat liver. Few cells near the central veins in a contain this protein. Next day after induction a clear-cut gradient of cytochrome P450 is formed. Indirect immunofluorescence. (Courtesy of Dr. A. Yu. Kolyada.)

albumin and 1% were homogeneously stained for fibrinogen. Only 0.1% of the liver cells were positive for both proteins (Hamashima *et al.*, 1964). Similar data for albumin, transferrin, or hemopexin were reported by different authors, including those from our laboratory (Lane, 1967; Engelhardt *et al.*, 1972, 1979; Gouillouzo *et al.*, 1975; Gleiberman, 1978; Foucrier *et al.*, 1979). These data were in good agreement with the hypothesis of liver mosaicism with respect to serum protein synthesis (e.g., see Fouerier *et al.*, 1979).

However, the basic observations on the mosaic distribution of serum albumin and transferrin in liver tissue turned out to be an artifact, as has been shown quite recently. It is well known that the immunohistochemical data are essentially dependent on the mode of tissue fixation and need special controls to exclude passive antigen uptake in the case of serum protein studies (Sternberger, 1974; Abelev *et al.*, 1979). An important control was suggested by Engelhardt *et al.* (1971); it consists of staining parallel sections for the test antigen and for endogenous IgG. Liver cells stained for IgG, which is not synthesized in the liver are excluded from the analysis because they are assumed to be dead or to have damaged permeability for serum proteins. It appears that this control is absolutely necessary but not enough. If the cells are damaged during the tissue treatment just before fixation and in the process of fixation, different serum proteins could penetrate the damaged cells at different rates. Thus, albumin and transferrin, which have a lower molecular weight than IgG and are present in higher concentration in the medium, could have a greater opportunity to penetrate the cells before precipitation with the fixative. Then, different proteins could be differentially precipitated by the fixative, and IgG could be fixed before serum albumin or transferrin. Hence, the IgG control is not sufficient to exclude all the possible fixation artifacts. Additional precautions and data are needed to localize the site of synthesis of different serum proteins. Among the recent techniques, several are especially informative. First of all, liver fixation by means of perfusion (Yokota and Fahimi, 1981) is particularly fruitful for immuno-electron microscopic studies. In addition, the control in which protein secretion from hepatocytes is inhibited with colchicine or other colchicine-like cytostatics is very useful. In this case, the preliminary treatment of the animal with a secretion-blocking agent leads to intracellular accumulation of the antigen, sometimes over the background, undetectable level (Stein *et al.*, 1974). Using this approach, Feldmann *et al.* (1975) demonstrated fibrinogen synthesis, not only in 1% of the liver cells, but actually in all hepatocytes. Besides, the pronounced portocentrolobular gradient of fibrinogen localization was shown to have a maximum near the triads. Further, Kushner and Feldmann (1978) established that all the hepatocytes in the acute phase of inflammation have the ability to synthesite C-reactive protein (CRP). The sharp portocentrolobular gradient of the hepatocyte involvement in CRP production was noted. The maximum of this gradient is also seen near the triads.

Absence of mosaicism in the liver tissue with reference to serum albumin synthesis was first conclusively demonstrated by Baranov and Rukosuev (1979) with immuno-electron microscopic techniques. They demonstrated, at the same time, that cells strongly positive for albumin exhibit by electron microscopy signs of destruction, while very weakly stained cells contained albumin in RER, Golgi cisternae, and secretory granules, i.e., in sites related to synthesis and secretion of proteins (Fig. 3). These data have received full confirmation in more recent studies in which the liver tissue was fixed by the perfusion technique (Yokota and Fahimi, 1981; Guillouzo *et al.*, 1982). Albumin and transferrin localization in all the hepatocytes of adult liver was also demonstrated by Gleiberman *et al.* (1981), using a secretion-inhibition technique. Delicate, dot-like, specific staining was observed in all liver cells (Fig. 4), while strong and homogeneous staining of single cells was considered to be an artifact. A porto-centrolobular gradient was noted for albumin and, somewhat less pronounced, for transferrin.

It must be noted that the synthesis of albumin in all the hepatocytes in embry-

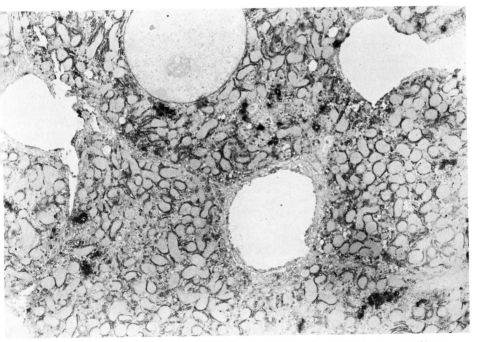

FIG. 3.   Immuno-electron microscopic detection of serum albumin in all the hepatocytes of intact mouse liver. Immunoperoxidase technique. Positive staining of RER, Golgi apparatus, and perinuclear cisternae. (Courtesy of Dr. V. N. Baranov.)

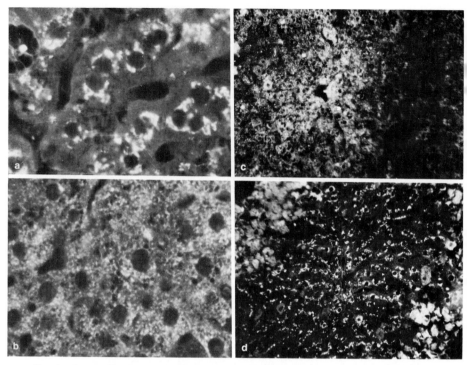

Fɪɢ. 4.   Immunofluorescent detection of serum albumin in the mouse liver. (a) Albumin "granules" in hepatocytes of regenerating mouse liver without blockade of secretion. (b) Increase of albumin staining in hepatocytes 1.5 hours after colchicine injection. (c) Gradient distribution of serum albumin with the maximum in the periportal area in the liver of a 14-day-old mouse (colchicine block of secretion). (d) Disappearance of albumin gradient in a CCl_4-poisoned mouse liver (without blockade of secretion).

onic and fetal liver in mice and humans has been very clearly shown earlier using immunofluorescence (Eraizer, 1977; Satoh, 1977) and a local hemolysis-in-gel method (Eraizer et al., 1977).

The above data demonstrated polyfunctionality of the hepatocytes and at the same time, dependence of their activity on the position in the liver lobule. This position determines the degree of expression of individual hepatocyte markers. It possesses in most cases a gradient-like character. Most probably the establishment of the gradient is associated with formation of the definitive, adult-type liver plate structure. The dependence of hepatocyte function on its position in the liver structure is related to a more general conception of "position information," developed by Wolpert (see, for example, Wolpert, 1982) to explain formation of a simple topographically regulated structure from similar cell elements. The mechanisms of such regulation in the liver remain completely unknown.

C. Embryo-Specific Hepatocyte Markers: Relationship with the Liver Structure

1. γ-Glutamyl Transpeptidase

γ-Glutamyl transpeptidase (GGT) is characteristic of embryonic and regenerating liver as well as of hepatocellular tumors. In the fetal murine liver, GGT appears to be revealed actually in all hepatocytes. The enzyme is localized mainly in the membrane regions bordering the bile capillaries. During liver maturation, the enzyme disappears from hepatocytes and is retained only in the bile duct epithelium of the adult liver (e.g., Kalengai and Desmet, 1978). GGT reappears in the proliferative foci of preneoplastic liver, in hyperplastic nodules, and in hepatocellular carcinomas (e.g., Laishes and Farber, 1978; Kalengai and Desmet, 1978). The possible role of cellular interactions in the control of GGT expression is suggested by the demonstration of GGT in proliferative foci of atypical hepatocytes. The nature and origin of these hepatocytes are unknown. They arise in response to carcinogen treatment; their number is proportional to the carcinogenic effect of the substance. They give rise to focal proliferation if the liver, treated with a subthreshold 2FAA dose, is stimulated to proliferation by partial hepatectomy. These hepatocytes are atypical in the sense that they are not sensitive to low doses of carcinogen and are able to respond to proliferative stimuli under such conditions. The atypical hepatocytes are not embryonal cells, they are indistinguishable morphologically from the typical mature liver cells (Laishes and Farber, 1978).

Spontaneous hepatomas are never seen in rats. However, with age some small GGT-positive foci are detected in the liver tissue. Their number and size increase in response to the introduction of nonmutagenic carcinogens (Ogawa et al., (1981; Schutte-Hermann et al., 1983). Such foci are positive for GGT. One can suggest that clonal growth of hepatocyte foci out of liver plate leads to partial reexpression of embryonic phenotype, GGT. This opinion is confirmed by the observations of Karavanova (1982), who found that GGT activity rose in primary monolayer cultures of nonproliferating hepatocytes of adult rats. Similar findings also have been obtained for murine hepatocytes (Klauning et al., 1982).

Unfortunately, there are actually no parallel investigations on AFP and GGT in proliferative foci or cultured hepatocytes. In the only work of Jalanko and Ruoslahti (1979), no correlation was found between these two embryo-specific markers in mice in the early stages of chemical hepatocarcinogenesis. More parallel studies are obviously needed in ontogenesis and carcinogenesis to under-

stand the relationship between AFP and GGT during the establishment of destruction of the liver plate structure.

2. α-*Fetoprotein*

Let us now consider AFP in relation to cell interactions in liver tissue.

a. *Ontogenesis.* The mammalian liver already contains AFP in the very
first stages of its formation. These findings have been obtained with immunohistochemical methods (Shipova *et al.*, 1974; Shipova and Goussev, 1976).
All hepatocytes in early livers of mice and humans are able to produce AFP, as
has been shown by immunofluorescence (Shipova and Goussev, 1976; Eraizer,
1977; Satoh, 1977) and by the local hemolysis-in-gel method (Eraizer *et al.*,
1977).

Herein, it may not be out of place to note that the immunohistochemical
localization alone of AFP in the embryo is quite insufficient to suggest the sites
of AFP synthesis (see Abelev *et al.*, 1979). In the head area of the embryo, in the
intestine, and in mesenchyme, the immunoflourescence (specific for AFP and in
the absence of endogenous IgG) is so bright that the liver does not stand out at all
against this ''background'' (Shipova *et al.*, 1974; Shipova and Goussev, 1976;
Basteris, 1976, 1979). Immunoelectron microscopic studies of different tissues
in this stage of development have not been carried out. However, very elegant
recent work by Dziadek and Andrews (1983) solved the problem equivocally.
They used ^{3}H-labeled cDNA to AFP mRNA for hybridization *in situ,* using the
sections of mouse embryo. Clear-cut localization was obtained only in the liver
and yolk sac visceral endoderm.

The synthesis of AFP in the fetal liver is clearly shown by different methods:
labeling AFP in fetal liver of humans, mice and rats with ^{14}C-labeled amino
acids (Abelev, 1965; Abelev and Bakirov, 1967a,b; Uriel and de Nechaud, 1972;
Gitlin *et al.*, 1972; Mackiewicz and Breborowicz, 1980); AFP production in
monolayer culture of fetal liver of humans and rats (Eraizer *et al.*, 1977); and
immunoelectron-microscopic data (Guillouzo *et al.*, 1976). Detection of mRNA
in situ in work by Dziadek and Andrews (1983) was specially mentioned above.

It is very important that AFP synthesis take place in all hepatocytes, as judged
by immunofluorescence and local hemolysis-in-gel methods (Eraizer *et al.*,
1977; see Abelev, 1980). Parallel investigations of albumin gave fully coinciding
results (Eraizer *et al.*, 1977; see Abelev, 1980). After birth in mice and rats, AFP
synthesis gradually fades, a change that is registered both by a drop of AFP level
in the serum and by the decrease in the number of AFP-positive cells in the liver
(Shipova *et al.*, 1974; see Abelev, 1980; Gleiberman *et al.*, 1979, 1981, 1983).
Most authors agree that the termination of AFP synthesis in mice and rats
coincides with pronounced morphological changes in the liver (Stratil *et al.*,
1976; Guillouzo *et al.*, 1976; Gleiberman *et al.*, 1979, 1981, 1983; see Abelev,
1980). In the first few days after birth, AFP is detected in all (or most)

hepatocytes, although with great and irregular heterogeneity. By the end of the first week of postnatal life in mice, one can observe a well-expressed gradient in AFP-positive cells. The brightest cells are located just around the central veins, whereas the portal areas are free of such cells. In the subsequent days, AFP gradually disappears from the hepatocytes. Only single AFP-positive cells could be found in the liver of 11- to 12-day-old mice, always close to the central veins (Shipova et al., 1974; Gleiberman et al., 1979, 1981, 1983). The situation is much the same in rats (Shipova and Goussev, 1976; Stratil et al., 1976; Basteris, 1976, 1979). The pronounced morphological patterns of this process suggest the critical role of liver plate formation in the repression of AFP synthesis in hepatocytes.

Synthesis can be "derepressed" in almost all hepatocytes when very young mice are treated with CCl_4 (Lazareva, 1977; Poltoranina, 1981). This finding provides strong evidence of "inducibility" of AFP synthesis in all hepatocytes, which cease its production. Hence, the morphologically organized process of reversible repression of AFP synthesis most probably underlies its dynamics in postnatal development. This period of liver ontogenesis suggests a number of intriguing problems and needs thorough investigation. We shall discuss some additional data relative to this period in Section III,C,2,d.

b. *Regeneration of the Liver.* Liver regeneration provides an excellent system for studying the cellular basis of AFP synthesis. It was investigated in detail in our laboratory by N. V. Engelhardt and her co-workers, V. S. Poltoranina and M. N. Lazareva. The data obtained permitted us to draw two main conclusions: (1) The ability to synthesize AFP is reversibly repressed in mature, fully differentiated hepatocytes. (2) Cell interactions in the definitive liver plate seem to be a critical factor in the repression (see Abelev, 1980). The evidence substantiating these conclusions is summarized below.

The first basic observation demonstrated that single cells, but not all hepatocytes, are responsible for the resumption of AFP synthesis in liver regeneration. This holds true for the liver regeneration following hepatectomy or hepatotoxin action. The serum level of AFP reflects the number of AFP-positive cells as well as their appearance and disappearance (Engelhardt et al., 1976a–c). The AFP-positive cells, which are revealed by immunohistochemical methods (immunofluorescence or immunoperoxidase) are cells actually synthesizing AFP. This was proved by immunoelectron microscopic investigations demonstrating AFP localization in the RER membranes, Golgi cisternae, and secretory vesicles, i.e., in the sites of protein synthesis and secretion (Baranov et al., 1981a, b, 1982; Engelhardt et al., 1982).

The fact that AFP reexpression does not take place in all hepatocytes but only in a small and clearly distinguishable fraction of their population was the key observation in the analysis of the phenomenon.

It was necessary to determine (1) whether this subpopulation is genetically different (noninterconvertible) from the rest of hepatocytes (or whether any hepatocyte is able to reexpress AFP); (2) whether the AFP-producing cells belong to the hepatocytes in their earlier developmental stages (i.e., to the transitory cells staying between the hepatocyte precursor and the young hepatocyte) or to mature liver cells; (3) whether the AFP-synthesizing cells are newly formed cells or whether they preexist in the liver tissue before its regeneration; whether there is a positive correlation between the proliferation phase of the cell cycle and AFP synthesis.

The study of mouse regenerating liver provided answers to all these questions. In the work by Engelhardt *et al.* (1976a–c) and Lazareva (1977), who used immunofluorescence detection of AFP combined with [^{3}H]thymidine determination in the same cells, it was clearly shown that a significant portion of the AFP-positive cells starts to synthesize this protein before entering the S phase. This finding means that AFP reexpression took place in preexisting cells, which did not originate from precursors in the process of regeneration. Obviously, these cells were AFP-negative before the regeneration stimulus was generated. Thus, the ability to synthesize was reversibly repressed in these cells.

The next question concerns the features of the AFP-positive cells that are different from those of AFP-negative cells. It was logical to assume that AFP-synthesizing cells belong, so to say, to young hepatocytes which still are able to reexpress AFP and that this ability is lost with their maturation. This possibility was entirely excluded in the work by Lazareva (1977), who investigated the synthesis of AFP in regenerating liver on the basis of hepatocyte maturity. It is known that maturation of the hepatocyte is accompanied by an increase in cell ploidy (Brodsky and Uryvaeva, 1977). This process could be enhanced by repeated waves of liver regeneration induced by repeated injuries with CCl_4. It was demonstrated that giant, polyploid cells are able to produce AFP in liver regeneration just like the typical hepatocytes of normal liver (Lazareva, 1977). This problem was reinvestigated with immuno-electron microscopic techniques by Baranov *et al.* (1981a,b, 1982) and Engelhardt *et al.* (1982). It was fully confirmed on the ultramicroscopic level that most AFP-synthesizing cells are typical mature hepatocytes and are not distinguishable morphologically from nonsynthesizing cells (Fig. 5).

At the same time, ultrastructural study revealed atypical hepatocytes in the regenerating liver of mice; these cells produce AFP and serum albumin (Baranov *et al.,* 1982) (Fig. 6). These cells are similar to the so-called oval cells, well known in the rat liver treated with carcinogen. Probably these atypical hepatocytes are young hepatocytes or their transitory forms. Their origin and prospective fate need special investigation. But, in any case, such atypical cells are in the minority, as compared with the overwhelming majority of typical hepatocytes. Hence, ultramicroscopic data are in line with the conclusion that the ability to synthesize AFP is reversibly repressed in mature hepatocytes.

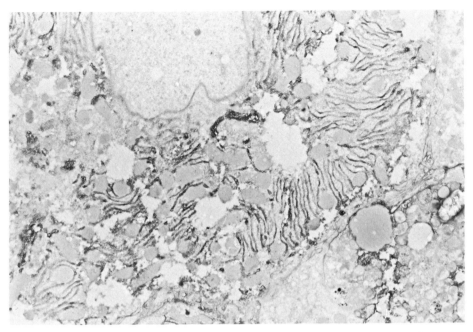

Fig. 5.   Electron microscopy of AFP in the hepatocyte of the regenerating mouse liver. Immunoperoxidase technique. Positive staining of RER and Golgi apparatus. (Courtesy of Dr. V. N. Baranov.)

The next question is whether all hepatocytes or only a certain fraction of them are able to reexpress AFP. The present evidence suggests that all hepatocytes can derepress AFP synthesis. This follows from the immunofluorescence data obtained on the regenerating liver of very young mice and adult "high AFP-producers." BALB/c/J mice. In both cases AFP can be found in practically all hepatocytes (Kuhlmann, 1981; Poltoranina, unpublished; see Abelev, 1980).

Mohanty *et al.* (1978) treated adult mice with CCl_4 and partial hepatectomy. This combination treatment results in AFP synthesis in the majority of hepatocytes. Obviously, the reversible repression is the basis of AFP regulation in the early postnatal period and in the adult liver.

The next problem concerns factor(s) responsible for such reversible repression. The regenerating liver of mice provides excellent opportunities for the search for the suggested factor(s).

The first and most logical possibility is that AFP expression is bound to a certain stage of the cell cycle or, more generally, is associated with hepatocyte proliferation. Indirect evidence in favor of such a view was obtained by Leffert and Sell (1974), who used fetal hepatocyte cultures synchronized *in vitro* by

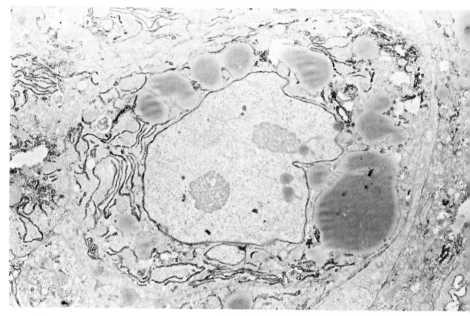

Fig. 6.   "Small" hepatocyte with positive staining for AFP in regenerating mouse liver. (Courtesy of Dr. V. N. Baranov.)

elimination of essential amino acids from the culture medium. AFP synthesis stopped in the surviving cultures but was resumed when the amino acid deficiency was corrected. Direct data on AFP synthesis in the late G_1–S period in rat hepatoma *in vitro* were reported by Tsukada and Hirai (1975). Thus, the possible association of AFP synthesis with hepatocyte proliferation and a certain phase of the cell cycle seemed quite plausible.

However, both possibilities were excluded by the elegant experiments of Lazareva (1981) and Poltoranina (1981). Lazareva syncrhonized regenerating mouse liver using hydroxyurea, which inhibits DNA synthesis and stops almost all hepatocytes in the late G_1 phase. After the treatment is stopped, the synchronized cell population enters S, G_2, M, and G_0 according to a clear-cut timetable (Rabes *et al.*, 1977). AFP-positive cells were detected in each stage of the cell cycle, including M and G_0, without any relation to certain stages. Quite recently V. N. Baranov (1983, personal communication), using immuno-electron microscopy, observed hepatocytes synthesizing AFP in the M phase (Fig. 7).

In the work by Poltoranina (1981), AFP-positive cells were induced in liver minimally damaged by a very small incision. Such damage did not lead to hepatocyte proliferation even at the site of injury—judging by [³H]thymidine incorporation and subsequent autoradiography. However, AFP-positive cells were clearly seen in the perinecrotic area of the resting liver parenchyma cells (Fig. 8a).

Hence, AFP synthesis in hepatocytes does not even need hepatocyte proliferation. The only constant property that is noted for the AFP-positive cells in the regenerating mouse liver is their characteristic topographic position—always in the perinecrotic area (Fig. 8b). These observations suggested that disintegration of the definitive liver tissue structure leads to depression of AFP synthesis in the area of injury. Rebuilding of the tissue structure blocks its synthesis (Abelev, 1978, 1979, 1980; Gleiberman et al., 1979, 1981, 1983). In other words, we assumed that cellular interactions in the definitive liver plate are the critical factor in the repression of AFP synthesis. This hypothesis unites the observations on AFP synthesis in postnatal and regenerating liver. It does not contradict the data on AFP synthesis in the mouse liver after partial hepatectomy, whee AFP-positive cells have a tendency to concentrate around the central veins in the very young animals and are dispersed irregularly throughout the liver lobule in more aged ones. There are no morphological patterns in this system in liver plate destruction or rearrangement. According to this model, there are no preferential

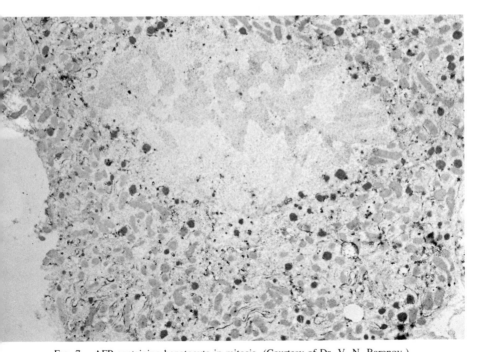

FIG. 7.   AFP-containing hepatocyte in mitosis. (Courtesy of Dr. V. N. Baranov.)

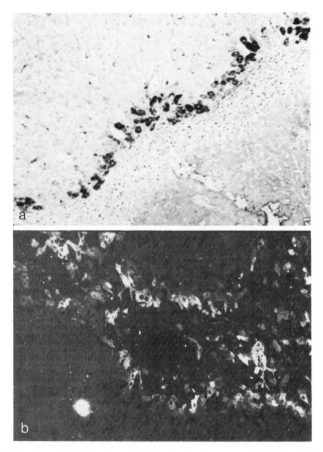

Fig. 8.   (a) Perinecrotic localization of AFP-producing hepatocytes in the liver of the BALB/c/J mouse with minimal surgical damage. Indirect immunoperoxidase. (Courtesy of Dr. V. S. Poltoranina.) (b) Perinecrotic localization of AFP-producing cells in the liver of SWR mice on the third day after CCl₄ poisoning. Indirect immunofluorescence.

sites for the localization of AFP-producing cells; in addition, there are no clear patterns in the degree of AFP production by the regenerating liver of partially hepatectomized mice (Poltoranina, unpublished).

The experiments with liver regeneration showed that the morphology of the AFP-positive cells at the peak of activity considerably differed from the morphology of the intact hepatocytes. The AFP-positive cells had, as a rule, an irregular stretched shape; and very often they were spindle-shaped. At the same time, the hepatocytes in the perinecrotic areas, where the inflammatory changes were not seen, did not contain AFP and retained their polygonal morphology. All this may well support the fact that it is not necrosis or damage to the liver plate structure, as such, that is responsible for the resumption of AFP synthesis, but only the process of the restitution of the liver plates. This process includes active movement of hepatocytes bordering necroses, and, hence, their "isolation" from the structure and local deterioration of intercellular contacts. Naturally, the reticuloendothelial cells must be involved in the process.

Perinecrotic distribution of the AFP-synthesizing hepatocytes might result from the action thereon of some factor that diffuses from the zone of necrosis or inflammation. It seems to us that this model is less probable than the aforementioned one: First, this model requires that the diffusing factor be characterized by an extremely narrow range of action, i.e., only into a layer one cell thick. Second, the graded distribution of the AFP-positive cells in the postnatal liver of mice is evidently not due to any "necrobiotic" or inflammatory factor. Third, the AFP-positive cells are sometimes detected in constricted parenchyma, around a neoplastic nodule (Shipova and Gleiberman, 1985), i.e., under the conditions of structural rearrangement occurring without necrosis or inflammation.

Yet, the possible existence of such a factor requires investigation. Pharmacological analyses of the inflammation using antiinflammatory drugs of known action, of induction of necrosis without inflammation, and of inflammation without necrosis might well be used for this study.

In our studies we adhered to the "structural model" because it could be tested directly. We tried to test it in two ways. In the first case, we investigated, in the same cells, AFP and membrane antigens, which could be used as markers of tissue arrangement and rearrangement. In other experiments AFP synthesis was studied in primary monolayer hepatocyte cultures of adult mice. In this case, dissociation of liver tissue into separate cells and their explantation into the culture were expected to be a strong "inducer" of AFP synthesis.

c. *Membrane-Associated Antigens of Hepatocytes in the AFP-Synthesizing Cells.*   The hepatocyte is a most peculiar epithelial cell. It is as though it had two apical surfaces, which participate in the secretion of various substances: the surface supporting the bile capillary and the surface contacting the blood and adjacent to Disse's space. Between these two regions there is an area of the surface with interhepatocyte contacts. One of the peculiarities of the hepatocyte as an epithelial cell is its lack of basal membrane (see Elias and Sherrick, 1969). Three different regions of the surface can be characterized on the basis of morphological and biochemical cahracteristics. These differences also can be revealed with immunohistochemical methods. In fact, the hepatocyte membrane contains a wide range of antigens of protein, glycoprotein, phospholipid, and glycolipid nature. We shall present the data concerning the three glycoprotein antigens of the hepatocyte plasma membrane related to different functional domains of murine hepatocyte surface (Beloshapkina and Abelev, 1964; Khramkova and Beloshapkina, 1974; Sulitzeany and Slavkin, 1968; Wisher and Evans, 1975).

Antigen I (Ag I), which is also an antigen of the bile capillaries, was first described by Khramkova and Beloshapkina (1974) in our laboratory. This glycoprotein has a molecular mass of about 115 kDa and is not a specific liver antigen. It is also found in the cuticle of the intestine and in kidney and lungs, but it is absent in the bile duct epithelium. In the murine liver, it is detected exclusively on the hepatocyte surfaces adjacent to the bile capillaries. Thus, in the liver, Ag I is not only a marker of hepatocytes, but it is also a marker of the specific parts of the cell surface that are included into the liver plate structure (Fig. 9a and b).

Antigen II (Ag II, molecular mass less than 54 kDa) is not a specific liver antigen either. It is detected, as is Ag I, in intestine and kidney. In the liver, Ag II is also related exclusively to the hepatocytes. It is found on the entire surface

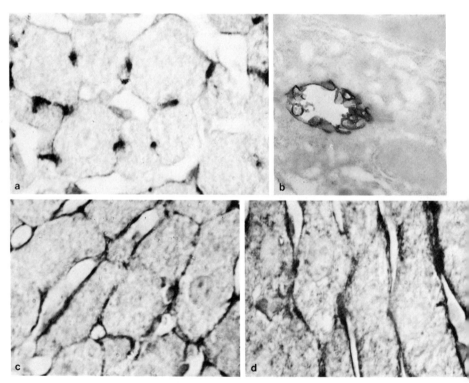

FIG. 9. Hepatocyte membrane-associated antigens in intact adult mouse liver. (a) Ag I is localized in the bile canaliculi. (b) Immunoelectron microscopy detection of Ag I. (Courtesy of Dr. V. N. Baranov.) Ag II (c) and Ag III (d) are localized on the sinosoidal parts of the hepatocyte surface. Indirect immunoperoxidase.

of parenchymatous cells, especially on the surface supporting sinusoids. The surface in the region of the bile capillaries does not contain Ag II (Fig. 9c).

Antigen III (Ag III, molecular mass about 40 kd) is the liver-specific, membrane-associated antigen. Its localization is similar to that of Ag II. In addition, in the intact adult mouse liver, it is clearly seen that the hepatocyte surface adjacent to Disse's space contains appreciably larger amounts of Ag III than do the other parts of the membrane. Like Ag II, Ag III is missing on the surface of the cells supporting the bile capillary (Fig. 9d). It is noteworthy that while Ag I is evenly distributed throughout the liver tissue, Ag II and Ag III are characterized by moderately expressed portocentrolobular gradients. The maximal levels of Ag II are found in the centrolobular areas, whereas those of Ag III are found in the periportal ones (Kuprina et al., 1981; Gleiberman et al., 1983).

Hence, this set of antigens enables us to clearly define in liver of adult mice distinct functional areas of the hepatocyte membrane which, however, are clearly expressed only when the hepatocyte belongs to the definitive liver plate.

As is well known, the liver of newborn mice is devoid of the definitive plate structure. The hepatocytes form the tubules in the center of which are located bile ductules. Among the hepatic tubules are sites of hemopoiesis. However, these structural peculiarities are poorly seen in the routine histological examinations. Simultaneous staining with antibodies to Ag I, Ag II, and Ag III easily reveals these structures in the liver parenchyma (Gleiberman et al., 1979, 1981, 1983; Kuprina et al., 1981). In the liver of newborn mice, Ag I is localized on the apical surface of hepatocytes which form the acinar structures. Ag III is mainly characteristic of the external basal surface of these acini. Ag II is located on the basal and lateral surfaces of hepatocytes. On apical cell surfaces bordering the lumen of acini and containing Ag I, Ag II and Ag III are missing (Fig. 10). Thus, both in the liver of adults and in the liver of newborn animals, all three antigens are characteristic of similar functional areas of the hepatocyte surface. These findings have provided the opportunity to use these antigens for studying hepatocyte rearrangements during the formation of the liver plates in postnatal ontogenesis in liver regeneration.

We mentioned earlier that AFP disappearance from the liver of mice in postnatal ontogenesis has a pronounced gradient character. The gradient-type redistribution of Ag I characterized the transition of the liver tissue from the acinar to the plate structure. The "adult" type of Ag I localization—small part of the surface of 2–3 contacting hepatocytes—usually makes its appearance in the area of the triads on the third to the fifth day after birth. Approximately at the same time, the AFP level gradually drops in the periportal areas. In parallel with AFP disappearance, the "adult" type of Ag I distribution extends to still greater areas. In the middle of the second week of postnatal life, one can regularly detect the Ag I gradient. It is typically localized in the periportal areas, whereas around

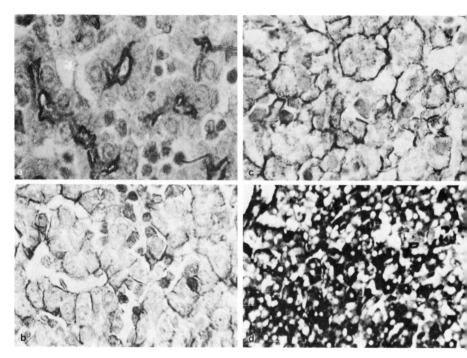

Fig. 10. Hepatocyte membrane-associated antigens in the liver of the newborn mice. (a) Ag I localization on the apical surface of tubules composed of fetal hepatocytes. (b) Ag II localization on the basal and lateral surfaces, and (c) Ag III on basal surfaces of hepatocytes. (d) At this stage of development, AFP was found in practically all hepatocytes. Peroxidase–antiperoxidase technique.

the central veins its level is very low or completely missing. It is very characteristic that all the AFP-containing cells on the tenth to the thirteenth day of postnatal life are located in the zones with low Ag I expression, or even in the zones in which it is missing entirely. AFP disappearance from the centrolobular hepatocytes correlates with the appearance on ther surface of Ag I (Fig. 11).

In parallel with the gradient-type disappearance of AFP from the liver and the gradient-like appearance of Ag I on the surface of hepatocytes, formation of the definitive gradients of Ag II and Ag III takes place; initially these antigens are distributed either evenly or heterogeneously, but without any pattern.

Thus, it can be seen from these data that the formation of the liver structure in postnatal ontogenesis has a gradient character—judging by the redistribution of the membrane-associated antigens. AFP disappearance from hepatocytes very clearly correlates with local rearrangements of the liver tissue toward the adult type.

Distinct correlation between AFP synthesis and membrane antigen redistribution was found in the liver recovering from hepatotoxin action.

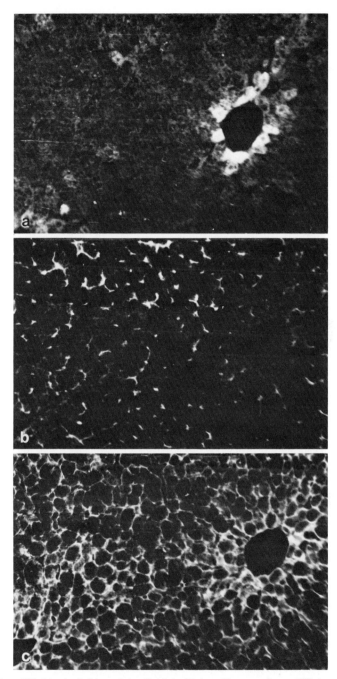

FIG. 11.   AFP (a), Ag I (b), and Ag II (c) in 11-day-old mouse liver. AFP is seen only in pericentral hepatocytes, which contain trace amounts of Ag I. A definitive portocentral gradient of Ag II, with the maximum around the central vein, can be seen. Indirect immunofluorescence.

We stated earlier that the maximal number of AFP-positive cells is detected on the third to the fourth day of regeneration in perinecrotic areas. First, usually weak and single AFP-containing cells make their appearance within 20–24 hours after poisoning. Up to 48 hours, their localization is not characterized by any pattern, although there is a tendency for them to extend from the periportal to the perinecrotic areas. Localization in the perinecrotic area is most stable and actually characteristic of all the AFP-positive cells 48 hours after CCl_4 action. Up to 48 hours, Ag I, Ag II, and Ag III are detected on the surfaces of all living hepatocytes, including the AFP-positive cells. By the time the number of AFP-positive cells has reached its maximum on the peripheries of the necrotic areas, zones have formed from hepatocytes that are, as a rule, devoid of or contain appreciably smaller amounts of Ag I. At this time all the AFP-positive cells are localized in these zones. Usually not all the cells that are devoid of Ag I are AFP positive (Fig. 12). In some cases Ag II and Ag III also disappear in these zones, or their amount is sharply decreased. AFP disappearance from the cells coincides with replacement of the damaged areas with hepatocytes. Simultaneously, the characteristic pattern of membrane antigen distribution is reestablished (Gleiberman et al., 1979, 1981, 1983). Various changes in localization of the membrane antigens have been reported by Poltoranina (1981) in the course of AFP synthesis in hepatocytes bordering the areas of the liver with minimal surgical or "mechanical" damage. These observations give further support to the aforementioned conclusion that local damage of the liver structure is the factor ensuring AFP expression in adult differentiated hepatocytes.

d. *AFP Expression in Primary Monolayer Cultures of Adult Murine Hepatocytes.* On the basis of the model in which liver structure has a role in regulation of AFP synthesis, one would expect that dissociation of liver tissue into a single-cell suspension and explantation of the hepatocytes into monolayer culture would lead to reexpression of AFP in the "adult" cells. Indeed, it was shown earlier that in adult murine hepatocyte cultures one can detect active accumulation of AFP in the culture medium (De Nechaud et al., 1979). Less intensive AFP synthesis was found in cultures of hepatocytes of adult rats (Leffert et al., 1978; Sirica et al., 1979).

We studied the AFP production by cultures of adult hepatocytes of different murine lines and the immunohistochecmical localization of this protein in the cultured cells (Gleiberman, 1982; Gleiberman and Elgort, 1982). Hepatocytes were isolated by a routine technique with collagenase perfusion. AFP in the medium and the AFP-positive cells usually make their appearance on the third to the fourth day of cultivation. The number of AFP-positive cells in the monolayer was in direct proportion to the AFP level in the culture medium. The highest percentage of AFP-positive cells is detected on the sixth to the twelfth day of cultivation; it reached 50–75%.

Of interest are the morphological patterns of AFP production in cultures. We

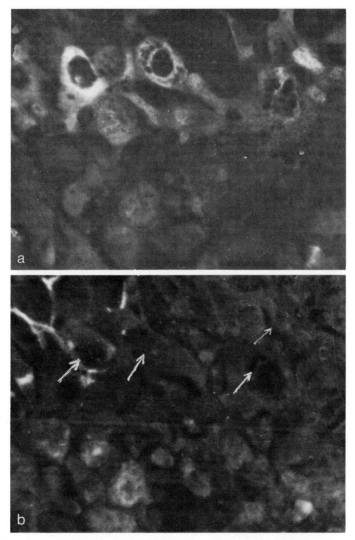

FIG. 12.   AFP-positive hepatocytes (a) in mouse liver on the third day after CCl$_4$ poisoning with absence of Ag I (b). Arrows indicate AFP-positive cells. Indirect immunofluorescence.

obtained, more or less regularly, the following stages: formation of a dense monolayer; hepatocyte proliferation; formation of a polylayer, including stretched spindle-shaped cells; occurrence of a great number of giant multi-nuclear hepatocytes. The AFP synthesis arises after the dense monolayer from the polygonal hepatocytes is transformed into the proliferating polylayer containing the spindle-shaped, stretched cells (Fig. 13). At the same time, proliferation does not appear to be a crucial factor for the particular hepatocyte to start AFP synthesis. Autoradiographic experiments combined with immunoperoxidase staining of AFP showed that the AFP-synthesizing cells are by no means always present in the proliferative pool. In addition, our data show that direct lack of contacts with other hepatocytes is not necessarily required for reexpression of AFP synthesis. At the same time, the interhepatocyte contacts in one way or another affect AFP synthesis, since in the areas of the culture in which the dense monolayer of hepatocytes is retained for a longer time, the AFP-containing cells occur far more rarely than they do in the hepatocyte polylayer.

Thus, explantation of hepatocytes into a monolayer is, indeed, a strong "inducer" of AFP synthesis. There is good reason to believe that *in vitro* studies would help to clarify the cellular mechanisms that are responsible for regulation of AFP synthesis. As yet, however, the mechanism(s) remains obscure.

The most interesting result reliably obtained in the liver culture studies is that most hepatocytes of C57BL/6 mice, which show extremely low "inducibility" *in vivo,* start to synthesize AFP in culture. Moreover, in a culture of hepatocytes from a high-inducibility strain, BALB/c/J mice, the percentage of AFP-producing cells does not exceed that of C57BL/6 cultures. The point is that the mice of these two strains differ 10- to 100-fold in both AFP background serum level and "AFP-inducibility" in regenerating liver. These differences are genetic. In the next section we shall present data on the genetic patterns of the regulation of AFP

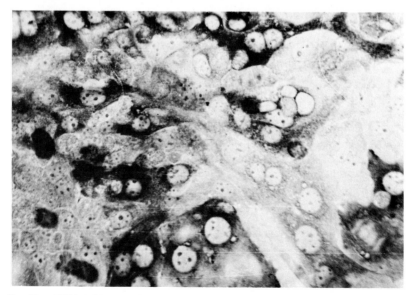

Fig. 13.   AFP in adult mouse hepatocytes cultivated during 5 days in monolayer culture. Peroxidase–antiperoxidase technique. Counterstaining with hematoxylin.

synthesis and try to define, proceeding from these data, a possible cell substrate of this regulation.

D. Genetics of AFP Regulation

1. Interline Differences in Background AFP Levels in the Blood Serum of Adult Mice

Olsson and co-workers (Olsson et al., 1977; Lindahl et al., 1978) attempted to find "allotypic" differences in AFP of various murine lines. These attempts met with failure. However, the authors succeeded in finding and analyzing interline differences in background AFP level revealed in the blood serum of adult mice. Whereas in the majority of lines the value of the background AFP level is close to 100 ng/ml, mice of the BALB/c/J line contain in their blood serum up to 2000/ng/ml. An analysis of hybrid strains revealed that low background level is dominant over high background level and that the trait is controlled by one gene. This gene was referred to as raf. Hence, it follows that BALB/c/J mice carry a recessive allele of the raf gene, ensuring very high background levels of AFP in the blood serum of adult mice without any liver pathologies. The different phenotypes of this gene do not manifest themselves in early postnatal ontogenesis. At the same time the strain differences in the level of AFP synthesis during liver regeneration correlate with the expression of the raf gene. BALB/c/J mice after CCl_4 poisoning have AFP serum levels 10–100 times higher than that of most other mouse strains.

Interline differences in AFP "inducibility" in adult mice were clearly demonstrated by Bakiriv and Abelev (see Abelev, 1968). The hybrid analysis of this phenomenon was attempted by Poltoranina and Sorokina (1978). The authors performed quantitative determinations of AFP serum levels during liver regeneration in 12 murine lines. The inheritance of this character proved to be more complicated than that of background AFP level. In F_1 hybrids, the AFP level in the blood serum during regeneration was intermediate with reference to the parent lines. Unlike background level, AFP level induced by liver injury has a distinct sex-linked difference in most of the lines studies (Poltoranina and Sorokina, 1978).

These findings suggest the polygenic control of AFP inducibility. The recent genetic analysis of the raf gene and AFP inducibility started by Tilghmann and co-workers (Belayew and Thilghmann, 1983) will throw more light on this intriguing problem.

2. Morphological Peculiarities in AFP Synthesis by the Regenerating Liver in Mice of Different Genotypes

The genetic differences in the serum level of AFP during regeneration are closely correlated with the number of cells involved in the synthesis of this protein. In BALB/c/J mice, on the third to the fourth day of regeneration almost all hepatocytes are able to synthesize AFP whereas in the majority of the other lines (e.g., SWR, AKR, BALB/c, C3HA) the number of AFP-positive cells was 5–10%. Low-inducible mice (C57BL/6, C57BL/10, B10.D2 strains) synthesize AFP at the lowest level; the number of AFP-containing cells is negligible and never exceeds 1%. Hence, regulation of the AFP synthesis at the cellular level is dependent on the number of hepatocytes involved into this synthesis (Engelhardt *et al.,* 1976a–c; Poltoranina and Sorokina, 1978).

It must be emphasized that distinct interline differences in the morphological characteristics of liver regeneration exist and are closely correlated with different levels of AFP synthesis. SWR, BALB/c, and C3HA mice are characterized by comparatively high AFP serum levels and a great (up to 10%) number of AFP-positive cells. In the process of healing, an invasion of liver cells with changed morphology into the damaged area occurs. The AFP-positive cells often look like "leaders" of the moving cords. In such situations, zones of cells losing the membrane-associated antigens can be seen.

As a rule, in C57BL/6 mice no active penetration of hepatocytes into the damaged areas occurs. Healing is achieved by "constricting" the damaged areas with the remaining intact parenchyma. In this case hepatocytes are often hypertrophic. In the perineocrotic zones, no loss of the membrane-associated antigens occurs and the AFP-positive cells occur extremely rarely and are weakly stained.

It should be noted that in BALB/c mice, characterized by wide variability of AFP synthesis during regeneration, one can identify both morphological types of regeneration: mice with high levels of AFP exhibit zones deficient in the membrane-associated antigens and the AFP-positive cells penetrating the damaged areas, whereas in mice with comparatively low levels of AFP in the blood serum the pattern of regeneration and localization of membrane-associated antigens and AFP is similar to that in C57BL/6 mice.

Thus, the data presented in this section indicate that the genetic differences in regulation of AFP synthesis during regeneration of the liver are closely correlated with the differences in the course of morphogenetic processes, ensuring the reconstitution of the liver.

At the same time, when hepatocytes are grown in culture, the genetic differences in AFP synthesis between C57BL/6 and BALB/c/J murine cells are completely unexpressed. It should be noted that induction of AFP synthesis by the explantation of adult hepatocytes into culture is much more effective for C57BL/6 mice than is any *in vivo* treatment. None of the "inductive actions" resulted in a detectable, significant number of AFP-positive hepatocytes in the liver of C57BL/6 mice.

The preceding data can be summarized in the following way: The existing genetic differences in the quantitative level of expression of AFP synthesis at the cellular level are dependent on the number of the hepatocytes involved into this process. The same genetic differences in C57BL/6, SWR, and BALB/c but not in BALB/c/J correlate with the differences in the morphological characteristics of the liver repair processes after CCl_4 poisoning as well as with the differences in the behavior of the hepatocyte membrane-associated antigens during regeneration of the liver.

Background AFP synthesis in the adult organism appears to be regulated by one gene (*raf*) whereas AFP synthesis induced by liver regeneration is probably regulated on a polygenic basis.

The reexpression of AFP synthesis in a primary culture of adult murine hepatocytes takes place without any external treatment; in this case the genetic differences in the level of AFP synthesis are fully lost.

Most probably, the action of the regulatory genes does not take place inside the hepatocyte, but rather is external.

Studies of *in vivo* AFP synthesis in postnatal ontogenesis and during regeneration of the liver indicate that AFP synthesis is related to the local reconstructions and rearrangements of the liver plate structure. On the basis of the results of experiments on cultivation of hepatocytes, one can suggest that the matter herein is not limited only to interhepatocyte interactions in the liver plate; it seems that the stroma is also involved into these interactions. The genetic control of AFP regulation, i.e., the action of the *raf* gene and other genes is possibly realized at the level of the hepatic stromal elements. This hypothesis can be tested experimentally in studies of AFP synthesis in mixed cultures of hepatocytes and nonparenchymal liver cells of various genotypes. Of course, the stated considerations are not the only possible ones.

E. On the "Structural" Control of AFP in Liver Tumors

AFP is commonly used as an immunodiagnostic marker of liver tumors (see Abelev and Elgort, 1982). Of the three main types of liver tumors—angiosarcomas, cholangiocarcinomas, and hepatocellular tumors—AFP is characteristic only of the third, the most frequently occurring group. This is quite natural, since numerous, aforementioned findings show that AFP is a marker of hepatocyte differentiation. There exists some correlation between the level of AFP synthesis and the degree of tumor anaplasia (see Abelev, 1965, 1968, 1974). However, there are numerous occasions when tumors with a similar degree of morphological and clinical malignancy sharply differ in the level of AFP synthesis. All that has been stated above on the mechanisms of the regulation of AFP synthesis can be applied to normal, nontransformed cells. But the mechanisms of expression of AFP synthesis in tumors have not, as yet, actually been elucidated.

We do not intend now to comprehensively consider the numerous data on cells able to synthesize AFP in early stages of chemical hepatocarcinogenesis. AFP synthesis in these conditions is mainly performed by the so-called oval cells, which combine the properties of young hepatocytes and cholangiocytes (Kitagawa *et al.*, 1972; Onoe *et al.*, 1975; Tchypysheva *et al.*, 1977; Kuhlmann, 1981). Most probably the oval cells are liver cell precursors (Inaoka, 1967).

The small AFP-containing cells, which are not typical hepatocytes, were also detected in mouse liver regenerating after CCl_4 poisoning, with the use of immuno-electron microscopic technique (Baranov *et al.*, 1982). However, we not only have accumulated few data on the mechanisms of AFP regulation in these cells, but moreover, in spite of numerous studies, as yet, neither the origin of these cells, nor their place in the histogenesis of liver tissue, nor their relation to the process of carcinogenesis have been elucidated.

Somewhat more data are available on AFP synthesis by the cells of the established hepatocellular tumor. In CBA mice, spontaneous hepatomas arise with age. Among them are morphologically highly differentiated tumors, which do not actually synthesize AFP, and moderately differentiated hepatomas, which contain numerous AFP-positive cells (Shipova *et al.*, 1983).

We were interested in identifying similarities in the mechanisms of AFP expression in highly differentiated hepatomas and the normal liver. A model of minimal surgical damages, developed by Poltoranina (1981) for the normal mouse liver was used to study this problem. Minimal mechanical damage—incision—of highly differentiated tumor nodules, which did not usually contain the AFP-positive cells, led to the appearance on the third day of AFP-positive neoplastic cells lying in the perinecrotic layer. These cells were clearly seen in

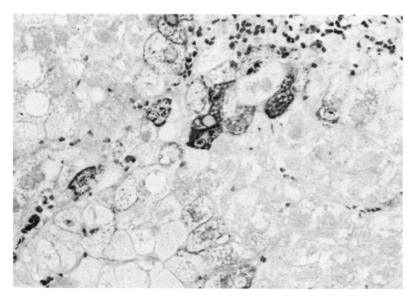

FIG. 14.   Perinecrotic localization of AFP-positive cells in the spontaneous highly differentiated mouse hepatoma after surgical damage. Indirect immunoperoxidase technique.

the animals with blocked protein secretion (Shipova and Gleiberman, 1985) (Fig. 14). Hence, on the basis of these data, one can suggest that in highly differentiated hepatomas the mechanisms of the regulation of AFP synthesis are basically the same as those in the normal liver.

How can one evaluate from this point of view the "spontaneous" AFP synthesis in poorly differentiated hepatomas? The cells of highly differentiated hepatomas are similar in their properties to adult hepatocytes, the cells of less differentiated tumors show closer similarity to embryonic hepatocytes. The embryonic hepatocytes are able to produce all the elements of their synthesis program the same as the adult ones. Their difference from the adult hepatocytes consists most probably in absence of sensitivity to the regulatory factors. For instance, such evolution from insensitivity toward sensitivity to regulators might be due to the appearance of membrane receptors to humoral AFP regulator(s), as was suggested by Eraizer (1977). Differences in the sensitivity to the humoral regulatory factors of adult and embryonic precursors of erythropoiesis can serve as an example of such a situation (Papayannopoulou et al., 1982).

IV. Conclusion

We tried to show in this article that a biochemical phenotype of the mature, differentiated hepatocyte in its different manifestations is dependent on its position in the structure of the liver lobule—in the synthesis of the characteristic proteins and in the competence to induce them. The data presented support and extend the conception of morphophysiological gradients in the liver, previously formulated by Rappoport (1958) and developed by Khruschov and Brodsky (1961). A new statement, which we would like to suggest in this article, is the dependence of the hepatocyte embryonic phenotype on its position in the liver structure. When included into the definitive structure, the hepatocyte "feels" its position and represses the embryonic synthesis. When located outside the structure, the hepatocyte displays an embryonic phenotype. The program of the hepatocyte differentiation consists in acquiring the capacity to "sense the structure," i.e., most likely, the capacity to acquire membrane-associated receptors, ensuring cell interactions, characteristic of the definitive liver tissue. According to this hypothesis, hepatocyte possesses the embryonic phenotype either in a stage when it is not yet able to form the structure due to the lack of the corresponding receptors or after destruction of the structure by external factors.

These two mechanisms are retained in liver tumors, which can be related in the type of regulation either to the embryonic liver (hepatoblastomas), with full expression of the embryonic phenotype, or to the adult liver, with retention of "the structural repression" of the embryonic synthesis, which manifests itself the same as in the liver damaged by various mechanical and toxic actions.

Such is the hypothesis. It excludes from consideration the problem on the nature of the relation between the structure and the biochemical phenotype of the cell. It only provides the system for studying this dependency. In the very general form the suggested relation can be realized by "over-cell" structural factors or the mode of the cell interactions. Since the gradients are strictly "bound" to the system of the lobular vessels, a concentration gradient of certain substance (for instance, O_2) coming to the lobule from the vessels of the portal tract, may be the simplest example of the "over-cell" regulator.

In the case of liver damage, this may be some or other mediator diffusing from the zone of necrosis, or, more likely, inflammation, which is able to induce AFP synthesis or other embryo-specific features in the hepatocyte. This type of humoral factors, characterized by regular topography, can be perfectly used as "morphogens" both for the normal physiological gradients in the liver and for the strict topography of the AFP synthesizing cells in the damaged liver.

If, however, the structural factors are due to cell interactions, creating well-expressed gradients, herein, one should think first of all about cell compartments based on metabolic cooperation (see Lowenstein, 1979).

Most situations presented in this article can receive a plausible explanation from both points of view. The aim is to find approaches allowing one to choose between the alternatives. It seems to us that the comparative study of the examined systems under the two circumstances—in toxic (or surgical)) damage of the liver and during partial hepatectomy—might prove to be the necessary approach, In toxic or mechanical damage of the liver, the structure of the lobule is always disarranged and necrosis and inflammation arise. Subsequent to this, a wave of hepatocyte proliferation occurs and is accompanied by "individualization" of hepatocytes with disappearance of the gap junctions between them (Yee and Revel, 1978; Traub *et al.*, 1983). Thus, the system includes four groups of factors: disarrangement of humoral gradients, appearance of the diffusion centers of "new" mediators, local disarrangements of the liver plate structure bordering necroses, and short-term isolation of the hepatocytes from the metabolic compartments. Each of these factors is sufficient to explain the pictures, observed in the damaged liver. On the contrary, during hepatectomy the intralobular structure of the liver is retained, no necroses are formed, but only temporal isolation of hepatocytes takes place. Studying the morphological patterns of the reexpression of AFP and GGT under these circumstances, combined with the immunoelectron microscopy of AFP-positive cells according to their gap junctions and membrane antigens seems to be very promising. A low level of AFP synthesis in mice with partial hepatectomy, as compared with CCl_4-poisoned mice, and wide scattering in the degree of induction created difficulties for this kind of experiments. Use of the "highly inducible" BALB/c/J mice seems to be more convenient.

We expect the systems described in this article to provide new impulses and approaches in the study of the old and fundamental problem of morphogenetic fields or positional information.

REFERENCES

Abelev, G. I. (1965). *Prog. Exp. Tumor Res.* **7**, 104–157.
Abelev, G. I. (1968). *Cancer Res.* **28**, 1344–1350.
Abelev, G. I. (1971). *Adv. Cancer Res.* **14**, 295–358.
Abelev, G. I. (1974). *Transplant. Rev.* **20**, 3–37.
Abelev, G. I. (1976). *In* "Onco-developmental Gene Expression" (W. Fishman and S. Sell, eds.), pp. 191–202. Academic Press, New York.
Abelev, G. I. (1978). *In* "Cell Differentiation and Neoplasia" (G. P. Saunders, ed.), pp. 257–269. Raven, New York.
Abelev, G. I. (1979). *In* "Carcino-Embryonic Proteins," Vol. 1, (F.-G. Lehmann, ed.), Vol. 1,*a* pp. 99–110. Elsevier, Amsterdam.
Abelev, G. I. (1980). *V. P. Skulachev, Sov. Sci. Rev. Sect. D, Biol. Rev.* **1**, 371–397.
Abelev, G. I., and Bakirov, R. D. (1967a). *Vopr. Med. Khim.* **13**, 378–383. (in Russian).
Abelev, G. I., and Bakirov, R. D. (1967b). Cited in Abelev, 1968.
Abelev, G. I., and Elgort, D. A. (1982). *In* "Cancer Medicine" (J. F. Holland and E. Frei, III, eds.), 2nd ed., pp. 1089–1099. Lea & Febiger, Philadelphia.
Abelev, G. I., Assercritova, I. V., Kraevsky, N. A., Perova, S. D., and Perevodchikova, N. I. (1967). *Int. J. Cancer* **2**, 551–558.
Abelev, G. I., Engelhardt, N. V., and Elgort, D. A. (1979). *Methods Cancer Res.* **18**, 1–37.
Abelev, G. I., Elgort, D. A., and Eraizer, D. A. (1981). *Bull. Exp. Biol. Med.* **92**, 333–335 (in Russian).
Adamson, E. D. (1982). *Dev. Biol.* **91**, 227–334.
Bakirov, R. D. (1968). *Bull. Exp. Biol. Med.* (2), 45–47 (in Russian).
Bannikov, G. A., Guelstein, V. I., and Tchypyshiva, T. A. (1977). *Vopt. Onkol.* **23** ,39–44 (in Russian-.
Baranov, V. N., and Rukosuev, V. S. (1979). *Bull. Exp. Biol. Med.* **87**, 482–485. (in Russian).
Baranov, V. N., Engelhardt, N. V., and Lazareva, M. N. (1981a). *Oncodev. Biol. Med.* **2**, 193.
Baranov, V. N., Engelhardt, N. V., Lazareva, M. N., and Goussev, A. I. (1981b). *Bull Exp. Biol. Med.* **91**, 736–738 (in Russian).
Baranov, V. N., Engelhardt, N. V., Lazareva, M. N., Goussev, A. I., Yazova, A. K., Shachlamov, V. A., and Abelev, G. I. (1982). *Bull. Exp. Biol. Med.* **93**, 82–84 (in Russian).
Baron, I., Redick, I. G., and Guengerich, F. P. (1978). *Life Sci.* **23**, 2627–2732.
Basteris, B. (1976). Thesis in Anatomy and Pathology, Marseille.
Basteris, B. (1979). *In* "Carcino-Embryonic Proteins." (F.-G. Lehmann, ed.) Vol. 2, pp. 353–356. Elsevier, Amsterdam.
Belayew, A., and Thilghmann, S. (1982). *Mol. Cell. Biol.* **2**, 1427–1435.
Beloshapkina, T. D., and Abelev, G. I. (1964). *N. F. Gamaleya Inst. Symp. Immunol., Moscow* pp. 25–38 (in Russian).
Bentley, P., Weschter, F. and Oesch, F. (1979). *Biochem. Biophys. Res. Commun.* **91**, 1101–1108.
Bernstine, E. G., Hooper, M. L., Grandchamp, S., and Ephrussi, B. (1973). *Proc. Natl. Acad. Sci. U.S.A.* **70**, 3899–3903.
Brodsky, W. Ya., and Uryvaeva, I. V. (1977). *Int. Rev. Cytol.* **50**, 275–332.
Bucher, N. L. R., and Malt, R. A. (1971). *In* "Regeneration of Liver and Kidney," pp. 17–161. Houghton, Boston.
Carriere, R. (1969). *Int. Rev. Cytol.* **25**, 201–277.
Damjanov, I., and Sell, S. (1977). *J. Natl. Cancer Inst.* **58**, 1523–1525.

De Nechaud, B., Viron, A., and Puvion, E. (1979). *C. R. Acad. Sci. (Paris)* **289** (Ser. D), 737–740.
De Nechaud, B., and Uriel, J. (1972). *Int. J. Cancer* **8**, 71–80.
Desmet, V. (1963). "Experimentele Levercarcinogenese. Histochemische Studie," pp. 1–367. Arcia et Presses Academiquess Europeenes, Brussels.
Ducibella, T., Albertini, D. F., Anderson, E., and Biggers, Y. D. (1975). *Dev. Biol.* **45**, 231–250.
Dziadek, M. (1978). *J. Embryol. Exp. Morphol.* **46**, 135–146.
Dziadek, M. (1979). *J. Embryol. Exp. Morphol.* **53**, 367–379.
Dziadek, M., and Adamson, E. (1978). *J. Embryol. Exp. Morphol.* **43**, 289–313.
Dziadek, M., and Andrews, G. K. (1983). *EMBO J.* **2**, 549–554.
Elias, H. (1955). *Biol. Rev.* **30**, 265–310.
Elias, H., and Sherrick, H. C. (1969). "Morphology of the Liver." Academic Press, New York.
Engelhardt, N. V., Goussev, A. I., Shipova, L. Ya., and Abelev, G. I. (1971). *Int. J. Cancer* **7**, 198–206.
Engelhardt, N. V., Goussev, A. I., and Poltoranina, V. S. (1972). *Bull. Exp. Biol. Med.* (9), 87–89 (in Russian).
Engelhardt, N. V., Poltoranina, V. S., and Yazova, A. K. (1973). *Int. J. Cancer* **11**, 448–459.
Engelhardt, N. V., Poltoranina, V. S., Shipova, L. Ya., Goussev, A. I., and Yazova, A. K. (1974). *In* Alpha-Feto-Protein" (R. Masseyeff, ed.), pp. 217–229. Inserm, Paris.
Engelhardt, N. V., Lazareva, M. N., Abelev, G. I., Uryvaeva, I. V., Factor, V. M., and Brodsky, V. Ya. (1976a). *Nature (London)* **263**, 146–148.
Engelhardt, N. V., Lazareva, M. N., Poltoranina, V. S., Perova, S. D., and Gleiberman, A. S. (1976b). *Bull. Exp. Biol. Med.* **82**, 1251–1254 (in Russian).
Engelhardt, N. V., Lazareva, M. N., Uryvaeva, I. V., Factor, V. M., Poltoranina, V. S., Gleiberman, A. S., Brodsky, V. Ya., and Abelev, G. I. (1976c). *In* "Onco-developmental Gene Expression" (W. Fishman and S. Sell, ed.), pp. 533–540. Academic Press, New York.
Engelhardt, N. V., Gleiberman, A. S., Lazareva, M. N., and Poltoranina, V. S. (1979). *In* "Carcino-embryonic Antigens: Chemistry, Biology, Clinical Applications" (F.-G. Lehmann, ed.), Vol. 1, pp. 111–119. Elsevier, Amsterdam.
Engelhardt, N. V., Baranov, V. N., Lazareva, M. N., Goussev, A. I., and Yazova, A. K. (1982). *Cytologia* **24**, 1115 (in Russian).
Eraizer, T. L. (1977). PhD thesis, Moscow.
Eraizer, T. L., Elgort, D. A., and Abelev, G. I. (1977). *Bull. Exp. Biol. Med.* **83**, 711–713 (in Russian).
Feldman, G., Maurice, M., Sapin, C., and Benhamon, J. P. (1975). *J. Cell Biol.* **67**, 237–241.
Foucrier, J., Kraemer, M., Vassy, J., and Chalumeau, M. T. (1979). *Cell. Differ.* **8**, 39–48.
Gitlin, D., and Boesman, M. (1967). *J. Clin. Invest.* **46**, 1010–1016.
Gitlin, D. A., Pericelli, A., and Gitlin, G. (1972). *Cancer Res.* **32**, 979–982.
Gleiberman, A. S. (1978). *Bull. Exp. Biol. Med.* **85**, 625–630 (in Russian).
Gleiberman, A. S. (1982). *Bull. Exp. Biol. Med.* **93**, 55–58 (in Russian.
Gleiberman, A. S., and Elgort D. A. (1982). *Cytologia* **24**, 1098 (in Russian).
Gleiberman, A. S., Khramkova, N. I., and Beloshapkina, T. D. (1979). *Bull. Exp. Biol. Med.* **87**, 607–610 (in Russian).
Gleiberman, A. S., Kuprina, N. I., and Rudinskaya, T. D. (1981). *Oncodev. Biol. Med.* **2**, 194.
Gleiberman, A. S., Kuprina-Khramkova, N. I., Rudinskaya-Beloshapkina, T. D., and Abelev, G. I. (1983). *Int. J. Cancer* **32**, 85–92.
Graham, C. F. (1971). *Br. Soc. Exp. Biol. Symp.* **25**, 371–378.
Guelstein, V. I., Tchipysheva, T. A., and Bannikov, G. A. (1980). *Oncodev. Biol. Med.* **1**, 389–403.
Guillouzo, A., Feldman, G., Boisnard, M., Sapin, C., and Benhamon, J. P. (1975). *Exp. Cell Res.* **16**, 239–246.

Guillouzo, A., Feldman, G., Maurice, M., Sapin, C., and Benhamon, J. P. (1976). *J. Microsc. Biol. Cell.* **26**, 35–41.

Guillouzo, A., Beamont, C., LeRumeur, E., Rissel, M., Latiner, M.-F., Ouguen-Guillouzo, C., and Bourel, M. (1982). *Biol. Cell.* **43**, 163–172.

Hamashima, J., Harter, J., and Coons, A. (1964). *J. Cell Biol.* **20**, 271–279.

Hillman, N., Sherman, M. I., and Graham, C. F. (1972). *J. Embryol. Exp. Morphol.* **28**, 263–278.

Hogan, B. L. M. Taylor, A., and Adamson, E. D. (1981). *Nature (London)* **291**, 235–237.

Hogan, B. L. M., Barlow, D. P., and Tilly, R. (1983). *Cancer Surveys* **2**, 115–140.

Inaoka, Y. (1967). *Gann* **58**, 355–366.

Jalanko, H., and Ruoslahti, E. (1979). *Cancer Res.* **39**, 3495–3501.

Janzen, R. G., Andrews, G. K., and Tamaoki, T. (1982). *Dev. Biol.* **90**, 18–23.

Jones, A. L., and Schmucker, D. L. (1977). *Gastroenterology* **73**, 833–851.

Kalengai, M. M. R., and Desmet, V. J. (1975). *Cancer Res.* **35**, 2836–2844.

Kalengai, M. M. R., and Desmet, V. J. (1978). *Scand. J. Immunol.* **8**, (Suppl. 8), 547–556.

Karavanova, I. D. (1982). *Cytology* **24**, 1099 (in Russian).

Karavanova, I. D., Tchipysheva, T. A., Guelstein, V. I., and Bannikov, G. A. (1980). *Oncodev. Biol. Med.* **1**, 375–388.

Khramkova, N. I., and Beloshapkina, T. D. (1974). *Nature (London)* **251**, 627–628.

Khruschow, G. Kh., and Brodsky, V. Ya. (1961). *Usp. Sov. Biol.* **52**, 181–207 (in Russian).

Kitagawa, T., Yokochi, T., and Sugano, H. (1972). *Int. J. Cancer* **10**, 368–381.

Klauning, Y. E., Goldblatt, P. J., Hinton, D. E., Lypsky, M. M., Knipe, S. M., and Trump, B. F. (1982). *Anat. Rec.* **204**, 231–243.

Kolyada, A. Yu. (1981). *Bull. Exp. Biol. Med.* **92**, 115–116 (in Russian).

Kolyada, A. Yu., Guelstein, V. I., and Koblyakov, V. A. (1982). *Bull. Exp. Biol. Med.* **94**, 96–100 (in Russian).

Kuhlmann, W. D. (1981). *Virchows Arch. (Pathol. Anat.)* **393**, 9–26.

Kuprina, N. I., Rudinskaya, T. D., and Yakimenko, E. F. (1981). *Oncodev. Biol. Med.* **2**, 198.

Kushner, I., and Feldmann, G. (1978). *J. Exp. Med.* **148**, 466–477.

Laishes, B. A., and Farber, E. (1978). *J. Natl. Cancer Inst.* **61**, 507–512.

Lane, R. S. (1967). *Nature (London)* **215**, 161–162.

Lazareva, M. N. (1977). *Bull. Exp. Biol. Med.* **83**, 97–101 (in Russian).

Lazareva, M. N. (1981). *Oncodev. Biol. Med.* **2**, 89–99.

Le Bouton, A. V. (1974a). *Anat. Rec.* **178**, 401.

Le Bouton, A. V. (1974b). *Dev. Biol.* **41**, 22–30.

Le Bouton, A. V. (1976). *Anat. Rec.* **184**, 679–688.

Le Bouton, A. V., and Marchaud, R. (1970). *Dev. Biol.* **23**, 524–533.

Leffert, H. and Sell, S. (1974). *J. Cell Biol.* **61**, 823–829.

Leffert, H., Moran, T., Sell, S., Skelly, H., Ibsen K., Muller, M., and Arias, I. (1978). *Proc, Natl. Acad. Sci. U.S.A.* **75**, 1834–1838.

Lindahl, J., Olsson, M., and Ruoslahti, E. (1978). *Scand. J. Immunol.* **8** (Suppl. 8), 209–212.

Loewenstein, W. R. (1979). *Biochim. Biophys. Acta* **560**, 1–65.

Mackiewicz, A., and Breborowicz, J. (1980). *Oncodev. Biol. Med.* **1**, 251–262.

Martin, G. (1975). *Cell* **5**, 229–243.

Martin, G. (1981). *Proc. Natl. Acad. Sci. U.S.A.* **78**, 7634–7638.

Masopust, J., Kithier, K., and Radl, I. (1968). *Int. J. Cancer*, **3**, 703–711.

Mintz, B., and Illmensee, K. (1975). *Proc. Natl. Acad. Sci. U.S.A.* **72**, 3385–3389.

Mohanty, M., Das, P., Mittal, A., and Nayak, N. (1978). *Int. J. Cancer* **23**, 181–188.

Ogawa, K., Onoe, T., and Takeuchi, M. (1981). *J. Natl. Cancer Inst.* **67**, 407–412.

Olsson, M., Lindahl, J., and Ruoslahti, E. (1977). *J. Exp. Med.* **145**, 819–827.

Onoe, T., Kaneko, A., Dempo, K., Ogawa, K., and Takashi, M. (1975). *Ann. N.Y. Acad. Sci.* **259**, 168–180.

Papayannopoulou, Th., Kenach, S., Nakamoto, B., Zanjani, E., and Stamatoyannopoulos, G. (1982). *Proc. Natl. Acad. Sci. U.S.A.* **79**, 6578–6583.

Poltoranina, V. S. (1981). *Bull. Exp. Biol. Med.* **91**, 212–215 (in Russian).

Poltoranina, V. S., and Sorokina, T. V. (1978). *Bull. Exp. Biol. Med.* **86**, 71–75 (in Russian).

Rabes, H. M., Iseler, G., Cziehos, S., and Tuerek, H. V. (1977). *Cancer Res.* **37**, 1105–1111.

Rappoport, A. M. (1958). *Anat. Rec.* **130**, 673–689.

Rappoport, A. M. (1963). *In* "The Liver" (C. Rouiller, ed.) Vol. 1, pp. 266–328. Academic Press, New York.

Rappoport, A. M. (1973). *Microvasc. Res.* **6**, 212–228.

Satoh, K. (1977). *Eur. Surg. Press,* **2**, 57–66.

Schmucker, D. L., Mooney, J. S., and Jones, A. L. (1978). *J. Cell Biol.* **78**, 319–327.

Schultze, B., Gerhardt, H., Shump, E., and Maurer, B. (1973). *Virchovs Arch. Abt. B Cell Pathol.* **14**, 329–343.

Schutte-Hermann, R., Timmermann-Trosiener, I., and Schuppler, J. (1983). *Cancer Res.* **43**, 839–844.

Schwartz, G. (1978). *Acta Histochem.* **62**(1).

Shapira, F. (1981). *Isosymes: Curr. Top. Biol. Med. Res.* **5**, 27–75.

Shipova, L. Ya., and Gleiberman, A. S. (1985). *Int. J. Cancer* **35**, 135–138.

Shipova, L. Ya., and Goussev, A. I. (1976). *Ontogenez,* **7**, 392–395 (in Russian).

Shipova, L. Ya., Goussev, A. I., and Engelhardt, N. V. (1974). *Ontogenez* **5**, 53–60 (in Russian).

Shipova, L. Ya., Kharkovskaya, N. A., and Ladygina, N. G. (1983). *Exp. Oncol.* **5**, 27–31 (in Russian).

Sirica, A. E., Richards, R. V., Tsukada, Y., Sattler, C. A., and Pitot, H. C. (1979). *Proc. Natl. Acad. Sci. U.S.A.* **76**, 283–287.

Solter, D., and Damjanov, I. (1979). *Methods Cancer Res.* **18**, 277–332.

Solter, D., and Knowles, B. (1975). *Proc. Natl. Acad. Sci. U.S.A.* **72.**

Stein, O., Sanger, L., and Stein, J. (1974). *J. Cell Biol.,* **62**, 93–103.

Sternberger, L. A. (1974). "Immunocytochemistry" Prentice-Hall, New York.

Stratil, P., Dolezalova, Y., Feit, J., and Kocent, A. (1976). *Neoplasma* **23**, 1–10.

Strickland, S., and Mahdavi, V. (1978). *Cell* **15**, 393–403.

Strickland, S., Smith, K. K., and Marotti, K. R. (1980). *Cell* **21**, 347–355.

Sulitceany, D., and Slavkin, M. (1968). *Clin. Exp. Immunol.* **3**, 1005–1008.

Suurmeijer, A. J. H., Oosterhuis, J. W., Marrink, J., De Bruin, H. W. A., Schrafford Koops, H., Sleijfer, D. T., and Fleugen, G. J. (1983). *Oncodev. Biol. Med.* **4**, 289–308.

Tchypysheva, T. A., Guelstein, V. I., and Bannikov, G. A. (1977). *Int. J. Cancer* **20**, 388–393.

Teilum, G. (1976). "Special Tumors of Ovary and Testis and Related Extragonadal Lesions: Comparative Pathology and Histological Identification," 2nd ed. Munkagaard, Copenhagen.

Teilum, G., Albrechsen, R., and Norgaard-Pedersen, B. (1975). *Acta Pathol. Microbiol. Scand.* **83**, 80–86.

Traub, O., Druge, P., and Willecke, K. (1983). *Proc. Natl. Acad. Sci. U.S.A.* **80**, 755–759.

Tsukada, Y., and Hirai, H. (1975) *Ann. N.Y. Acad. Sci.* **259**, 37–44.

Wachstein, M. (1963). *In* "The Liver" (C. Rouillier, ed.), Vol. 1, pp. 137–194. Academic Press, New York.

Wisher, M. H., and Evans, W. A. (1975). *Biochem. J.* **146**, 375–378.

Wolpert, L. (1982). *In* "Evolution and Development" (J. T. Bonner, ed.), pp. 169–188, Springer-Verlag, Berlin and New York.

Yee, A. G., and Revel, J.-P. (1978). *J. Cell Biol.* **78**, 554–564.

Xie, H.-X., Takeichi, M., Ogou, S.-I., and Okada, T. S. (1982). *Dev. Growth Differ.* **24**, 513–520.

Yokota, S., and Fahimi, H. D. (1981). *Proc. Natl. Acad. Sci. U.S.A.* **78**, 4970–4974.

INTERNATIONAL REVIEW OF CYTOLOGY, VOL. 95

Primitive Never-Dividing Macronuclei of Some Lower Ciliates[1]

IGOR B. RAIKOV

Institute of Cytology of the Academy of Sciences, Leningrad, USSR

I. Introduction

The nuclei of all proliferating cells are generally supposed to be able to divide. This is certainly true of all mononucleate cells. It is, however, conceivable that in multinucleate cells only some nuclei reproduce while other nuclei remain undivided. But practically all the nuclei divide in most multinucleate cells, for example in some slime molds (*Physarum*) or in multinucleate amebae (*Chaos*). Even in the cases of *nuclear dualism* (heteronuclearity), when the cell contains two different nuclei (or many nuclei of two kinds), both nuclei are usually able to divide, though by different methods. The best example is the heterokaryotic

[1]The author dedicates this paper to Professor George Poljansky on the occasion of his eightieth birthday, March 15, 1984.

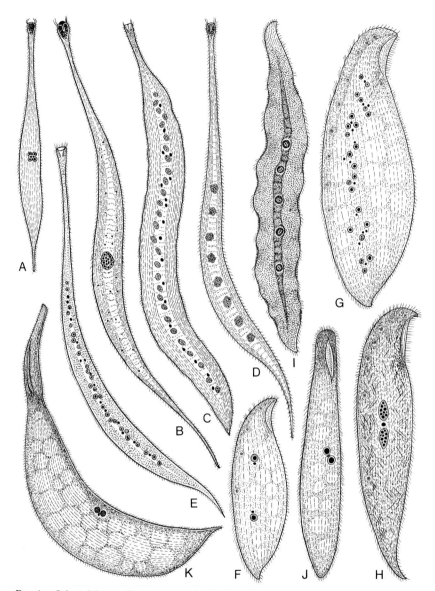

Fig. 1. Selected karyorelictids as seen *in vivo* (semidiagrammatic), with nuclei added from stained preparations. (A) *Trachelocerca coluber;* (B) *Tracheloraphis phoenicopterus;* (C) *T. dogieli;* (D) *T. kahli;* (E) *Trachelonema sulcata;* (F) *Loxodes striatus;* (G) *L. magnus;* (H) *Remanella rugosa;* (I) *Kentrophoros latum;* (J) *Geleia nigriceps;* (K) *G. orbis* (a strongly contracted specimen). Magnifications: C, I, x 90; A, x 120; B, D, E, x 150; G, K, x 210; H, J. x 300.

nuclear apparatus of the vast majority of the ciliates, in which the small *generative nucleus* (or *micronucleus*) divides by mitosis whereas the large *somatic nucleus* (or *macronucleus*) divides by apparent amitosis, e.g., in *Paramecium, Tetrahymena*, or *Stylonychia* (reviewed by Raikov, 1982, Chapter 8).

However, more than 100 species of lower ciliates have macronuclei (somatic nuclei) which do not divide at all. These ciliates now constitute a special order Karyorelictida (Corliss, 1979) or even a primitive class Karyorelictea (Small and Lynn, 1981). Most karyorelictids, namely, members of the genera *Trachelocerca, Tracheloraphis, Trachelonema, Remanella, Kentrophoros, Geleia, Avelia*, and some others, are marine ciliates, are often vermiform or ribbon-shaped (Fig. 1), and live mainly in the interstices of sandy sediments (for details, see Dragesco, 1960; Corliss and Hartwig, 1977). Only species of *Loxodes* (Fig. 1F and G) occur in fresh water (Rylov, 1923; Goulder, 1980).

It is in *Loxodes* that the inability of the macronuclei to divide was first noted more than a century ago (Bütschli, 1876). A generally correct understanding of the nuclear transformations during cell division in species of this genus was soon gained (Balbiani, 1890; Joseph, 1907; Kasanzeff, 1910; Rossolimo, 1916). However, for about half a century the nuclei of *Loxodes* were considered an isolated curiosity. The nuclei of the marine Trachelocercidae remained, despite Lebedew's (1909) study, little known and poorly understood. Fauré-Fremiet (1954) first stressed the cytological and evolutionary importance of the never-dividing macronuclei of *Loxodes* and demonstrated that some marine ciliates (*Remanella* and *Kentrophoros*) may have similar nuclei. Almost simultaneously, the macronuclei of the Trachelocercidae were shown to belong to the same type (Raikov, 1955, 1957a). This finding permitted investigators to specify for the first time the cytological peculiarities of the never-dividing macronuclei and to formulate a hypothesis about their place in the evolution of the nuclear dualism in ciliates (Raikov, 1957b, 1963a; Poljansky and Raikov, 1961).

Since karyorelictid macronuclei never divide, a question arises as to how the normal composition of the nuclear apparatus is maintained from one cell generation to another. Other problems of interest are the following: Why and how did the macronuclei lose their ability to divide? Are they capable of DNA synthesis? Is their chromatin transcribed? What is the function of these nuclei in the cell? And, finally, what are their fine structural peculiarities? A treatment of these questions is the subject of this article.

II. Organization of the Nuclear Apparatus

A. General Organization

1. Number and Size of the Nuclei

All karyorelictids are multinucleate ciliates. No species among them has a single macronucleus, unlike other ciliates where most species have but one (able-

TABLE I

COMPOSITION OF THE NUCLEAR APPARATUS OF SOME SELECTED KARYORELICTIDA[a]

Species	Number of macronuclei	Number of micronuclei	Presence and number of nuclear groups[b]	References
Family Trachelocercidae				
Trachelocerca coluber	4	2	1	Raikov (1963e, 1969)
T. geopetiti	4 or 8	2 or 4	1	Raikov and Kovaleva (1981)
Tracheloraphis sp.	4	2	1	Torch (1961)
T. phoenicopterus	12	6	1	Raikov (1955, 1958a, 1962); Raikov and Kovaleva (1978)
T. totevi	16–22	2	1	Kovaleva *et al.* (1979)
T. kahli	24–88	12–44	3–11	Raikov (1962)
T. caudatus	28–200	14–100	7–50	Dragesco and Raikov (1966)
T. margaritatus (White Sea)	9–35	2–29	—	Raikov (1957a, 1958a, 1962)
T. margaritatus (English Channel)	17–101	5–61	—	Dragesco and Raikov (1966)
T. dogieli	6–30	2–17	—	Raikov (1957a, 1958a, 1962, 1974)
Trachelonema oligostriata	8–18	4–9	4–9	Raikov (1962)
T. sulcata	9–60	3–18	±	Kovaleva and Raikov (1973)
Family Loxodidae				
Loxodes rostrum	2	1	1	Raikov (1959a)
L. striatus	2(3)	2(3)	2	Raikov (1959a); Foissner and Rieder (1983)
L. magnus	8–47	5–32	±	Raikov (1959a); Bobyleva (1981); Foissner and Rieder (1983)
L. rex	132–181	39–138	—	Dragesco (1970)
Remanella rugosa	2(3)	1	1	Raikov (1963b)
R. granulosa	2(3)	1	1	Raikov (1963b)
R. multinucleata	7–35	2–16	±	Raikov (1963c)
Kentrophoros latum	6–42	2–14	1–7	Raikov (1972b)
Family Geleiidae				
Geleia nigriceps	2(3)	1	1	Raikov (1959b)
G. orbis	2(3–6)	1(2–3)	1(2–3)	Raikov (1963d, 1984); Nouzarède (1976)
G. murmanica	8–32	4–16	±	Raikov (1962, 1963d)
Avelia martinicense	2	1	1	Nouzarède (1975, 1976)

[a]Rare variants of the number of nuclei are shown within parentheses.

[b]± means that the nuclear groups are unstable.

to-divide) macronucleus. The minimum number of nuclei in karyorelictids is two macronuclei and one micronucleus (Fig. 1H, J, and K). Many species have, however, many more nuclei of both types (Fig. 1C, E, and G). Table I presents data about the number of nuclei in the species which were studied cytologically. The table shows that in some forms the nuclear set is relatively constant and species specific (especially in species with a few nuclei), whereas in other forms it varies within very wide limits.

In most species, the macronuclei are more numerous than the micronuclei, often twice as numerous (Table I). There are, however, examples both of a much higher numerical prevalence of the macronuclei over the micronuclei (*Tracheloraphis totevi*) and of equal numbers of the two nuclei (*Loxodes striatus*).

While the micronuclei of the Karyorelictida have a size typical of the generative nuclei of most ciliates (usually within 1 to 5 μm), their macronuclei are considerably smaller than those of the ciliates which have able-to-divide somatic nuclei. The diameter of karyorelictid macronuclei usually varies from 5 to 10 μm only. The smallest macronuclei (2.5–5 μm) occur in *Kentrophoros fistulosum* (see Fig. 9I), the largest ones (10–20 μm), in *Trachelocerca geopetiti, Tracheloraphis dogieli,* and *Remanella rugosa* (cf. Fig. 9B and H; for references, see Table I). The relative volume of the whole nuclear apparatus as compared with the volume of the cytoplasm is sometimes surprisingly small, e.g., in *Geleia orbis* (Fig. 1K).

2. *Clustering of the Nuclei*

In many karyorelictids, all the nuclei are united into peculiar groups or *nuclear complexes* which include both macro- and micronuclei. In the simplest case, a

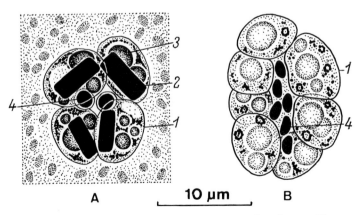

FIG. 2.   Nuclear complexes in Trachelocercidae. (A) A rosette-shaped group of four macronuclei (1) and two micronuclei (4) in *T. coluber,* stained for protein with mercuric Bromophenol Blue; the macronuclei contain crystalloids (2) and nucleoli (3). (From Raikov, 1969). (B) A morula-like complex of 12 macronuclei (1) and 6 micronuclei (4) in *T. phoenicopterus.* Feulgen staining. (From Raikov, 1962.)

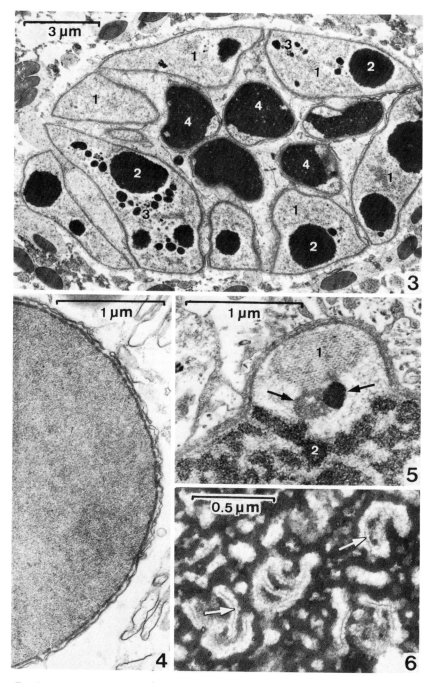

Fig. 3. Electron micrograph of a section of the nuclear complex of *T. phoenicopterus*. The macronuclei (1) contain nucleoli (2) and chromocenters (3); five micronuclei (4) are seen. (From Raikov and Kovaleva, 1978.)

single group including all the nuclei of a cell is formed, e.g., in *R. rugosa, Geleia nigriceps,* or *G. orbis* (Fig. 1H, J, and K) in which the group consists of two macronuclei and one micronucleus. In other cases, the single nuclear complex includes more nuclei (cf. Table I); and then it is either rosette-shaped usually with four macronuclei and two micronuclei (e.g., in *Trachelocerca coluber,* Figs. 1A and 2A), or morula-shaped, with the macronuclei at the periphery and the micronuclei near the center of the cluster (e.g., in *Tracheloraphis phoenicopterus,* Figs. 1B and 2B). In still other cases, the numerous nuclei are united into several or many nuclear complexes aligned along the body (Fig. 1D and I), rather than into a single cluster. The number of such complexes may be rather large (up to 50) and highly variable, e.g., in *Tracheloraphis kahli, Tracheloraphis caudatus,* or *K. fistulosum* (Table I).

Electron microscopy has shown that the envelopes of the individual macronuclei and micronuclei always remain intact within a nuclear complex (Fig. 3), e.g., in *T. phoenicopterus* (Raikov and Kovaleva, 1978) or *T. totevi* (Kovaleva *et al.,* 1979). From the outside, the entire nuclear complex is usually covered by an additional cytoplasmic membrane which belongs to the perinuclear lacuna of the smooth endoplasmic reticulum (Raikov and Dragesco, 1969). Finally, the whole morula-like cluster of nuclei can be isolated from the cytoplasm with a heavy capsule which consists of stacked flattened vesicles of the smooth reticulum, e.g., in *Kentrophoros latum* (cf. Fig. 14).

Along with this, many multinucleate karyorelictids have free macro- and micronuclei which either form no groups at all (Fig. 1c) or form only unstable groups (Fig. 1E and G; cf. Table I).

B. The Micronuclei

A detailed consideration of the karyorelictid micronuclei is beyond the scope of this article. Therefore, only a brief summary of the main peculiarities of these nuclei will be given.

1. Interphasic Micronuclei

The micronuclei of all karyorelictids belong to the "spermal" type of nuclei (cf. Raikov, 1982, Chapter 1). This is characterized by a very dense packing of chromatin in a small volume. The micronuclei always intensely stain with

---

Fig. 4. Part of a micronucleus of *T. sulcata* filled with compact chromatin. (From Kovaleva and Raikov, 1978.)

Fig. 5. A crystalloid (1) beneath the micronuclear envelope in *G. orbis,* with two associated bodies of different electron density (at arrows); 2, chromatin. (From Raikov, 1984.)

Fig. 6. Part of an interphase micronucleus of *T. geopetiti* showing persisting kinetochores (arrows) in the lacunae of the chromatin. (From Raikov and Kovaleva, 1981.)

Feulgen (Figs. 2B, 8A, 9A–F, H–J, and L, 25, and 29), but no RNA could be cytochemically revealed in them (Raikov, 1958a, 1959a, 1963b–d, etc.).

Electron microscopy has shown the karyorelictid micronuclei to possess a typical two-membrane envelope bearing numerous pore complexes. The micronuclear chromatin is fully condensed and is either a solid mass filling the entire nucleus (Fig. 4) or a spongy structure (Figs. 5 and 6). The former case is typical of *Trachelonema sulcata* (Kovaleva and Raikov, 1970, 1973, 1978), *T. caudatus* (Raikov and Dragesco, 1969), or *T. phoenicopterus* (Raikov and Kovaleva, 1978); the latter, of *T. dogieli, Loxodes magnus,* or *Remanella multinucleata* (Raikov, 1974, 1975, 1979). The condensed chromatin usually consists of densely packed 10-nm fibrils which apparently correspond to nucleosome fibrils. Such chromatin is readily bleached with ethylenediaminetetraacetic acid (EDTA) during Bernhard's ultracytochemical staining (Raikov and Kovaleva, 1980, 1981). However, in *G. orbis* the micronuclear chromatin consists of granules of supranucleosome size (about 30 nm) which are resistant to EDTA bleaching (Raikov, 1984).

Neither nucleoli nor intranuclear ribonucleoprotein (RNP) particles exist in the micronuclei. However, in *L. magnus* and *R. multinucleata,* these nuclei often contain finely fibrillar spheres which seem to be proteinaceous (Raikov, 1975, 1979); and in *G. orbis* they display small crystalloids (Fig. 5). Finally, in *T. geopetiti,* the cleftlike lacunae pervading the micronuclear chromatin contain peculiar lamellae in which RNP was ultracytochemically detected (Fig. 6); these lamellae proved to be kinetochores of the micronuclear chromosomes which persist throughout the interphase (Raikov and Kovaleva, 1981, 1982).

According to their fine structure, the karyorelictid micronuclei thus correspond to transcriptionally inert nuclei, which has also been confirmed with autoradiography: no incorporation of [³H]uridine into the micronuclei was revealed in either *Tracheloraphis* sp. (Torch, 1964a) or *L. striatus* (Ron and Urieli, 1977). As to the replication of DNA, it immediately follows mitosis in the micronuclei of *L. magnus,* as demonstrated by both autoradiography (Raikov and Morat, 1977) and cytofluorimetry (Bobyleva *et al.,* 1980). These nuclei are consequently in the G_2 period during almost the entire interphase. However, in *T. sulcata,* most micronuclei of a nondividing cell are in G_1 (Kovaleva and Raikov, 1978).

2. *Micronuclear Mitosis*

The micronuclei of the karyorelictids fully justify their name of generative nuclei since they, and only they, are able to divide (by mitosis) in these ciliates. Morphologically, the mitosis is rather similar in various species. Chromosome counts yielded diploid numbers ranging from 34 in *T. phoenicopterus* (Raikov, 1958a,b) to 56 in *T. sulcata* (Kovaleva, 1972); however, some species have even higher numbers (> 100 in *L. magnus*).

At the light optical level, micronuclear mitosis was studied in *T. phoenicop-*
terus, Tracheloraphis margaritatus, T. dogieli (Raikov, 1955, 1957a, 1958a), *L.*
striatus, L. magnus (Raikov, 1959a), and *G. nigriceps* (Raikov, 1959b). The
mitotic spindle is always blunt-ended, oval or nearly spherical; a clear equatorial
plate is formed in metaphase, and no strong elongation of the spindle occurs in
telophase (cf. Figs. 25, 28, and 29).

At the fine structural level, micronuclear mitosis was studied in *L. magnus*
(Raikov, 1973, 1976a) and *T. geopetiti* (Raikov and Kovaleva, 1982). The
mitosis occurs, as it usually does in ciliates, inside the intact nuclear envelope.
The mitotic apparatus is thus entirely intranuclear and displays an axial symme-
try ("closed intranuclear orthomitosis" according to Raikov, 1982, Chapter 2).
The spindle is acentric and consists in metaphase of parallel bundles of microtubules, some of which are attached to conspicuous chromosomal kinetochores
(Fig. 7A, and B). During telophase, the envelopes of the two daughter nuclei are
formed anew inside the envelope of the mother micronucleus which still sur-
rounds the entire spindle. They form by fusion of membrane-bounded vesicles

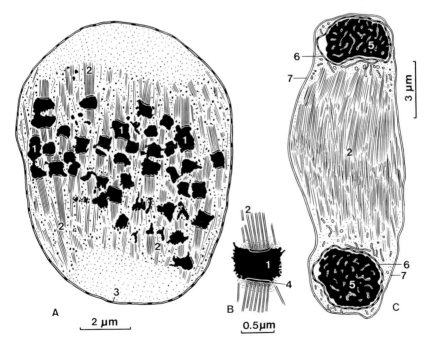

Fig. 7.   Micronuclear mitosis in *L. magnus* (tracings from electron micrographs). (A) Metaphase
(B) a metaphase chromosome with two kinetochores; (C) telophase. 1, Chromosomes; 2, microtubules; 3, nuclear envelope; 4, kinetochore; 5, daughter micronucleus; 6, its new nuclear envelope;
7, old nuclear envelope of the mother micronucleus. (From Raikov, 1973.)

which have previously pinched off the inner membrane of the old nuclear envelope (Fig. 7C). The latter disintegrates in late telophase, liberating the two
daughter nuclei. The chromosomes are small and compact in *Loxodes* but are
larger and have a crenated outline in *Trachelocerca*.

III. Morphology and Cytochemistry of Adult Macronuclei

A. Light Microscopic Morphology and Cytochemistry

The macronuclei of the Karyorelictida are usually spherical or oval and vesicular in appearance. They generally stain faintly with Feulgen. In *L. magnus*, only
small chromatin granules at the periphery of a macronucleus are stained (Fig.
8A). The same granules light up when a fluorescent staining for DNA is carried

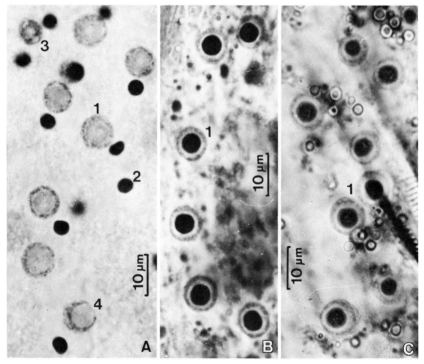

Fig. 8. Light micrographs of the macronuclei (1) and micronuclei (2) of *L. magnus*. (A) Feulgen
straining. 3, Macronuclear anlage; 4, old macronucleus. (B) Methyl Green and Pyronin staining (the
macronuclear nucleoli strongly stain with Pyronin). (C) Mercuric Bromophenol Blue staining (mainly the nucleoli are stained). (From Raikov, 1982.)

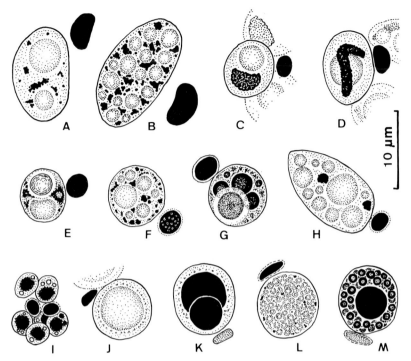

FIG. 9. Light microscopic morphology and cytochemistry of karyorelictid macronuclei. In all figures except I, a micronucleus is shown for comparison near the macronucleus. (A) *T. margaritatus* (Feulgen staining); (B) *T. dogieli* (Feulgen); (C) *T. drachi* (Feulgen); (D) *T. drachi* forma *bi-micronucleata* (Feulgen); (E) *T. sulcata* (sphere at top; Feulgen); (F) *R. multinucleata* (Feulgen); (G) the same (mercuric Bromophenol Blue; nucleoli and a sphere are stained); (H) *R. rugosa* (Feulgen); (I) *K. fistulosum;* an entire group of four macronuclei and two micronuclei are shown (Feulgen); (J) *G. nigriceps* (Feulgen); (K) the same (Methyl Green and Pyronin; a nucleolus and a sphere are stained); (L) *G. orbis* (Feulgen; the numerous nucleoli are unstained); (M) the same (Methyl Green and Pyronin; nucleoli and a central sphere are stained with Pyronin).

out (Bobyleva *et al.,* 1980). The center of a *Loxodes* macronucleus is occupied by a large Feulgen-negative nucleolus which intensely stains for RNA (Fig. 8B) and for protein (Fig. 8C). In some karyorelictids, the chromatin is so dispersed that the macronuclei become practically Feulgen negative, e.g., in *G. nigriceps* and *G. orbis* (Fig. 9J and L) or *Tracheloraphis* sp. (Torch, 1961). In most species, however, the small granules of chromatin aggregate to form several *chromocenters* (Figs. 2B, 9A, B, E, F, and H). Finally, in some species all the condensed chromatin of a macronucleus unites into a single large chromocenter, e.g., in *Tracheloraphis drachi* (Fig. 9C, and D), *Trachelonema lanceolata* (Rai-kov, 1962), or *Kentrophoros fistulosum* (Fig. 9I).

The number of *nucleoli* per macronucleus is relatively species specific. In all *Loxodes* species (Fig. 8B and C), as well as in *Remanella granulosa, G. nigriceps* (Fig. 9J), *Trachelonema oligostriata,* the nucleolus is generally single. In *T. coluber* (Fig. 2A), *T. geopetiti, T. phoenicopterus* (Fig. 2B), *T. caudatus, T. margaritatus* (Fig. 9A), *R. multinucleata* (Fig. 9F), and *K. latum,* there are several nucleoli per macronucleus. In *T. dogieli* (Fig. 9B) and *R. rugosa* (Fig. 9H), they usually number more than 10, and in *G. orbis* (Fig. 9L and M) and *Geleia murmanica,* more than 100 (for references, see Table I). In all cases checked, much RNA and nonhistone protein was cytochemically revealed in the nucleoli (Raikov, 1958a, 1959a, b, 1963b, c. etc.).

Along with the chromatin elements and the nucleoli, the macronuclei of marine karyorelictids (but not those of the freshwater *Loxodes* species!) frequently contain refractile Feulgen-negative *spheres* or *crystalloids.* These inclusions are, however, facultative, occurring in the macronuclei of only some cells. Nonhistone protein is always clearly revealed in both the spheres and the crystalloids (Figs. 2A and 9G), but the presence of RNA in them is somewhat uncertain. In some species, much RNA has been found in the spheres, which are clearly basophilic (Fig. 9K and M) and RNase sensitive, e.g., in *G. nigriceps, G. orbis, R. granulosa, R. rugosa, R. multinucleata* (Raikov, 1959b, 1963b–d). In other species, the spheres are pyroninophilic as well, but their basophilia is RNase resistant, e.g., in *T. sulcata* (Kovaleva and Raikov, 1970) or *K. latum* (Raikov, 1972a). The crystalloids of *T. coluber* (Fig. 2A; Raikov, 1969) and *T. caudatus* (Raikov and Dragesco, 1969) also belong to the latter category. The basophilia of the spheres and crystalloids appears to be caused in these cases by acid proteins rather than by RNA. Ultracytochemical data (see Section III,D,5) also indicate a purely proteinaceous nature of the spheres in Trachelocercidae.

B. DNA STUDIES

1. *DNA Content*

Microscopic studies of various karyorelictids suggest a proportionality between the DNA contents of their macronuclei and micronuclei. Species with large, brilliantly staining micronuclei usually show more chromatin also in the macronuclei (Fig. 9B); species with small micronuclei generally have macronuclei which stain faintly for chromatin (Fig. 9J). The single chromocenter present in each macronucleus of some species usually resembles a micronucleus in both size and stainability (Fig. 9C, D, and I). In all these cases, the visually estimated DNA quantity in a macronucleus resembles that in a micronucleus.

Using cytophotometry, Raikov *et al.* (1963) have shown the average DNA content of the adult macronuclei of *L. magnus* to be only 11% higher than that of G_2 micronuclei, i.e., to equal about 4.4 c (Fig. 10). However, the DNA content

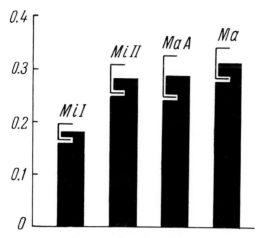

F IG. 10.   Mean DNA content (arbitrary units) of the micronuclei in G_1 and S (MiI), of those in G_2 (MiII), of macronuclear anlagen (MaA), and of adult macronuclei (Ma) of *L. magnus*. (From Raikov *et al.*, 1963).

of individual macronuclei strongly varied (from 2 to 6 c). In the paper cited, this variation was unjustly attributed to measurement errors, and a conclusion was drawn that the macronuclei of *Loxodes* remained diploid, though blocked at the postsynthetic level, and that they were likely to differentiate from micronuclei already in G_2.

This interpretation later proved to be not quite correct. A reinvestigation using a more sensitive cytofluorimetric method (Bobyleva *et al.*, 1980) has shown that nearly all micronuclei of nondividing *L. magnus* are already in G_2; only in dividing cells are there many micronuclei in G_1 or S (Fig. 11). The developing macronuclei always differentiate, however, from G_1 micronuclei, and at first they contain only 2 c DNA. Then, a single round of DNA replication occurs in them, so that young macronuclei already have about 4 c DNA. Adult macronuclei of nondividing cells actually vary in their DNA content; most of them contain (in one of the clones studied) from 4.5 to 7 c DNA (Fig. 11B). In other clones, the range of this variability can be both narrower (4–5.5 c; 5–6 c) and wider (5–10 c). Such variations are inconsistent with the hypothesis of simple diploidy (or even tetraploidy) of the macronuclei of *Loxodes*. This caused Bobyleva and associates (1980) to presume a partial replication of DNA in the adult macronuclei, leading to its gradual accumulation above the diploid postsynthetic level.

In *T. sulcata,* the adult macronuclei contain, according to cytophotometric data, approximately as much DNA as the micronuclei (Kovaleva and Raikov, 1978). Most nuclei of either category have about 2 c DNA, but some of them

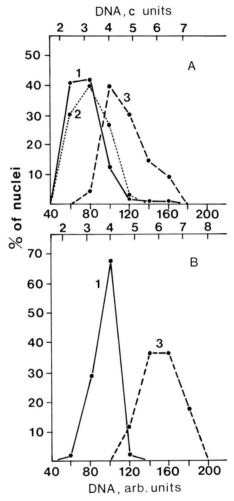

FIG. 11.   Variation curves of the DNA content of the nuclei in a clone of *L. magnus*. (A) In dividing cells; (B) in nondividing cells. 1, Micronuclei; 2, macronuclear anlagen; 3, macronuclei. (From Bobyleva *et al.*, 1980.)

contain from 2 to 4 c (Fig. 12a and d). In the case of the micronuclei, this apparently means that their S period occurs near the end of the interphase. As for the macronuclei, these data could argue for "simple diploidy" of these nuclei were it not for the existence of a temporary drop of the DNA content in developing macronuclei (Fig. 12b and c) which indicates some kind of reorganization of their genetic apparatus (see Section IV,C, 3). Moreover, some macronuclei, like those in *Loxodes,* accumulate DNA in excess of 4c, probably as a result of partial DNA replication (Fig. 12e).

Finally, in *G. orbis* (Nouzarède, 1976), the DNA content of the macronuclei clearly exceeds that of the micronuclei. The macronuclei may contain from 4.5 to 32 c DNA (frequent values, from 8 to 16 c). These data are rather hard to

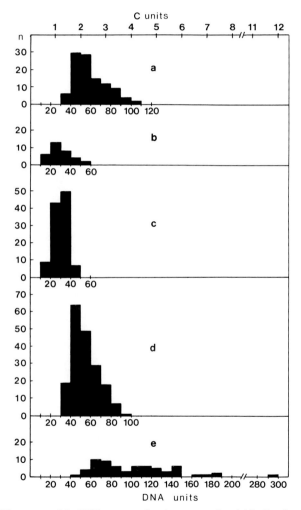

FIG. 12. Histograms of the DNA content of various types of nuclei in *T. sulcata.* (a) In micronuclei; (b) in macronuclear anlagen; (c) in young macronuclei; (d) in adult macronuclei; (e) in old macronuclei. Abscissas: DNA quantity in arbitrary units (bottom) and in c units (top). Ordinates: frequencies. (From Kovaleva and Raikov, 1978.)

interpret since they may mean either polyploidy of the macronuclei or accumulation in them of some specific DNA, e.g., of nucleolar DNA, in addition to the basically tetraploid (diploid postsynthetic) genome. Nouzarède himself favors the latter explanation.

Thus, in no case so far studied is the DNA content of the macronuclei exactly the same as the diploid (pre- or postsynthetic) micronuclear content. In *Loxodes* and *Geleia*, the minimum (initial?) DNA content of the macronuclei lies near 4 c, but in *Trachelonema*, near 2 c. The nature of the subsequent accumulation of DNA in some of the macronuclei remains to be studied (see Section V). In general, the macronuclei of the karyorelictids can apparently be called *paradiploid* or *hyperdiploid* nuclei (Kovaleva and Raikov, 1978).

2. DNA Replication

The comparatively low DNA content of the karyorelictid macronuclei, in conjunction with their inability to divide, have lead to an idea that both phenomena might be caused by a block of DNA replication in the macronuclei (Raikov, 1957b, 1963a; Poljansky and Raikov, 1961). This idea found support in the autoradiographic data of Torch (1964a), who failed to obtain any incorporation of [³H]thymidine into the macronuclei of *Tracheloraphis* sp.

The question about DNA synthesis in the macronuclei was later investigated with autoradiography in *L. magnus* (Raikov and Morat, 1977) and *L. striatus* (Ron and Urieli, 1977). In *L. magnus,* no strongly labeled macronuclei were obtained following a 3-hour incubation with [³H]thymidine, provided the fixation was done after a relatively short period of chase (up to 7 hours). Only some micronuclei and some anlagen of differentiating macronuclei were then labeled. Strongly labeled macronuclei appeared only after a 20-hour chase, which meant that new macronuclei could have developed during the chase period from anlagen or even from micronuclei which were already labeled. At the same time, a minor DNA synthesis (2–3 silver grains per nucleus) was found in many macronuclei even with short times of chase. These data support the idea that replication of the bulk DNA is blocked in the macronuclei, but they do not exclude partial replication of some DNA sequences which may be responsible for the gradual accumulation of DNA in the macronuclei, found in *L. magnus* with cytofluorimetry (see Section III, B, 1).

In *L. striatus*, the results look somewhat different, at least at the first glance. After an incubation with [³H]thymidine for 2 to 6 hours and with immediate fixation, more than 90% of the macronuclei were unlabeled, but about 9% displayed some label over the whole nucleus or over the nucleolus only. Unfortunately, Ron and Urieli (1977) do not mention the intensity of the labeling of these macronuclei, and therefore it is hard to say whether a minor DNA synthesis or a replication of the bulk DNA was involved. It is also possible that some developing macronuclear anlagen got into the category of labeled macronuclei. After long incubations with [³H]thymidine (1 to 3 days), the percentage of labeled macronuclei sharply increased (to 60% or more), as did the percentage of nuclei with only the nucleolus labeled (up to 50%). This increase can be explained by accumulation of the label incorporated as a result of minor DNA synthesis and/or by the development of new macronuclei from labeled anlagen or micronuclei during the incubation itself. The data of Ron and Urieli about thymidine labeling of only the nucleolus apparently reflect a partial replication (amplification) of the nucleolar DNA in some macronuclei.

Thus, the autoradiographic evidence concerning *Loxodes* is on the whole consistent with the hypothesis postulating a block of replication of the bulk DNA in the macronuclei and the existence of a partial replication of some DNA fractions in them, e.g., of an amplification of the ribosomal RNA genes.

Finally, an autoradiographic study of the incorporation of [¹⁴C]- and [³H]thymidine has been carried out in *G. orbis* by Nouzarède (1976). A strong labeling of the peripheral zone of the macronuclei and of the perinuclear cytoplasm was observed at the light microscopic level. The macronuclear sphere remained, however, unlabeled. At the electron microscopic level, only some incorporation of [³H]thymidine into the macronuclear matrix was demonstrated, but many membrane-bounded vesicles in the perinuclear cytoplasm were also labeled. The labeling of the macronuclei apparently depends on the DNA synthesis that is responsible in *Geleia* for the increase of the DNA content of these nuclei from 4 to 8–16 c and even more (see Section III,B,1). It is more difficult to explain the labeling of the cytoplasm outside of the mitochondria. Nouzarède supposes that some vesicles of the perinuclear cytoplasm may contain replicating and transcribed DNA which has been extruded from the macronuclei. However, there is not enough evidence to prove it.

C. RNA Content and Synthesis

As already mentioned (Section III,A), the karyorelictid macronuclei have large nucleoli which strongly stain for RNA, and sometimes also RNA-containing spheres. But no quantitative studies of the RNA content of these nuclei exist yet.

As to the synthesis of RNA, the macronuclei of *Tracheloraphis* sp. readily incorporate [³H]uridine (Torch, 1964a); however, the macronuclear crystalloids always remain unlabeled, which confirms the absence of RNA in them. In 24 hours, the labeled RNA appears also in the cytoplasm. The RNA synthesis in the macronuclei of *Tracheloraphis* can be inhibited with actinomycin D (Torch, 1965). This drug also blocks the regeneration of the anterior body end, but only after 48 hours of incubation with it (Torch, 1964b). This seems to mean that the macronuclei of *Tracheloraphis* synthesize, along with rRNA, a long-lived form of mRNA which is necessary for the regeneration. Since regeneration is not blocked immediately and since even anucleate fragments of *Tracheloraphis* can regenerate during some time (Torch, 1962), this mRNA must be stored in the cytoplasm.

In *L. striatus* and *L. magnus,* the macronuclei intensely incorporate [³H]uridine (Ron and Urieli, 1977; Raikov and Morat, 1977). Especially the nucleolus is labeled, but some label also gets into the peripheral zone of the macronucleus. A gradual decrease of the labeling of macronuclei isolated after a chase of increasing duration (from 1.5 to 27.5 hours) indicates that the newly synthesized RNA moves from the macronuclei into the cytoplasm (Raikov and Morat, 1977).

In *G. orbis,* mainly an accumulation of [³H]uridine-labeled RNA in the perinuclear cytoplasm was observed (Nouzarède, 1976). Since only long incubations with the precursor (19 and 24 hours) followed by long periods of chase (5, 19, and 72 hours) were used, this labeled RNA is likely to have a macronuclear origin (rather than to be synthesized in the cytoplasm, as supposed by Nouzarède). No uridine incorporation into the macronuclear spheres was observed in *Geleia,* despite the fact that they contain RNA (see Section III,A).

D. FINE STRUCTURE AND ULTRACYTOCHEMISTY

The macronuclei of the karyorelictids vary considerably in their fine structural organization (Figs. 13–23). These variations mainly depend on the degree of chromatin condensation and morphology of the chromocenters, on the number and size of the nucleoli, and on the presence and type of the nuclear bodies which may be either spheres or crystalloids. The main features of the karyorelictid macronuclei studied with the electron microscope are shown in Table II.

1. Nuclear Envelope

The karyorelictid macronuclei have a nuclear envelope of conventional structure. It carries numerous pore complexes (Fig. 13B). The number of pores per 1 μm^2 of the nuclear surface is about 24 in *K. latum* and *T. dogieli,* 40 in *T. caudatus,* 60 in *L. magnus, R. multinucleata,* and *T. totevi,* 85 in *T. phoenicopterus,* and up to 120 in *G. orbis.* In the last case the pores are arranged hexagonally (for references, see Table II). When macronuclei are united into nuclear complexes, the frequency and morphology of the pores as well as the structure of the envelope itself are the same at the sides of the nuclei facing the surface of the complex and at those turned to other macronuclei (Figs. 3 and 14A).

The fibrous lamina at the inner side of the macronuclear envelope is usually poorly developed. It is clearly seen only in *K. fistulosum* (Raikov, 1972b).

2. Chromatin Elements

As in other cell nuclei, a part of the chromatin of the karyorelictid macronuclei is decondensed while the other is condensed. The chromatin in the macronuclei

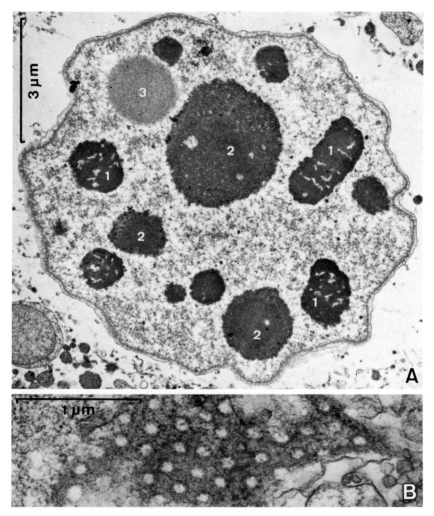

FIG. 13.   Fine structure of the macronucleus in *T. dogieli*. (A) Entire nucleus showing chromo-centers (1), nucleoli (2), and a sphere (3); (B) pore complexes in a tangential section of the macronuclear envelope. (From Raikov, 1974.)

of *Geleia orbis* is almost completely decondensed (Fig. 23A and C); bodies of condensed chromatin are quite rare (Raikov, 1984). A considerable part of the chromatin also seems to be decondensed in the macronuclei of *T. caudatus* (Raikov and Dragesco, 1969) and *L. magnus* (Raikov, 1975).

Small bodies of condensed chromatin, 0.1–0.3 μm in diameter, occur in *L. magnus* and *R. multinucleata*. They are usually numerous and distributed

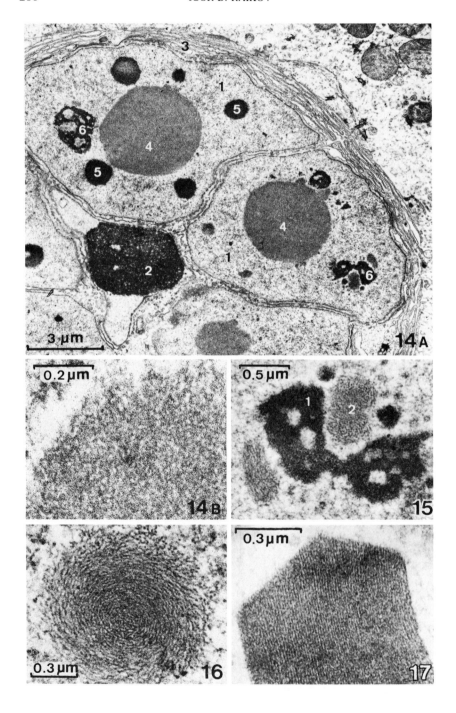

throughout the nucleus (Fig. 18). However, some macronuclei of *R. multi-nucleata* already show an aggregation and fusion of many small bodies into larger (1.5 μm) chromocenters which are often vacuolized (Raikov, 1979). And in most karyorelictids studied, all the condensed chromatin is united into chromocenters and there are practically no free "small bodies" left over (see Table II).

The number, size, and structure of the macronuclear chromocenters can vary. Most frequent are large (up to 3μm) spongy chromocenters which are pervaded with cleftlike lacunae or are sometimes vacuolized. Such are the chromocenters of *T. dogieli* (Fig. 13A), *T. geopetiti, T. sulcata* (Fig. 22A and B), and *K. latum* (Figs. 14A and 15). These chromocenters seem to be formed by a cord of condensed chromatin folded upon itself. Also frequent are chromocenters consisting of many chromatin bodies which are aggregated but not fused (*T. caudatus, T. phoenicopterus, T. totevi*). In *T. phoenicopterus*, the chromatin bodies are usually arranged around a mass of fibrous material, so that the entire chromocenter looks ring-shaped (Fig. 19). Finally, the single large chromocenter present in each macronucleus of *K. fistulosum* has a dense core and a spongy cortex (Raikov, 1972b). The chromocenters never have any membranous or other envelope.

The chromocenters always consist of densely packed 10-nm thick fibrils corresponding in diameter to nucleosome fibrils of the chromatin. The material of the chromocenters is completely bleached with EDTA after Bernhard (Fig. 20), which is typical of deoxyribonucleoprotein (DNP). A loss of stainability of the chromocenters following a sequential treatment of the sections with Pronase and DNase was also obtained in *T. dogieli* and *T. geopetiti* (Raikov and Kovaleva, 1980, 1981).

3. Nucleoli

The nucleoli of karyorelictid macronuclei generally display a dense fibrillar core and a looser granular cortex, sometimes pervaded with lacunae (Figs. 13A, 19, and 22A). Small fragments of granular structure ("micronucleoli") may detach from the cortex, e. g., in *T. caudatus* (Raikov and Dragesco, 1969) or *T.*

FIG. 14.   Parts of the nuclear complex of *K. latum*. (A) Two macronuclei (1), a micronucleus (2), and the multimembranous capsule around the complex (3) are seen. The macronuclei contain spheres (4), nucleoli (5), and chromocenters (6). (B) Part of a sphere showing its component filaments. (From Raikov, 1972a).

FIG. 15.   A chromocenter (1) of *K. latum* showing stacks of filaments (2) of the future sphere which form in contact with it. (From Raikov, 1972a.)

FIG. 16.   A sphere from a macronucleus of *K. fistulosum* showing spiral arrangement of its component filaments. (From Raikov, 1972b.)

FIG. 17.   A crystalloid from a macronucleus of *T. phoenicopterus*. (From Raikov and Kovaleva, 1978.)

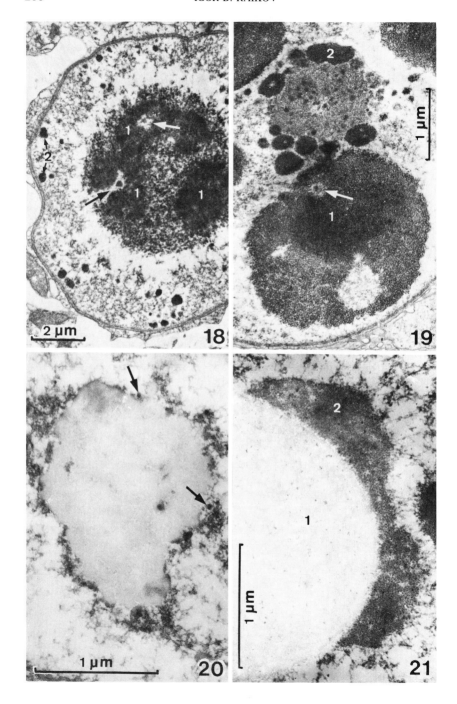

totevi (Kovaleva *et al.*, 1979). In *K. fistulosum,* the granular cortex is almost absent and the nucleoli are entirely fibrillar (Raikov, 1972b).

Profiles of a channel, filled with loose fibrillar matrix and sometimes showing a denser axis which resembles condensed chromatin, are frequently seen inside the nucleolar fibrillar core or at its outer edge (Figs. 13A and 19). This channel, meandering inside the nucleolus, apparently corresponds to the nucleolar organizer. Such channels have been observed in the nucleoli of all Trachelocercidae studied so far, as well as in *R. multinucleata* (see Table II). The chromatin nature of the dense axis has been checked ultracytochemically: in *T. dogieli* and *T. geopetiti* it becomes bleached with Bernhard's EDTA and is digested with Pronase followed by DNase (Raikov and Kovaleva, 1980, 1981). Moreover, treatment of the sections with DNase considerably decreases the contrast of the entire fibrillar core of the nucleolus in *T. dogieli.* This means that some DNA fibrils of the nucleolar organizer are decondensed and spread throughout the fibrillar zone, serving there as templates for rRNA transcription. All other nucleolar components (both the fibrils and the granules) retain full contrast after Bernhard's staining, which is typical of RNP (Raikov and Kovaleva, 1980, 1981; Raikov, 1984).

In *L. magnus* (Raikov, 1975), the sole nucleolus of a macronucleus proved to be composite and has several fibrillar cores inside a common granular zone (Fig. 18). It forms during the development of a macronucleus by fusion of several unit nucleoli (Raikov, 1959a). Each fibrillar core has its own organizer, which looks like a chromatin body deeply invaginated into the nucleolus (Fig. 18). A composite nucleolus also forms by fusion of unit nucleoli in *T. sulcata* (Kovaleva and Raikov, 1970); it also displays several organizer regions (Fig. 24D–G).

A problem that remains unsolved is whether the intranucleolar chromatin is chromosomal or extrachromosomal, e.g., amplified. The latter is more likely in *L. magnus* and *T. sulcata,* where partial replication of DNA exists in the adult macronuclei (see Section III,B).

The numerous (more than 100) nucleoli of the macronuclei of *G. orbis* usually unite with each other pairwise or form larger aggregates (Fig. 23A). The unit nucleoli are sometimes arranged in such aggregates along a spiral line (Fig. 23B), but they never really fuse (Raikov, 1984).

Fig. 18.   Fine structure of a macronucleus of *L. magnus.* The composite nucleolus containing three fibrillar zones (1) with nucleolar organizers (arrows) is seen; the nuclear periphery contains chromatin bodies (2). (From Raikov, 1975.)

Fig. 19.   Part of a macronucleus of *T. phoenicopterus* showing a nucleolus (1) with its organizer (arrow) and a composite "annular" chromocenter (2). (From Raikov and Kovaleva, 1978.)

Fig. 20.   A chromocenter of *T. geopetiti* bleached with EDTA. The rim of perichromatin fibrils and some perichromatin granules (arrows) are seen. (From Raikov and Kovaleva, 1981.)

Fig. 21.   Part of a Pronase-digested sphere (1) in a macronucleus of *T. geopetiti.* The sphere is surrounded by nucleolar material (2). (From Raikov and Kovaleva, 1981.)

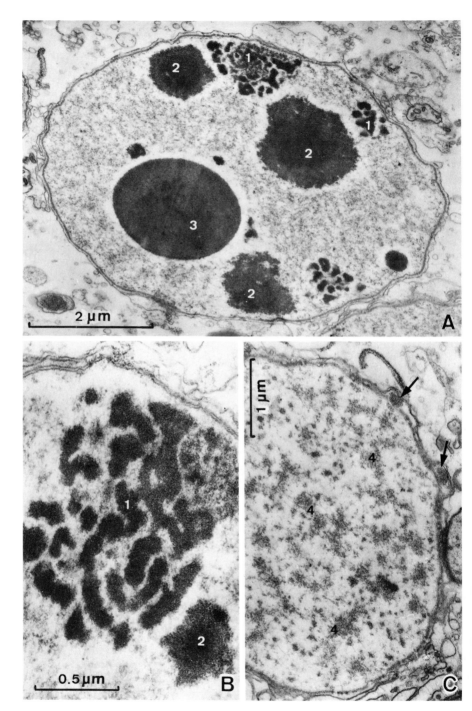

4. Nuclear Matrix and RNP Particles

The matrix of the karyorelictid macronuclei is a network of filaments of various thicknesses (5–20 nm). Some of them are certainly fibrils of decondensed chromatin. Other filaments may consist of protein or RNP; in *T. geopetiti*, most of them are digested with either Pronase alone or Pronase followed by RNase (Raikov and Kovaleva, 1981). The macronuclear matrix of *G. orbis* contains also bundles of microfilaments which form septae dividing the nucleus into a number of compartments (Raikov, 1984).

The matrix usually contains RNP particles of various types. Macronuclei of *T. geopetiti* stained after Bernhard show a rim of electron-dense, 5- to 6-nm thick fibrils at the periphery of bleached chromocenters; many granules ranging in size from 35 to 140 nm (usually about 50 nm) are implanted into this rim (Fig. 20). Both the fibrils and the granules are DNase resistant but can be digested with Pronase followed by RNase (Raikov and Kovaleva, 1981). They apparently correspond to the RNP-containing perichromatin fibrils and perichromatin granules which are typical products of transcription in higher organisms (reviews: Bouteille *et al.*, 1974; Puvion and Moyne, 1981; Hancock and Boulikas, 1982). In *T. dogieli*, the perichromatin fibrils occur mainly in the lacunae inside the chromocenters, while perichromatin granules (40–70 nm in size) occur both in the lacunae and at the outer surface of the chromocenters (Raikov and Kovaleva, 1980). In both species, the presence of perichromatin fibrils and granules indicates that masses of condensed chromatin are capable of peripheral transcription which is likely to occur on DNA loops protruding into the nuclear matrix.

The macronuclei of *G. orbis* have no chromocenters and almost no condensed chromatin. As a result of this, perhaps, they also lack typical perichromatin fibrils and granules; the nuclear RNP particles are here somewhat different (Raikov, 1984). Among the intramacronuclear compartments already mentioned, some appear to be active in transcription (Fig. 23C). Such compartments contain electron-dense strands with fuzzy outlines, some 50 nm thick, which are not bleached with EDTA and apparently consist of RNP. Possibly these are transcription complexes, i.e., nascent threads of RNA or RNP attached to a DNA axis. Besides this, the ''active'' compartments contain clusters of granules about 20 nm in size, resembling interchromatin granules; these also retain contrast after Bernhard's staining. Both the fibrils and the granules seem to be products of nonnucleolar transcription occurring on decondensed chromatin threads.

FIG. 22. Fine structure of the macronucleus in *T. sulcata*. (A) An aging macronucleus containing chromocenters (1), nucleoli (2), and a sphere (3). (B) A chromocenter showing its component chromatin cords. (C) A macronuclear anlage which contains decondensed chromatin strands (4) and accumulations of material extruded from the analge (arrows). [From Kovaleva and Raikov, 1973 (A, B) and 1978 (C).]

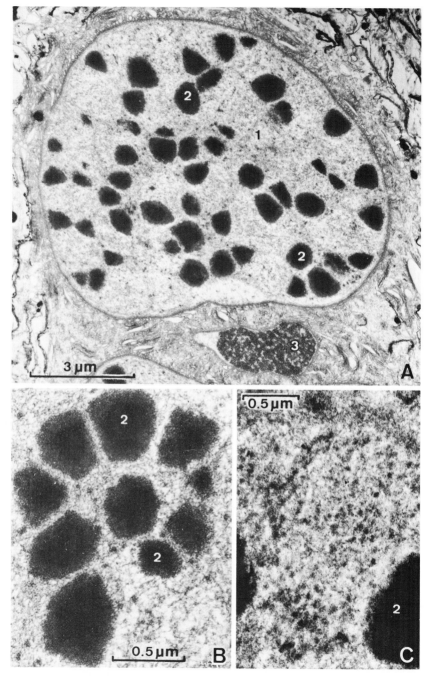

Fig. 23. Macronuclear fine structure in *G. orbis*. (A) A macronucleus (1) containing numerous nucleoli (2), and a micronucleus (3). (B) A nucleolar aggregate. (C) An active compartment in a macronucleus, containing fuzzy strands (transcriptional complexes?). (From Raikov, 1984.)

5. Nuclear Bodies

As mentioned earlier (Section III,A), the macronuclei of the karyorelictids may contain larger inclusions (nuclear bodies) in the form of either spheres or crystalloids, which consist of protein and sometimes of RNA as well. In several species they have been studied with the electron microscope (see Table II). The fine structural and cytochemical features of the nuclear bodies are summarized in Tables III and IV.

a. *Spheres.*   Each macronucleus usually forms a single sphere, 1 to 8 μm in diameter. In most species, the spheres arise asynchronously, i.e., in only some of the macronuclei of a given cell (*T. geopetiti, T. dogieli, T. sulcata, K. fistulosum;* see Table III). They seem to form in aging macronuclei and to be absent in young ones (Kovaleva and Raikov, 1970, 1978). However, in *R. multinucleata* and *G. orbis* the spheres appear synchronously in all (or both) adult macronuclei of a cell. It is interesting to note that in these same two species the spheres contain RNA in addition to protein (Table III). This observation suggests that the spheres are formed in these two species for a limited time only and then synchronously disappear, e.g., by extrusion of their contents into the cytoplasm. Such an extrusion has actually been seen by light microscope in both species (Raikov, 1963c, 1963d), as well as in *R. granulosa, R. rugosa* (Raikov, 1963b), and *G. nigriceps* (Raikov, 1959b), which also have synchronously form- ing and RNA-containing spheres.

The spheres always lack envelopes (Figs. 13A, 14A, 16, and 22A). They usually consist of a random plexus of 7- to 8-nm thick filaments of medium electron density (Table III; Fig. 14B). However, in *K. fistulosum* the same filaments are spirally arranged (Fig. 16). Only nonhistone protein is cytochem- ically revealed in the spheres consisting of such filaments (Table III). This finding has recently been confirmed with fine structural cytochemistry in *T. dogieli,* the spheres of which can be completely digested with Pronase (Raikov and Kovaleva, 1980). Also the spheres of *T. geopetiti* proved to be Pronase- sensitive (Fig. 21), though no 7- to 8-nm filaments were found in them. It is, however, possible that such filaments are here masked as a result of their ex- tremely dense packing (Raikov and Kovaleva, 1981).

The fine structure of RNA-containing spheres is not uniform. The spheres of *G. orbis* consist of somewhat thicker filaments (10–12 nm), which are possibly RNP fibrils (Raikov, 1984). But the spheres of *R. multinucleata,* which also contain RNA and protein, seem to be made of tiny granules and/or very thin fibrils, less than 2.5 nm in diameter (Raikov, 1979). Thus, so far no definite correlation has been established between the fine structure of the sphere and the presence of RNA in it.

The mode of formation of the spheres also varies (see Table III). In most species investigated, they form while in contact with the condensed chromatin. In *T. dogieli,* the sphere appears in a depression of a chromocenter and remains

TABLE II

Fine Structural Peculiarities of the Macronuclei of the Karyorelictida[a]

Species	Arrangement of macronuclei	Chromatin elements	Nucleoli	Nuclear bodies	References
Tracheloarca geopetiti	In a group	Up to 10 chromocenters	Up to 10 typical	Protein sphere	Raikov and Kovaleva (1981)
Tracheloraphis dogieli	Free	Up to 15 chromocenters	10–15 typical	Protein sphere	Raikov (1974); Raikov and Kovaleva (1980)
T. caudatus	In many groups	Up to 4 small chromocenters	1–5 typical	Crystalloids	Raikov and Dragesco (1969)
T. phoenicopterus	In a nuclear complex	Several composite chromocenters	1–3 typical	Crystalloids	Raikov and Kovaleva (1978)
T. totevi	In a nuclear complex	Several composite chromocenters	3–6 typical	Crystalloids	Kovaleva et al. (1979)
Trachelonema sulcata	Free	1–3 composite chromocenters	Up to 4 typical or 1 composite	Sphere	Kovaleva and Raikov (1970, 1973, 1978)

Loxodes magnus	Free	Small bodies	1, composite	—	Mashansky (1963); De Puytorac and Njiné (1970); Raikov (1975)
Remanella multinucleata	Free	Small bodies and several chromo-centers	Up to 10 typical	Sphere	Raikov (1979)
Keutrophoros latum	In several nuclear complexes	Several chromocenters	1–4 typical	Large sphere	Raikov (1972a)
K. fistulosum	In many groups	1 large chromocenter	2–4 small	Several spheres	Raikov (1972b)
Geleia orbis	In a group	Decondensed, rarely small bodies	More than 100, small	Large sphere	Raikov (1984)
Avelia martinicense	In a group	?	Many small (?)	Large sphere	Nouzarède (1975, 1976)

[a]Modified from Raikov (1982).

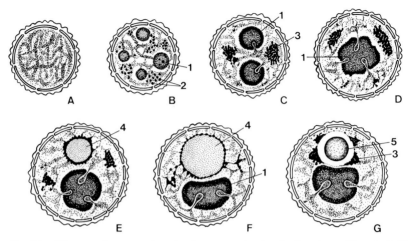

Fig. 24. Diagram of macronuclear development and aging in *T. sulcata*. (A and B) Macronuclear anlagen; (C) young macronucleus; (D and E) adult macronuclei; (F and G) aging macronuclei. 1, Nucleoli; 2, chromatin bodies; 3, chromocenters; 4, fibrillar material inside a distended chromocenter (precursor of the sphere); 5, sphere. (From Kovaleva and Raikov, 1970.)

adjacent to one or several chromocenters (Raikov, 1974). In *T. sulcata,* the sphere forms by condensation of fibrous material accumulated inside a large chromocenter (Fig. 24E–G). In *K. fistulosum* also, the precursors of the spheres are loose masses of fibrils which first appear in vacuoles of the single large chromocenter (Raikov, 1972b). Finally, in *K. latum* stacks of 8-nm filaments are formed in the cavities of several chromocenters (Fig. 15), but later they fuse with the central sphere (Fig. 14A).

However, the spheres may also develop in contact with the nucleoli. Thus, in *T. geopetiti* the sphere primordium first appears inside the granular cortex of a nucleolus (Raikov and Kovaleva, 1981), and the grown sphere remains in close contact with several nucleoli (Fig. 21). In *G. orbis,* the sphere is also adjacent to several nucleoli and, moreover, its filaments seem to be continuous with some filaments of the nuclear matrix (Raikov, 1984). In the former species, the sphere is purely proteinaceous; in the latter, it also contains RNA.

One may suppose that the spheres are intranuclear stocks of proteins, which are sometimes chromatinic proteins and sometimes nucleolar proteins and/or RNP. This is consistent with the general notion of nuclear bodies as proteinaceous structures which may sometimes be laden with RNA (Dupuy-Coin *et al.,* 1972). The exact functional significance of the macronuclear spheres is, however, unknown.

b. *Crystalloids.* The crystalloids have so far been studied only in the macronuclei of some Trachelocercidae (Table IV). It is worth noting that other

TABLE III

FINE-STRUCTURE CHARACTERIZATION OF MACRONUCLEAR SPHERES

Species	Incidence (percentage of nuclei or animals)	Diameter (μm)	Components	Mode of formation	Contacts	Chemical nature	References
T. geopetiti	30% of nuclei	Up to 8	Fibrils 2 nm (?)	Inside a nucleolus	Nucleoli	Protein	Raikov and Kovaleva (1981)
T. dogieli	10% of nuclei	Up to 3	Fibrils 8 nm	Close to a chromocenter	Chromocenters	Protein	Raikov (1974); Raikov and Kovaleva (1980)
T. sulcata	40% of nuclei	1–3	Fibrils 7 nm	From loose fibrils inside a chromocenter	Chromocenters	Protein	Kovaleva and Raikov (1970, 1973)
R. multinucleata	20% of animals	Up to 3	Granules 2.5 nm (?)	In nuclear matrix	—	Protein and RNA	Raikov (1979)
K. latum	?	Up to 4	Fibrils 8 nm	Stacks of fibrils near chromocenters	Chromocenters	Protein, (RNA ?)	Raikov (1972a)
K. fistulosum	10% of nuclei	Up to 1.5	Fibrils 8 nm	From loose fibrils inside the chromocenter	—	Protein	Raikov (1972b)
G. orbis	10–50% of animals	Up to 8	Fibrils 10–12 nm	In nuclear matrix (?)	Nucleoli	Protein and RNA	Raikov (1984)

TABLE IV

FINE STRUCTURE CHARACTERIZATION OF MACRONUCLEAR CRYSTALLOIDS

Species	Incidence	Length (μm)	Period of subunit packing	Mode of formation	Contacts	Chemical nature	References
T. caudatus	?	Up to 5	13 × 8 nm	?	Nucleoli	Protein	Raikov and Dragesco (1969)
T. phoenicopterus	20% of animals	Up to 5	13 × 8 nm	Inside chromo-centers	—	Protein	Raikov and Kovaleva (1978)
T. totevi	?	Up to 3.5	?	Close to nucleoli	Nucleoli	Protein	Kovaleva et al. (1979)

species of the same family and sometimes of the same genera form spheres. The spheres and the crystalloids thus seem to be homologous. Like the spheres, the crystalloids are facultative formations. The number of crystalloids per macronucleus may reach three (in *T. phoenicopterus*) but usually there is only one. The crystalloids are generally prismatic in shape (Fig. 2A).

With the electron microscope, the crystalloids of *T. phoenicopterus* and *T. caudatus* show a longitudinal striation with a period of 13 nm; this is caused by parallel packing of 8-nm filaments (Fig. 17). The crystalloids thus contain the same kind of filaments as the spheres, but only in a regularly packed form. There is also a weaker cross periodicity of the crystalloids (about 8 nm). According to light microscopic cytochemistry (see Section III,A), the crystalloids of trachelocercid macronuclei are proteinaceous.

The crystalloids are formed in *T. phoenicopterus* (Raikov and Kovaleva, 1978) by crystallization of an amorphous proteinaceous material which accumulates inside "ring-shaped" chromocenters (Fig. 19). Crystalloids already formed lose contact with the chromocenters. However, in *T. caudatus* and *T. totevi* the crystalloids frequently contact nucleoli and micronucleoli; it is still unknown whether this has something to do with their formation.

As in the case of the spheres, the functions of the crytalloids are unknown. Their extrusion into the cytoplasm was never observed.

6. Interpretation of Fine-Structure Patterns

The differences in the fine structure of the macronuclei of various karyorelictids apparently reflect the functional (transcriptional) activity of these nuclei. The macronuclei which have a single large chromocenter and small, mainly fibrillar nucleoli are likely to be the least active ones (*K. fistulosum*, cf. Table II). The next grade is represented by macronuclei which have large chromocenters but at the same time typical nucleoli (*T. geopetiti, T. dogieli, T. sulcata, K. latum*). Still more active seem to be the macronuclei which have a strongly developed nucleolar apparatus and little condensed chromatin (*T. caudatus, T. phoenicopterus, L. magnus, R. multinucleata*). This series will then be completed by *G. orbis*, the macronuclei of which possess a fully decondensed chromatin and an extremely developed nucleolar apparatus. It is perhaps meaningful that the nucleocytoplasmic ratio is extremely low in *Geleia* (Fig. 1K), so that the activity of the small macronuclei must support the metabolism of a very large cell.

IV. Macronuclei during Cell Division

A. BEHAVIOR OF THE EXISTING MACRONUCLEI

1. Segregation of the Macronuclei

Macronuclear division has never been observed in any karyorelictid species. This inability of the karyorelictid macronuclei to divide, called *caryosterosis* by

Fauré-Fremiet (1954), implies that during division of the ciliate itself the existing macronuclei segregate in some way or another between the two daughter cells.

In species with many free nuclei, the macronuclei are randomly partitioned between the daughter cells, usually not in equal numbers. This type of cell division is seen in *T. margaritatus* (Fig. 25A) and *T. dogieli* (Raikov, 1957a, 1958a), *L. magnus* (Fig. 26C and D; Fauré-Fremiet, 1954; Raikov, 1959a; Bobyleva, 1981), *R. multinucleata* (Fauré-Fremiet, 1954; Raikov, 1963c), *G. murmanica* (Raikov, 1963d). In most of these cases, either the micronuclei do

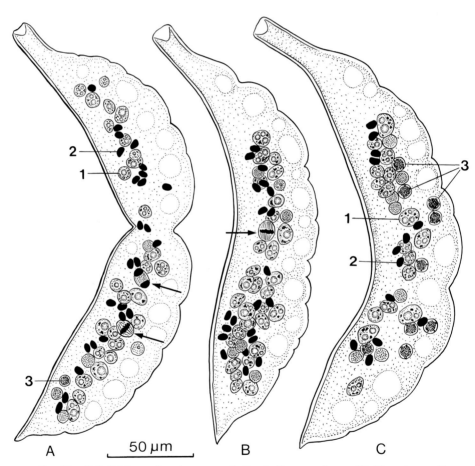

FIG. 25. Cell division and nuclear reorganization in *T. margaritatus*. (A) Plasmotomy with segregation of the nuclei; single micronuclear mitoses are seen (arrows). (B) Daughter cell showing an asynchronous micronuclear mitosis (arrow). (C) Nondividing cell with several macronuclear anlagen (3). 1, Macronuclei; 2, micronuclei. Feulgen staining. (From Raikov, 1957a).

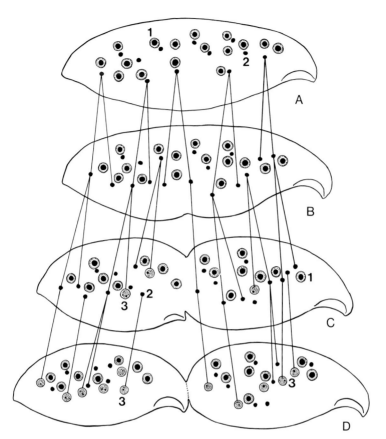

FIG. 26.   Diagram of cell division and nuclear reorganization in *L. magnus*. (A) Reproduction of some micronuclei. (B and C) Early cytokinesis; the micronuclei continue to divide and some of them differentiate into macronuclear anlagen. (D) Late cytokinesis; formation of macronuclear anlagen continues, the existing macronuclei are segregated. 1, Macronucleus; 2, micronucleus; 3, macronuclear anlage. (Modified from Raikov, 1957b.)

not divide during the cytokinesis, or only a few of them divide (Fig. 25A). Thus, the division of multinucleate karyorelictids is essentially plasmotomy.

Such karyorelictids apparently become able to divide only when the number of macronuclei in a cell reaches a certain threshold level. This level, however, varies even within a clone. Thus, in actively growing cultures, the cells of *L. magnus* can start dividing when the number of their macronuclei reaches 18–20, but in stationary cultures of the same clone, when it is not less than 31 (Bobyleva, 1981). At the same time, dividing cells showing a highly unequal distribution of the macronuclei between the two daughter animals (e.g., 28:5) become

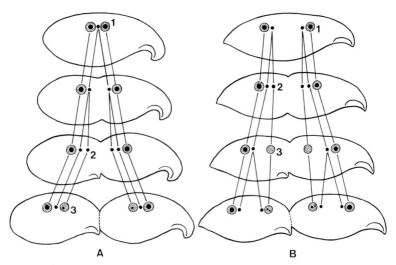

Fig. 27.   Diagrams of nuclear reorganization during cytokinesis in *L. rostrum* (A) and *L. striatus* (B). 1, Macronucleus; 2, micronucleus; 3, macronuclear anlage. (From Raikov, 1957b.)

much more frequent in inhibited cultures, which leads to a strong variation of the nuclear numbers in the progeny.

In paucinucleate karyorelictids, the segregation of the existing macronuclei is, on the contrary, quite exact. For instance, in species with two macronuclei, each daughter cell always receives one of them (Figs. 27 and 28). This type of cytokinesis is found in *L. striatus, L. rostrum* (Raikov, 1959a), *R. granulosa, R. rugosa* (Raikov, 1963b), *G. nigriceps,* and *G. orbis* (Raikov, 1959b, 1963d). In species having a single nuclear group or complex (see Section II,A,2), usually the partitioning of the macronuclei is also exact. Thus, in *T. coluber,* the four macronuclei forming the group are regularly segregated by twos between the daughter cells (Fig. 29). Also the reorganization processes leading to the reconstruction of the normal nuclear apparatus in the daughter cells occur in paucinucleate species simultaneously with the segregation of the existing macronuclei (see Section IV,B).

Finally, in *T. caudatus,* a form with many nuclear groups of four macronuclei and two micronuclei in each, the nuclear reorganization precedes cytokinesis and leads to a doubling of the number of nuclear groups (Dragesco and Raikov, 1966). During the plasmotomy which follows, the reorganized nuclear groups are randomly segregated.

2. Cyclical Changes of the Macronuclei

Although the karyorelictid macronuclei do not divide during cytokinesis, this does not mean that they cannot undergo some changes at this time. Thus, it has been demonstrated that the mean DNA content of the adult macronuclei of *L. magnus* is always significantly lower (by 10–20%) in dividing animals than in nondividing ones (Bobyleva *et al.*, 1980). The entire variation curve of the DNA content is shifted toward lower values (Fig. 11A). These data apparently mean that an elimination of some part of the "additional" DNA, which has been accumulated by the macronuclei above the 4-c level (cf. Section III,B,1), must occur at the beginning of cytokinesis. This DNA is likely to be synthesized anew in the next cell cycle, and so on. Unfortunately, we do not know whether some cyclical changes of the transcription in the macronuclei are coupled with these changes in DNA content.

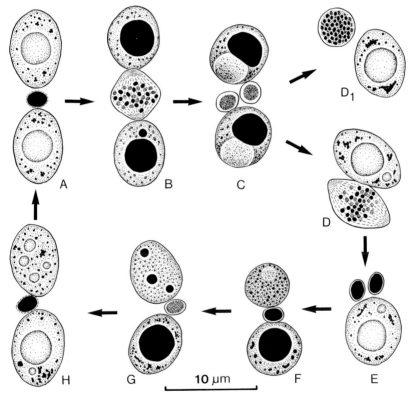

FIG. 28. Reorganization of the nuclear apparatus during cytokinesis in *R. granulosa*. (A) Nuclear apparatus of a nondividing cell (two macronuclei, one micronucleus); (B) first mitosis of the micronucleus; (C) two macronuclei and two micronuclei; (D and D₁) the two daughter nuclear groups (in each the micronucleus is in metaphase of the second mitosis). E–H show the nuclei of only one future daughter cell. (E) One macronucleus and two micronuclei; (F–H) formation and development of the anlage of the second macronucleus (at top). Staining: A, D, E, H, Feulgen reaction; B, C, G, Methyl Green and Pyronin; F, iron hematoxylin. (Modified from Raikov, 1963b.)

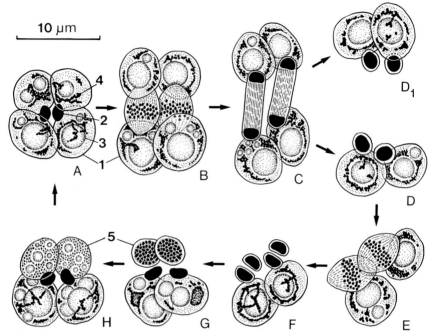

FIG. 29.   Nuclear reorganization during cytokinesis in *T. coluber*. (A) Group of four macro and two micronuclei; (B and C) mitosis of both micronuclei; (D and D₁) separation of the nuclear group in two (two macronuclei and two micronuclei in each); (E) second mitosis of the micronuclei in a daughter group; (F) stage following the second mitosis (four micronuclei); (G and H) differentiation of two micronuclei into macronuclear anlagen. 1, Macronuclei; 2, micronuclei; 3, nucleolus; 4, chromatin; 5, macronuclear anlagen. Feulgen staining. (From Raikov, 1969.)

Morphological changes of the macronuclei which can be related to cytokinesis are generally rare. In most species which form spheres in the macronuclei, no relation between their presence and the cell division could be established, e.g., in *R. rugosa, R. granulosa, R. multinucleata,* and *G. orbis* (Raikov, 1963b–d). In *G. nigriceps,* however, the spheres which contain RNA and protein occur in the macronuclei of only nondividing cells and are absent from those of dividing ones (Raikov, 1959b). Their extrusion from the macronuclei into the cytoplasm was reported to precede cytokinesis. This phenomenon may ensure the transport of some additional nuclear RNA into the cytoplasm where divisional morphogenesis is beginning.

B. Formation of New Macronuclei

The segregation of the existing macronuclei during cytokinesis obviously leads to a halving of their number in the daughter cells. To maintain a constant number of nuclei from one cell generation to another, a regular formation of new macronuclei must therefore occur in the karyorelictids in the cycle of every cell division (rather than during the sexual process only, as in other ciliates). Such a phenomenon does exist in all species studied; it occurs during a process of *nuclear reorganization,* which includes additional mitotic divisions of the micronuclei and differentiation of some of them into new macronuclei.

In multinucleate species, the nuclear reorganization is usually asynchronous and is not directly coupled with cytokinesis. Thus, in *T. margaritatus,* asynchronous mitoses of some micronuclei occur both in dividing and nondividing cells (Fig. 25A and B). Likewise asynchronous is the formation of the anlagen of new macronuclei which occur in most cells (Fig. 25A–C). In *T. dogieli,* the micronuclear mitoses and formation of the macronuclear anlagen appear more synchronized (approximately to 70%) but still occur mostly in nondividing cells (Raikov, 1957a, 1958a). In *L. magnus,* the nuclear reorganization is asynchronous and unrelated to cytokinesis in some strains (Raikov, 1959a) but rather synchronous in others (Fig. 26). In the latter strains, the micronuclei divide by mitosis mainly at early stages of the cytokinesis, and macronuclear anlagen (which always differentiate from just-divided micronuclei) mostly occur in dividing cells (Bobyleva *et al.,* 1980).

It is obvious that at least some micronuclei must divide more than once per cell cycle in order to reestablish the original number of nuclei. The first mitotic division ensures doubling of the micronuclei themselves, the second (and sometimes the following) produce an excess of micronuclei which later differentiate into macronuclei. If the number of macronuclei (Ma) is twice that of the micronuclei (Mi), as is frequently the case (see Section II,A,1), all the micronuclei must divide twice per cell cycle: $2x$ Ma + xMi→ (first mitosis) → $2x$ Ma + $2x$ Mi → (second mitosis) → $2x$ Ma + $4x$ Mi → (differentiation of the anlagen, MaA) → $2x$ Ma + $2x$ MaA + $2x$ Mi→ (development of new Ma) → $4x$ Ma + $2x$ Mi (double the initial number). These numerical relationships are especially evident in species with only a few nuclei ($x = 1$ or 2), as shown below.

In paucinucleate karyorelictids, the nuclear reorganization is always synchronous and occurs during cytokinesis. In species with 2 Ma and 1 Mi (e.g., *L. rostrum*), the sole micronucleus divides two times in succession, so that each daughter cell at first receives an old macronucleus and two micronuclei; then, one of the latter differentiates into a second macronucleus (Fig. 27A). The nuclear events in *R. granulosa* (Fig. 28), *R. rugosa, G. nigriceps, G. orbis* (Raikov, 1959a,b, 1963b,d) are exactly the same. But in *L. striatus* (2 Ma, 2 Mi), only one derivative of the first division of each micronucleus divides for the second time, while the other directly differentiates to produce a new macronucleus (Fig. 27B).

When a single nuclear group or complex is present, the sequence of the nuclear events is also fixed and coupled with cytokinesis. Thus, in *T. coluber* (4 Ma, 2 Mi), both micronuclei divide synchronously for the first time (Fig. 29B and C), and then the entire group of nuclei falls in two (Fig. 29D). Thereafter, all the micronuclei divide for the second time (Fig. 29E); and of the four micronuclei formed in each daughter cell (Fig. 29F), two become macronuclear anlagen (Fig. 29G and H) (Raikov, 1969). The reconstruction of the nuclear group in *Tracheloraphis* sp. is similar (Torch, 1961). In *T. phoenicopterus* (12 Ma, 6 Mi), which has a compact nuclear complex (Fig. 2B), this falls into two groups of nuclei in early cytokinesis; all six micronuclei synchronously divide twice and six anlagen of new macronuclei are formed in each daughter cell (Raikov, 1955, 1958a).

Among species with many nuclear groups (cf. Fig. 1D), the nuclear reorganization has thus far been studied only in *T. caudatus* (Dragesco and Raikov, 1966). The duplication of each nuclear group (4 Ma, 2 Mi in each) here occurs exactly like that of the sole group of *T. coluber* (cf. Fig. 29). This process occurs synchronously in all nuclear groups during early cytokinesis. The daughter groups of nuclei are almost formed when the two cells separate. The replication of the many nuclear groups in *K. fistulosum* appears to be similar but not coupled with cytokinesis (Raikov, 1972b).

C. Development of Macronuclear Anlagen

1. Light Microscopy and Cytochemistry

The development of new macronuclei has been followed light microscopically in *T. phoenicopterus, T. margaritatus, T. dogieli* (Raikov, 1955, 1957a, 1958a), *T. sulcata* (Kovaleva and Raikov, 1970), *L. striatus, L. magnus* (Raikov,

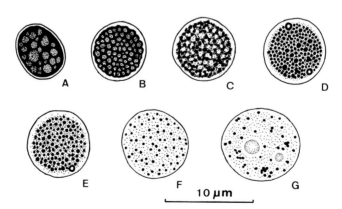

Fig. 30.   Macronuclear development in *T. margaritatus*. (A) Vacuolization of a micronucleus; (B and C) stage of chromatin reticulum; (D) stage of chromatin granules; (E and F) dechromatinization stage; (G) appearance of nucleoli. Feulgen staining. (from Raikov, 1957a.)

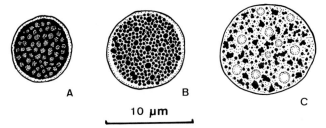

A   B
                                                              C
                   10 µm

FIG. 31.   Macronuclear development in *T. dogieli*. (A) Vacuolization stage; (B) granular stage;
(C) appearance of nucleoli and aggregation of the chromatin graunules. Feulgen staining. (From
Raikov, 1957a.)

1959a), *G. nigriceps, G. orbis* (Raikov, 1959b, 1963d), *R. granulosa, R. rugosa,* and *R. multinucleata* (Raikov, 1963b, c).

The development of an anlage begins with swelling of the micronucleus and vacuolization of its chromatin (Figs. 30A and B and 31A). At the next stage, a Feulgen-positive reticulum is usually formed (Fig. 30C). Less frequently, a skein of threadlike chromosomes is seen in the anlage, resembling a mitotic prophase (in *T. phoenicopterus* and *G. nigriceps*). Alternatively, condensed rod-shaped chromosome-like bodies may occur (in *G. orbis*). In all species studied, the chromatin of the macronuclear anlage later becomes a mass of uniform Feulgen-positive granules, with only a few larger and ring-shaped bodies among them (Figs. 30D and 31B). These granules are smaller and more numerous than the metaphase chromosomes of a micronucleus, which is especially obvious in *Tracheloraphis* species. They are particularly tiny in *Geleia*. At the stage of granular chromatin, no RNA was ever revealed in the anlagen. Their protein content proved to be rather low.

The further development of the anlagen may proceed somewhat differently. In some species (*T. margaritatus, T. sulcata*), there is a marked decrease of both number and size of the chromatin granules: the so-called dechromatinization of the anlagen (Fig. 30E and F). At that time, no substantial growth of the anlagen occurs and therefore the decrease of their Feulgen stainability cannot be attributed to a dispersion of the DNA in a larger volume. In other cases, e.g., in *T. dogieli* or species of *Loxodes* and *Remanella,* there is no apparent dechromatinization of the anlagen: the number and size of the chromatin granules remain unchanged (Fig. 31). It will be shown later that these differences correspond to actual changes of the DNA content of the anlagen (see Section IV, C,3). In no species studied has a visual increase of the DNA content of the anlagen been reported; and no signs of polyploidization or polytenization of the anlagen were ever seen.

At the late stages of development, the anlagen grow again and produce the first RNA-containing nucleoli (Figs. 28G, 30G, and 31C). The number of the nucleoli is sometimes constant (e.g., four in *G. nigriceps*), a finding which implies a connection of the first nucleoli with definite chromosomes. However, in *Tracheloraphis dogieli*, many nucleoli are formed (Fig. 31C). The chromatin granules often unite at this stage into larger blocks (chromocenters), especially in the species lacking dechromatinization (Fig. 31C). In other cases, however, the granules grow smaller and become dispersed in the nucleus, although no overall loss of Feulgen stainability occurs (species of *Loxodes* and *R. multinucleata*). Finally, the chromatin granules become almost fully decondensed in *Geleia* species. Fusion of several nucleoli into a single central nucleolus, typical of the adult macronuclei, occurs in some species (*Loxodes* spp., *G. nigriceps*, *R. granulosa;* cf. Fig. 28).

2. *Electron Microscopy*

The earliest stage of development of the macronuclear anlagen thus far studied with the electron microscope is the dechromatinization stage, which has been observed in *T. sulcata* (Kovaleva and Raikov, 1978). Such anlagen contain chromatin elements in the form of fibrous strands, 0.1–0.2 μm thick (Fig. 22C; cf. Fig. 24A). No bodies of condensed chromatin and no nucleoli exist in them yet. Small fibrogranular masses often occur at the outer side of the nuclear envelope of the anlagen (Fig. 22C); these are likely to consist of material which has been extruded from the macronucleus due to a "lock-gate" activity of the nuclear membranes. A macronuclear anlage of *T. sulcata* is at this stage only slightly larger than a micronucleus, but the density of packing of its chromatin is greatly reduced (cf. Fig. 4).

The fine structure of the anlagen during formation of the first nucleoli has been studied in *T. sulcata* (Kovaleva and Raikov, 1978), *L. magnus* (Raikov, 1975), *K. fistulosum* (Raikov, 1972b), and *G. orbis* (Raikov, 1984). In all cases, most of the chromatin is still a reticulum of loose strands. However, a few bodies of condensed chromatin also appear. The nucleolar primordia are at first entirely fibrillar. In *Loxodes*, a body of condensed chromatin is adjacent to each forming nucleolus; it possibly contains amplified ribosomal DNA. This body later becomes surrounded by the fibrillar core of the nucleolus (cf. Fig. 18). In *Geleia*, the anlage is already subdivided into a number of compartments by microfilamentous partitions.

Late macronuclear anlagen have been studied in *T. sulcata, L. magnus, K. fistulosum*, and *T. dogieli* (Raikov, 1974). At this stage the nucleoli produce a granular cortex. The number of chromatin bodies increases and the amount of loose fibrillar chromatin decreases. In *T. dogieli*, also larger spongy chromocenters are formed by aggregation of the chromatin bodies. In *K. fistulosum*, however, almost all the chromatin still remains decondensed. The large single chromocenter is here formed only in adult macronuclei (see Section III,D,2). The macronuclear anlagen never contain spheres or crystalloids.

3. DNA Cytophotometry

The changes in DNA content accompanying the development of the macronuclear anlagen were studied in two karyorelictids: *T. sulcata,* a species with a well-expressed dechromatinization stage (Kovaleva and Raikov, 1978), and *L. magnus,* a species without apparent dechromatinization (Bobyleva *et al.,* 1980).

In *T. sulcata,* the DNA content of the macronuclear anlagen (at the stage corresponding to Figs. 22C and 24A) proved to be only half of that of the G_1 micronuclei (Fig. 12b). The dechromatinization of the anlagen, first reported only visually (cf. Fig. 30E and F), thus corresponds to a real diminution of the DNA during the development of the new macronucleus. Some parts of the micronuclear genome seem to be discarded from the macronuclear anlagen. The fibrogranular bodies, extruded at this stage from the anlagen into the cytoplasm, may contain the eliminated DNA or its degradation products. At the late stages of macronuclear development, when nucleolar primordia are already formed (Fig. 24B), the DNA content of the anlagen remains low and equals about 1 c (Fig. 12c). During the "maturation" of the new macronuclei, however, when small chromatin bodies fuse to form chromocenters (Fig. 24C), the DNA content of the anlagen returns to about 2–3 c (Fig. 12d). The fact that it almost coincides with the DNA content of the micronuclei (cf. Fig. 12a and d) thus seems to be a mere coincidence.

Anyway, the genome of the adult macronucleus of *T. sulcata* must result from a substantial processing of the micronuclear genome which occurs during the development of the anlage. This processing is likely to involve both destruction of some DNA sequences (DNA diminution) and additional replication of all or some of the sequences preserved (DNA resynthesis). Some micronuclear genes, perhaps those coding for the nuclear division, may become eliminated during this time (Kovaleva and Raikov, 1978).

In *L. magnus,* there is no significant decrease of the DNA content of the macronuclear anlagen as compared with that of the micronuclei (Bobyleva *et al.,* 1980). The anlagen at first contain 2 c DNA. Then, a single round of replication of the DNA occurs in them (simultaneously with the DNA replication in their sister micronuclei), which brings their DNA content to 4 c. The DNA content of nonsynchronous anlagen actually varies from 2 to 4 c (Fig. 11A). These data are consistent with the autoradiographic evidence that [^{3}H]thymidine is incorporated into many macronuclear anlagen of *L. magnus* (Raikov and Morat, 1977; see also Section III,B,2). Thus, a species lacking dechromatinization of the anlagen shows no DNA diminution in them but only a single replication of their genome, after which the replication of the bulk DNA is apparently blocked in G_2. Nevertheless, one cannot exclude the possibility that elimination of some minor parts of the genome can exist in *Loxodes* as well, provided it is too small to be detected by cytofluorimetry.

It is important that in both *Trachelonema* and *Loxodes* the macronuclear development involves no manifold DNA replication, i.e., it is not connected with polyploidization of the anlagen or with polytenization of their chromosomes.

V. Aging of the Macronuclei

Since karyorelictid macronuclei segregate at cytokinesis and since their set is supplemented in every cell cycle with an approximately equal number of young nuclei (see Section IV), the macronuclei of every cell necessarily differ in age, a fact first pointed out by Fauré-Fremiet (1954). Thus, in a cell of any multinucleate species, some 50% of the macronuclei are those formed after the last cytokinesis, 25% are one cell generation older, 12.5% are two generations older, 6.25% are three generations older, etc. In a cell having but two macronuclei (*Loxodes rostrum* and others, cf. Fig. 27), one of them is always young and formed during the last cytokinesis (in *Loxodes*, this is always the anterior macronucleus), while the other one may in principle have any age from +1 cell generation to infinity. An interesting question arises of whether the longevity of each individual macronucleus is restricted or not, i.e., whether it can pass from one generation into another indefinitely, being "potentially immortal."

This problem is little studied yet; no labeling of the macronuclei in order to identify them several generations later has been done. However, light microscopic data indicate that individual macronuclei live during several cell generations, after which they degenerate. The cells of multinucleate species usually show some atypical macronuclei, likely to be aged and degenerating, among the normal ones. In *L. magnus*, such macronuclei have irregular shapes; their nucleoli are eccentric (Fig. 8A) or even missing, and their peripheral Feulgen-positive granules fuse into larger pycnotic blocks (Fauré-Fremiet, 1954; Raikov, 1959a; Bobyleva *et al.*, 1980). They incorporate labeled uridine much more slowly than normal (Raikov and Morat, 1977). The frequency of such macronuclei ranges from 10 to 1% in *L. magnus*, which corresponds to their age of three to seven cell generations.

Degenerating macronuclei have been observed also in *T. margaritatus, G. nigriceps, G. murmanica,* and *K. fistulosum* (Raikov, 1958a, 1959b, 1963d, 1972b). They are usually irregularly shaped; in *T. margaritatus* they almost lack chromatin but in *K. fistulosum* they have, on the contrary, a hypertrophied chromocenter. In *G. murmanica,* the numerous macronuclear nucleoli become larger but less basophilic. In *K. fistulosum*, the aging macronuclei contain protein spheres.

The age-related changes of the macronuclei have been studied with the electron microscope only in *T. sulcata* (Kovaleva and Raikov, 1970, 1978). In this species, the old macronuclei are larger than the mature ones and are often polymorphous; they always contain a protein sphere (Fig. 24G), sometimes even two spheres. The number of both chromocenters and nucleoli also increases in them (Fig. 22A).

A cytophotometric study (Kovaleva and Raikov, 1978) has shown that aging macronuclei of *T. sulcata* are very diverse in their DNA content. While mature macronuclei contain 2 to 4 c DNA (Fig. 12d), old ones contain from 2 to 12 c (Fig. 12e). Among the latter, about 50% of the nuclei have 2 to 4 c; about 40%, from 4 to 6 c; and about 10%, more than 6 c DNA. The partial replication (amplification?) of some DNA sequences, typical of the mature macronuclei of this species (see Section IV,C,3), seems to continue in the aging macronuclei. The DNA thus accumulated is apparently stored in the extra chromocenters.

In *L. magnus,* some macronuclei also contain much DNA in excess of the diploid, postsynthetic level, especially in the nondividing cells (see Section III,B,1 and IV,A,2; and Fig. 11). When the division rate of the cultures is low, these macronuclei can accumulate up to 10 c DNA (Bobyleva *et al.,* 1980). It is likely (although not yet definitely proved), that the DNA-rich macronuclei are the old ones.

Finally, if the old macronuclei eventually degenerate, they must be somehow replaced with new ones, especially in the species with a small and constant number of nuclei. The replacement of the degenerating macronucleus must then find a morphological expression. ''Nuclear abnormalities'' were actually found

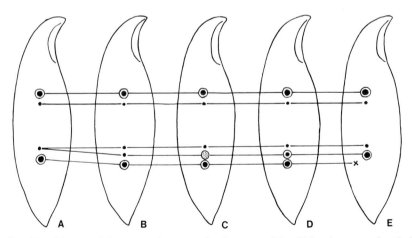

FIG. 32.   Diagram of the supposed process of replacement of the old (rear) macronucleus in *L. striatus*. (A) A typical cell with two macronuclei and two micronuclei; (B) asynchronous division of the rear micronucleus; (C) differentiation of one of its derivatives into a macronucleus anlage; (D) formation of a new (third) macronucleus; (E) degeneration of the old macronucleus (X) and return to the normal set of nuclei.

in 2 to 7% of the cells of *L. striatus* which normally have two macronuclei and two micronuclei (Fig. 1F); at least some of them may be related to the replacement of the aging macronucleus (Raikov, 1959a). Among these "abnormalities" are cases of asynchronous mitotic division of the micronucleus which lies near the rear (i.e., old) macronucleus and also cases when one of the two micronuclei thus formed differentiates into the anlage of a third macronucleus (Fig. 32A–C). Also specimens with three macronuclei occur (Fig. 32D). It only remains to suppose, in the absence of direct data, that the old macronucleus included into the rear group of nuclei would degenerate and become replaced with the new one (Fig. 32E).

VI. The Never-Dividing Macronuclei during Conjugation

In the vast majority of the ciliates, except only the Karyorelictida, it is during the sexual process (conjugation or autogamy) that the old macronucleus degenerates and becomes replaced by a new one (reviewed by Raikov, 1972c). But since the renewal of the macronuclear apparatus occurs in the Karyorelictida throughout the period of asexual reproduction, as shown earlier, a question arises of what happens to the macronuclei during conjugation.

The nuclear phenomena during the conjugation of karyorelictids have been studied light microscopically in *L. striatus* (Kasanzeff, 1910; Bogdanowicz, 1930). *T. phoenicopterus* (Raikov, 1958a,b), *T. margaritatus* and *T. caudatus* (Dragesco and Raikov, 1966). *T. coluber* (Raikov, 1963f), *T. sulcata* (Kovaleva, 1972), and some Geleiidae (Nouzarède, 1976). These observations are, however, mostly fragmentary and restricted to the progamic period (up to the formation of the synkarya). During this time, the macronuclei undergo almost no changes which can be seen with the light microscope. The nuclear groups or complexes generally disintegrate, however, and all the macronuclei become free. The micronuclei undergo two meiotic and one postmeiotic division, after which some of their haploid derivatives differentiate into pronuclei. Unlike other ciliates, the karyorelictids produce many pronuclei and synkarya per conjugant (for details and interpretation see Raikov, 1972c). At the fine-structure level, only the meiotic prophase of the micronuclei has been studied in *L. striatus* (Bobyleva, 1984) and *G. orbis* (Nouzarède, 1976).

In karyorelictids, conjugation as a rule begins between individuals whose nuclear apparatus is not yet fully reconstructed after the last cell division. Along with adult macronuclei, the conjugants therefore contain macronuclear anlagen from the very beginning of the process (*Loxodes, T. phoenicopterus, T. coluber, T. sulcata*). These anlagen become blocked in development for the whole period of conjugation.

No degeneration of the adult macronuclei has so far been found in any karyorelictid species. This was first briefly reported by Bogdanowicz (1930), but his data on *Loxodes* exconjugants remained unpublished. Among the karyorelictids, the exconjugation period has up to now been described only in *Tracheloraphis phoenicopterus* (Raikov, 1958a, b). The adult macronuclei do not degenerate at all during this period, but the macronuclear anlagen which persisted from the preconjugant stage do become pycnotic and degenerate in the exconjugants. They are replaced by six new macronuclear anlagen which differentiate from the derivatives of one of the multiple synkarya. These anlagen, together with the micronuclei and the adult macronuclei of the preconjugants, re-form the nuclear complex at the end of the exconjugation period.

It is thus very likely that the existing macronuclei do not perish during conjugation in the karyorelictids, but rather persist and degenerate later, when their natural longevity comes to an end. However, further research is needed to prove this supposition.

The fine-structure changes occurring in the macronuclei during conjugation have so far been studied only in the progamic period of *T. totevi* (Kovaleva, 1984) and *G. orbis* (Nouzarède, 1976). In *T. totevi,* an increase of the pore frequency in the macronuclear envelope, a proliferation of the granular cortex of the nucleoli which produce many micronucleoli, and an appearance of fibrogranular masses in the nuclear matrix is reported. All these features indicate an intensive functioning of the macronuclei during the conjugation rather than their degeneration. During the meiotic prophase in *G. orbis,* the macronuclei always lack spheres, have a plicated envelope, and contain relatively little DNA—only about 4 c (cf. Section III, B, 1). The nucleoli (Nouzarède's "chromatin bodies") form no aggregates but are still united pairwise; the compartments inside the macronucleus (cf. Section III,D,4) are inconspicuous. Nouzarède supposes all these changes to be features of degeneration, but it is more likely that they are features of a high functional activity of the macronuclei, the more so as they occur at the earliest stages of conjugation.

VII. Nature and Mechanism of Macronuclear Differentiation

Passing from evidence to interpretation, we may ask what is the difference, in genetic terms, between the macronuclei and the micronuclei. The answer to this question must be consistent with the following facts:

1. The nondeterminate nature (the omnipotency) of the micronuclei, as a result of which any micronucleus can in principle become a macronucleus.

2. The irreversibility of macronuclear differentiation: No transformation of a macronucleus or even a macronuclear anlage back into a micronucleus was ever observed.

3. The inability of the macronuclei to autoreproduce (by division or any other means).

4. The physiological (transcriptional) activity of the macronuclei compared with that of the micronuclei.

I believed for a long time that the never-dividing macronuclei remained diploid and that the entire micronuclear genome was conserved unaltered in them (Raikov, 1957b, 1963a, 1969, etc.). This idea logically implied that the nature of macronuclear differentiation in the karyorelictids was *epigenetic,* i.e., that it was based on stable activation of certain genes and irreversible repression of other genes in the macronuclei (Raikov, 1969, 1976b; Poljansky, 1974). Specifically, it was supposed that transcription of the genes coding for various types of RNA was activated, and expression of the genes responsible for autoreproduction of the genome itself and for nuclear division was repressed.

The notions about the possible nature of the differentiation of karyorelictid macronuclei somewhat changed when it became known that, first, these nuclei often contain significantly more DNA than the diploid (even postsynthetic) quantity; second, they are capable of a partial replication of DNA; and third, a DNA diminution can occur during their development, a finding indicating a reduction of the genome size (see Sections III, B, 1–2 and IV,C,3). Then, it has been suggested that at least some of the properties of the macronuclei (e.g., their complete inability to divide) can have a *genetic* basis, i.e., can depend on a physical loss of the respective genes during the reorganization of the genome (Kovaleva and Raikov, 1978; Raikov, 1982). In other words, the micronuclei would have a full genome (and therefore be omnipotent), and the macronuclei would have a reduced one (and therefore be irreversibly differentiated). Of course, this interpretation does not exclude some epigenetic phenomena as well, especially those directed toward activation of the genes coding for the various RNAs (since micronuclei clearly contain the same genes but in a nonfunctional state).

The phenomena of partial replication (amplification) of some DNA sequences may also play a part in the process of activation of the transcription. Possibly the same sequence can be silent when incorporated into a chromosome and transcribed when excised from the chromosome and amplified.

Thus, the problem of the nature of macronuclear differentiation in the karyorelictids still awaits solution. One can only suppose that the nuclear differentiation has here partly a genetic and partly an epigenetic basis.

The mechanism of macronuclear differentiation is also almost unknown in the karyorelictids. Future experiments are needed to answer the questions, why do only some micronuclei differentiate into the macronuclei, despite the omnipotency of the former, and why does it occur only at certain moments of the cell cycle. Only some suppositions based on indirect evidence can be made now in this field.

For instance, it is unlikely that differentiation of the micronuclei into macronuclei were induced in the karyorelictids by their localization in some specific area of the cytoplasm. Such is the mechanism of differentiation of the macronuclear anlagen in the exconjugants of many higher ciliates, where either the anterior or the posterior areas of the cell possess inducing properties (Raikov, 1972c; Mikami, 1980; Ossipov, 1981; Grandchamp and Beisson, 1981). In the karyorelictids, however, the macronuclear anlagen do not show any specific localization in the cell which is different from that of the micronuclei.

More likely is the existence, in the karyorelictids, of a mechanism of nuclear differentiation based on the feedback principle. Such a mechanism has already been discovered in heterokaryotic foraminiferans (reviewed by Grell, 1958a, 1973, 1979; see also Section VIII,B,2). In this case, the somatic nucleus which differentiates first inhibits further transformation of the remaining generative nuclei into somatic ones. If the somatic nucleus is destroyed, another generative nucleus differentiates (Czihak, 1964; Zech, 1964). If the cell is big, several somatic nuclei differentiate and together they inhibit further differentiation. This mechanism requires no spatial separation of the presumptive somatic nuclei from the presumptive generative ones within the cell.

One may note that in those karyorelictids the nuclei of which are clustered, it is always the micronuclei which are the most distant (inside the nuclear group) from the existing macronuclei which differentiate into the anlagen of new macronuclei (Figs 27–29). This phenomenon has been observed in *T. coluber, T. phoenicopterus, T. caudatus, L. rostrum, L. striatus, R. granulosa, R. rugosa, G. nigriceps,* and *G. orbis* (for references, Table I). One one hand, it tends to confirm the supposition about the inhibiting action of the existing macronuclei upon the differentiation of new macronuclei. On the other hand, this fact implies that the inhibitory influence of a macronucleus is spatially limited to a narrow zone around it (such phenomena of "near-neighbor interaction" are widely distributed in the cortex of the ciliates; see Sonneborn, 1975). Moreover, one can imagine that, in species with synchronous nuclear reorganization, the zone of inhibition around each macronucleus widens in nondividing cells and narrows down in dividing ones (e.g., as a result of some changes of the functional activity of the macronuclei coupled with cytokinesis). This would explain why new macronuclei can differentiate during cytokinesis only. Therefore, it would be very interesting to study the changes of the transcriptional activity of the never-dividing macronuclei during the cell cycle (cf. Section IV,A,2).

VIII. Phylogenetic Significance of the Never-Dividing Macronuclei

Ever since the existence of the paradiploid never-dividing macronuclei became known, their possible phylogenetic significance has been discussed. The controversy has been centered on whether the nuclear apparatus of the karyorelictids is primitive or secondarily simplified compared with that of the majority of the ciliates.

A. Hypotheses of Secondary Simplification of the Macronuclei

1. *Hypothesis of Regressive Evolution*

The idea that never-dividing macronuclei of the karyorelictids could have arisen by regressive evolution from polyploid, able-to-divide macronuclei of other ciliates was first suggested by Fauré-Fremiet (1954). Later, Fauré-Fremiet (1961) proposed that reduction of the size of the macronuclei, decrease of their DNA content, and loss of their ability to divide could all result from convergent restrictive adaptation of the ciliates to the specific conditions of life in the interstices of marine sand.

Using evidence that the stomatogenesis of *Loxodes* is not primitive, Fauré-Fremiet (1970) argued that both the karyorelictids themselves and their macronuclei could not be considered primitive, either. Finally, in the 1950s and 1960s the three families Trachelocercidae, Loxodidae, and Geleiidae, now united into the order Karyorelictida, were thought to be unrelated. This was also used by Fauré-Fremiet to support his hypothesis. According to him, the never-dividing macronuclei must have arisen from "usual" macronuclei many times and independently in various ciliate taxa. This point of view was shared by Dragesco (1960).

2. *Hypothesis of Arrest in Development*

An interesting explanation of the properties of *Loxodes* nuclei was given by Schweyer (1925). He proposed that the exconjugation period was extended in *Loxodes* to cover the whole asexual part of the life cycle. The micronuclei of *Loxodes* were considered by him as "synkaryal nuclei" which permanently retain their ability to differentiate into macronuclear anlagen. Correspondingly, the macronuclei of *Loxodes* were considered as macronuclear anlagen arrested in their development. This idea explained both the division inability of the macronuclei (since macronuclear anlagen of the exconjugants of other ciliates generally do not divide until their development is over) and the small amount of chromatin in them. This ingenious hypothesis was supported by Bogdanowicz (1930) but was never discussed later.

Schweyer's explanation is basically a variant of the hypothesis of the origin of karyorelictid macronuclei by secondary simplification of "typical" macronuclei. It can in principle be applied to other karyorelictids as well. It does not contradict Fauré-Fremiet's ideas and even supplements them, postulating a mechanism by which a "simplification" of the macronuclear organization might have occurred.

On the whole, however, the argumentation of the hypothesis of secondary origin of karyorelictid macronuclei is rather weak. To begin with, it is difficult to see what can be the adaptive significance of the decreased chromatin content of these nuclei and/or of the loss of their ability to divide, were it by arrest in development or otherwise. Then, it is well known that different systems of characters can evolve more or less independently; therefore, ciliates with a rather advanced stomatogenesis (as in *Loxodes*) and at the same time with a primitive nuclear apparatus may well exist (Corliss, 1975; Corliss and Hartwig, 1977). Finally, the taxonomic remoteness of the Trachelocercidae, Loxodidae, and Geleiidae proved to be strongly exaggerated, the most conservative features of the fine structural organization of the somatic cortex being almost identical in the three families (De Puytorac and Njiné, 1970; Raikov, 1971/72, 1978; De Puytorac *et al.*, 1973; Raikov *et al.*, 1975). As a result, it became possible to unite them in a common order Karyorelictida (Corliss, 1979). Some specialists even put the karyorelictids (as a class Karyorelictea) at the very base of the ciliate's phylogenetic tree, considering their cortical features to be primitive as well (Small and Lynn, 1981).

B. Hypothesis of Primitiveness of the Macronuclei

1. *Arguments for Primitiveness*

The hypothesis claiming that the never-dividing karyorelictid macronuclei are primitive as compared with the macronuclei of the rest of ciliates has been developed by Raikov (1957b, 1958a, 1963a, 1969, 1976b, etc.) and supported by Poljansky (Poljansky and Raikov, 1961, 1976; Poljansky, 1974, etc.), Grell (1962, 1964, 1973), Corliss (1974, 1975), Corliss and Hartwig (1977), Small and Lynn (1981), and some others. According to it, the karyorelictid macronuclei originated in phylogenesis from usual diploid nuclei, reproducing by mitosis, as a result of a process which has been called *primary differentiation of somatic nuclei* (Raikov, 1963a, b). This occurred in the karyorelictid ancestors only once. Therefore, the profound similarities among the macronuclei of the Trachelocercidae, Loxididae, and Geleiidae are due to the common origin of these nuclei rather than to convergent evolution.

Formerly, when the three families were thought to be unrelated, their extant representatives were considered to be remnants of a vast but now extinct spectrum of ancestral forms which all had never-dividing macronuclei (Raikov, 1969). In other words, they were thought to represent an entire ancestral level of organization and thus to be true *karyological relicts* (Grell, 1962). Now, when the three families are known to be related, it is more likely that paradiploid never-dividing macronuclei developed in only one line of ciliate evolution, which branched off the main trunk very early. In this case it is justifiable to separate the karyorelictids into an order or even a class of their own (Small and Lynn, 1981). The karyorelictid nuclear apparatus, while remaining primitive, will then represent an alternative to the nuclear apparatus of the other ciliates rather than a necessary step in its phylogenetic development, an idea first suggested by MacKinnon and Hawes (1961, p. 230) and supported by Orias (1977).

The main arguments for the primitiveness of the karyorelictid macronuclei (i.e., for their origin from normal diploid nuclei rather than from polyploid macronuclei) are the following (see also Raikov, 1963b, 1969, 1982; Corliss, 1975; Corliss and Hartwig, 1977):

1. Such macronuclei occur only among the lower ciliates. According to the system of Corliss (1979), they occur only in the lower subclass Gymnostomata, belonging to the lower ciliate class Kinetofragminophora. According to the system of Small and Lynn (1981), they are typical of the lower class Karyorelictea belonging to the lower subphylum Postciliodesmatophora. Such macronuclei never occur in the higher ciliate taxa (Oligohymenophora and Polyhymenophora), despite the fact that these classes include many obligate and perfectly adapted sand-dwelling species.

2. According to modern concepts, the karyorelictids are corticorelicts, too. Their paired somatic kinetosomes seem to represent the ancestral dikinetid (Lynn and Small, 1981; Small and Lynn, 1981). And, in general, the somatic cortex of the ciliates is a much more conservative system than their oral apparatus (Lynn, 1981).

3. The never-dividing macronuclei are typical of actively moving predatory ciliates which are unlikely to react to selective pressure by undergoing a morphophysiological regression.

4. Such macronuclei occur not only in marine sand-dwelling ciliates but also in the freshwater benthic and planktonic species of *Loxodes,* a finding which is hard to explain from the viewpoint of their convergent and adaptive origin.

5. It is well known that the interstitial biotop of marine sand is generally a niche which favors the conservation of many ancient relict animals (Swedmark, 1964).

6. There are close analogies between the karyorelictid macronuclei and the somatic nuclei of some representatives of quite another protistan phylum—the heterokaryotic foraminiferans. In these, the somatic nuclei have clearly originated by primary differentiation of ordinary diploid nuclei (see the following section).

2. *An Analogous Case: The Foraminiferan Somatic Nuclei*

As already mentioned, nuclear dualism occurs at the diploid phase of the life cycle (in the so-called *agamonts*) of some foraminiferans. This phenomenon was discovered and studied by Grell (reviews: Grell, 1958a, 1979) in some species of the family Rotaliidae; it is now known to occur in other families as well (see Raikov, 1982, Chapter 7).

The single diploid nucleus of the young agamont at first divides mitotically several times. In *Rotaliella* it divides twice, and the agamont becomes quadrinucleate. Then, one of the four nuclei grows and forms peripheral nucleoli; this is the *somatic nucleus*. The other three nuclei remain small and dense; these are *generative nuclei* (Grell, 1954, 1957). In other genera, the number of nuclei of both types may vary: one somatic and one generative in *Metarotaliella simplex* (Grell, 1979), one somatic and five generative in *Rubratella* (Grell, 1958b), up to five somatic and several generative in *Glabratella* (Grell, 1958c), up to 10–15 somatic and 40–70 generative in *Rosalina* (Voronova, 1971), one large somatic and hundreds of generative in *Cibicides* (Voronova, 1976), etc. The foraminiferan somatic nuclei thus resemble the karyorelictid macronuclei morphologically, and they are also formed during the asexual period by differentiation of some generative nuclei which resemble the micronuclei.

Cytophotometric studies (Zech, 1964) have shown that, like the macronuclear anlagen of *Loxodes* (see Section IV,C,3), the developing somatic nuclei of *Rotaliella* undergo a single round of DNA replication, after which they become blocked in G_2. Consequently they remain diploid. Simultaneously, the generative nuclei undergo a premeiotic replication of their DNA. The content of RNA and protein increases in the somatic nucleus of *Rotaliella* much more than it does in the generative nuclei, a finding which argues for the transcriptional activity of the former. However, *Cibicides* shows a gradual accumulation of DNA in the somatic nucleus well above the diploid level, namely, up to 12–30 c, as in *Geleia* (see Section III,B,1), which may indicate an amplification of the ribosomal or some other genes (Voronova and Selivanova, 1976). The somatic nuclei of the foraminiferans thus resemble the karyorelictid macronuclei also in their DNA and RNA contents.

When the agamont ceases to grow, the generative nuclei undergo meiosis and give rise to the haploid nuclei of the agametes (uninucleate cells serving for asexual reproduction). At the same time the somatic nucleus degenerates in one way or another. Sometimes it enters the prophase of an abortive asynaptic meiosis, but later its chromosomes are scattered in the cytoplasm since they cannot attach spindle fibers (Grell, 1956). Like karyorelictid macronuclei, the foraminiferan somatic nucleus is thus unable to divide. This is perhaps due to a loss of some genes responsible for pairing of the chromosomes and/or for their attachment to spindle fibers.

It has been shown experimentally that the somatic nucleus is irreversibly differentiated and doomed to degeneration. Even if one destroys all generative nuclei (with an ultraviolet microbeam), the somatic nucleus never dedifferentiates (Czihak, 1964). Such agamonts normally grow. This proves that it is the somatic nucleus which supplies the cell with all the templates necessary for growth and morphogenesis. But later such agamonts perish following degeneration of the somatic nucleus. At the same time the generative nuclei (like the karyorelictid micronuclei) are omnipotent. If the existing somatic nucleus is excised or destroyed, another generative nucleus differentiates to replace it (Czihak, 1964; Zech, 1964). The number of the somatic nuclei is apparently controlled by a feedback mechanism (cf. Section VII), i.e., the existing somatic nucleus inhibits the differentiation of the remaining generative nuclei (Grell, 1958a).

The similarities between the karyorelictid macronuclei and the foraminiferan somatic nuclei are consequently rather close, but they cannot result from a common origin since these two protistan taxa are phylogenetically very remote. One can speak only of analogies in their nuclear organization, which seem to be based on some general laws of primary differentiation of the somatic nuclei. Most foraminiferans are homokaryotic, and therefore it is natural to admit that heterokaryotic forms descended from homokaryotic ones which had several identical diploid nuclei at the agamont stage. Since no foraminiferans with highly polyploid somatic nuclei are known, an origin of the diploid somatic nuclei by "simplification" of polyploid ones is practically excluded. Although based only on analogy, one may suppose that the karyorelictids also descended from a hypothetical homokaryotic ancestor which had identical diploid able-to-divide nuclei.

C. Origin of the Nuclear Dualism

Practically all authors who discuss this problem admit that some flagellates with several identical nuclei must have been the ancestors of the ciliates. These flagellates could have evolved at first into primitive homokaryotic ciliates. Until recently, such primary ciliates were thought to exist even now and to be represented by the genus *Stephanopogon*. These are small, marine, ciliated protists which feed by phagotrophy and externally resemble true ciliates. But their nuclear apparatus proved to consist of several identical vesicular nuclei which all can divide by mitosis (Lwoff, 1936; Dragesco, 1963; Borror, 1965; Raikov, 1969). However, it has recently been demonstrated that, according to fine-structure criteria (organization of the mitochondria, kinetosomes, and their fibrillar derivatives), *Stephanopogon* cannot be a ciliate; it must be classified as a flagellate carrying multiple flagella (Lipscomb and Corliss, 1982). Moreover, as this flagellate has no fine-structure similarities with the ciliates, it has nothing to do with their origin, even remaining outside the phylum Ciliophora. As a result, the "homokaryotic ancestor" of the ciliates has become a hypothetical organism again.

Lwoff (1936) proposed that the ciliates descended from forms with two identical nuclei (like small specimens of *Stephanopogon*) by a gradual hypertrophy of one nucleus, which became the macronucleus as its mitosis transformed into amitosis. Raikov (1957b, 1958a, 1963a, 1969) held, on the contrary, that the evolution of the ciliate nuclear dualism must have included an obligatory stage when macronuclei, while remaining diploid, lost their ability to divide altogether (as in the extant karyorelictids). This idea was based on the opinion (which later proved erroneous) that the karyorelictid families were unrelated and thus represented relics of a vast complex of ancestral ciliates (cf. Section VIII,B,1). According to Raikov's hypothesis, the macronuclei of the higher ciliates must have acquired their ability to divide *de novo* rather than by transformation of the mitosis, perhaps via fusion of several diploid macronuclei into polyploid complexes capable of fragmentation.

An updated version of this hypothesis (Raikov, 1976b) presumes the existence of several stages of phylogenetic development of the nuclear dualism in the ciliates. At the first stage, the nuclear dualism was absent (this stage is now represented by only hypothetical eociliates or even flagellates). At the second stage, a primary differentiation of the nuclei into generative and somatic types took place at the diploid level. The extant karyorelictids can now be more appropriately considered as an early side branch of evolution, in which the primary differentiation of the macronuclei was coupled with a loss of their ability to divide. The main trunk of evolution of the ciliates, however, would include hypothetical forms in which differentiation of the macronuclei also occurred but their ability to divide was conserved. Finally, at the third and subsequent stages, the diploid able-to-divide macronuclei became polyploid (polygenomic) and underwent various more or less drastic reorganizations of their genetic apparatus, which cannot be analyzed within the scope of this review (see Raikov, 1976b, 1982).

IX. Conclusion: Never-Dividing Macronuclei as a Cytological Model

I have tried to review the advances of the last three decades in the study of a practically unknown class of cell nuclei—that of paradiploid, transcriptionally active, but never-dividing somatic nuclei of some lower ciliates. It has also been noted that such nuclei occur elsewhere, e.g., in the Foraminiferida. The somatic paradiploid nuclei have thus far been investigated mainly by morphological and cytochemical methods, much less with methods of developmental biology. Biochemical and molecular investigation of these nuclei remains entirely an open field. Such studies have thus far been hindered by difficulties in obtaining pure cultures of the karyorelictids, which are necessary for mass isolation of the nuclei and for obtaining chromatin and other components from them. However, cloning of *Loxodes* (Bobyleva, 1981) and even axenic cultivation of *Tracheloraphis* sp. (Lenk *et al.*, 1984) have recently been achieved. This permits one to hope that biochemical studies of the karyorelictid nuclei will become possible in the near future; their potential importance has been duly stressed by Hutner and Corliss (1976).

The interest that paradiploid never-dividing macronuclei present for general cytology consists primarily in the fact that they can become useful natural models for the study of quite a number of problems.

Thus, the heteromorphic nuclear system of the karyorelictids is a model showing a remarkably neat separation of the two functions of the genome—that of self-reproduction (only in the micronuclei) and that of transcription (only in the macronuclei), despite the fact that both types of nuclei share a common cytoplasm. If pure fractions of macronuclei and of micronuclei are obtained, this system is worth using for studies of the configuration of the chromatin in either nucleus (e.g., with the spreading technique), and also for studies of the template activity of the DNA, of the properties of the nuclear proteins and enzymes, etc.

Then, paradiploid macronuclei may turn out to be a good model of nuclei in which the ability to form a mitotic apparatus is blocked. This block must be in the nuclei themselves rather than in the cytoplasm (since micronuclei, which have the same cytoplasmic environment, are fully capable of mitosis). Such a model may be useful for studies of the nature of the G_2 block of the nuclear cycle, be it genetic or epigenetic. This system can prove of some use also for the studies of internuclear interactions between blocked and cycling nuclei and between blocked nuclei and their cytoplasmic environment as well (e.g., changes in the transcriptional activity of the blocked nuclei coupled with mitosis of the other nuclei and/or with cytokinesis can be investigated).

The model of paradiploid macronuclei seems to be a good one also for the investigation of the nuclear bodies, since these nuclei regularly form proteinaceous and sometimes also RNA-containing inclusions. The question as to what class of proteins and what types of RNAs are stored in these bodies can be studied with karyorelictid macronuclei. Immunofluorescent and biochemical approaches appear to be the most promising here.

In a farther perspective, the never-dividing macronuclei and their developing anlagen may become an interesting model for the analysis of the ''genetic processing'' which is likely to happen to the chromosomes when the nucleus is somatically differentiated. This would necessitate a molecular analysis of both the micronuclear and the macronuclear DNAs at various stages of development of the somatic nuclei.

Finally, the paradiploid macronuclei may prove to be a useful system for studies of the alterations of the genome during aging of nondividing nuclei. In particular, one may try to find out whether the gradual accumulation of the DNA in aging nuclei is an amplification of coding and transcribed DNA or, on the contrary, a synthesis and stockage of noncoding, satellite, excess, or even defective DNA which remains in the nuclei until they degenerate.

The never-dividing macronuclei of the lower ciliates thus constitute by far not only a protozoological problem. These nuclei are interesting and promising models for studies of the general structural and functional properties of the cell nuclei.

REFERENCES

Balbiani, E. G. (1890). *Ann. Microgr.* **2**, 401–431.
Bobyleva, N. N. (1981). *Tsitologiya (Leningrad)* **23**, 1073–1077.
Bobyleva, N. N. (1984). *Tsitologiya (Leningrad)* **26**, 138–142.
Bobyleva, N. N., Kudrjavtsev, B. N., and Raikov, I. B. (1980). *J. Cell Sci.* **44**, 375–394.
Bogdanowicz, A. (1930). *Zool. Anz.* **87**, 209–222.
Borror, A. C. (1965). *Trans. Am. Microsc. Soc.* **84**, 550–565.
Bouteille, M., Laval, M., and Dupuy-Coin, A. M. (1974). *In* "The Cell Nucleus" (H. Busch, ed.), Vol. 1, pp. 3–71. Academic Press, New York.
Bütschli, O. (1876). *Abhandl. Senckenberg Naturforsch. Ges.* **10**, 213–464.
Corliss, J. O. (1974). *J. Protozool.* **21**, 207–220.
Corliss, J. O. (1975). *BioSystems* **7**, 338–349.
Corliss, J. O. (1979). "The Ciliated Protozoa. Characterization, Classification and Guide to the Literature," 2nd ed. Pergamon, Oxford.
Corliss, J. O., and Hartwig, E. (1977). *Mikrofauna Meeresboden* **61**, 65–88.
Czihak, G. (1964). *Exp. Cell Res.* **35**, 372–380.
De Puytorac, P., and Njiné, T. (1970). *Protistologica* **6**, 427–444.
De Puytorac, P., Raikov, I., and Nouzarède, M. (1973). *C. R. Soc. Biol.* **167**, 982–985.
Dragesco, J. (1960). *Trav. Station Biol. Roscoff, New Ser.* **12**, 1–356.
Dragesco, J. (1963). *Cah. Biol. Mar.* **4**, 91–119.
Dragesco, J. (1970). "Ciliés Libres du Cameroun." Univ. Fédérale du Cameroun, Yaoundé.
Dragesco, J., and Raikov, I. B. (1966). *Arch. Protistenk.* **109**, 99–113.
Dupuy-Coin, A. M., Kalifat, S. R., and Bouteille, M. (1972). *J. Ultrastruct. Res.* **38**, 174–187.
Fauré-Fremiet, E. (1954). *J. Protozool.* **1**, 20–27.
Fauré-Fremiet, E. (1961). *Cah. Biol. Mar.* **2**, 177–186.
Fauré-Fremiet, E. (1970). *C. R. Acad. Sci. Paris D* **270**, 523–524.
Foissner, W., and Rieder, N. (1983). *Zool. Anz.* **210**, 3–13.
Goulder, R. (1980). *Hydrobiologia* **72**, 131–158.
Grandchamp, S., and Beisson, J. (1981). *Dev. Biol.* **81**, 336–341.
Grell, K. G. (1954). *Arch. Protistenk.* **100**, 268–286.
Grell, K. G. (1956). *Z. Naturforsch.* **11b**, 759–761.
Grell, K. G. (1957). *Arch. Protistenk.* **102**, 147–164.
Grell, K. G. (1958a). *Naturwissenschaften* **45**, 25–32.
Grell, K. G. (1958b). *Arch. Protistenk.* **102**, 291–308.
Grell, K. G. (1958c). *Arch. Protistenk.* **102**, 449–472.
Grell, K. G. (1962). *Fortschr. Zool.* **14**, 1–85.
Grell, K. G. (1964). *In* "The Cell" (J. Brachet and A. Mirsky, eds.), Vol. 6, pp. 1–79. Academic Press, New York.
Grell, K. G. (1973). "Protozoology." Springer-Verlag, Berlin.
Grell, K. G. (1979). *J. Foraminiferal Res.* **9**, 1–13.
Hancock, R., and Boulikas, T. (1982). *Int. Rev. Cytol.* **79**, 165–214.

Hutner, S. H., and Corliss, J. O. (1976). *J. Protozool.* **23**, 48–56.
Joseph, H. (1907). *Arch. Protistenk.* **8**, 344–368.
Kasanzeff, W. (1910). *Arch. Protistenk.* **20**, 79–96.
Kovaleva, V. G. (1972). *Protistologica* **8**, 83–90.
Kovaleva, V. G. (1984). *Tsitologiya (Leningrad)* **6**, 258–263.
Kovaleva, V. G., and Raikov, I. B. (1970). *Tsitologiya (Leningrad)* **12**, 1446–1455.
Kovaleva, V. G., and Raikov, I. B. (1973). *Protistologica* **9**, 471–480.
Kovaleva, V. G., and Raikov, I. B. (1978). *Chromosoma* **69**, 177–192.
Kovaleva, V. G., Vinnikova, N. V., and Raikov, I. B. (1979). *Tsitologiya (Leningrad)* **21**, 280–286.
Lebedew, W. (1909). *Arch. Protistenk.* **13**, 71–114.
Lenk, S. E., Small, E. B., and Gunderson, J. (1984). *Origins of Life,* **13**, 229–234.
Lipscomb, D. L., and Corliss, J. O. (1982). *Science* **215**, 303–304.
Lwoff, A. (1936). *Arch. Zool. Exp. Gen.* **78**, 117–132.
Lynn, D. H. (1981). *Biol. Rev.* **56**, 243–292.
Lynn, D. H., and Small, E. B. (1981). *BioSystems* **14**, 377–385.
MacKinnon, D. L., and Hawes, R. S. J. (1961). "An Introduction to the Study of Protozoa." Clarendon, Oxford.
Mashansky, V. F. (1963). *In* "Morfologiya i Fiziologiya Prostejshikh (Proc. Inst. Cytol. Acad. Sci. USSR, No.3), pp. 3–8. Nauka Press, Moscow and Leningrad.
Mikami, K. (1980). *Dev. Biol.* **80**, 46–55.
Nouzarède, M. (1975). *C. R. Acad. Sci. Paris D* **280**, 625–628.
Nouzarède, M. (1976). *Bull. Station Biol. Arcachon, Suppl.* **28**, 1–315.
Orias, E. (1977). *Proc. Int. Congr. Protozool., 5th, New York* 459.
Ossipov, D. V. (1981). "Problems of Nuclear Heteromorphism in the Unicellular Organisms." Nauka Press, Leningrad, (In Russian).
Poljansky, G. (1974). *Priroda (Moscow)* (4), 14–23.
Poljansky, G., and Raikov, I. B. (1961). *Bull. Soc. Zool. France* **86**, 402–411.
Poljansky, G. I., and Raikov, I. B. (1976). *Trans. Am. Microsc. Soc.* **95**, 314–326.
Puvion, E., and Moyne, G. (1981). *In* "The Cell Nucleus" (H. Busch, ed.), Vol. 8, pp. 59–115. Academic Press, New York.
Raikov, I. B. (1955). *Zool. Zhurn. (Moscow)* **34**, 747–759.
Raikov, I. B. (1957a). *Zool. Zhurn. (Moscow)* **36**, 344–359.
Raikov, I. B. (1957b). *Vestn. Leningrad. Univ.* (15), 21–37.
Raikov, I. B. (1958a). *Arch. Protistenk.* **103**, 129–192.
Raikov, I. B. (1958b). *Zool. Zhurn. (Moscow)* **37**, 781–800.
Raikov, I. B. (1959a). *Arch. Protistenk.* **104**, 1–42.
Raikov, I. B. (1959b). *Tsitologiya (Leningrad)* **1**, 566–579.
Raikov, I. B. (1962). *Cah. Biol. Mar.* **3**, 325–361.
Raikov, I. B. (1963a). *Proc. Int. Congr. Protozool., 1st, Prague, 1961* pp. 253–258.
Raikov, I. B. (1963b). *In* "Morfologiya i Fiziologiya Prostejshikh" (*Proc. Inst. Cytol. Acad. Sci. USSR,* No. 3), pp. 20–34. Nauka Press, Moscow and Leningrad.
Raikov, I. B. (1963c). *Acta Biol. Acad. Sci. Hung.* **14**, 221–229.
Raikov, I. B. (1963d). *Acta Protozool.* **1**, 21–30.
Raikov, I. B. (1963e). *Zool. Zhurn. (Moscow)* **42**, 1753–1767.
Raikov, I. B. (1963f). *Tsitologiya (Leningrad)* **5**, 685–689.
Raikov, I. B. (1969). *In* "Research in Protozoology" (T. T. Chen, ed.), Vol. 3, pp. 1-128. Pergamon, Oxford.
Raikov, I. B. (1971/72). *Ann Station Biol. Besse-en-Chandesse* **6/7**, 21–53.
Raikov, I. B. (1972a). *Protistologica* **8**, 299–313.

Raikov, I. B. (1972b). *Acta Protozool.* **10**, 227–248.
Raikov, I. B. (1972c). *In* "Research in Protozoology" (T. T. Chen, ed.), Vol. 4, pp. 147–289. Pergamon, Oxford.
Raikov, I. B. (1973). *C. R. Acad. Sci. Paris D* **276**, 2385–2388.
Raikov, I. B. (1974). *Acta Protozool.* **13**, 85–96.
Raikov, I. B. (1975). *Tsitologiya (Leningrad)* **17**, 1009–1017.
Raikov, I. B. (1976a). *Tsitologiya (Leningrad)* **18**, 144–151.
Raikov, I. B. (1976b). *Annu. Rev. Genet.* **10**, 413–440.
Raikov, I. B. (1978). *Protistologica* **14**, 413–432.
Raikov, I. B. (1979). *Arch. Protistenk.* **121**, 1–19.
Raikov, I. B. (1982). "The Protozoan Nucleus. Morphology and Evolution". (*Cell Biol. Monogr.* **9**). Springer-Verlag, Wien and New York.
Raikov, I. B. (1984). *Arch. Protistenk.* **128**, 231–252.
Raikov, I. B., and Dragesco, J. (1969). *Protistologica* **5**, 193–208.
Raikov, I. B., and Kovaleva, V. G. (1978). *Protistologica* **14**, 269–282.
Raikov, I. B., and Kovaleva, V. G. (1980). *Tsitologiya (Leningrad)* **22**, 1139–1145.
Raikov, I. B., and Kovaleva, V. G. (1981). *Protistologica* **17**, 113–130.
Raikov, I. B., and Kovaleva, V. G. (1982). *Tsitologiya (Leningrad)* **24**, 1153–1159.
Raikov, I. B., and Morat, G. (1977). *Protistologica* **13**, 391–399.
Raikov, I. B., Cheissin, E. M., and Buze, E. G. (1963). *Acta Protozool.* **1**, 285–300.
Raikov, I. B., Gerassimova-Matvejeva, Z. P., and De Puytorac, P. (1975). *Acta Protozool.* **14**, 17–42.
Ron, A., and Urieli, S. (1977). *J. Protozool.* **24**, 150–154.
Rossolimo, L. L. (1916). *Dnevn. Zool. Otd. Imp. Obsch. Ljubit. Estestvozn. Antropol. Etnogr. (Moscow), New Ser.* **3**, 1–18.
Rylov, W. M. (1923). *Int. Rev. Ges. Hydrobiol. Hydrogr.* **11**, 179–192.
Schweyer, A. (1925). *Trav. Soc. Natur. Leningrad* **54**, 127–175.
Small, E. B., and Lynn, D. H. (1981). *BioSystems* **14**, 387–401.
Sonneborn, T. M. (1975). *Année Biol.* **14**, 565–584.
Swedmark, B. (1964). *Biol. Rev.* **39**, 1–42.
Torch, R. (1961). *Biol. Bull.* **121**, 410–411.
Torch, R. (1962). *Biol. Bull.* **123**, 467.
Torch, R. (1964a). *J. Cell Biol.* **23**, 98A.
Torch, R. (1964b). *Biol. Bull.* **127**, 393.
Torch, R. (1965). *Biol. Bull.* **129**, 394.
Voronova, M. N. (1971). *Vestnik Leningrad. Univ.* (3), 19–27.
Voronova, M. N. (1976). *Tsitologiya (Leningrad)* **18**, 509–512.
Voronova, M. N., and Selivanova, G. V. (1976). *In* "Karyologiya i Genetika Prostejshikh" (Ser. *Protozoologiya*, No. 1), pp. 144–150. Nauka Press, Leningrad.
Zech, L. (1964). *Arch. Protistenk.* **107**, 295–330.

INTERNATIONAL REVIEW OF CYTOLOGY, VOL. 95

The Unicellular Tetrahymena as a Model Cell for Receptor Research

G. Csaba

Department of Biology, Semmelweis University of Medicine, Budapest, Hungary

I. Basic Evolution of Chemical Recognition

Although signal communication and reception were "invented" by Nature long ago, in the present era of mechanization and computerization the terms characterizing the flow and processing of biological information have been "borrowed" from the technical nomelature (Ashby, 1956). In this sense, there is a flow of signals between emitter and receiver, and the latter not only receives, but also processes the signals. Signal communication makes sense if the emitter and the receiver operate in the same system and if the signal emitted is such as can be recognized and processed by the receiver. The mechanism furnishings recognition is the code; the signals are emitted in a code system which is recognized and decoded by the receiver. The area in which the signals flow is the channel, which may be as narrow as single file in a cable-rope or as a single fiber in a fiber optics device, or as wide as space is for radio waves. If the emitter and receiver systems are properly "tuned," signal reception is also possible in a broad region.

Usually a multitude of signals flows through the channel, but the receiver "tuned" to a given code perceives the "nonsense" signals as mere noise, which interferes with the reception of the adequate signal only if it is similar enough to the code to "mislead" the receiver.

Trying to apply the technical conceptions to the primordial communication system which is an integral part of Life, one soon finds that *even the most primitive forms of life could not exist without communication, i.e., exchange of information.* Even the most primitive living being requires a continuous supply of information from (and about) its immediate environment, and an appropriate source of information is vitally important for both simple (low) and complex (higher) organisms. It follows that a signal receiver (receptor) necessarily has existed since the first living entity came into being, while a (live) signal emitter may have appeared later, since signals are also emitted by lifeless objects. When, however, living beings began to appear in masses, one "willy-nilly" emitted signals to the other, even at the most primitive levels of life. Since life emerged to terrestrial habitats from the sea, where the channel had been represented by water, the mass of which is enormous compared to that of the signals emitted by aquatic forms of life, various problems of biological signal emission and reception can be analyzed and explained on that basis.

The transition from unicellular to multicellular forms of life has not fundamentally altered the system of information exchange, only rendered it more reliable and more specific. *Whereas the encounter between receptor and signal molecule is a chance coincidence at the unicellular level, it is regular in multicellular organisms.* The channel becomes narrower and the receptor-bearing cell inevitably becomes subject to the influence of the signal molecule. Since, however, narrowing of the channel results in an enormous increase in the number of signal molecules flowing through the given channel region, the "noise" may become intolerable. This can be averted either by a (qualitative) decrease in the set of signal molecules or by an increase in receptor specificity, which may involve a reduction in the types of receptors presented. A reduction in the number of signal molecules is impossible since increasing multicellularity and evolutionary progression involve an increasing degree of organization, which presupposes the differentation (and quantitative increase) of the signal molecule types. A reduction in the number of interacting structures can therefore take place exclusively at the receptor level.

The salient point of the foregoing considerations is the hypothesis that receptors also exist at the unicellular level. It is known that prokaryotes and eukaryotes are extraordinarily responsive to environmental (chemical) stimuli (Meglitsch, 1967). It is also known that phenomena resembling reception in higher organisms *have been* demonstrated on the membrane (Josefson and Johannson, 1979; Csaba, 1980a, 1981; Weiss *et al.*, 1983) or in the cytosol (Loose and Feldman, 1982; Csaba and Cserhalmi, 1982) of *unicellular organisms. The most obvious proof is nevertheless the simple fact that the multicellular forms of life derive from the unicellular forms, whose survival, growth, and evolution were impossible without an adequate mechanism(s) of reception, which is the main prerequisite of adaptation to the environment.* Very likely, however, the reception mechanisms and receptors differ to a certain degree between the low and the high levels of phylogenesis.

At the unicellular level, the (chemical) reception is externally oriented and covers, among others, the functions of the sensory organs of higher organisms. It provides for the nutrition, protection, and reproduction of the cell, in all probability not exclusively, since sensations other than reception (e.g., of mechanical and thermal effects) also may play a role in these life functions. *Multicellularity,* however, *involves the inward orientation of chemical reception,* which ultimately gives rise to hormonal control as one element of chemical control.

At the unicellular level, the encounter between the signal receiver and the signal molecule is a chance coincidence, since the environment of the unicellular organism and the number of active environmental molecules is equally changeable. Since the survival of the unicellular organism depends primarily on its adaptation to the environment, such chance encounters presuppose the availability of a wide range of "ad hoc" receptors and an adequate responsiveness to "foreign" materials—in other words, an extraordinary adaptability of the "receiver." The receptor system of unicellular organisms is, therefore (presumably), considerably more adaptive, sensitive, and dynamic than is the receptor system of higher organisms. In the latter, however, the encoding of the signal–receptor relationship becomes possible (by "previous agreement") because the receptor always—and necessarily—encounters the same molecules, and this interaction is an integral element of organization. The receptor system of higher organisms is, therefore—as is already known—more or less stable in a given cell type, and its qualitative aspects vary little, if at all, once the receptor structure has become established; the dynamic property of the receptor system stems primarily from quantitative changes. Encoding of the receptor–hormone relationship ensures that receptor–hormone binding takes place regularly to normal conditions, and the receptor is insensitive to "noise," i.e., it qualifies all signals incapable of specific binding to it as a nonspecific signal (noise). *The diminished dynamism of cellular reception, characteristic of the individual cells of higher organisms, is thus a prerequisite of multicellular existence and reproduction, exactly as the greater dynamism of the receptor system serves the survival and reproduction of unicellular organisms.*

The tetrahymena, used as model cell in our experiments, is a ciliated unicellular organism and as such a protozoan, the systematic position of which is very low in the phylogenetic order (Meglitsch, 1967; Hill, 1972). Since, however, most ciliated unicellular organisms existing today are highly differentiated, they are considered primarily as independent organisms, and only secondarily as single cells. As a unicellular organism, dependent greatly on its own resources for survival in a changing environment, the tetrahymena seems to be a suitable experimental model for the study of hormone receptors and their evolution.

II. Hormone Reception of the Tetrahymena

Although the tetrahymena simultaneously represents a single cell and an independent organism, its response to hormones is not unequivocal in either capacity. *As an organism,* it lacks the organs characteristic of higher organisms, such as gonads and thyroid gland, and is, therefore, incapable of a direct response to the hormones acting on these, whereas, *although a single cell,* it does respond directly to insulin, having a glucose metabolism of its own. On the other hand, the tetrahymena possesses organelles for certain functions which are cell-associated at the vertebrate level; for example, it has the cytopharynx for phagocytosis, which is the specific function of the macrophages in higher organisms. In other functional contexts, such as division and RNA synthesis, the tetrahymena behaves exactly as do the single cells of higher organisms. Experimental approachs to the study of the tetrahymena's hormone reception should therefore be based on the kind of response that unicellular organism shows to a given hormone, on the system in which the hormonal signal molecule is transmitted, and on the quality, binding capacity, kinetics, etc. of the receptor structure itself.

A. RESPONSE OF THE TETRAHYMENA TO HORMONES

The hormones are characteristic signal molecules in the multicellular organisms. They have presumably arisen by evolutionary selection (Barrington, 1978, 1979) from among those molecules which, by virtue of their steric structure, have been capable of binding to cellular receptors and have not yet been involved in some other function. As to the intracellular synthesis of hormones, that of the oligo- and polypeptides seems to be the simplest process, since these molecules are by-products of the cellular protein synthesis. Steroid and amino acid-like hormones arise by a more complex process since their synthesis presupposes transformation of a common simple (sterane, amino acid) molecule (Csaba, 1977). This does not, of course, imply the phylogenetic priority of the oligo- and polypeptide hormones since all types of hormones, or immunobiologically demonstrable hormone-like molecules, also appear at very low levels of phylogenesis (Le Roith *et al.* 1980). As to the type of hormone (s) that could occur in the natural environment of the tetrahymena, of all types the amino acid hormones are most wide spread in the living world.

The hormone-like molecule serotonin and histamine are very widespread in the plant and animal kingdoms (Garattini and Valzelli, 1965). In higher organisms, one of the multiple functions of these hormones is the stimulation of phagocytosis (Jancsó, 1955; Kushinsky *et al.,* 1955; Lison and Smoulders, 1949). They have a similar effect on the tetrahymena, also at very low concentrations (Csaba and Lantos, 1973). Histamine is superior in action to serotonin, and both hormones are toxic at higher concentrations; their activity reaches a maximum in the range 10^{-7} to 10^{-9} M and tends to decline as the concentration rises (Fig. 1). Epinephrine also stimulates the phagocytosis of the tetrahymena (Csaba and Lantos, 1976), although to a lesser degree; this hormone acts as a metabolic stimulant at different levels of phylogenesis, including the unicellular one (Kariya et al., 1974). Thyroxine and its precursors have no influence (Fig. 2), and insulin has little effect, if any, on phagocytosis (Csaba and Lantos 1975a). It follows that the tetrahymena is able to respond to those hormones, which presumably occur in its natural environment, and its sensitivity to these matches that of the hormone receptors of higher organisms, to judge from the similar molality of the active concentration ranges for man and unicellular organisms. It does not, however, follow from the foregoing considerations that the tetrahymena were irresponsive to those hormones which do not usually, occur in its natural environment. While neither insulin nor thyroxine stimulated the phagocytosis of the unicellular organism to a measurable degree, the former did stimulate its glucose metabolism (Csaba and Lantos, 1975b) and the latter (Table I) its division (Csaba et al., 1979b). Thus, the tetrahymena is in principle capable of interacting with higher hormones which (probably) are not present at its level, if we find the response (index) which (possibly) differes from that considered specific in the physiological environment of the hormone.

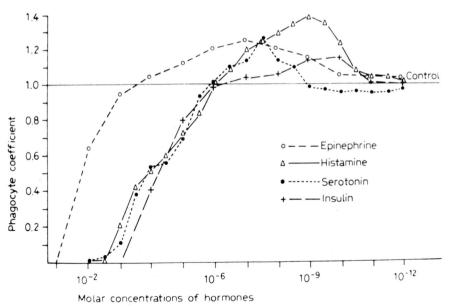

FIG. 1.   Effects of epinephrine, histamine, serotonin, and insulin on the phagocytic activity of tetrahymena. Phagocyte coefficient = phagocyte capacity relative to control value of 0. (Csaba and Lantos, 1973, 1975a; Csaba, 1981).

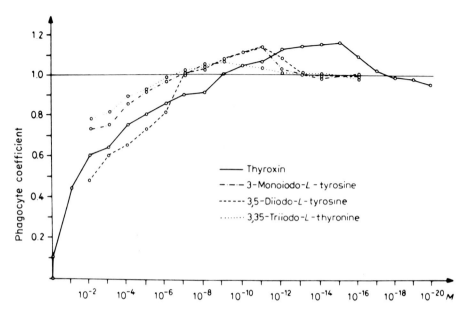

FIG. 2.   Effects of thyroxine and its precursors on the phagocytic activity of tetrahymena (Csaba and Lantos, 1975a; Csaba, 1981).

TABLE I

MULTIPLICATION INDICES[a] OF TETRAHYMENA AFTER TREATMENT WITH DIFFERENT SUBSTANCES[b,c]

Group	Hormone concentration (M)									
	10^{-3}	10^{-4}	10^{-5}	10^{-6}	10^{-7}	10^{-8}	10^{-9}	10^{-10}	10^{-11}	10^{-12}
Triiodothyronine	0.011	0.07	0.10	0.23	0.44	0.67	1.24	1.36	1.21	1.08
Serotonin	—	0.14	0.63	0.78	0.83	1.88	1.68	1.33	0.96	—
Epinephrine	—	0.014	0.20	0.30	0.53	1.04	1.00	1.01	1.05	—
Gibberellin A_3	—	0.02	0.18	0.63	0.74	0.87	0.03	1.00	—	—
Gramine	—	—	0.42	1.40	1.45	1.77	1.48	1.04	—	—

[a]Calculated from cell counts, relative to control as 1.

[b]Values represent statistically significant results: $p < 0.001$ for all substances and concentrations, with the exception of the serotonin values, the significance of which is $p < 0.05$ and $p < 0.02$ at the 10^{-7} and 10^{-10} M doses, respectively.

[c]Csaba (1981).

As already mentioned, the polypeptide hormones have no direct effect on the tetrahymena for lack of a target organ. Their influence on the unicellular organism may nevertheless be studied indirectly, by assessment of their impact, e.g., on RNA synthesis. Thyrotropin (TSH) and glucagon stimulated RNA synthesis of the tetrahymena considerably by a lasting effect at a concentration of $10^{-8} M$, whereas insulin and gonadotropin depressed it (Fig. 3.). Adrenocorticotropic hormone (ACTH) and follicle stimulating hormone (FSH) initially depressed RNA synthesis but did not interfere with it later (Csaba and Ubornyák, 1982a). Apparently the tetrahymena also possessed receptors for those polypeptide hormones which are lacking in its natural environment, to judge from its response to these. Experiments along this line have also disclosed some information on receptor selectivity, since the tetrahymena did not respond to all polypeptide hormones and responded differently to certain similar hormones.

Changes in RNA synthesis caused by other hormones (Fig. 4) that influence the tetrahymena in other measurable parameters also has been demonstrated (Csaba and Ubornyák, 1981).

By systematic classification, the unicellular tetrahymena has been assigned to the animal kingdom, yet it is capable of responding to certain natural or synthetic plant hromones, such as indoleacetic acid, trichlorophenoxyacetic acid, and α-

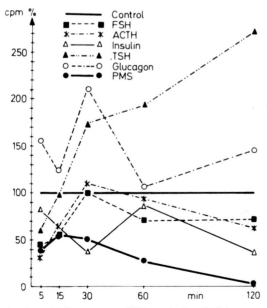

Fig. 3. Effect of polypeptide hormones on RNA synthesis, which is measured by [^{3}H]uridine uptake and is expressed as a percentage of the control value defined as 100 cpm/10^5 cells PMS, (Csaba and Ubornyák, 1982a.)

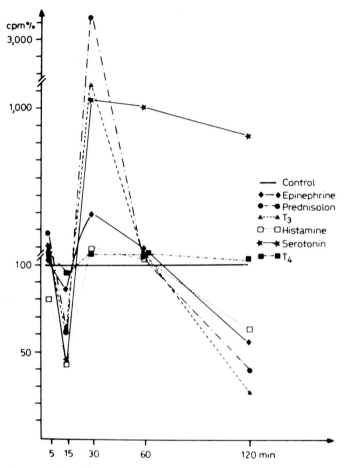

FIG. 4.   Incorporation of [³H]uridine by RNA in tetrahymena pyriformis cells exposed to different hormones (relative to the control value defined as 100 cpm/10⁶ cells) (Csaba and Ubornyák, 1981).

naphthylacetic acid, whose effect on it can be assessed from changes in RNA synthesis (Fig. 5) or in growth rate (Fig. 6) (Csaba and Ubornyák, 1982b; Csaba and Darvas, 1984).

It would appear from the foregoing considerations that the tetrahymena possessed receptors to all hormone-like materials examined, regardless how different the parameters portraying the interaction are. In view of this, the question may justly be posed whether or not the interacting structure is a genuine receptor, i.e., to what extent would it satisfy the criteria set for defining of complex organisms, with special regard to selectivity.

It has already been noted that the tetrahymena can differentiate one polypeptide hormone from the other, as shown by the direction of its responses. The differentiating capacity is also displayed in the case of related hormones (precursors, hormone families) or hormone analogues (antagonists). As mentioned earlier, the tetrahymena responds to serotonin with increased phagocytic activity, whereas it responds to indoleacetic acid with increased division and RNA synthesis. These two hormone-like molecules are closely related to one another, yet indoleacetic acid fails to stimulate phagocytosis in the tetrahymena (Fig. 1). The selectivity of response is obvious, but the question remains whether selection takes place at the receptor level or after the receptor–ligand interaction. To obtain more information on this problem, we examined the behavior of the tetrahymena toward hormone families.

Of the thyroxine series, thyroxine (T_4), triiodothyronine (T_3), diiodotyrosine (T_2), and monoiodotyrosine (T_1) all acted on the tetrahymena as growth stim-

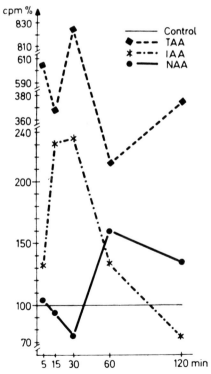

FIG. 5. Effect of plant hormones on RNA synthesis of tetrahymena, which is measured by [^{3}H]uridine uptake expressed as a percentage of the control value, which is defined as 100 cpm/10^5 cells. TAA, Trichlorophenoxyacetic acid; IAA, indoleacetic acid; NAA, naphthylacetic acid. (Csaba and Ubornyák, 1982b.)

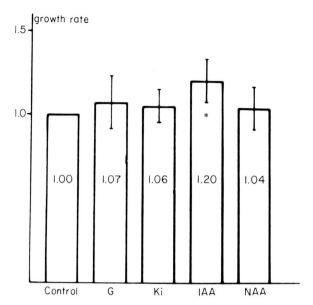

Fɪɢ. 6. Effect of plant hormones (G Gibberelline; Ki, kinetine; IAA, indoleacetic acid; NAA, naphthylacetic acid) on the growth of tetrahymena (Csaba and Darvas, 1984).

ulants, but their actions differed in intensity. Contrary to our expectations, T_2 proved to be the most active molecule, followed in the sequence by T_1, T_3, and T_4 (Fig. 7.). The activity of T_4 was very low relative to T_2. Thus, the tetrahymena was able to differentiate thyronine from tyrosine, and its response also varied with the number of iodine molecules present. Interestingly, the intensity of action differed little between T_1 and T_2, yet the latter represented the optimal interacting molecular structure (Csaba and Németh, 1980b).

In another hormone family, serotonin proved to be more active than its precursors tryptamine and 5-hydroxytryptophan (Fig. 8.)

While selectivity was readily obvious within a hormone series, it was less unequivocal in the case of hormone antagonists. The ethylenediamine-like and phenothiazine-like antagonists of histamine stimulated phagocytosis of the tetrahymena in a manner similar to that of histamine, although to a lesser degree; but they failed to inhibit histamine action when added to the culture before histamine (Csaba and Lantos, 1975c). The serotonin precursor tryptamine and its antagonist 5-methoxytryptamine both stimulated phagocytosis to a lesser degree than serotonin itself and inhibited slightly the action of serotonin when added prior to it. Of the antagonists studied, only the barley alkaloid gramine failed to influence the phagocytosis of the tetrahymena and the stimulant action of the serotonin added after it as well.

The conclusion remains that the receptor of the tetrahymena is not inferior in selectivity to the receptor of the cells of higher organisms. Sharp differentiation between related hormones, as displayed by the receptor of the tetrahymena, unequivocally indicates a high selectivity which was, however, less pronounced in the case of synthetic antagonists. We nevertheless believe that the receptor selectivity displayed by the tetrahymena is appreciable even in comparison to receptor activities in higher organisms.

1. Hormone Binding and Signal Transmission at the Level of the Tetrahymena

A functional response is necessarily consequent upon hormone binding. However, although experimental monitoring of a direct or indirect response is relatively easy, that of hormone binding to the tetrahymena is less so. Receptor analysis leads to results different from those for cells of higher organisms.

Binding of the hormone insulin is extremely low. However, the tetrahymena

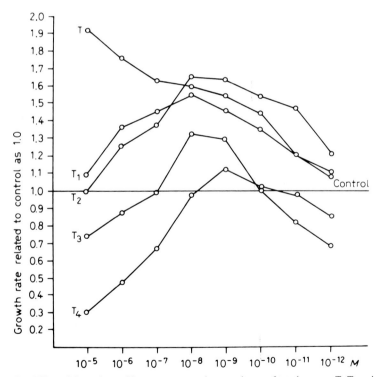

FIG. 7. Effect of thyroxine and its precursors on the growth rate of tetrahymena. T, Tyrosine; T_1, monoiodotyrosine; T_2, diiodotyrosine; T_3, triiodothyronine; T_4, thyroxine (Csaba and Németh, 1980b).

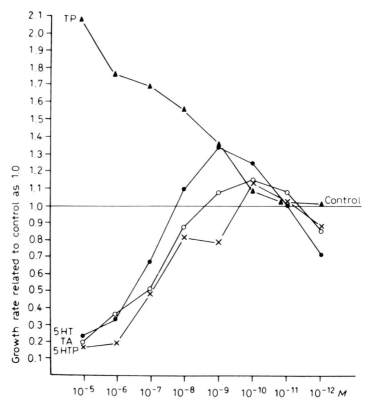

Fig. 8.   Effect of serotonin and its precursors on the growth rate of tetrahymena. TP, Tryptophan; TA, tryptamine; 5HTP, 5-hydroxytryptophan; 5HT, serotonin (Csaba and Németh, 1980b).

does bind the hormone; and the receptor-bound hormone can be displaced by unlabeled insulin (and not by glucagon), a finding which shows the specificity of the binding (Takeda *et al.*, 1984). Autoradiographic studies at the light and electron microscopic levels provided evidence that labeled hormone [T_3 and T_4 (Table II), insulin and histamine (Table III)] was chased to a measurable degree from the membrane binding sites by either pretreatment or posttreatment with unlabeled (cold) hormone (Csaba *et al.*, 1977; Csaba and Ubornyák, 1979).

Thus, hormone binding is measurable, but cellular response presupposes mediation of the signal conveyed by the membrane-bound hormone molecule to the "executive" system of the cell. In higher organisms the signals represented by polypeptide and other hormones are usually mediated via the adenylate cyclase–cAMP system. Adenylate cyclase and cAMP are also present in the tetrahymena (Kassis and Kindler, 1975), but the question remains whether the hormone is able to activate that system at the unicellular level.

TABLE II

BINDING OF TRIIODOTHYRONINE BY TETRAHYMENA[a]

Cells	[^{125}I]Triiodothyronine (cpm/10^5 cells)[b]
Control	271.11 ± 44
Pretreated with unlabeled hormone	$167.8 \pm 29*$
Posttreated with unlabeled hormone	$194.25 \pm 42**$

[a]Csaba and Ubornyák (1979); Csaba (1981).
[b]Significance, relative to control: *, $p < 0.01$; **, $p < 0.001$.

Of the hormones studied, those also acting on cellular functions unequivocally elicited a rise of the cAMP level in the tetrahymena (Csaba and Nagy, 1976a). The cyclic phosphodiesterase inhibitor theophylline also accounted for elevation of the cAMP (Table IV). It follows that the adenylate cyclase—cAMP system is not only present in the tetrahymena, but it also begins to operate under hormonal influence. Nevertheless, the functional response is as a rule not proportional to the degree of elevation of cAMP—it appears that the concentration increase is in itself sufficient to precipitate the given function. Exogenous cAMP added to the tetrahymena culture increased the intracellular cAMP level several hundred times, but was hardly more effective than the hormones (Table V), which elicit only a 20–40% concentration increase (Csaba et al., 1978b).

2. Why Does the Tetrahymena Possess Hormone Receptor(s)?

The tetrahymena, being a unicellular organism, does not, by nature, possess an endocrine system. It therefore seems incomprehensible, at first thought, why it should possess a hormone receptor. As mentioned earlier, response to all events and chemicals which occur in its environment is a life condition for the tetrahymena. The nutrition and survival of the unicellular organism thus presup-

TABLE III

BINDING OF HISTAMINE BY TETRAHYMENA[a]

Cells	[^{3}H]Histamine (cpm/10^5 cells)[b]
Control	$4,287.17 \pm 679$
Pretreated with unlabeled hormone	$3,035.69 \pm 510**$
Posttreated by unlabeled hormone	$3,645.97 \pm 565*\dagger$

[a]Csaba and Ubornyák (1979); Csaba (1981).
[b]Significance, relative to control: *, $p < 0.01$, **, $p < 0.001$; relative to pretreated: $\dagger$, $p < 0.02$.

pose the presence of receptors for recognition of the nutrients, and of other receptors for differentiation of advantageous or disadvantageous environmental influences or materials. The latter receptor function is probably acquired empirically—we shall come back to this problem later.

Amino acids, oligopeptides, and polypeptides may well be present in the natural environment of the tetrahymena and may be utilized by it as nutrients. The experiments with hormone families (Csaba and Németh, 1980b) have disclosed that the principal amino acids (tyrosine in the thyroxine series and tryptophan in the serotonin series) acted on the unicellular organism in a manner similar to that of the hormone proper at the concentrations at which the latter was most active; whereas at the higher concentrations the principal amino acids (as nutrients) enhanced the division of the unicellular organism in a dose-dependent way. while the hormones itself became increasingly toxic. This result suggests that, in all probability, the nutrient receptors of the tetrahymena are capable of responding to amino acid-like hormones, above all to those bearing the closest structural resemblance to amino acids, such as T_1 and T_2 in the case of the tyroxine series (Fig. 7). Conversely, from the serotonin series, serotonin itself proved to be most active (Fig. 8). Serotonin is omnipresent in the living world, presumably also in the natural environment of the tetrahymena, an environment in which thyroxine is certainly missing and tyrosine is present. This probably explains why the tetrahymena recognizes as a hormone proper the molecules that serve as hormone precursors at higher levels of phylogenesis. At the low phylogenetic level of the tetrahymena, the lower evolutionary level of the hormone may be more active than the hormone proper; experimental evidence of this has also been presented in connection with another invertebrate organism (Csaba et al., 1980a). The hypothetical conclusion remains that, on exposure to a hormone, the nutrient receptors of the tetrahymena are transformed into hormone

TABLE IV

EFFECT OF HORMONES AND THEOPHYLLINE ON THE cAMP LEVEL OF TETRAHYMENA[a]

Group	Concentration	cAMP (pmol per assay)	Significance
Control	—	18.21 ± 2.95	
Epinephrine	10^{-8} M	30.3 ± 4.81	$p < 0.05$
Insulin	10^{-3} mg/ml	36.25 ± 7.19	$p < 0.01$
Glucagon	10^{-3} mg/ml	32.11 ± 4.6	$p < 0.05$
Thyrotropic hormone	10^{-3} mg/ml	25.45 ± 7.73	$p < 0.3$
Theophylline	10^{-8} M	33.11 ± 5.93	$p < 0.02$

[a]Csaba (1981).

TABLE V

A COMPARISON BETWEEN PHAGOCYTOSIS, GLUCOSE UPTAKE AND cAMP LEVEL

Group	Glucose (mg/100 ml)	Significance	Phagocytic coefficient	Significance	cAMP (%)	Significance
Control	54.4		1.0		100 (=19 pmol/mg)	
Theophylline (10^{-8} M)	56.7	—	1.29	$p < 0.01$	183	$p < 0.02$
Epinephrine (10^{-8} M)	55.7	—	1.35	$p < 0.01$	166	$p < 0.05$
Control	47.9		1.0		100	
Serotonin (10^{-8} M)	46.4	—	1.41	$p < 0.01$	135	
cAMP (10^{-4} M)	45.9	—	1.34	$p < 0.01$	847	$p < 0.005$
Control	49.1		1.0		100	
Gramine (10^{-8} M)	43.9	—	1.07	$p < 0.01$	16	$p < 0.01$
Epinephrine (10^{-4} M)	41.3	$p < 0.01$	1.13	$p < 0.01$	88	—

[a]Csaba (1981).

receptors (Lenhoff, 1974). The underlying mechanism of transformation being presumably less simple than the above conclusion, we shall come back to the evolutionary aspects of this problem later.

3. Resemblance between Receptors of the Tetrahymena and of Higher Organisms

Ginsberg and colleagues 1977), as well as Muggeo and colleagues (1979a, b) have demonstrated that the insulin of higher organisms binds to the receptors of lower animals separated from the higher vertebrates by an evolutionary gap of several hundreds of thousands of years. As described in the foregoing sections the higher hormones are able to bind to the receptors of the unicellular tetrahymena. The close resemblance of the receptors of the tetrahymena to those of higher animals, and the chance operation of the former's food receptors as hormone receptors has been substantiated by direct immunological evidence. Antibodies to a purified receptor preparation obtained from rat hepatocellular membrane inhibited the binding of insulin to the membrane of the tetrahymena by having bound to it themselves (Figs. 9 and 10). This phenomenon presupposes *a close resemblance of the receptor structures at the distant phylogenetic levels represented by the unicellular organism and the rat* (Csaba et al., 1984c). A more detailed discussion of the problem will follow in Section II, C.

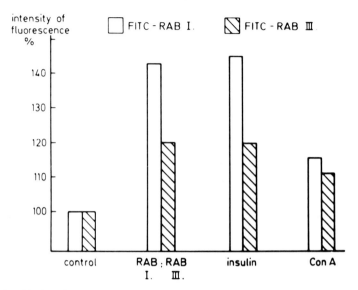

Fig. 9. Binding of FITC-labeled rat liver receptor antibodies (FITC-RAB I, strong; FITC-RAB III, weak) to control and differently pretreated (abscissa: RAB, rat liver receptor antibody; I, strong; III, weak) tetrahymena cells. Con A, Concanavalin A. (Csaba *et al.*, 1984c.)

B. Receptor Formation and Receptor "Memory" in the Tetrahymena

Although receptor development is genetically encoded in higher organisms (mammals), the receptors are immature at birth. They mature gradually after birth, in all probability in association with membrane differentiation. Receptor immaturity could explain the observation that the hormone binding capacity of the receptors is generally much lower at birth than later in life (Blazquez *et al.*, 1976; Gluckman *et al.*, 1983); for example, the hormone receptors of the rat reach full maturity 21–28 days postpartum. However, certain hormones show a decline in binding capacity with progressing age (Thorrson and Hintz, 1977; Neufeld *et al.*, 1980; Peyrat *et al.*, 1981) presumably because they had played an important-morphogenetic—role in prenatal life and tend to lose importance postnatally along with the morphogenetic function. The perinatal period is critical for the receptor, since receptor maturation requires the presence of the appropriate hormone. If the latter appears at the optimal concentration, the receptor matures and its normal binding capacity (affinity or number) becomes established (Csaba and Nagy, 1984). Perinatal qualitative or quantitative deviations of the hormone from the normal requirement account for anomalous development of the receptor (Csaba, 1980a, b, 1981). Too low or too high concentrations of the appropriate hormone may injure the developing receptor for the animal's lifetime. A still greater injury results if molecules analogous or related to the appropriate hormone are involved in the first interaction with the receptor; depending on the degree of structural discrepancy, such interactions may either amplify or deform the receptor structure (Csaba *et al.*, 1980b). For example, rats neonatally treated with a large dose of gonadotropin (Csaba and Nagy, 1976b) showed a considerable decrease in adult thyroid response to TSH (the two hormones have a common α subunit and similar β subunits), whereas exposure of 1-day-old chicks to thyrotropin accounted for a later increase in gonadal binding capacity for gonadotropin (Csaba *et al.*, 1981; Dobozy *et al.*, 1981). These experimental observations have unequivocally indicated that the establishment of the receptor–hormone relationship presupposes a perinatal hormonal imprinting, which amplifies the genetically encoded, but initially plastic receptor for interaction with the appropriate hormone. This happens if the appropriate molecule had been involved in the first interaction, whereas faulty imprinting by a ''foreign'' molecule pushes the receptor function onto a false track. Hormonal imprinting is presumably part of a complex of perinatally operative imprinting mechanisms, such as behavioral imprinting, which adjust the genetically encoded, but plastic interacting structures to *their own patterns* of interaction (Csaba, 1981).

At the level of the tetrahymena, genetic encoding of the receptor structure(s) is out of question, since the environment of the unicellular organism is extraordinarily changeable. More probably only the subunits, which form the receptor,

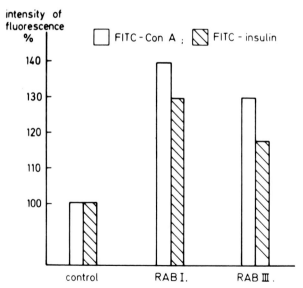

FIG. 10. Binding of FITC-labeled Con A and insulin to tetrahymena cells pretreated with rat liver receptor antibody. Designations as in Fig. 9 (Csaba *et al.*, 1984c).

are encoded structures (Koch *et al.*, 1979); the subunits assemble as dictated by the actual environmental influences and furnish thereby a considerably greater variety of receptors than are found in the single cells of higher organisms. In this light, the question necessarily arises how hormonal imprinting, the role of which in higher organisms has been discussed earlier, affects later response to the hormone at the level of the tetrahymena.

Tetrahymena cells preexposed to histamine, washed, returned to normal medium, and reexposed to histamine again, showed a considerable increase in phagocytic activity relative to the first response, which had itself increased markedly over the not-preexposed control (Csaba and Lantos, 1977). Experiments with other amino acid-like hormones, e.g., with diiodotyrosine (T_2), which stimulates the division of the tetrahymena, had essentially similar results: The growth response at the second exposure was considerably greater than that at the first exposure (Csaba *et al.*, 1982b). Preexposure to polypeptide hormones (Fig. 11) also accounted for a greater hormone binding on reexposure (Kovács and Csaba, 1984). Two important conslusions can be drawn from the these observations. First, the *first interaction with the hormone had a major impact on the tetrahymena,* which resulted in the amplification (in affinity or number?) of its hormone receptor, and second, since the life span of the tetrahymena is so short that several new generations arise within 24 hours, *the influence of the first interaction obviously lasted over many progeny generations.*

It follows that the first interaction of the receptor with the hormone gives rise to hormonal imprinting, not only in the higher organisms, but also in the tetrahymena. The question is what importance hormonal imprinting could have for

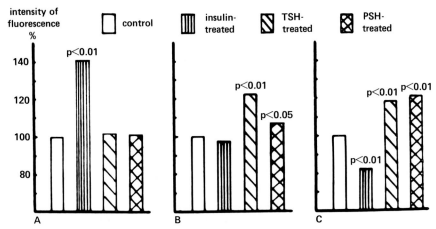

FIG. 11.   Binding of FITC-labeled insulin (A), TSH (B), or FSH (C) to the control, and insulin-, TSH-, or FSH-pretreated tetrahymena cells (Kovács and Csaba, 1984).

TABLE VI

INFLUENCE OF TREATMENT WITH PHYSIOLOGICALLY AND BIOLOGICALLY
ACTIVE, NONPHYSIOLOGICAL MATERIALS ON THE CLONAL GROWTH
RATE OF THE TETRAHYMENA[a]

Culture	First treatment	Second treatment	Growth rates[b,c]
1	—	—	12.5
2	—	Epinephrine	12.5
3	—	Gibberellin	14.4 (14.2)
4	—	Prednisolone	15.4 (16.4)
5	—	Benzpyrene	17.8 (18.5)
6	Epinephrine	Epinephrine	16.3
7	Gibberellin	Gibberellin	17.8
8	Prednisolone	Prednisolone	19.9
9	Benzpyrene	Benzpyrene	20.0

[a]Csaba et al. (1982f).

[b]All cultures (1) treated (first treatment) for 24 hours in mass culture; (2) returned to plain medium for 6 hours; (3) treated (second treatment) for 24 hours in subculture. Growth rate values in parentheses are for cells treated in subculture only. There is no significant difference between the two values in any relation.

[c]Growth rate equals the number of cells arising from one cell after 24 hours.

the tetrahymena at the level of the individual cell or the species, or in the evolutionary context.

In higher organisms, *"natural" imprinting* by the endogenous hormone essentially *represents a modulation of* the receptor (signal receiver) *to "self"* (to the signal emitters). This modulation endows the receptor with the potential of selecting between "self" and "nonself." Nonphysiological interference with that mechanism is like replacing the adequate signal by a noise, which confuses the receptor and depresses thereby its selectivity. *For the tetrahymena, the hormone represents just a signal, as would any other molecule with a steric structure suitable for interaction.* Imprinting could, in fact, be induced in the tetrahymena by nonhormone molecules (Table VI), such as benzpyrene (Csaba et al., 1982f) or digoxine (Darvas et al., 1984b), or by nonsignal molecules which do not bind to the receptors of higher organisms, e.g., bovine serum albumin. The advantage of the hormone over other signal molecules is the specificity of its steric structure, which facilitates its recognition also for the tetrahymena—to judge from the more specific response of the latter to hormones than, for example, to serum albumin. If the tetrahymena is under the influence of a given molecule (has received the signal), this may be to its advantage or disadvantage, since the "signal" may as well represent a nutrient as a toxic molecule. Whichever is the case, the "memory" of the interaction necessarily remians preserved and induces the tetrahymena to adjust its reactions to the beneficent or hostile nature of the signal molecule. The processing and the memory of each signal is therefore vitally important at the level of the individual tetrahymena cell. However, that entity exists only between two divisions, after which the properties of each individual cell are transmitted to two daughter cells. Presumably the "memory" of various signals also is transmitted. The same applies to the higher organisms, in which the cells involved in adult response also represent distant progeny generations of those involved in neonatal imprinting. Thus, the tetrahymena is a suitable model for the experimental study of receptor development and imprinting and of signal processing and memory transmission as well.

C. Tetrahymena, the Cellular Model of Receptor Evolution

However similar the mechanisms of imprinting in the tetrahymena and in the single cell of higher organisms, there is one substantial difference. Whereas at the higher phylogenetic levels the receptors are genetically encoded structures and no receptor can arise without encoding, the *tetrahymena is an open system* in that respect—a "virgin" cell in which receptor formation can be provoked by a wide variety of signal molecules; and if the receptor so arisen persists, it may acquire an evolutionary importance.

As already noted, exposure of the tetrahymena to histamine (even for as short a time as 10 minutes) enhanced markedly its phagocytic activity (Csaba and Lantos, 1973). Tetrahymena cells continuously exposed to a low concentration of histamine for 5 weeks showed a gradual increase in phagocytic activity, until it reached a peak at which it persisted (Fig. 12). Those cells which were subsequently returned to normal medium for 1 week showed no significant difference from the control with respect to phagocytic activity, but they did show a significant increase over it and over the once-exposed cells as well if reexposed to histamine, be it for as short a time as 10 minutes (Csaba and Lantos, 1977). Similar observations were made with T_2, which stimulates the growth of the tetrahymena (Fig. 13); the cell population preexposed to T_2 still "remembered" the first interaction with the hormone after as many as 500 generation changes (Csaba *et al.*, 1982e), although the increased response to reexposure (and along with it the difference from the control) tended to diminish with progressing time.

Experiments with single-cell subcultures (clones) have thrown some light on the factors involved in the stimulation of the phagocytosis or the growth of the tetrahymena by hormones. It appears that *selection and amplification both play a role in transmission of the established hormone receptor from one generation to the other* (Csaba *et al.*, 1982a). Selection presupposes that part of the tetrahymena cells *ab ovo* possess potential receptor structures, which are either complementary to the given hormone or are exactly in that stage of receptor formation (which takes place continuously in the cell membrane) in which a complementary structure (potential binding site) is taking shape. These potential

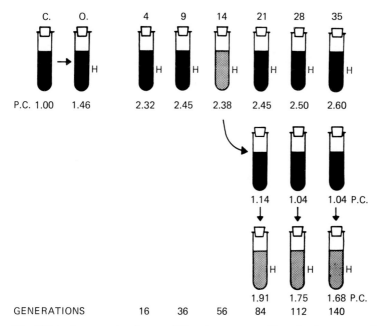

C. O. 4 9 14 21 28 35

P.C. 1.00 1.46 2.32 2.45 2.38 2.45 2.50 2.60

1.14 1.04 1.04 P.C.

1.91 1.75 1.68 P.C.

GENERATIONS 16 36 56 84 112 140

Fig. 12. Effect of permanent and repeated histamine treatment (H) on the phagocyte coefficient (P.C.) of the tetrahymena. After a 2-week incubation in 10^{-4} M histamine-containing media (top) the tetrahymena were transplanted to normal medium, in which the previously high phagocyte coefficient returned to normal levels (middle). After a second histamine treatment of only 3 minutes (bottom) the phagocyte coefficient significantly increased (Csaba and Lantos, 1977).

receptors receive in the presence of the hormone a functional (mitotic, phagocytic) stimulus, which endows them with a selection advantage (improved nutrition, greater number of progeny) that accounts for the predominance of their progeny in the next generation(s). The other (more feasible) alternative is that each tetrahymena cell is capable of forming an adequate receptor in presence of a given hormone, and the "memory" of that receptor persists over several subsequent generations. Comparative studies on interclonal and intraclonal variation have suggested that receptor development in the membrane of the tetrahymena depends to a lesser degree on genetic factors than on the genetic variability of the membrane itself, which could account for the stabilization of the membrane receptor after the first interaction with the hormone.

In the hormone experiments, the tetrahymena modeled a cell at a low level of phylogenesis, a level at which no specific receptors exist for given molecules but at which *nonspecific (nutrient-specific) and/or potential receptor structures are present;* the potential signal molecules either do or do not appear in the environment of the cell. If the tetrahymena is exposed to a specific signal molecule in

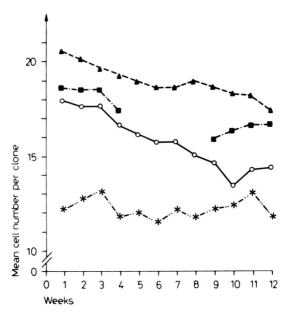

FIG. 13. Mean rate of multiplication of tetrahymena populations under different experimental conditions. ▲, Subcultures treated repeatedly, once a week with T_2; ■, subcultures from the same stock as used for repeated treatment, but treated only once with T_2, at the beginning of the experiment; ○, subcultures from another stock treated only once with T_2, at the beginning of the experiment; *, control stock (not treated) (Csaba *et al.*, 1982c).

adequate concentrations and for an adequate time, the signal molecule—the "future hormone"—may elicit those membrane alterations which ultimately lead to receptor formation (Csaba, 1980b, 1981). Thus the originally nonspecific membrane structure becomes stabilized as a receptor and the nonspecific signal molecule acquires the "sense" of a hormone. *If this interrelationship is advantageous for the cell* (the tetrahymena cell, in this instance) *or for the macroorganism of which the cell is a part, the hormone-responsive cells acquire a selection advantage over the irresponsive cells and will survive.* This hypothetical explanation also fails to throw light on the mode of the genetic encoding of receptor formation.

The hypothesis that the receptors of the tetrahymena are not preformed, but arise under hormonal influence, has been substantiated by immunological evidence. Treatment with antiserum (against tetrahymena) immobilizes the tetrahymena cell, and antibodies against tetrahymena pretreated with insulin for induction of receptor formation have the same effect. If, however, other cells (e.g., rat hepatocytes in culture) are treated with antisera to tetrahymena cells pretreated and not pretreated with insulin, the antiserum against the insulin-pretreated cells binds to the hepatocytes in a considerably greater amount than does the plain antiserum; this result accounts for a corresponding difference in the quantitative relations of insulin binding to the hapatocytes (Figs. 14 and 15). It appears that *insulin treatment induced in the tetrahymena the formation of receptors;* therefore the immune globulins formed against these cells were complementary to the insulin receptor and bound readily to such receptors of the rat (Kovács *et al.,* 1985). This result provides immunological evidence that the insulin receptor of the tetrahymena is very similar to that of the rat. This seems surprising because of the great phylogenetic distance between the tetrahymena and the rat, but is less surprising if we take into consideration the fact that *receptor formation has been induced in the unicellular organism with a mammalian insulin preparation.* The marked functional difference between the immune globulins formed against tetrahymena cells pretreated and not pretreated with insulin can be regarded as an immunological proof that *receptor formation was induced by insulin. The behavior of the hormone as a signal molecule may thus have represented one evolutionary factor responsible for receptor formation in the originally nonspecific membrane.* Presumably this phenomenon collab-

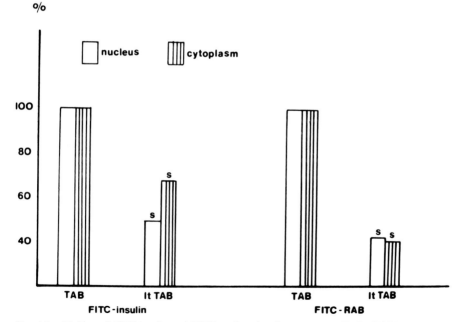

FIG. 14. Binding of FITC-insulin and FITC-rat liver insulin receptor antibody (RAB) to rat hepatocytes treated after fixation with rabbit IgG against intact (TAB) and insulin pretreated tetrahymena cells (ItTAB). Significance between TAB and ItTAB, $p < 0.01$ (Kovács *et al.,* 1984a).

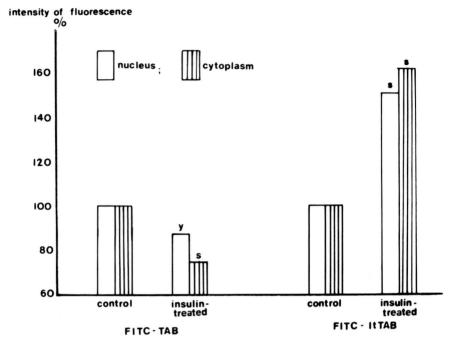

FIG. 15. Binding of FITC-TAB (antibody against tetrahymena) and FITC-ItTAB (antibody against insulin-pretreated tetrahymena) to rat hepatocytes pretreated or not pretreated (control) with insulin before fixation. Significance to control: for S, $p < 0.01$; or y, $p < 0.05$. (Kovács *et al.*, 1984a.)

orating with selection factors represents the underlying mechanism of receptor formation.

D. INVESTIGATIONS INTO THE MECHANISM OF HORMONAL IMPRINTING AND RECEPTOR "MEMORY" IN THE TETRAHYMENA MODEL SYSTEM

It follows from the foregoing considerations that the tetrahymena not only possesses (forms) receptors for hormones of higher organisms but also is operated on by the mechanims of hormonal imprinting (receptor "memory"). Since in higher organisms investigations into receptor memory are hampered by the complexity of the system (and the extraordinarily high level of "noise"), the tetrahymena has been chosen as the model for studies along that line.

Evidence has been presented that receptor memory is transmitted to many (more than 500) tetrahymena generations (Fig. 13). As a matter of fact, the duration of imprinting greatly depends on the concentration of, and length of exposure to, the hormone at the first interaction.

Pertinent experimental studies have suggested that the time factor plays a more decisive role than the hormone concentration itself (Csaba *et al.*, 1982b). Induction of imprinting in mass cultures of the tetrahymena required at least a 1-hour hormone exposure, and the establishment of imprinting took 4 hours (Table VII). The effective hormone concentration was, however, very low; for example, T_2 elicited full imprinting at the concentration of 10^{-18} M (Table VIII). This is remarkable, since at that concentration T_2 does not appreciably alter the cellular growth rate at the first interaction (Table IX). The "memory" of the interaction nevertheless seems to persist, to judge from the characteristic increase in cellular response at reexposure(s).

The decisive role of the length of exposure could be explained by postulating

TABLE VII

INFLUENCE OF THE LENGTH OF EXPOSURE TO 10^{-9} M T_2
ON GROWTH RESPONSE OF THE TETRAHYMENA[a]

A. Mean growth rate

Sampling times	Period of first exposure					
	10 min	30 min	1 hr	4 hr	8 hr	24 hr
Immediately after first exposure	17.8	18.9	20.8	21.1	21.0	22.3
At 1 week after first exposure	13.3	14.2	13.8	15.1	16.5	17.9
After 24-hr re-exposure for identical periods	13.4	14.1	15.8	21.8	21.6	21.5
At 2 weeks	12.4	13.2	13.2	19.0	20.0	20.0
At 2 + 3 weeks	14.2	13.5	16.0	20.0	20.8	21.2
At 2 + 3 + 4 weeks	16.0	17.7	18.8	20.5	20.5	20.8

B. Variance table

Source of variation	Sum of squares	Degrees of freedom	Mean square	F	P
	Values assessed immediately after treatment[b]				
Regression	236.5	1	235	55	$\ll 0.001$
Deviation from linearity	34.4	4	8.6	2.0	> 0.05
Error	494.3	114	4.34		
	Values assessed 1 week after treatment[c]				
Regression	284	1	284	66	$\ll 0.001$
Deviation from linearity	31.5	4	7.9	1.8	> 0.05
Error	488.8	114	4.29		

[a]Csaba *et al.* (1982b).
[b]Equation of regression $y = 20 + 0.8x$, where y = growth and x = log time.
[c]Equation of regression: $y = 14 + 0.9x$ where y = growth and x = log time.

TABLE VIII

Growth Response of Tetrahymena to Application of Different Hormone Levels for First and Second Exposure[a]

A. Mean growth rates

Hormone concentration for second exposure (M)	Hormone concentration for first exposure (M)			
	10^{-9}	10^{-12}	10^{-15}	10^{-18}
10^{-9}	21.2	19.7	19.2	18.1
10^{-18}	19.9	18.8	17.6	16.3

B. Variance table

Source of variation	Sum of squares	Degrees of freedom	Mean square	F	P
At first exposure	242.32	3	80.8	15.9	< 0.001
At reexposure	79.81	1	79.81	15.8	< 0.001
Interaction	5.27	3	1.76	0.35	> 0.05
Error	768.40	152	5.05		

[a]Csaba et al. (1982b).

that although potential receptor structures might exist it is more probable that a certain time is required until the appropriate subunits of the fluid membrane assemble to form an adequate receptor for the hormone. In this light, receptor formation can be interpreted as an issue of the "inquiry" of the membrane

TABLE IX

Growth Response of Tetrahymena to a Single Treatment with T_2[a]

A. Mean growth rates at different hormone levels

Hormone conc. (M)	10^{-9}	10^{-12}	10^{-15}	10^{-18}	K[b]
Mean growth rate in 24 hours	21.0	17.6	14.6	12.2	12.4

B. Variance table[c]

Source of variation	Sum of squares	Degrees of freedom	Mean square	F	P
Regression	870.25	1	870.25	184	$\leqslant 0.001$
Deviation from linearity	6.30	2	3.15	0.67	> 0.05
Error	358.20	76	4.71		

[a]Csaba et al. (1982c).
[b]K, Control culture; no hormone in medium.
[c]Equation of regression: $y = 29.7 + 0.98x$, where y = growth and x = log concentration.

structures (Koch *et al.*, 1979) for complementary environmental structures. The low concentration required for hormonal imprinting indicates that the receptor mechanisms of the tetrahymena are extraordinarily sensitive, which is probably a fundamental prerequisite of its survival. It appears in this light that *the "memory" of interaction with an environmental molecule is superior to the threshold of a functional response to the same* (hormone) *molecule.*

If hormones (combinations) are used which inhibit the function (e.g., growth) of the tetrahymena, this also could provoke positive imprinting (Csaba and Németh, 1980a). It appears that amplification of the receptor by the hormone does take place at the first encouter regardless of whether the response of the cells was positive or negative (Fig. 16.)

1. Membrane-Level or Gene-Level Effects?

The tetrahymena "communicates" with its environment through its membrane. It follows that the primary changes also are membrane associated in the case of hormone reception, at both the first and second interaction(s). The membrane of the tetrahymena is, in fact, extraordinarily sensitive to external influences (Nozawa, 1980), as indicated by its involvement in hormone binding and hormonal imprinting. Any alteration in membrane fluidity, be it an increase or a decrease, reduces the intensity of imprinting, or may even result in faulty imprinting (Kovács *et al.*, 1984d).

Evidence of the decisive role of the membrane in imprinting has emerged from experiments with liposome-enclosed hormone, which was engulfed by the cell without membrane involvement. Imprinting failed to take place under those conditions (Nozawa *et al.*, 1984).

The close association of the hormone binding and imprinting mechanisms with the membrane cannot in itself explain the transmission of imprinting to the progeny generations. Transmission of membrane-associated information to daughter cells via division would imply a gradual fading of the "memory" unless a "reconstruction" of the structure originally involved in imprinting via self-assembly is postulated. More probably, however, the information "communicated" by the hormone at the induction of receptor formation is transmitted at the nuclear (gene) level.

Internalization of hormones after interaction with the membrane has frequently been observed also in cells of higher organisms (Baldvin *et al.*, 1981; Goldstein *et al.*, 1979; Steinmann *et al.*, 1983), but it is still a matter of dispute whether internalization is a prelude to intracellular degradation or to a secondary (intracellular) action of the hormone molecule. The degradation theory is more popular, but much evidence has also been presented that the internalized hormones appeared on the nuclear membrane, or even intranuclearly (Horvat *et al.*, 1975; Goldfine *et al.*, 1977a, b; Horvat, 1978; Rao and Chegini, 1983). In hormone-exposed tetrahymena cells, amino acid-type hormones have been detected inside

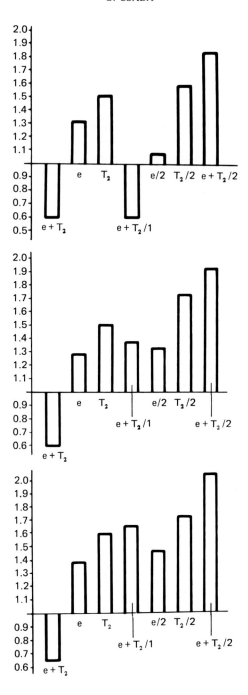

the nucleus, usually in a heterochromatic localization, and polypeptide hormones have been detected along the nuclear membrane (Csaba *et al.*, 1980c, 1983d, 1984g). This finding implies that some nuclear (gene) level effect of the hormone could be responsible for lifelong imprinting and for its transmission to the progeny as well. Morphological evidence has in fact been obtained that hormonal notion differs appreciably between first exposure and reexposure. The first exposure of tetrahymena cells to T_2 was followed by appearance of enormous nucleoli in the nucleus (Fig. 17), and of characteristic, but structurally obscure corpuscles in the cytoplasm (Csaba and Madarász, 1985); the latter also appeared after reexposure(s) (Fig. 18). This supports the hypothesis that the gene structures responsible for encoding the membrane subpatterns assemble to form a complex which thus carries all the information required for encoding a given receptor structure. Recent immunological theories also seem to support this hypothesis (Fristrom and Spieth, 1980; Leder, 1982).

One proof of a gene-level effect is that the first interaction with the hormone gives rise, not only to hormonal imprinting, but also to a certain change in cellular function. For example, the growth rate changes permanently under the influence of T_2 in the generation directly involved in interaction with the hormone, and in the progeny generations as well, without another exposure to the hormone (Csaba *et al.*, 1982e). Although the response to reexposure is still greater, the fact that a single exposure accounts for a measurable increase in the mitotic rate over as many as 500 generations strongly suggests that a gene-level effect is responsible for the ''modulation'' of the mitotic function (Fig. 13). This also applies to other functions, e.g., to the alteration (stimulation) of phagocytic activity by histamine (Darvas *et al.*, 1984a).

On the basis of the preceding results, we can postulate that *while in vertebrate organisms (mammals, birds) the genetically encoded receptor structures become amplified by parinatal interaction with the hormone, in the unicellular tetrahymena certain nonencoded receptor structures become encoded under the influence of the hormone.*

It would be hard to define the time parameters of cell ''birth'' and individual cellular life span (from origination to decay), yet it appears that hormonal imprinting takes effect differently in the various stages of the cell cycle (Csaba *et*

FIG. 16.   Effect of 24-hour (A), 72-hour (B), and 148-hour (C) single or combined hormonal treatment on the growth of tetrahymena. E, Epinephrine; T_2, diiodotyrosine. The columns above e + T_2, e, and T_2 indicate the response of untreated (absolute) controls; e + $T_2/1$ designates clonal growth after pretreatment in the mass culture and a subsequent 24-hour withdrawal period. The designations e/2, $T_2/2$, and e+$T_2/2$ show the cell growth after pretreatment, a 24-hour withdrawal, and a 24-hour second exposure to epinephrine, T_2, and epinephrine + T_2, respectively, in mass culture. The horizontal axis represents unity, i.e., the control value (baseline) to which the growth in variously treated culture was compared (Csaba and Németh, 1980a).

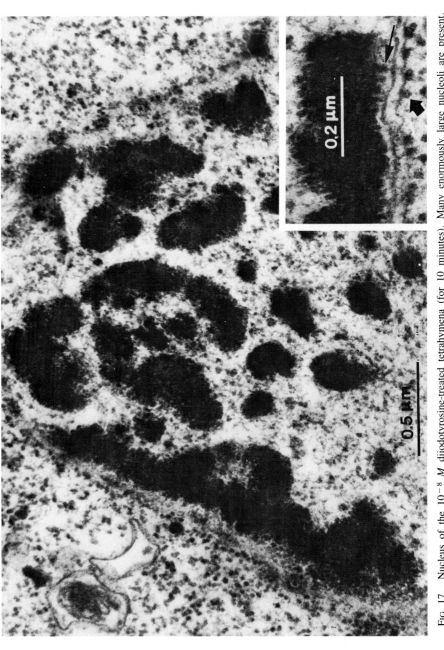

FIG. 17. Nucleus of the 10^{-8} M diiodotyrosine-treated tetrahymena (for 10 minutes). Many enormously large nucleoli are present. Ribosome-like particles are detaching from the nucleoli and attaching to the nuclear membrane arrows in the insert) (Csaba and Madarász, 1985).

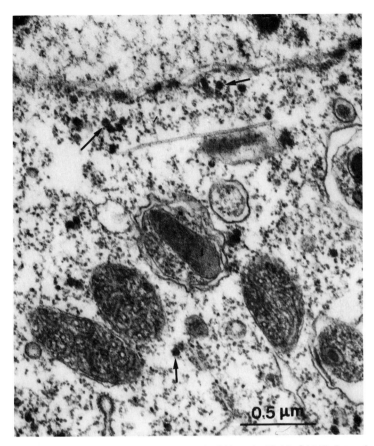

Fig. 18.   Cytoplasm of a tetrahymena pretreated (for 24 hours) with $10^{-9}\,M$ diiodotyrosine, and 72 hours later repeatedly treated with $10^{-8}\,M$ diiodotyronine for 4 hours The arrows indicate the spherical corpuscles in the cytoplasm (Csaba and Madarász, 1985).

al., 1984f). Tetrahymenas first exposed to the hormone in phase G_1 showed a more distinct imprinting than those exposed in phase S or G_2, although imprinting also takes effect in these. This finding indicates either that, by analogy with higher organisms, the early postnatal period (phase G_1) is the most critical stage of receptor development at the cellular (unicellular) level, or that the membrane alterations taking place during the cell cycle have a dissimilar impact on the potential (future) receptor structures.

   The inhibitability of hormonal imprinting has also disclosed some information on its underlying mechanism. Treatment of the cells with inhibitors of protein synthesis, of DNA–RNA transcription, or of receptor motility all had a depressive effect on hormonal imprinting, but they did not inhibit it completely

(Csaba *et al.*, 1982d). Complete inhibition if imprinting could be achieved only by altering the fluidity of the membrane either by thermal influence or by ergosterol incorporation (Kovács *et al.*, 1984c). It follows that the normal stage of the cell membrane is of primary importance for receptor formation, but intracellular processes also play a decisive role in it.

2. Interrelatedness of Imprinting and Receptor "Memory" in the Tetrahymena

As already mentioned, inhibitors of protein or RNA synthesis depress markedly, but do not inhibit completely, hormonal imprinting in the tetrahymena. However, exposure of the tetrahymena to an excessive amount of a material either similar to or different from the hormone responsible for imprinting, but acting at the receptor level, has an entirely different effect. Exposure and reexposure to T_2 or serotonin account for a nearly twofold increase of the growth rate over the control (Csaba and Németh, 1982), but if first exposure to T_2 is followed 3, 5, and 14 days later by reexposure to a growth stimulant different from T_2 (serotonin, gramine, and, finally, serotonin + gramine), the growth rate does not appreciably differ from the control, although T_2, which had been responsible for imprinting, was included in the combined treatment (Table X). It appears that excessive foreign (nonself) information can delete the established information.

TABLE X

EFFECT OF COMBINED AND REPEATED HORMONE TREATMENTS ON THE GROWTH OF TETRAHYMENA, AS ASSESSED FROM MEAN COUNTS OF SUBCULTURES SET UP ON DAY 14 OF THE EXPERIMENT[a]

Experimental group	Treatment[b]				Mean cell count
	Day 1	Day 3	Day 5	Day 14	
1	T_2	5HT	Gramine	All	13.50
2	Gramine	5HT	T_2	All	15.50[c,d,e]
3	5HT	T_2	Gramine	All	16.25[c,d,e]
4	All	—	—	All	13.55
5	All	All	All	All	13.60[f]
6	Gramine	Gramine	Gramine	Gramine	14.45[c]
7	T_2	T_2	T_2	T_2	21.00[c,d,e]
8	5HT	5HT	5HT	5HT	23.65[c,d,e]
9	Control	Control	Control	Control	12.55

[a]Csaba and Németh (1982).
[b]5HT, Serotonin; All, combination of gramine, 5HT, T_2; Control, no hormones added to medium.
[c]Significance versus control (group 9), $p < 0.01$.
[d]Significance versus group 1, $p < 0.01$.
[e]Significance versus group 4, $p < 0.01$.
[f]Significance versus control (group 9), $p < 0.05$.

TABLE XI

EFFECT OF THYROXINE AND ITS PRECURSORS ON RECEPTOR MEMORY IN THE TETRAHYMENA[a]

Culture	First exposure (Day 1)		Second exposure (after 1 week)		Third exposure (after 2 weeks)	
	Treatment	Growth rate	Treatment	Growth rate	Treatment	Growth rate
Control	—	12.2	—	$11.9-12.5^b$		
Test	T_2	20.85				
	T_2		T_1	18.95	T_1	19.6
	T_2		T_2	22.5	T_2	21.7
	T_2		T_3	16.95	T_3	17.5
	T_2		T_4	19.0	T_4	17.4

[a]Csaba and Németh (1982).
[b]Confidence limits.

Not only "loading" by excessive information, but also information very similar to the adequate one, in other words the "noise" recognized as "almost self" can adversely affect imprinting and, thereby, the receptor "memory." Treatment of tetrahymena cells first with T_2, than 1 week later with different hormones of the thyroxine series (T_1, T_2, T_3, or T_4), and after another week, i.e., for a third time, with T_2 again (Table XI) has shown that T_1 depressed the influence of imprinting by T_2 to a minor (nonsignificant) degree, T_2 amplified it, and T_3 and T_4, being of a different (thyronine, not tyrosine) structure yet able to bind to the receptor, extinguished a substantial part of the receptor "memory" (Csaba et al., 1982c).

A molecule similar in action to, but different in structure from, the given hormone may also interfere with imprinting if applied immediately after its completion; but then interference is of a much lesser degree than in the case of structural similarity and functional disparity (Csaba et al., 1983c).

When imprinting with T_2 was followed without delay by treatment with a combination of five hormones, each of which had acted on the tetrahymena by itself, the imprinting induced by T_2 was completely extinguished without being replaced by imprinting by any hormone included in the combination (Table XII). Each of the five hormones depressed imprinting when applied singly after T_2— but to a lesser degree than did the combination. It appears that, by analogy to the neuronal "memory," retroactive interference, i.e., deletion of the freshly acquired individual information by excessive "foreign" information, also exists at the phylogenetic level of the tetrahymena (Csaba et al., 1984e).

There are also other indications in support of the resemblance between neuronal memory and receptor "memory" in the tetrahymena. As already noted, exposure of the tetrahymena to T_2 at a concentration as low as 10^{-18} M had in

TABLE XII

Mean Growth Rates of Tetrahymena Cultures Reexposed to Hormones, Hormone-Like Materials, or a Combination of These after 4-Hour Preexposure to T_2[a]

Culture[b]	Second treatment (first reexposure)		Third treatment (second reexposure)	
	Treatment	Mean growth rate	Treatment	Mean growth rate
1 (Control)	—	12.5	—	12.1
	T_2	14.8	T_2	18.2
2	T_2	19.4	T_2	20.0
3	Serotonin	19.5	T_2	18.2
			Serotonin	19.1
4	Gramine	12.5	T_2	15.8
			Gramine	14.0
5	Epinephrine	12.2	T_2	13.9
			Epinephrine	14.0
6.	Histamine	14.4	T_2	16.5
			Histamine	16.3
7	Dopamine	14.5	T_2	15.0
			Dopamine	14.0
8	Combination	14.4	T_2	12.2
			Combination	11.6

[a]Csaba et al. (1984e).
[b]All cultures, except control culture, received a 4-hour preexposure (first treatment) to T_2.

itself no influence on the growth rate of the unicellular organism but was sufficient to induce imprinting (Table XIII)—to judge from the increased response of the unicellular organism to reexposure(s) at the same low concentration (Csaba et al., 1982b, 1984e). Four exposures for 1 hour each to $10^{-9} M$ T_2 were significantly more effective in inducing receptor "memory" (Table XIV) than was a single exposure to the same concentration for 4 hours (Csaba et al., 1984e). This greatly resembles neuronal memory.

It has been shown that receptor "memory" persists in the tetrahymena over as many as 500 generations. Investigations into the persistence of receptor "memory" in individual cells with an extremely prolonged life span had somewhat different results.

It is known that tetrahymena cells may survive on rat intestine under paraffin oil as long as a year, but fail to divide under the anaerobic conditions (Williams et al., 1980). Tetrahymenas maintained in such conditions after hormonal imprinting still "remembered" the first interaction with the hormone after 3 months, having shown an increased response to it on reexposure (Fig. 19). A less distinct increase over the control was still noted *after 6 months, but after 9 and 12 months, the "memory" of the first interaction was completely extinguished.*

TABLE XIII

MEAN GROWTH RATES OF TETRAHYMENA
CULTURES PREEXPOSED TO
10^{-18} M T_2[a]

Time interval between pre- and reexposure (weeks)	Mean growth rate	
	Without reexposure	After reexposure
Single reexposure		
1	15.2	15.6
3	15.0	15.9
5	13.4	15.8
Multiple reexposure		
1	14.4	16.2
2	15.4	16.8
3	15.6	17.6
4	14.2	16.8
5	14.4	17.2

[a]Csaba et al. (1984e).

The loss of "memory" is part of the loss of general responsiveness under the given conditions of maintenance and, as such, reversible (Csaba et al., 1984a).

If tetrahymena cells maintained under the above anaerobic conditions for 9 months are returned to normal medium (to aerobic conditions), the normal growth potential reappears within 4 days, whereas recovery of the alteration induced in the growth potential by a single interaction with the hormone (imprinting) takes 48 days without reexposure (Fig. 20). With reexposure, return of the receptor "memory" is already demonstrable at 21 days. It appears that *the "rejuvenation" of the tetrahymena cells involves the refreshing of their receptor*

TABLE XIV

MEAN GROWTH RATES OF TETRAHYMENA CULTURES
REEXPOSED TO T_2 1 WEEK AFTER 1×4 AND 4×1 HOUR
PREEXPOSURE TO T_2[a]

Experiment	Mean growth rate	Percentage difference
1×4 hours	17.85	43.3
Control	12.45	
4×1 hours	20.95	76.0
Control	11.9	

[a]Csaba et al. (1984e).

"memory," which strongly suggests that hormonal imprinting takes effect at, and is transmitted at, the gene level by a hitherto obscure mechanism.

3. *Hormone Overlap and Hormonal Imprinting*

In higher organisms, hormones of the same family bind to one another's receptors without functional consequence in adulthood (Azukizawa *et al.,* 1977; Amir *et al.,* 1978; Reichert and Bhalla, 1974), whereas in the perinatal period, in which receptor maturation takes place, hormone overlap on the binding sites does involve a functional overlap as well. For example, the pituitary hormones, thyrotropin (TSH) and follicle stimulating hormone (FSH), which have a common α subunit and similar β subunits (Ward, 1974; Pierce *et al.,* 1976), overlap not only on the gonadal, but also on the thyroid receptors (TSH being even more active on the gonads than FSH) and imprint these for themselves and each other as well (Csaba *et al.,* 1979a; Csaba 1980b; Dobozy *et al.,* 1980).

TSH and FSH both bind to the tetrahymena. Pretreatment with TSH accounts for a significant increase of both TSH and FSH binding over the control, whereas pretreatment with FSH amplifies the receptor to a greater degree for FSH than for TSH, although the effect is significant in both instances (Kovács and Csaba, 1984). *Similar experiments on mammalian cells exposed to pituitary hormones in the perinatal period (Csaba et al., 1981) and in cell cultures (Csaba et al., 1984g, h) had similar results:* TSH always induced a stronger imprinting for

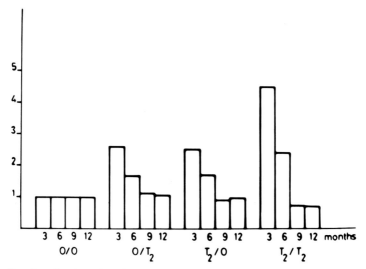

Fig. 19.   Growth values of tetrahymena (relative to control growth value) after different periods (months) of incubation in paraffin-sealed tubes. O/O, Control; O/T_2, not pretreated/treated with T_2; T_2/O, pretreated with T_2/not treated; T_2/T_2, pretreated with T_2/treated with T_2 (Csaba *et al.,* 1984a).

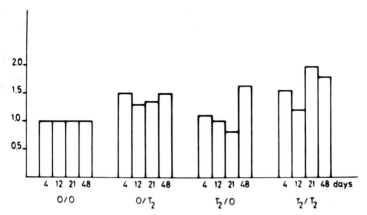

Fig. 20. Growth values of tetrahymena after 9 months of incubation in paraffin-sealed tubes for different lengths of time (days) of cultivation in normal media. Designations as in Fig. 19 (Csaba *et al.*, 1984a).

FSH than for itself, whereas FSH was more active in the FSH–FSH than in the FSH–TSH relation. These findings also indicate that the *receptor formed in the tetrahymena under hormonal influence bears a close resemblance to that possessed by the target cells of higher organisms* and that the dissimilarity of FSH–TSH and TSH–FSH imprinting is due to structural differences in the hormone rather than in the receptor.

The question naturally arises whether the receptor involved in both imprinting mechanisms considered is a common polypeptide receptor (Kovács and Csaba, 1984), since TSH and the gonadotropins are all polypeptide hormones. The primitive polypeptide receptor does in all probability play a certain role, since insulin-pretreated tetrahymena cells bound both TSH and FSH to a lesser degree than those not pretreated. At the same time, pretreatment with either TSH or FSH had no appreciable influence on insulin binding. This is, of course, no proof of the existence of a general polypeptide receptor because if it existed, insulin should have amplified rather than inhibited the binding of TSH and FSH, and vice versa. However, the problem is obviously not as simple as that. Probably the polypeptide–sugar subunit of the membrane can in fact serve as a general peptide binding site *until* it encounters a specific hormone (i.e., a peptide signal molecule) which renders it specific by amplifying itself. This accords well with the experimental observations on the lectin (concanvalin A)—insulin overlap (to be discussed later), in which insulin forms (amplifies) the receptor for Con A (as a fully specific hormone), whereas Con A, being a sugar-specific but not a receptor-specific molecule, fails to amplify the receptor for insulin (Kovács *et al.*, 1984b).

E. The Cytosolic Receptor of the Tetrahymena

In higher organisms certain hormones bind, not to the membrane, but to a cytosolic receptor, which transports them to the cellular nucleus for development of action. The hormones interacting with cytosolic receptors are all morphogenetic; not only lipid-soluble materials, such as steroids, penetrate the membrane for binding to a cytosolic receptor, since thyroxine, which is water soluble, also develops action intracellularly, after binding to a cytosolic or to nuclear receptor. Morphogenesis probably involves a direct gene-level effect, whereas the hormones involved in adaptive reactions seem to be able to develop full action at the membrane level, through mediation by the adenylate cyclase–cAMP system. It seems unlikely that the tetrahymena would *ab ovo* possess cytosolic receptors because its life functions, such as nutrition and protection against adverse influences, all involve a communication with the environment through the membrane, and because its morphogenesis seems to depend under physiological conditions on endogenous rather than exogenous hormones. On the other hand, lipid-soluble morphogenetic hormones, such as steroids, cannot normally be present in the natural environment of the tetrahymena in a dissolved state.

Experimental exposure of the tetrahymena to steroid hormones has shown that although these do appear in the cytoplasm since they can penetrate the membrane, they do not appear in the nucleus (Csaba *et al.,* 1978a). Cytosolic (receptor) protein, isolated from the tetrahymena by methods used for similar purposes in cells of higher organisms, failed to give a specific reaction either with natural steroids, such as estradiol, or with synthetic steroids (dexamethasone and triamciolone), and displacement of labeled hormone with inactive one on the cytosolic receptor preparation also failed, a result indicating that no specific binding had taken place (Csaba *et al.,* 1978a, 1984b).

On exposure of whole tetrahymena cells to tritiated dexamethasone in the presence of the inactive competitor (unlabeled dexamethasone), specific binding was demonstrable at a very low level. Cells preexposed to unlabeled dexamethasone for 24 hours showed 72 hours later a twofold increase in tritiated dexamethasone binding over the control in the presence of the competitor, and a threefold increase was observable after treatment with unlabeled dexamethasone for 72 hours (Csaba and Cserhalmi, 1982.)

Specific binding of dexamethasone to the cytosolic protein was demonstrable by both saturation and displacement (chasing) techniques in cells preexposed to dexamethasone for 72 hours, and returned subsequently to normal medium for 48 hours (Csaba *et al.,* 1984b). It appears that the tetrahymena, which possesses very little steroid binding capacity, if any, in normal conditions, is able to form a specific binding site for these after interaction with the steroid (Fig. 21). Thus the steroids can induce imprinting in the tetrahymena also presumably by a mechanism similar to that in mammals during the perinatal period.

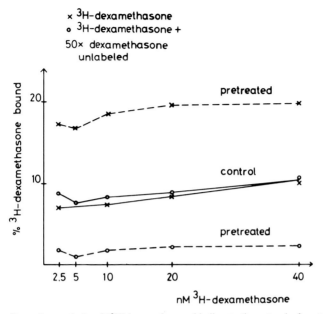

FIG. 21. Saturation analysis of [³H]dexamethasone binding to the cytosol of control and dexamethasone-pretreated (before 72 hours) tetrahymena with or without the presence of unlabeled dexamethasone (Csaba *et al.*, 1984b).

The origin of the cytosolic protein which is capable of binding the steroid, or of "remembering" the interaction with it, is obscure. Certain experimental observations indicates that steroids also bind to the membrane (Pietras and Szego, 1977, 1979) and may enter the cytosol via membrane internalization (Csaba, 1980a). In this case the mechanism of imprinting is in every respect similar to that observed with polypeptide or amino acid-type hormones. Hypothesizing the presence of a potential interacting protein in the cytosol presupposes that the steroid entering the cytoplasm is capable either of its activation or of inducing the assembly of a specific and stable (receptor) structure. "Stability" applies, not only to the cell directly involved in interaction with the steroid, but also to its progeny generations, since the tetrahymena undergoes 10 to 15 generation changes during a culturing time of 72 hours. The experimental fact—that the receptor binding capacity tended to increase rather than to decrease in the progeny generations—implies that the "memory" of the information received by the mother cell at interaction with the hormone remains preserved in the daughter cells.

The cytosolic receptor of the tetrahymena is in all probability more "vulnerable" than that of the higher animals—to judge from the experimental fact that specific binding to the isolated cytosol failed to take place without hormone pretreatment, whereas it did take place in the case of whole cells not subjected to the (drastic?) procedures of cytosol isolation.

Loose and Feldman (1982) detected in *Candida albicans* a special corticosterone binding protein and supposed it to represent the primitive form of either the mammalian glycocorticoid receptor or of the glycocorticoid-binding plasma protein. At all events, it is remarkable that a binding protein lacking in the tetrahymena appears to be inherent in the phylogenetically lower *Candida albicans* species. Nevertheless, it cannot be ruled out that *Candida albicans,* which is pathogenic for humans, who not infrequently receive steroid therapy, may have had a contact with steroids and had, consequently, received from them the imprinting stimulus.

III. Lectin Binding to the Tetrahymena

The lectins are proteins of large molecular size which bind to certain sugars (Barondes, 1981). Since the cell membrane contains sugar components, these may be located by lectin binding (Collard, 1979). The sugar components are linked either with receptor or with marker structures, thereby increasing their

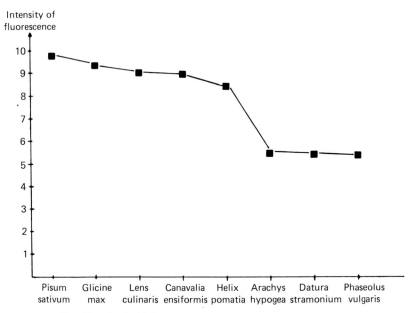

FIG. 22. Lectin binding by tetrahymena cells (Kovács and Csaba, 1982).

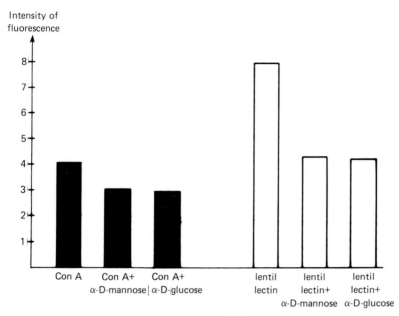

Fig. 23. α-D-Glucose and α-D-mannose supersede FITC-labeled Con A, and *Lens culinaris* lectin bound to receptors of the tetrahymena (Kovács and Csaba, 1982).

specificity. Thus, the localization of the sugars simultaneously involves the localization of the receptor (marker) structures as well.

Certain lectins are able to bind to unicellular organisms, among others to the tetrahymena (Richmond, 1979). However, they display a dissimilar affinity to the different membrane regions, their sites of preference apparently being the cilia above all the tips of them (Csaba and Madarász, 1979). The quantitative relations of binding differ not only between membrane regions, but also between lectin types (Figs. 22 and 23). Lectins with a binding affinity for simple sugars, e.g., Con A, *Lens* and pea lectin, bind to the tetrahymena to a greater degree than do those linking exclusively with amino sugars or oligomeres (Kovács and Csaba, 1982).

Lectin binding to the tetrahymena has different effects on the unicellular organism (Richmond, 1979), e.g., immobilization (Frisch *et al.,* 1976) or alteration of the incorporation of environmental molecules, or alteration of division. Experiments centered on lectin influence on the growth of the tetrahymena are particularly important, since the lectins have been applied as mitogens in various experimental systems. For the tetrahymena, the lectins that bind to simple sugars (such as Con A, *Lens* lectin, and pea lectin) have no approciable influence on division, whereas *Helix* lectin (Fig. 24.), which binds to amino sugars, is strong-

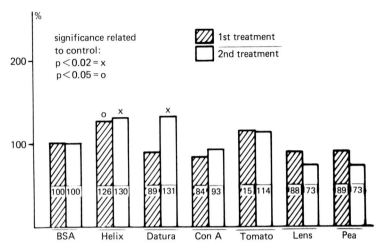

Fig. 24.   Effect of lectins on the growth of pretreated and non-pretreated tetrahymena. Effects are expressed as percentages of the control value, which is assigned a value of 1. BSA, Bovine serum albumin (control) (Csaba *et al.*, 1983b).

ly mitogenic for the tetrahymena (Csaba *et al.*, 1983b). Since the lectins bind to the sugar component of the receptor, it was postulated that they could induce imprinting in the tetrahymena. However, of all lectins studied, only the *Datura* lectin, which binds to oligomeric amino sugars, gave rise to imprinting (Fig. 24.). It appears that while lectin binding to simple sugars has no functional influence, and binding to amino sugars does have some functional influence but does not induce imprinting, the oligomeric amino sugars are those structures which on interaction with a ligand can furnish a "memory" (imprinting) of the event.

The localization of the receptors, and of the associated sugar components as well, may vary during the cell cycle. Such variations are indicated by qualitative and quantitative changes in lectin binding. For example, while the binding patterns of Con A and pea lectin were similar, both having peak at 60 minutes—in phase S of the cell cycle (Fig. 25), tomato and bean lectin (Fig. 26), which bind to oligomeres, showed minimum binding exactly in phase S (Kovács *et al.*, 1984).

The movement and aggregation of protein molecules, and of the associated sugars, in the membrane of the tetrahymena has been demonstrated experimentally. Perioral or aboral cap formation, unrelated to the presence of lectin, but detectable by lectin binding, was observed in a certain phase of the cell cycle. The fact that Con A binding also was demonstrable in different membrane regions in synchronized cell populations (Figs. 27 and 28) indicates that the

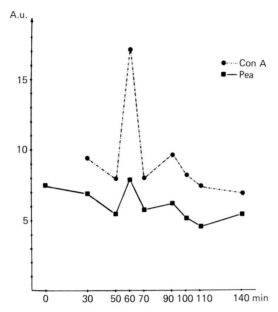

Fig. 25. Binding of Con A and pea lectin to the tetrahymena membrane, in different stages of the cell cycle, A.u., Arbitrary unit (Kovács *et al.*, 1984d).

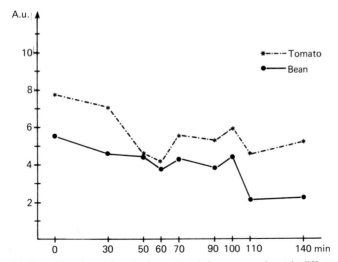

Fig. 26. Binding of tomato and bean lectins to the tetrahymena membrane in different stages of cell cycle. A.u., Arbitrary units (Kovács *et al.*, 1984d).

localization of the sugars and of the structures binding to them depends not only on cyclic but also on individual factors (Köhidai *et al.*, 1984).

In mammalian cells, lectins of a given sugar specificity are capable of interacting with the hormone (Costlow and Gallagher, 1979; Sandra *et al.*, 1979) by occupying its binding sites, and vice versa; bound hormone prevents lectin binding in the same system. This finding suggests that certain lectins and certain hormones have common binding sites. This also applies to the tetrahymena, for preexposure to insulin or to histamine inhibited lectin binding, and, conversely preexposure to Con A inhibited the binding of insulin to the tetrahymena, results indicating that the binding site for Con A, insulin, and histamine is in all probability common (Csaba and Kovács, 1982a). Surprisingly, however, like insulin, the hypophyseal hormones TSH, FSH, and PMSG also depressed the binding of Con A to the membrane of the tetrahymena (Kovács and Csaba, 1984). On the basis of these results, the existence of a primitive polypeptide receptor, at least with respect to the sugar component, can well be postulated. At the same time, the three pituitary hormones have a common binding site, not only with Con A, but also with *Helix* lectin, which is, however, not a binding site

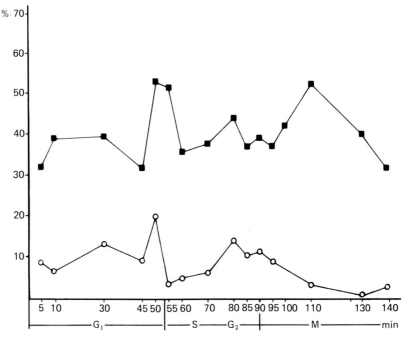

Fɪɢ. 27.　Localization of Con A binding sites on the tetrahymena during the cell cycle; demonstrated by horseradish peroxidase. ■, Peroxidase-positive cells per total cell number; ○, periorally capped cells per total cell number (Köhidai *et al.*, 1984).

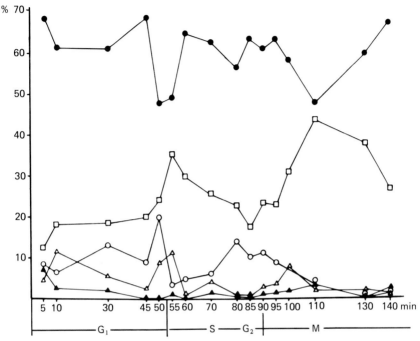

FIG. 28.   Different types of binding of Con A by the tetrahymena during the cell cycle related to the total cell number demonstrated by horseradish peroxidase. ○, Periorally capped cells; △, completely stained cells; □, completely stained rounded cells; ▲, aborally capped cells; ●, peroxidase-negative cells (Köhidai *et al.,* 1984.)

for insulin. It appears that in addition to availability of a general binding site, variations in the sugar component of the receptor also play a role in specific binding.

Whereas insulin inhibited the binding of Con A and all other polypeptide hormones, the action of histamine appeared to be specific, since other biogenic amines, such as epinephrine, dopamine, or serotonin did not interfere with the binding of Con A (Csaba and Kovács, 1982b). This is a plain fact, but it remains obscure why histamine, radically differing in structure from insulin and the other polypeptide hormones, interacts with a binding site that has a sugar composition that suits the polypeptide hormones.

A still greater confusion arises if the functional context is also taken into consideration (Csaba *et al.,* 1983a). As noted earlier, histamine stimulates the phagocytosis of the tetrahymena by a durable action. Con A, which binds to the same site as insulin and which inhibits insulin binding if given before it, has in itself no influence on phagocytosis. Thus, the binding of Con A, although inhibitory for insulin, does not represent a functional stimulus. Nevertheless, something more must happen than a mere occupation of the binding site, since tetrahymena cells preexposed to Con A failed to show a significant increase in phagocytic activity in response to histamine exposure 1 week later. A certain receptor alteration may thus have been consequent upon the binding of Con A. Yet, however, grossly Con A interferes with histamine binding, it is in itself incapable not only of stimulating phagocytosis but also of utilizing for itself the histamine-induced imprinting, since it fails to activate phagocytosis in cells preexposed to histamine.

The antagonistic action of lectins on hormone binding has been utilized to identify the sugar components of the basic (general) (Kovács *et al.*, 1981) receptors. The histamine receptors represent two classes, designated H_1 and H_2. Lectin binding studies have revealed that the sugar components of the H_1 receptor, which is complementary to both histamine and its antagonists, are primarily simple sugars, such as glucose and mannose derivatives, and secondarily glucosamine and acetyl glucosamine oligomeres. The sugar components of the H_2 receptor consist, in contrast, primarily of galactosamine and related compounds, and only in a minor part of simple sugars. Studies along this line have been limited to the tetrahymena, but an evolutionary study could probably disclose how far the sugar components of the tetrahymena's receptor corresponded to those of higher organisms.

The tetrahymena not only binds but also contains lectins. Binding studies with fluorescein-labeled antilectins prepared in rabbit have shown that the lectin-like proteins naturally present in the body of the tetrahymena entered into a cytochemically demonstrable reaction with antibodies to various plant lectins and snail lectin (Csaba and Kovács, 1983). The lectins were detected not only on the cell surface, but also intracellularly, which is not surprising if we take into consideration the fact that Barondes (1981) and colleagues detected 98% of the lectins possessed by *Dictyostelium* in intracellular localizations. The cytochemical evidence of lectin localization equally supports the hypothesis of a primitive lectin which is generally capable of interacting with various antibodies, as that of the occurrence of diverse types of lectins within the same cell.

Evidence has been accumulating that the lectins are specific ligands which play a role in both cell–cell recognition and intracellular recognition. Their presence in the tetrahymena is therefore not surprising, but it is certainly remarkable that lectins characteristic of higher animals also occur in the tetrahymena. Since, however, certain hormones which obtain a functional importance only in higher organisms, and other materials, which have no obvious function at the higher vertebrate level either (e.g., digoxin, Darvas *et al.*, 1984b) also appear in the tetrahymena, the presence of plant and *Helix* lectins in it does not seem to be extraordinary.

IV. Conclusion: Is the Tetrahymena a Suitable Model Cell for Receptor Research?

Biological research frequently relies on model cells, either because the target cells cannot be made available for study or because studies on simple model cells are more conclusive than direct examinations of target cells. A classic example of this is the use of *Escherichia coli* cells in genetic research; the simplicity of the bacterial chromosomes has promoted the understanding of many general genetic laws, and the rapid reproduction of the bacterial cell has enabled comprehensive generation studies within a relatively short time. However, the conclusions drawn from *E. coli* studies cannot be directly extrapolated to eukaryotic cells, and still less to multicellular organisms, in which information and regulation systems are infinitely more complex. No up-to-date genetic outlook would, however, exist without *E. coli* studies. The characteristic model cell of developmental biological studies is the *Acetabularia,* in which the entire process of differentiation can be followed up within a single cell to promote the understanding of the fundamental processes of genetic control. The single-cell model for embryological research is the fertilized amphibian egg, the study of which has contributed the theory of ontogenetic regulation. Naturally, the observations made on the *Acetabularia,* the amphibian egg, or any other model cell are *not fully* applicable to the ontogenetic development of higher organisms.

In this light we may question whether the tetrahymena can be regarded as a realistic model cell for hormone receptor research or, in other words, how far the observations made on the receptor structure and activity of the tetrahymena apply to those of genuine target cells. It appears that, with respect to receptor function, the tetrahymena is at the same time inferior and superior to the target cells of higher organisms. It is inferior because, being itself devoid of a hormonal system, its response to most hormones is indirect, or can be read only as such. Furthermore, although it binds the steroid hormones in the same way in every respect as do higher organisms, and is therefore suitable also for receptor kinetic studies, its interaction with the polypeptide hormones is less informative—as shown by saturation and displacement studies with low-molecular-weight hormones—than the interactions of mammalian cells. This certainly limits the methodical approach to hormone binding studies on the tetrahymena, but the fact remains that binding necessarily must take place whenever an action is developed, since the functional response, which is biologically more important than binding, presupposes binding, whereas binding does not necessarily result in a functional response.

The superiority of the tetrahymena model to cells of higher organisms derives from the fact that it permits a comprehensive study of receptor formation and development, from both the phylogenetic and the ontogenetic point of view—

partly because the membrane of the tetrahymena is an intact ("virgin") structure with respect to hormonal influence and partly because, being a unicellular organism, its membrane is more dynamic than that of the cellular elements of organized tissues (exactly on account of this dynamism has the tetrahymena been preferred as a model, not only for receptor studies, but also for membrane studies; Nozawa, 1980). Thus, the tetrahymena lends itself to the study of events which occur at the vertebrate level partly perinatally and partly in adulthood. The fact that the tetrahymena simultaneously represents a single cell and an independent biological entity has the advantage that the response of the cell and the entity can be examined simultaneously, since it responds to cellular level impulses as a complete organism. Its behavior is, therefore, more conclusive of cell–hormone interaction than that of cultured cells, which are necessarily studied in artificial conditions outside their natural environment and cannot usually be regarded as intact with respect to hormonal influence, since a hormonal system operates in all higher organisms from which cell cultures are derived, from the early stage of prenatal life on.

Another important advantage of the tetrahymena is its rapid growth, which enables a short-term followup of adverse or advantageous influences on the receptors over many generations, and since it is known that the functioning of the receptor of the tetrahymena is, including the postreceptor effects, similar to that of target cell receptors in higher organisms, it is obvious that the observations made on the model cell can be more reliably extrapolated to higher organisms than those obtained on *E. coli*.

As a matter of fact, complementary studies on genuine target cells are by no means unnecessary. In the usually simpler model system the fundamental mechanisms are as a rule more conspicuous and their knowledge promotes focused investigations into certain important phenomena on the genuine target cell. The tetrahymena, being a phylogenetically low, but highly differentiated eukaryotic cell, and having a structure and fundamental life functions that have long been mapped, has served as a suitable model for receptor research. It is to be hoped that it will serve as such in the future.

ACKNOWLEDGMENTS

The author is grateful for the permission to use the figures and tables of S. Karger A. G., Basel-New York, Verlag der Zeitschrift für Naturforschung, Tübingen, Comparative Biochemistry and Physiology, Cell Biology International Reports and another journals. The experiments done by the author and his co-workers had been supported by the Scientific Research Council, Ministry of Health, Hungary, 16/1-04/432/Cs.

REFERENCES

Amir, S. M., Sullivan, R. C., and Ingbar, S. H. (1978). *Endocrinology* **103**, 101–111.
Ashby, W. R. (1956). "An Introduction to Cybernetics." Chapman & Hall, London.
Azukizawa, M., Kutzman, G., Pekary, A. E., and Hersmann, J. K. (1977). *Endocrinology* **101**, 1880–1889.
Baldwin, D., Prince, M., Tsai, P., Johnson, C., Lotan, R., and Rubinstein, A. H. (1981). *Am. J. Physiol.* **241E**, 251–260.
Blazquez, E., Rubalcava, B., Montesano, R., Orci, L., and Unger, R. H. (1976). *Endocrinology* **98**, 1014–1023.
Barondes, S. H. (1981). *Annu. Rev. Biochem.* **50**, 207–231.
Barrington, E. J. W. (1978). *In* "Comparative Endocrinology" (P. J. Gaillard and H. Boer, eds). Academic Press, New York.
Barrington, E. J. W. (1979). "Hormones and Evolution." Academic Press, New York.
Collard, G. J. (1979). *Biol. Cell.* **36**, 309–312.
Costlow, M. E., and Gallagher, P. E. (1979). *Biochim. Biophys. Acta* **587**, 129–201.
Csaba, G. (1977). *Biol. Rev. (Cambridge)* **52**, 295–303.
Csaba, G. (1980a). *Acta Biol. Hung.* **31**, 405–474.
Csaba, G. (1980b). *Biol. Rev. (Cambridge)* **55**, 47–63.
Csaba, G. (1981). "Ontogeny and Phylogeny of Hormone Receptors." Karger, Basel.
Csaba, G., and Cserhalmi, M. (1982). *Endokrinologie* **79**, 431–433.
Csaba, G., and Darvas, Zs. (1984). *Cell Biol. Int. Rep.* **8**, 181.
Csaba, G., and Kovács, P. (1982a). *Cell. Mol. Biol.* **28**, 153–158.
Csaba, G., and Kovács, P. (1982b). *Cell Mol. Biol.* **28**, 509–512.
Csaba, G., and Kovács, P. (1983). *Acta Histochem.* **73**, 53–61.
Csaba, G., and Lantos, T. (1973). *Cytobiologie* **7**, 361–365.
Csaba, G., and Lantos, T. (1975a). *Acta Protozool.* **13**, 410–413.
Csaba, G., and Lantos, T. (1975b). *Experientia* **31**, 1097–1098.
Csaba, G., and Lantos, T. (1975c). *Cytobiologie* **11**, 44–49.
Csaba, G., and Lantos, T. (1976). *Endokrinologie* **68**, 239–240.
Csaba, G., and Lantos, T. (1977). *Differentiation* **8**, 54–59.
Csaba, G., and Madarász, B. (1979). *Experientia* **35**, 1181–1182.
Csaba, G., and Madarász, B. (1985). *Z. Anat. Forsch.* (in press).
Csaba, G., and Nagy, S. U. (1976a). *Acta Biol. med. Germ.* **35**, 1399–1401.
Csaba, G., and Nagy, S. U. (1976b). *Experientia* **32**, 651–652.
Csaba, G., and Nagy, S. U. (1985). *J. Endocrinol. Invest.* In press.
Csaba, G., and Németh, G. (1980a). *Acta Biol. Hung.* **31**, 43–47.
Csaba, G., and Németh, G. (1980b). *Comp. Biochem. Physiol.* **65B**, 387–390.
Csaba, G., and Németh, G. (1982). *Acta Biol. Hung.* **33**, 87–89.
Csaba, G., and Ubornyák, L. (1979). *Acta Protozool.* **18**, 491–496.
Csaba, G., and Ubornyák, L. (1981). *Comp. Biochem. Physiol.* **68C** 251–253.
Csaba, G., and Ubornyák, L. (1982a). *Acta Biol. Hung.* **33**, 381–384.
Csaba, G., and Ubornyák, L. (1982b). *Acta Biol. Hung.* **33**, 423–424.
Csaba, G., Lantos, T., Nagy, S. U., Arányi, P., and Náray A. (1978a). *Acta Biol. Med. Germ.* **37**, 1377–1380.
Csaba, G., Nagy, S. U., and Lantos, T. (1978b). *Acta Biol. Med. Germ.* **37**, 505–507.
Csaba, G., Dobozy, O., and Kaizer, G. (1979a). *Horm. Metab. Res.* **11**, 662–665.
Csaba, G., Németh, G., and Prohászka, J. (1979b). *Exp. Cell Biol.* **47**, 307–311.
Csaba, G., Bierbauer, J., and Fehér, Zs. (1980a). *Comp. Biochem. Physiol.* **67C** 207–209.

Csaba, G., Rónai, A., Lázló, V., Darvas, Zs., and Berzétei, I. (1980b), Horm. Metab. Res. **12,** 28–31.

Csaba, G., Sudár, F., and Pados, R. (1980c). *Endokrinologie* **76,** 340–343.

Csaba, G., Dobozy, O., and Kaizer, G. (1981). *Horm. Metab. Res.* 177–179.

Csaba, G., Németh, G., Juvancz, I., and Vargha, P. (1982a). *BioSystems* **15,** 59–63.

Csaba, G., Németh, G., and Vargha, P. (1982b). *Comp. Biochem. Physiol.* **73B** 357–360.

Csaba, G., Németh, G., and Vargha, P. (1982c). *Acta Biol. Hung.* **33,** 425–427.

Csaba, G., Németh, G., and Vargha, P. (1982d). *Endokrinologie* **80,** 341–346.

Csaba, G., Németh, G., and Vargha, P. (1982e). *Expl. Cell Biol.* **50,** 291–294.

Csaba, G., Németh, G., and Vargha, P. (1982f). *Z. Naturforsch.* **37C,** 1042–1044.

Csaba, G., Darvas, Zs., and László, V. (1983a). *Comp. Biochem. Physiol.* **78A,** 457–460.

Csaba, G., Darvas, Zs., and László, V. (1983b). *Cell Biol. Int. Rep.* **7,** 403.

Csaba, G., Németh, G., and Vargha, P. (1983c). *Acta Physiol. Hung.* **61,** 131–136.

Csaba, G., Sudár, F., and Ubornyák, L. (1983d). *Exp. Clin. Endocrinol.* **82,** 61–67.

Csaba, G., Darvas, Zs., László, V., and Vargha, P. (1984a). *Expl. Cell Biol.* **52,** 211–216.

Csaba, G., Inczefi-Gonda, Á., and Fehér, T. (1984b). Submitted.

Csaba, G., Kovács, P., and Inczefi-Gonda, Á. (1984c). *Z. Naturforsch.* **39C,** 183–185.

Csaba, G., Németh, G., Kovács, P., Vargha, P., and Vas, Á. (1984d). *Biosystems,* in press.

Csaba, G., Németh, G., and Vargha, P. (1984e). *Expl. Cell Biol.* **52,** 370–375.

Csaba, G., Németh, G., and Vargha, P. (1984f). *Acta Biol. Hung.,* in press.

Csaba, G., Török, O., and Kovács, P. (1984g). *Acta Physiol. Hung.* **64,** 135–138.

Csaba, G., Török, O., and Kovács, P. (1984h). *Acta Physiol. Hung.* **64,** 57–63.

Darvas, Zs., Csaba, G., and László, V. (1984a). *Biológia,* in press.

Darvas, Zs., Swydan, R., Csaba, G., László, V., and Nagy, S. U. (1984b). *Acta Physiol. Hung.,* in press.

Dobozy, O., Csaba, G., Shahin, M. A., and Lazáry, G. (1980). *Acta Morphol. Hung.* **28,** 11–20.

Dobozy, O., Shahin, M. A., and Csaba, G. (1981). *Acta Morphol. Hung.* **29,** 19–25.

Frisch, A., Bessler, W., Lip, H. J., and Ammermann, D. (1976). *J. Protozool.* **23,** 427–430.

Fristrom, J. W., and Spieth, P. (1980). "Principles of Genetics." Blackwell, Oxford.

Garattini, S., and Valzelli, L. (1965). "Serotonin." Elsevier, Amsterdam.

Ginsberg, B. H., Kahn, C. R., and Roth, J. (1977). *Endocrinology* **100,** 520–525.

Gluckman, P. D., Butler, J. H., and Elliot, T. B. (1983). *Endocrinology* **112,** 1607–1612.

Goldfine, I. D., Smith, G. J., Wong, K. Y., and Jones, A. L. (1977a). *Proc. Natl. Acad. Sci. U.S.A.* **74,** 1368–1372.

Goldfine, I. D., Vigneri, E., Cohen, D., Pliam, N. B., and Kahn, C. R. (1977b). *Nature (London)* **269,** 698–700.

Goldstein, J. L., Anderson, R. G. W., and Brown, M. S. (1979). *Nature (London)* **279,** 679–685.

Hill, D. L. (1972). "The Biochemistry and Physiology of Tetrahymena." Academic Press, New York.

Horvat, A. (1978). *J. Cell. Physiol.* **97,** 37–48.

Horvat, A., Li, E., and Katsoyannis, P. G. (1975). *Biochim. Biophys. Acta* **382,** 609–620.

Jancsó, M. (1955). "Speicherung." Hung. Acad. Sci., Budapest.

Josefson, J.-O., and Johannson, P. (1979). *Nature (London)* **282,** 78–80.

Kariya, K., Saito, K., and Iwata, H. (1974). *J. Pharmacol.* **24,** 129–134.

Kassis, S., and Kindler, S. H. (1975). *Biochim. Biophys. Acta* **391,** 513.

Koch, A. S., Fehér, J., and Lukovics, I. (1979). *Biol. Cybernet.* **32,** 125–138.

Köhidai, L., Kovács, P., and Csaba, G. (1984). *Acta Morphol. Hung.* in press.

Kovács, P., and Gsaba, G. (1982). *Acta Protozool.* **21,** 69–75.

Kovács, P., and Csaba, G. (1984). *Acta Protozool.,* in press.

Kovács, P., Darvas, Zs., and Csaba, G. (1981). *Acta Biol. Hung.* **32,** 111–117.

Kovács, P., Csaba, G., and Bohdaneczky, E. (1985). *Comp. Biochem. Physiol.* **80A**, 41–42.

Kovács, P., Csaba, G., and László, V. (1984b). *Acta Physiol. Hung.* **64**, 19–23.

Kovács, P., Csaba, G., and Nozawa, Y. (1984c). *Comp. Biochem. Physiol.* **78A**, 763–766.

Kovács, P., Köhidai, L., and Csaba, G. (1984d). *Acta Biol. Hung.*, in press.

Kushinsky, G., Hille, W., and Shimassek, A. (1955). *Arch. Pharmakol.* **266**, 1–8.

Leder, P. (1982). *Sci. Am.* **246**, 72–83.

Lenhoff, H. M. (1974). *In* "Coelenterate Biology" (L. Muscatine and H. M. Lenhoff, eds.), pp. 238–239. Academic Press, New York.

Le Roith, D., Shiloach, J., Roth, J., and Lesniak, M. A. (1980). *Proc. Natl. Acad. Sci. U.S.A.* **77**, 6184–6188.

Lison, L., and Smoulders, J. (1949). *C.R. Séanc. Soc. Biol.* **143**, 575–577.

Loose, D. S., and Feldman, D. (1982). *J. Biol. Chem.* **257**, 4925–4930.

Meglitsch, P. A. (1967). "Invertebrate Zoology." Oxford Univ. Press, London.

Muggeo, M., Ginsberg, B. H., Roth, J., Neville, G. M., Meyts, P. de, and Kahn, C. R. (1979a). *Endocrinology* **104**, 1393–1402.

Muggeo, M., Obberghen, E., von, Kahn, C. R., Roth, J., Ginsberg, B. H., Meyts, P., de, Emdin, S. O., and Falkmer, S. (1979b). *Diabetes* **28** , 175–181.

Neufeld, N. D., Scott, M., and Kaplan, S. A. (1980). *Dev. Biol.* **78**, 151–160.

Nozawa, Y. (1980). *In* "Membrane Fluidity: Biophysical Techniques and Cellular Regulation" (M. Kates and A. Kuksis, eds.), pp. 399–410. Humana Press, Clifton New Jersey.

Nozawa, Y., Kovács, P., Okhi, K., and Csaba, G. (1985). *Cell. Mol. Biol.*, in press.

Peyrat, J.-P., Meusy-Derolle, N., and Garnier, J. (1981). *Endocrinology* **108**, 625–631.

Pietras, R. J., and Szego, C. M. (1977). *Nature (London)* **265**, 69–72.

Pietras, R. J., and Szego, C. M. (1979). *J. Cell. Physiol.* **98**, 145–160.

Rao, C., and Chegini, N. (1983). *In* "Evolution of Hormone-Receptor Systems", pp. 413–423. Liss. New York.

Reichert, L. E., and Bhalla, V. K. (1974). *Endocrinology* **94**, 483–491.

Richmond, J. E. (1979). *Comp. Biochem. Physiol.* **64B**, 161–165.

Sandra, A., Leon, M. A., and Przybilski, J. R. (1979). *Endocrinology* **105**, 391–401.

Steinmann, R. M., Mellmann, I. S., Muller, W. A., and Cohn, Z. A. (1983). *J. Cell Biol.* **96**, 1–27.

Takeda, N., Yasuda, K., Miura, K., and Nozawa, Y. (1984). Yet unpublished data (personal communication).

Thorrson, A. V., and Hintz, R. L. (1977). *N. Engl. J. Med.* **297**, 908–912.

Ward, D. M. (1974). *In* "Invertebrate Endocrinology and Hormonal Heterophylly" (W. J. Burdette, ed.). Springer-Verlag, Berlin.

Weiss, M., Ingbar, S. H., Winblad, S., and Kasper, (1983). *Science* **219**, 1331–1333.

Williams, N. E., Wolfe, J., and Bleyman, L. K. (1980). *J. Protozool.* **27**, 327–328.

Index

Contents of Recent Volumes

387